Greetings
Operation Bookshelf
Scarsdale Woman's Club
Scarsdale, N. Y., U. S. A. 10583

ADDISON-WESLEY BOOKS IN
NUCLEAR SCIENCE AND METALLURGY

Bishop—Project Sherwood—The U. S. Program in Controlled Fusion

Chastain—U. S. Research Reactor Operation and Use

Claus—Radiation Biology and Medicine

Clegg and Foley—Uranium Ore Processing

Cullity—Elements of X-Ray Diffraction

Cuthbert—Thorium Production Technology

Goldstein—Fundamental Aspects of Reactor Shielding

Goodman—Introduction to Pile Theory
   (The Science and Engineering of Nuclear Power, I)

Goodman—Applications of Nuclear Energy
   (The Science and Engineering of Nuclear Power, II)

Guy—Elements of Physical Metallurgy

Holden—Physical Metallurgy of Uranium

Hughes—Pile Neutron Research

Kaplan—Nuclear Physics

Kramer—Boiling Water Reactors

Lane, MacPherson, and Maslan—Fluid Fuel Reactors

Norton—Elements of Ceramics

Rough and Bauer—Constitutional Diagrams of Uranium and Thorium

Sachs—Nuclear Theory

Schuhmann—Metallurgical Engineering
      Vol. I: Engineering Principles

Seaborg—The Transuranium Elements

Starr and Dickinson—Sodium Graphite Reactors

USAEC—Shippingport Pressurized Water Reactor

Zinn and Dietrich—Solid Fuel Reactors

URANIUM ORE
PROCESSING

TN 490 .U7 C55

Clegg, John W.

Uranium ore processing

DATE DUE

Demco, Inc. 38-293

Yellow

URANIUM ORE PROCESSING

Edited by

JOHN W. CLEGG

and

DENNIS D. FOLEY

Battelle Memorial Institute

669.29
C

PREPARED UNDER CONTRACT WITH THE
UNITED STATES ATOMIC ENERGY COMMISSION

ADDISON-WESLEY PUBLISHING COMPANY, INC.

READING, MASSACHUSETTS, U.S.A.

WITHDRAWN FROM
J. EUGENE SMITH LIBRARY
EASTERN CONN. STATE UNIVERSITY
WILLIMANTIC, CT 06226-2295
J. EUGENE SMITH LIBRARY
EASTERN CONN. STATE UNIVERSITY
WILLIMANTIC, CT 06226

√c

Copyright © 1958

by

ADDISON-WESLEY PUBLISHING COMPANY, INC.

and assigned to the General Manager
of the United States Atomic Energy Commission

———————————

Printed in the United States of America

ALL RIGHTS RESERVED. THIS BOOK, OR PARTS THERE-
OF, MAY NOT BE REPRODUCED IN ANY FORM WITH-
OUT WRITTEN PERMISSION OF THE PUBLISHER.

Library of Congress Catalog Card No. 58–12597

First printing, September 1958

669.39
C58
4586

PREFACE

This book brings together in one volume a description of the technology of winning uranium from its ores. The first four chapters contain background information which sets the stage for presentation of the physical and chemical processes applied from the time uranium ore appears on the receiving dock at the processing plant until the product leaves the plant as a "concentrate" containing 40 to 85 percent uranium (reported as U_3O_8).

The four brief orientation chapters treat occurrence and sources, exploration and mining, sampling and analysis and mineralogy. They are written as synopses for the nonspecialist in geology, mining, chemical analysis, and mineralogy by authorities in each field. Use of specialized terms is held to a minimum.

The body of the book covers the steps of technology roughly in the order in which they are applied: preliminary treatments like roasting and physical concentrations, leaching with acid or alkaline reagents; separation of the pregnant leach liquor from the unwanted solid gangue; and recovery of the uranium product from the solution, principally by ion exchange and solvent extraction. No attempt has been made to discuss the basic principles of such unit operations as conveying, crushing and grinding, thickening, filtration, solvent extraction, and drying. It is assumed that the reader will already have a knowledge of these principles, or lacking it, will refer to a standard text.

The next chapter describes in considerable detail six typical plants employing the techniques set forth in preceding chapters. Of the last two chapters, one is on such currently minor sources (but major reserves) of uranium as shale, lignite, and phosphate rock, while the other covers health and safety in mining and milling.

For those who want additional information, there are numerous references. The references include a number of publications issued by the Atomic Energy Commission. These are available for inspection at the Commission's depository libraries in the United States and abroad and are sold by the Office of Technical Services, U. S. Department of Commerce, Washington 25, D. C.

The foremost debt which must be acknowledged for a book of this sort is to its 32 authors. Their names are given immediately following the preface. This volume was made possible by their willingness to take time from busy schedules, their diligence, and their erudition.

71726

While the selection of data, its evaluation, and the conclusions reached are the work of the authors writing in consultation with the editors, those who reviewed the manuscript technically made an important contribution. For such review the editors are grateful to Richard H. Kennedy and Ernest C. Van Blarcom and their associates of the Atomic Energy Commission's Raw Materials Division, and to Charles K. McArthur and others of the Commission's Raw Materials Development Laboratory at Winchester, Massachusetts. Special appreciation is expressed to John D. Sullivan, of Battelle Memorial Institute, for his painstaking review and unstinting assistance. We acknowledge the cooperation of several in the Commission's Industrial Information Branch of the Technical Information Service, including Van A. Wente, who paved the way to completion at rough spots in the course of the work; DeWitt O. Myatt, who pointed out ways of simplifying involved drawings so that they could be included in the book; and James R. Aswell and Jefferson D. Bates, who improved the readability of the manuscript by skilled editorial work.

J. W. CLEGG
D. D. FOLEY

Columbus, Ohio
June 1958

LIST OF AUTHORS

The following is a list of contributors to this volume. Specific credit is given with each chapter.

A. E. BEARSE	ROBERT KUNIN
ROMAN CHELMINSKI	I. M. LEBARON
J. B. CLEMMER	P. D. V. MANNING
FOSTER CRAMPTON	L. A. MCCLAINE
MERLE E. CREW	LEW PAINTER
M. A. DESESA	G. B. PECK
R. P. EHRLICH	H. G. PETROW
D. A. ELLIS	E. S. PORTER
D. L. EVERHART	A. F. PREUSS
M. N. GAINES	J. E. QUINN
D. R. GEORGE	J. B. ROSENBAUM
M. D. HASSIALIS	F. M. STEPHENS
W. C. HAZEN	O. F. TANGEL
A. V. HENDRICKSON	A. THUNAES
D. A. HOLADAY	T. B. UPCHURCH
THEODORE IZZO	R. J. WOODY

CONTENTS

CHAPTER 1.   URANIUM OCCURRENCE AND SOURCES 1

1-1.   Introduction 1
1-2.   Uranium Geology 3
1-3.   Uranium Sources in the United States 7
1-4.   Uranium Sources in Canada 14
1-5.   Uranium Sources in the Union of South Africa 17
1-6.   Other Uranium Sources of the Western World 17

CHAPTER 2.   URANIUM EXPLORATION AND MINING 24

2-1.   Radiation Detection Equipment 24
2-2.   Exploration 27
2-3.   Mining 33

CHAPTER 3.   SAMPLING AND ANALYSIS 44

PART I.   SAMPLING OF URANIUM ORES AND CONCENTRATES

3-1.   Introduction to Sampling 44
3-2.   Weighing Mine-Run Ore 45
3-3.   Ore Sampling for Moisture Content 45
3-4.   Ore Sampling for Uranium Content 48
3-5.   Accessory Operations 53
3-6.   Concentrate Sampling 57

PART II.   ANALYSIS OF URANIUM ORES

3-7.   Introduction to Analysis 65
3-8.   Volumetric Methods 65
3-9.   Fluorometric Methods 69
3-10. Spectrophotometric Methods 73
3-11. Polarographic Methods 78
3-12. Coulometric Methods 81
3-13. X-ray Spectrochemical Methods 81
3-14. Analysis for Other Elements 83

CHAPTER 4.   MINERALOGY OF URANIUM AS IT RELATES TO
             HYDROMETALLURGICAL PROCESSING 89

4-1.   Introduction 89
4-2.   Uranium Minerals 89
4-3.   Metallurgical Classification of Uranium Ores 93

ix

CHAPTER 5. PRELIMINARY ORE TREATMENT 103
  5–1. Roasting of Uranium Ores 103
  5–2. Physical Concentration of Uranium Ores 108

CHAPTER 6. ACID LEACHING OF URANIUM ORES 115
  6–1. Introduction 115
  6–2. Leaching Conditions 116
  6–3. Leaching Methods and Equipment 125
  6–4. Milling Practice 138

CHAPTER 7. CARBONATE LEACHING OF URANIUM ORES 153
  7–1. Introduction 153
  7–2. Chemistry of Carbonate Dissolution 154
  7–3. Methods of Dissolution 162

CHAPTER 8. LIQUID-SOLIDS SEPARATIONS 172
  8–1. Introduction 172
  8–2. Developments in Use of Flocculants 173
  8–3. Liquid-Solids Separations in Alkaline Systems 183
  8–4. Liquid-Solids Separation in Acid Systems 185

CHAPTER 9. URANIUM RECOVERY BY ION EXCHANGE 191
  9–1. Introduction 191
  9–2. Chemistry of the Ion-Exchange Process 192
  9–3. Columnar Ion Exchange 207
  9–4. Resin-in-Pulp Ion Exchange 216
  9–5. Special Problems in Ion-Exchange Recovery 219

CHAPTER 10. URANIUM RECOVERY BY SOLVENT EXTRACTION . . . 237
  10–1. Introduction 237
  10–2. Chemistry of Solvent Extraction 238
  10–3. Equipment Used in Solvent Extraction 255
  10–4. Current Solvent Extraction Processes for Uranium 261

CHAPTER 11. EXAMPLES OF URANIUM MILLING OPERATIONS . . . 272
  11–1. Introduction 272
  11–2. Uranium Mills in the Blind River Area 273
  11–3. Development of the Beaverlodge Mill 306
  11–4. Uranium Recovery by Vitro Uranium Company 323
  11–5. Shiprock Uranium Mill 331
  11–6. Moab Mill of Uranium Reduction Company 345
  11–7. South African Uranium Mills 354

CHAPTER 12. URANIUM RECOVERY FROM PHOSPHATE ROCK
MONAZITE, LIGNITE, AND SHALE 372

12–1. Introduction 372
12–2. Recovery from Phosphate Rock 375
12–3. Uranium Recovery from Monazite 386
12–4. Uranium Recovery from Lignite 390
12–5. Recovery from Chattanooga Shale 396

CHAPTER 13. HEALTH AND SAFETY PROBLEMS ASSOCIATED WITH
URANIUM MINING AND MILLING 406

13–1. Introduction 406
13–2. General Health and Safety Considerations 406
13–3. Uranium Mining 407
13–4. Uranium Milling 411

APPENDIX. MAJOR URANIUM DISTRICTS OF THE UNITED STATES . . 414

A–1. The Colorado Plateau 414
A–2. The Wyoming Basins 417
A–3. Other Uranium Producing Districts 419

Index 423

CHAPTER 1

URANIUM OCCURRENCE AND SOURCES*

1-1. INTRODUCTION

Since the advent of atomic energy and the sudden emergence in the early 1940's of uranium as the key raw material, knowledge has steadily accumulated on uranium geology and sources in the United States and throughout the world.

Early in the Atomic Energy Commission program, the general belief was that a few districts rich in pitchblende veins—such as Shinkolobwe in the Belgian Congo, Great Bear Lake in Canada's Northwest Territories, and Joachimsthal in Czechoslovakia—were the only really good sources of uranium ore in the world. This opinion was based on extensive wartime exploration by the Manhattan Engineering District, the predecessor of AEC. The seemingly unique carnotite deposits in the Salt Wash part of the Morrison formation on the Colorado Plateau were known but were considered relatively unimportant.

Shortly after the Commission was established in 1947, new sources of uranium ore appeared. In South Africa, Rand gold ores and mine tailings were developed for uranium, thereby adding powdery uraninite in metamorphosed conglomerates as an ore type. At about the same time the Happy Jack copper-uranium deposits in Utah sandstone came to light. In 1949, ore was also discovered in the Todilto limestone near Grants, New Mexico. Three years later the Anaconda Mining Company found the Jackpile mine, on the Colorado Plateau, with its large deposits of primary black uraninite and coffinite.

By 1952, increasing numbers of new types of ore deposits in various geologic "provinces" had been reported and examined—in the Black Hills of South Dakota, the Gunnar claims in Saskatchewan, the famous Mi Vida and Delta mines in Utah, the large vein deposits of France, and in a number of other localities around the world. New uranium districts have continued to develop at an unprecedented rate. As a result, the science of uranium geology is in a continual process of re-evaluation and change. Some of the more significant uranium deposits are shown on the map in Fig. 1-1.

In the early years, ore was so desperately needed that geologic methods used were, of necessity, empirical. For example, drilling projects of both individual mining companies and the Federal government consisted largely

---

* By Donald L. Everhart, U. S. Atomic Energy Commission.

1

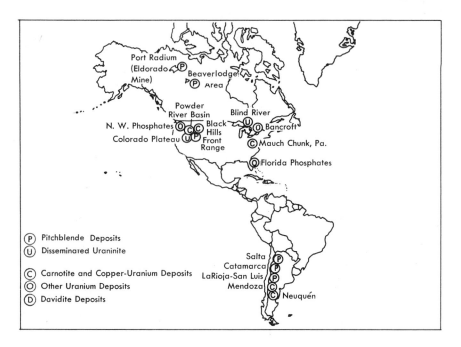

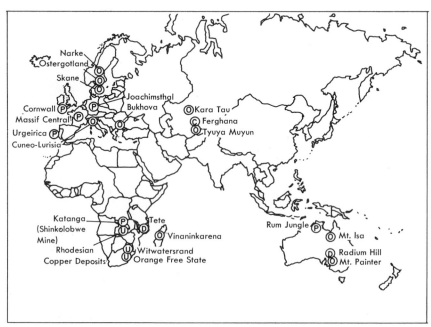

Fig. 1–1. Significant uranium occurrences in the world.

of following the projected trends of known ore bodies. In the past few years, however, geologists have amassed great amounts of data and basic information to enable them to locate uranium in the earth's crust, to explain how and why it is concentrated under certain geologic conditions, and to indicate generally how much ore they can reasonably expect to discover in given areas during coming years.

This chapter summarizes some of the basic tenets of uranium geology, as known at the present time. More detailed information may be obtained from the references at the end of the chapter.

1–2. URANIUM GEOLOGY

1–2.1 Geochemistry of uranium. Uranium makes up about 1 to 2 ppm (parts per million) of the earth's crust. Its crustal abundance is greater than that of antimony, bismuth, mercury, silver, and gold, and is about the same or slightly less than that of cobalt, lead, and molybdenum. Its average concentration in some typical general geologic entities is as follows [1]*:

	Concentration of U, ppm
Low-silica igneous rocks	1
Intermediate igneous rocks	2
High-silica igneous rocks	4
Sedimentary rocks	2
Ground and stream water	0.0002
Ocean water	0.002
Petroleum	0.1

The tetravalent uranium ion is by far the most abundant in nature. It is stable under reducing conditions, as in magmas, or in sedimentary environments in which organic material is preserved. However, in nearly all solutions instrumental in its transfer, uranium is in a hexavalent state and under oxidizing conditions moves as the uranyl ion $(U^{+6}O_2)^{+2}$. In solutions ranging in pH from 1 to 5, the uranyl ion is most commonly in association with sulfates in the earth's crust. At the same time, several kinds of basic carbonate solutions with a pH of 8.5 or higher hold uranium as complex ions at temperatures above 150°C.

Although uranium in general is a comparatively soluble element, there are a number of effective precipitants. One of the most spectacular is carbonaceous matter, which acts in at least two ways: (1) it creates

---

* References are listed at the ends of the chapters.

reducing conditions, during decomposition, with the production of H_2S, thereby radically changing the pH; and (2) it possesses powerful capacity to adsorb uranium from many kinds of solutions. High base-exchange clays also have a high affinity for uranium. In areas where uraniferous solutions have a pH of 5 or less, any kind of carbonate acts as a precipitating agent.

Concentrations of uranium more than 10 times the average in the earth's crust, or more than 0.002 percent uranium, are formed by a variety of igneous and sedimentary rock-forming processes, as well as by ore-forming processes as they are ordinarily understood. The nearly ubiquitous geologic distribution of uranium stems from its chemical and physical properties, particularly its polyvalence, its large atomic radius, its chemical reactivity, the relative solubility of many of its hexavalent compounds in aqueous solutions, and its relative abundance compared with some other ore metals. These attributes permit uranium to form compounds with many other elements, to enter the structure of a wide variety of minerals, to take part in many chemical reactions, and hence to be deposited in many rocks and minerals of diverse origins and compositions. The same properties that lead to the wide geologic distribution of uranium also lead to its dispersion. Uranium concentrations, therefore, are not as great as those of other, less active metals of comparable abundance, such as lead and molybdenum. The partition of uranium from other elements and its subsequent concentration in valuable deposits seem to be favored by its large radius and high valence, which deter its concentration in ordinary rock-forming minerals; also, the relative insolubility of its common tetravalent compounds in aqueous solutions leads to the precipitation of uranium in a wide variety of environments where reducing conditions prevail.

1–2.2 Geology of uranium districts. Considering the geochemical behavior of uranium, its has been recognized that at least three general geologic factors must be considered together in interpreting the geology of a uranium district: (1) the nature of the mineralizing solutions, (2) the structural framework through which they have moved, and (3) the nature of the host rocks in which the ore has been deposited.

Knowledge of the nature of the ore-bearing solution has come largely through study and interpretation of the varied mineral assemblages and alteration effects that occur with uranium ore types which have been developed. Experience has shown that many different kinds of solutions, containing a wide assortment of other metals and nonmetallic elements, carry uranium through the rocks.

For example, three important mineralogic types of uraniferous veins have been recognized: (1) nickel-cobalt-native-silver veins, (2) silica-iron-lead veins, and (3) iron-titanium veins [2]. The nickel-cobalt-native-silver veins are characterized by pitchblende, a complex assemblage of sulfides and carbonates, and minor amounts of silica. They occur typically in sedimentary and volcanic rocks, and are represented by large deposits such as those at Shinkolobwe and Great Bear Lake. The silica-iron-lead veins are also characterized by pitchblende, but the assemblage of asso-ciated minerals is generally simple—mainly pyrite, galena, relatively minor molybdenum minerals, and quartz or jasper. They occur chiefly in intrusive rocks, such as deposits at Urgeirica, Portugal, and Marysvale, Utah. The iron-titanium veins are characterized by uranium titanates such as davidite, together with ilmenite, rutile, and quartz. For the most part, they occur in metamorphic rocks and are typified by the deposits at Radium Hill, South Australia. Disseminated iron oxides are widespread in all these deposits.

The temperature of the transporting fluids and the depth and pressure at the site of deposition of the uranium veins are believed to have varied widely. Field evidence strongly indicates that most of the pitchblende veins were formed at depths shallow enough and at pressures low enough to provide open spaces along regular fissures.

Uranium is associated principally with vanadium minerals in the eastern part of the Colorado Plateau and with copper minerals in the western part. In the Silver Reef district of southwestern Utah, silver, copper, and uranium are associated in deposits contained in the Chinle formation. In the Wyoming Basins there are various phosphate, arsenate, carbonate, and oxide minerals of copper and other metallic elements associated with uranium. In Texas, high arsenic and molybdenum analy-ses have been reported from uranium deposits in the Jackson formation. Arsenic and molybdenum also are prominent in the uraniferous lignites of North Dakota. The molecular structures of the vanadates, phosphates, and arsenates are remarkably similar, and the elements involved are exactly those which have a chemical reactivity, like that of uranium, that permits their extensive migration and diffusion from ultimate sources.

In certain types of deposits, the prime importance of geologic structure and its effect on the shape and size of ore deposits is clear and has been recognized for many years. Almost without exception, the pitchblende-bearing vein deposits show a marked control by structural features and have a tendency to produce the richest ore where open spaces are abun-dant. Recently, in hydrothermal vein deposits, it has been found that rich and extensive orebodies occur in groups of fractures along areas of structural flattening, or on structural "terraces." Excellent examples of this relationship are seen in the Verna mine of the Lake Athabasca dis-trict, in Canada, and in the Schwartzwalder mine, Ralston Creek district, Colorado. The regional distribution of areas undergoing tension in the earth's crust during geologic history can be related to known uranium deposition in the Plateau and the Wyoming Basins. The strong influence of structural flats and terraces in sedimentary deposits has been demonstrated by U. S. Geological Survey studies in the Black Hills [3].

Any consideration of favorable types of host rocks must go hand in hand with the chemistry of ore solutions and the mineralogy of the ores. For example, the fact that most important uranium-bearing vein deposits are found in either granitic rock, continental sedimentary rocks, or volcanic flows probably means that these rocks are chemically effective in precipitating uranium from most hydrothermal solutions. Hot sulfate solutions, which are characteristically acid, are known to have the ability to alter and mineralize granitic rocks. As a group, these feldspar- and quartz-rich rocks also tend to neutralize alkaline solutions. They are relatively permeable and so act as good "soakers" of volatile or aqueous ore carriers.

The common denominators for favorable sedimentary rocks are horizons of high permeability interfingered with low permeability, and the presence of precipitants that may be carbonaceous matter (causing chemical reduction), carbonate cement (having a neutralizing effect on sulfate solutions), interstitial clays (with high absorption effect), or perhaps others. Most of the sediments are arkosic, i.e., rich in feldspar and quartz (therefore approximating favorable granitic rocks chemically) and are stream-deposited (which provides the contrasting permeability).

1–2.3 Uranium provinces. Early in the attempt to understand and systematize uranium geology, it was recognized that certain areas or belts in the earth's crust may be regarded as "uranium provinces." Known deposits of significant size and grade tend to form groups that are related in their distribution to certain broad geologic features. With the discovery of hundreds of new deposits throughout the world during the past 13 years, this concept has been strengthened, for each significant new discovery has tended to confirm the existence of previously established "provinces."

At least five broad uranium provinces outside the Soviet bloc can be outlined:

(1) A broad area including the granitic intrusives of Appalachian age in western Europe and parts of North Africa.

(2) The borders of the African Shield.

(3) The western and southern borders of the Canadian Shield.

(4) Portions of the Cordillera of North and South America, from Montana and Washington in the United States (possibly from Alaska) southward to central Chile and Argentina.

(5) Areas including granitic intrusives in Australia.

In several of these uranium areas, early experience has led to expectation of only certain types of deposits. Thus, for example, disseminated deposits in continental sediments are more commonly sought in the United States than in other parts of the world. Similarly there is a tendency to expect only vein deposits in the area of igneous intrusives. In view of the many possibilities for varied types of deposits everywhere, many areas in all known uranium belts have yet to be thoroughly explored. From this point of view, uranium geology, exploration, and development throughout the world are still very young, in spite of the tremendous effort that has been put into them in the past few years.

1–2.4 Classification of types of deposits. The interrelationship of all geologic factors controlling uranium deposition permits a more or less systematic classification of deposits. Table 1–1 lists only the so-called high-grade uranium ore deposits of the types that have produced, or show definite promise of producing, raw materials for the atomic energy industry under present economic conditions. Not included are such possible low-grade sources as black shales, phosphate beds, or granites, which are discussed below. In the group of ores listed, the most substantial reserves of the world are in one general type—disseminated deposits in sedimentary or metamorphosed sedimentary rocks.

1–3. URANIUM SOURCES IN THE UNITED STATES

The major uranium-producing districts of the United States are in the central and southern parts of the Colorado Plateau, in the Tertiary basins of Wyoming, on the flanks of the Black Hills of South Dakota and Wyoming, in southern Oregon, and in northeastern Washington. Other promising deposits of ore grade are known in eastern Colorado, and on the Gulf Coast of Texas. In addition, low-grade sources, not now used in commercial production, exist in certain lignite, phosphate, and black shale beds throughout the United States. The map of Fig. 1–2 shows the principal uranium districts in the United States.

Known uranium ore reserves in the United States have increased markedly in the past few years. The distribution of these reserves by areas, as of December 1957, is shown in Table 1–2. Uranium ore production in the United States reached an annual rate of more than 4,000,000 tons by the end of 1957. Ore production figures for 1957 and the last half of 1956 are shown in Table 1–3.

1–3.1 Colorado Plateau area. The Colorado Plateau region is a segment of the great Cordillera of North America, comprised of adjoining parts of the states of Colorado, Utah, Arizona, and New Mexico, and encom-

TABLE 1-1

Classification of Some Important Uranium Deposits

Typical mineral associations, depositional environments listed in descending order of their temperatures, left to right

Host rock	Davidite with ilmenite, quartz, and biotite	Uraninite with Cu, Mo, and Fe, and quartz, actinolite, and chlorite	Uraninite with Ni, Co, Ag, and Cu minerals, and carbonate (with minor quartz) gangue	Uraninite and/or brannerite with gold and iron sulfides	Uraninite with galena, pyrite, and silica minerals	Uraninite with Cu minerals (Cu–U deposits)	Uraninite and/or coffinite with Mo and As minerals	Uraninite and black minerals	"Carnotite ores" (or tyuyamunite)	Uranium phosphates and arsenate	Autunite–torbernite with limonite	Uraniferous lignite
Granite		Copiapo District, Chile*	Caribou, Colorado*		Urgeiriça, Portugal						Spokane, Washington*	
Rhyolitic rocks											Lakeview, Oregon*	North and South Dakota
Continental conglomerates, sandstones, mudstones, and shale					Los Ochos Mine, Colorado	Happy Jack Mine, Wyoming	Lucky Mc Mine, Wyoming	Mi Vida Mine, Utah	Oxidized Uravan Belt Deposits, Colorado; Haystack Buttes, New Mexico	Oxidized Wyoming Basin Deposits		
Fresh-water limestone											Pryor Mountains, Montana*	
Altered conglomerates				Witwatersrand, South Africa and Blind River, Ontario					Eastern Pennsylvania*			
Quartzite			Shinkolobwe, Belgian Congo									
Gneiss	Radium Hill, Australia			Colorado Front Range	Gunnar Deposit, Saskatchewan							
Schist			Joachimsthal, Czechoslovakia		Schwartzwalder Mine, Colorado			Ace Mine, Saskatchewan			Cunco District, Italy	
Volcanics					Ace Mine, Saskatchewan							

* Nonproducer at present.

TABLE 1–2

MEASURED, INDICATED, AND INFERRED DOMESTIC
ORE RESERVES (DECEMBER 31, 1957)

Area	Tons	Percent of total ore reserves	Grade, percent U_3O_8
New Mexico	53,300,000	68.3	0.26
Wyoming	9,200,000	11.8	0.26
Utah	5,700,000	7.3	0.37
Colorado	4,100,000	5.3	0.29
Arizona	1,400,000	1.8	0.32
Washington, Oregon, and Nevada	1,900,000	2.4	0.23
North and South Dakota	600,000	0.8	0.25
Others	1,800,000	2.3	0.23
Total	78,000,000	100.0	0.27 average

TABLE 1–3

ORE PRODUCTION IN THE UNITED STATES

	Production rate, tons of dry ore per year
1956 Second half	1,660,000
1957 First half	1,706,000
1957 Second half	1,970,000
1957 Total	3,676,000

passing about 140,000 square miles. The region is made up of many plateau-like areas, ranging from 4500 to 7000 feet in elevation, but there are possibly more areas of valleys, plains, mesas, buttes, and mountains than of plateaus. Uranium-vanadium-copper deposits in the Colorado Plateau are widely distributed and have many common geologic characteristics [4]. Deposits in this area have constituted the principal source of uranium in the United States. The major uranium mining districts are:

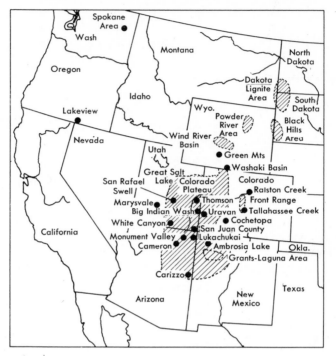

FIG. 1–2. Principal uranium districts in the United States.

San Rafael Swell district, Emery County, Utah
Thompson district, Grand County, Utah
Uravan mineral belt, Mesa, Montrose, and San Miguel Counties, Colorado
Big Indian Wash district, San Juan County, Utah
White Canyon district, San Juan County, Utah
Monument Valley district, Navajo County, Arizona
Luckachukai district, Apache County, Arizona
Cameron district, Coconino County, Arizona
Ambrosia Lake district, McKinley County, New Mexico
Grants district, McKinley and Valencia Counties, New Mexico
Laguna district, Valencia County, New Mexico

Vanadium-bearing uranium ores were discovered in the eastern part of the Colorado Plateau in 1898, and there have followed, with only short recesses, nearly 60 years of mining these ores—first for radium, then for vanadium, and finally for uranium. For years the production was from oxidized ore in shallow mines, and the Plateau ores were known as "carnotite" ores. Recent extensive exploration and deeper mining have developed black, unoxidized vanadium-bearing uranium ore below or close

Location

to the water table, and uranium ore with other associated metals, both oxidized and unoxidized.

Three examples of the more important uranium districts of the Colorado Plateau are described in the Appendix. They are the Big Indian Wash-Lisbon Valley, the Laguna, and the Ambrosia Lake districts.

1–3.2 Wyoming basins. A group of Tertiary sedimentary basins in central and northeastern Wyoming and northwestern Colorado make up the second-largest uranium "province" in the United States.

The discovery, in 1951, of carnotite ores in sandstone strata of the Wasatch formation (Eocene) in the Powder River Basin of Wyoming was the forerunner of other uranium finds in Wyoming and in adjacent Moffat County, Colorado.

The deposits all have similar geologic environments in sedimentary host rocks of Eocene, Oligocene, or Miocene age [8]. Most occur in medium- to coarse-grained or conglomeratic sandstones. Cross-bedding is a common feature of these sandstones, and they characteristically contain carbonaceous material and calcareous, ferruginous, or phosphatic cement.

Uranium vanadates are abundant in the Powder River Basin; phosphates and arsenates are the common minerals in the Wind River Basin; and silicates and sulfates are plentiful in the Green Mountains, Great Divide Basin, and Washakie Basin. The presence of uraninite has been established in the Wind River Basin, Powder River Basin, Green Mountains, and the Washakie Basin. Deposits containing uranium minerals disseminated in sandstone strata as grain coatings and cement seem to be of most significance.

Additional description of the Wyoming Basins is given in the Appendix.

1–3.3 Other uranium-producing districts of the United States. Although approximately 90 percent of current uranium ore production in the United States comes from the Colorado Plateau and Wyoming, there are other smaller but significant uranium districts, some showing promise of greatly increased production in the future. Among these are the following eight:

    Black Hills of South Dakota and Wyoming
    Marysvale, Utah
    Spokane Indian Reservation, Washington
    Cochetopa district, Saguache County, Colorado
    Ralston Creek district, Jefferson County, Colorado
    Tallahassee Creek district, Fremont County, Colorado
    Lakeview district, Oregon
    Texas Gulf Coastal Plain

Brief descriptions of these districts are given in the Appendix.

1–3.4 Possible future uranium sources in the United States. In addition to the above, there are great tonnages of other, lower-grade materials that may be potential sources. They are not worked now because of low grade or the fact that suitable ore processing techniques have not been developed.

Uraniferous lignitic deposits. In the lignite deposits of western North and South Dakota, uranium concentrations of 0.1 percent U_3O_8 or more are found in an area about 100 miles square north and east of the contiguous corners of the Dakotas and Montana. The deposits lie between the Black Hills Uplift and the Williston Basin, a few miles west of the Cedar Creek anticline. The uraniferous lignite is found almost entirely in the Paleocene Fort Union formation [16]. This formation, the principal coal-producing unit of the Dakotas, contains many lignite beds, ranging from thin layers to beds more than 20 feet thick. Discoveries of ore-grade uraniferous lignite, however, have been confined to the beds less than about 3 feet thick. The thicker beds examined do not contain uranium in significant quantities.

Uranium is known in various lignite beds at many horizons in the Fort Union formation. Age of the host bed has no known relationship to uranium deposition. The truncated Fort Union strata dip gently into the Williston Basin; the progressively older beds are exposed from north to south. All known deposits lie within 200 feet of this upper erosional contact.

The mineralogy of the uraniferous lignites is very complex. Visible uranium minerals account for only a small proportion of the total uranium content. Autunite, zeunerite, abernathyite, torbernite, and uranophane have been identified from various properties in Cave Hills and Slim Buttes. They are in the strongly weathered and oxidized zone, near the surface, and in the richest portions of the deposits. Most of the uranium is disseminated through the lignite and is adsorbed on the organic material.

The uranium grade of the Dakota lignite is comparable to that of other ore types and other areas. Many picked samples contain several percent uranium and a few contain 10 percent and more, but they are not representative of the average grade of any orebody. Nearly all exposed lignite is weathered, and most contains oxidized minerals such as limonite and jarosite. Pyrite, which is not uncommon, may be expected in greater proportions as mining progresses beyond the weathered zone. Gypsum in joints, fractures, and along bedding surfaces is common in some areas.

Semiquantitative spectrographic analyses, made by the U. S. Geological Survey on samples of ashed lignite, show significant concentrations of arsenic and molybdenum. A plot of the U-As-Mo values indicates that all three elements tend to peak together. Other analyses have indicated that molybdenum is widely distributed in the lignite and that many trace elements exist.

Large potential reserves of uranium in concentrations of less than 0.1 percent U_3O_8 are also contained in coal and lignite, particularly in Cretaceous and Tertiary sedimentary rocks, in other regions of the United States [17]. The concentration of uranium in the ash of coal provides a possible means of recovering uranium as a by-product. Uranium-bearing lignite occurs in the Salt Lake formation of Pliocene age in southern Idaho, and in Tertiary sediments in Nevada and southern California. Uranium-bearing coal is present in the Wasatch Eocene formation in Wyoming, in the Laramie Cretaceous formation in Colorado, in the Mesaverde Cretaceous formation in New Mexico, and in the Bear River Cretaceous formation in southeastern Idaho. Paleozoic bituminous and anthracite coals in the North Central and Eastern United States contain only very small quantities of uranium. The distribution of uranium in coal is erratic. In many areas uranium is preferentially concentrated at the top of the stratigraphically highest coal beds. In the Red Desert area of Wyoming, it is concentrated in coal beds adjacent to permeable units of the enclosing strata.

Uranium is thought to have been deposited in coal by epigenetic solutions. When there was more than could be chemically combined with the coal, uranium minerals such as carnotite, autunite, torbernite, metazeunerite, and coffinite may have formed.

Uraniferous phosphate rock. Marine phosphate rocks in the United States commonly contain 0.005 to 0.03 percent uranium. The uranium content increases roughly with increasing phosphate content, but is generally low in rocks that contain more than a few percent CO_2 [18]. Aluminum phosphate deposits derived from the weathering of phosphate rocks and phosphatic nodules in some marine black shale formations contain similar amounts of uranium. Most of the uranium in these materials does not occur as a separate mineral phase but substitutes for calcium in carbonate fluorapatite or crandallite. A few occurrences of tyuyamunite and torbernite have been reported from highly weathered phosphate rocks, however, and these and other secondary uranium minerals, such as carnotite and autunite, are not uncommon in fossil bones and teeth that have been exposed to uranium-bearing solutions after burial. Because marine phosphate deposits are of wide extent, they contain large tonnages of uranium, some of which can be recovered under favorable conditions as a by-product of the manufacture of triple superphosphate.

Principal uraniferous phosphate rocks in the United States are the Phosphoria formation of Permian age in Montana, Wyoming, Idaho, Utah, and Nevada, and the Hawthorn Miocene formation and the Bone Valley Pliocene formation in Florida.

Uraniferous marine black shales. Uranium is disseminated in minor amounts, generally not exceeding 0.02 percent, in many marine black shales in the United States. Two hundred or more formations, ranging in age from pre-Cambrian to Tertiary, consist wholly or in part of black shale, and one or more of these is present in nearly every state [19].

Most uraniferous black shale units are thin blanketlike deposits of Paleozoic age that have very little variation in thickness or lithology over wide areas and were deposited at an exceedingly slow rate. The Chattanooga shale and its equivalents, such as the New Albany, Ohio, and Woodford formations, which range from late Devonian to early Mississippian age, are made up of such a blanket deposit that was laid down in the eastern and central parts of the United States. This shale, which averages about 50 feet in thickness over much of the area, contains between 0.001 and 0.01 percent uranium. Several thin and widespread black shales of Pennsylvanian age in the mid-continent and thin beds of Permian phosphatic black shales in the Phosphoria formation in Idaho, Montana, and Wyoming have comparable uranium contents.

1–4. URANIUM SOURCES IN CANADA

Four principal areas along the western and southern margins of the Canadian Shield have contributed, and are contributing, many thousands of tons of uranium to the supply of the Western world. They are (1) the Great Bear Lake district, Northwest Territories; (2) the Beaverlodge district, Saskatchewan; (3) the Blind River district, Ontario; and (4) the Bancroft district, Ontario. These districts are shown in the map of Fig. 1–3.

1–4.1 Great Bear Lake district. The Eldorado mine, on the east shore of Great Bear Lake in the Northwest Territories (developed about 1930 for radium) was one of the first sources of uranium for the United States. It was in operation at the beginning of the United States atomic program.

The region is characterized by deposits of pitchblende or native silver, or both [20], and some also contain an unusually large number of other metallic minerals. The most common gangue minerals are quartz and the carbonates, which occur as small pitchblende-bearing stringers or lenses, large complex orebodies in fault zones, quartz veins containing a little pitchblende, or "giant quartz veins" carrying a little pitchblende. Principal deposits are in rocks of the Archean complex, but some have been found in younger granitic rocks.

The only settlement in the region other than small camps is the establishment of Eldorado Mining and Refining (1944) Limited, at Labine Point, about midway along the east shore of Great Bear Lake. The name of this camp is Port Radium.

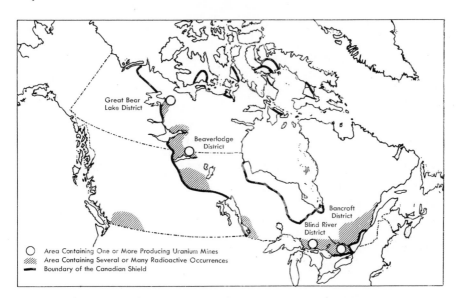

FIG. 1–3. Principal uranium districts in Canada.

In the Eldorado mine, orebodies range from narrow, high-grade veins to stock-works up to 40 feet wide that are only partly of ore grade. Individual veins are from less than an inch to about 10 feet wide. The orebodies are distributed at irregular intervals within four more or less parallel fault zones, some of which eventually coalesce in the northeastern part of the mine. The average strike is north 65 degrees east, and dips range from 60 degrees north to vertical. Ore shoots of minimum stoping width are from 50 to 700 feet long, and have been followed vertically for more than 600 feet. Where multiple stringer zones and masses of pitchblende occur the ore bodies widen to as much as 15 feet.

1–4.2 Beaverlodge district. Another very important uranium-producing area of Canada is the Beaverlodge district, lying north of Lake Athabasca in northwestern Saskatchewan, where numerous deposits were discovered in the late 1940's. Deposits are of two main types: (1) pitchblende in veins, lenses, pods, stringer systems, and disseminations in Archean or Proterozoic rocks; and (2) pegmatite containing uraninite [20]. Pitchblende deposits are the more important.

Mineralogically, the pitchblende occurrences are divisible into complex and simpler types. The complex, represented by the deposits at the Nicholson property and at Fish Hook Bay, contain in addition to pitchblende considerable amounts of cobalt-nickel and other metallic minerals. The common gangue consists of carbonate minerals, but quartz or chlorite is also found in some deposits. Deposits of this class have been found only within a small part of the Beaverlodge region, in or near strata of dolomite and ferruginous quartzite, which suggests that zoning, or the type of host rock, may have been responsible for the restricted distribution of deposits. The simpler type consists mainly of hematite, with different proportions of pitchblende; other metallic minerals are generally lacking or found in minor amounts. Carbonate is the most common nonmetallic constituent, but, in many deposits quartz and chlorite are plentiful.

Often deposits are in fractures and brecciated zones close to a fault. Several of the most important are close to the prominent northeast-trending St. Louis fault. Faults are, therefore, believed to have been the main loci of mineralization. In contrast with the principal deposits of Great Bear Lake, which lie within fault zones, very few have thus far been found within the main Beaverlodge fault zones. Instead, most of those believed to be related to faults are in fracture and crush zones in the walls of the faults. The pitchblende deposits, believed to be of late Proterozoic age, were derived from granitic rocks that are not exposed in the area.

The single property with the largest ore reserves for future production is the Gunnar mine, in the southwest part of the Beaverlodge district. This deposit is largely overlain by overburden and until recently had been explored almost wholly by vertical diamond-drill holes [21]. The ore occurs in a mass of albite monzonite overlying well-banded gneiss and amphibolite, which strike north 60 degrees east and dip between 45 and 70 degrees southeast. Drill holes show that this monzonite passes into well-banded gneisses at depth. The albite monzonite is overlain locally by outcrops of "grey capping granite."

This deposit is unusual in that pitchblende and secondary uranium minerals are disseminated through the monzonite without any observed structural control. In fact, they are dispersed so widely that boundaries of the orebody can be defined only by assay. Most high-grade shoots are zones of brecciation, often marked by red hematite, and a few are in veins carrying massive hematite and pitchblende. The primary deposits have been affected by widespread secondary alteration. Pitchblende is the only recognized primary uranium mineral. Other metallic minerals are hematite and traces of pyrite, chalcopyrite, and galena. Nonmetallic introduced minerals are calcite, dolomite, chlorite, and quartz.

1–4.3 Blind River district. The Blind River district is adjacent to the north shore of Lake Huron, in Ontario, some 90 miles east of Sault Ste. Marie. Here, all the uranium ore of present importance is found in quartz-pebble conglomerate (Mississagi quartzite) [22]. The quartzite containing the ore-bearing conglomerates is characteristically cross-bedded and green colored.

The unique and important feature of the uranium mineralization here is its uniform distribution throughout very large masses. The Pronto, the two Nordic, and the Quirke orebodies have individual lengths ranging from 3800 to 7500 feet and consistent thicknesses that range from 8 to 13 feet. These mineralized masses are ore-bearing to the maximum depth explored in the Pronto of over 2000 feet and in the Algom-Quirke of over 3400 feet. The uranium content, surprisingly uniform both throughout an individual orebody and between those found miles apart, averages between 2.0 and 2.5 pounds U_3O_8 per ton (0.100 to 0.125 percent U_3O_8).

Minerals present are pyrite or pyrrhotite, chalcopyrite, galena, molybdenite, rutile, anatase, scheelite, cobaltite, magnetite, and gold. The uranium-bearing minerals are brannerite, pitchblende, uraninite (?), and "thucholite." Pyrite and/or pyrrhotite content of the ore ranges from 3 to 15 percent by weight and averages about 5 percent; all other minerals named are very sparsely distributed and are only occasionally seen by the unaided eye.

1–4.4 Bancroft area. In the Bancroft area of eastern Ontario, uranium occurs generally in pegmatitelike deposits of the Grenville Sub-Province along the southern part of the Canadian Shield. The relatively highly uraniferous pegmatites of this area were the first in the western hemisphere to be exploited profitably for their uranium content.

1–5. URANIUM SOURCES IN THE UNION OF SOUTH AFRICA

In the Union of South Africa, uranium is principally a by-product of the gold ores and tailings of the world-famous Witwatersrand conglomerates of pre-Cambrian age. Here nearly 15 million tons of slime residue per year, mostly from current gold production works and partly from old dumps, are treated for their uranium content. This tonnage is handled in 17 uranium processing plants scattered throughout the "Rand."

In the original ores, the uranium occurs in a mixture of hydrocarbon and pitchblende or uraninite or both, known as "thucholite." It is a uranium-bearing variety of the so-called "carbon," well known upon the Rand, occurring in flecks, streaks, and impregnations in the matrix and as a replacement of both matrix and pebbles of the conglomerates. The thorium content of these radioactive hydrocarbons is low [23].

1–6. OTHER URANIUM SOURCES OF THE WESTERN WORLD

There are a number of other mining districts from which significant amounts of uranium ore are being extracted. A few of the more important are briefly described below.

1–6.1. Shinkolobwe, Belgian Congo.   In the early days of atomic energy development, the principal source of uranium for the United States was the Shinkolobwe mine in the Katanga region of the Belgian Congo. This mine still remains an appreciable contributor to the world's uranium supply.

The host rocks in the Shinkolobwe deposit are the so-called Mine Series of the Katanga System of pre-Cambrian age [24]. A characteristic structural feature of the Katanga is a series of folds bowed northward, with their axial planes dipping to the north.   Great overthrust faults are particularly prominent in the western Katanga.   In these faults, rocks of the Mine Series have been thrust from the northeast over the Kundelungu Series.

The Shinkolobwe mine is in one of many complex fault structures. One of many structural complications in this orebody is a westward-trending fault zone crossing the strike of the Mine Series at a low angle. This zone of faulting is characterized by numerous irregular cross faults of varying length and dip. The mineralization in these cross faults is localized where they intersect the favorable ore horizons—the thin-bedded quartzites, cellular quartzites, and the dolomitic shales (the three middle members of the Mine Series), and in the brecciated zones adjacent to the principal vein structures.

Veins may contain almost pure pitchblende with little other filling material, or they may consist predominantly of cobalt or copper sulfides with or without pitchblende. In other instances, pitchblende accompanied by cobalt minerals occurs in a quartz-carbonate vein matrix. Clearly, the existence of open fissures and brecciated rocks favored pitchblende ore deposition. Cobalt mineralization, on the other hand, is not confined to brecciated zones and cross faults but is disseminated through the more massive dolomitic wall rocks.

In addition to the principal pitchblende-cobalt mineralization, the Shinkolobwe ores carry significant quantities of copper, molybdenum and iron sulfides, thorium and tungsten, and gold, platinum, and palladium. Oxidation of the orebodies has extended several hundred feet in depth. A host of complex hydrous oxides, phosphates, and silicates such as becquerelite, curite, uranophane, and torbernite are in the near-surface deposits.

1–6.2 Australia.   Increasing amounts of uranium ore are being mined and processed in three Australian states—the Northern Territory, South Austraila, and western Queensland.

In the Northern Territory, at Rum Jungle, uranium minerals occur in carbonaceous shale which has been folded, sheared, and dragged by faulting [25]. The orebodies are close to the margin of granite, intruding pre-Cambrian sediments, and also close to a major fault that displaces the southern part of the granite to the southwest. The two most important deposits are White's and Dyson's. At White's and adjacent prospects, pyrite and chalcopyrite are associated with the uranium. Fine-grained disseminated lead and cobalt minerals are also present in the vicinity. The primary uranium mineral is uraninite but secondary minerals occur to shallow depths below the surface. At Dyson's deposit the uranium mineral is princrpally saleite. Although most geologists regard the deposits as of the hydrothermal replacement type, possibly all the minerals except the chalcopyrite were deposited with the sediments. The ore averages about 0.3 percent U_3O_8.

In South Australia, at Radium Hill, near Olary, uranium ore is being mined and concentrated and the concentrates sent for treatment to Port Pirie. Deposits consist of several parallel lodes occupying fissures in pre-Cambrian gneiss. The lodes contain quartz, black and bronze biotite, and ilmenite, and the uranium mineral is davidite. Coatings of carnotite occur near the surface. Average grade is less than 0.2 percent U_3O_8.

At Crocker's Well, near Olary, coarse disseminations of brannerite occur in granitic rocks. Davidite is also present, at Mt. Victoria. In northwestern Queensland, in the Mt. Isa area, the Mary Kathleen deposit is in rock consisting mainly of allanite, garnet, and apatite, and containing uraninite and rare earths. A new mineral (a barosilicate of cerium, etc.) has been reported and the name "stillwellite" proposed for it. Uraninite also occurs as inclusions in allanite and stillwellite. The deposit is in a calc-silicate sequence of metamorphosed sedimentary rocks but its structural relationships and origin need further study.

1–6.3 France. During the past few years, considerable capacity for uranium ore production has been developed in a number of French mines. Several more are being developed. At present, nearly all uranium deposits in France are in areas underlain by granitic intrusive rocks, namely the Massif Central, the Massif of Britanny, and the Vosges. Aside from the uranium-bearing carbonaceous schists of the Schaentzel, in the Vosges, all French deposits are of the hydrothermal vein type. Pitchblende, commonly associated with fluorite and silica gangue, occurs in vein fillings in granitic rocks. Common secondary minerals derived therefrom are parsonite, autunite, and chalcolite.

1–6.4 Portugal. Discovery of uranium deposits in Portugal dates back to 1907 [26]. Some were mined for radium as early as 1911 and were brought to peak production in 1926, when Portugal was fourth among the world producers. As in France, the most important deposits in Portugal are concentrated in granitic intrusives, known as the Douro and Beira granitic masses. These consist essentially of two mica granite porphyries, in which biotite predominates. There are, however, variations of medium- to fine-grained granite, and related rock types.

Uranium-bearing veins are nearly exclusively in the granite porphyry and form a metallogenic province with three distinct mineral zones: (1) Viseu-Nelas-Carregal do Sal (including the Urgeirica mine), (2) Guarda-Belmonte-Sabugal, and (3) Trancoso-Aguiar da Beira-Moimenta da Beira.

Portuguese uranium deposits are of the low-temperature primary vein type and are characterized by the presence of quartz, jasper, and chalcedony. The uranium occurs as the primary mineral, pitchblende, and as the secondary minerals, i.e., phosphates, silicates, oxides, hydrates, and sulfates, associated with pyrite, marcasite, galena, sphalerite, and chalcopyrite.

1–6.5 Argentina. Uranium deposits have been known in Argentina since 1936, but not until 1952, when the Argentina National Committee on Atomic Energy (now the Comisión Nacional de la Energía Atómica) and a government uranium program were established, were producing mines developed [27]. Today several mines, with varied types of deposits, are in modest production. Average grade for all types of deposits is about 0.25 percent U_3O_8, with the vein deposits averaging somewhat higher.

Hydrothermal vein deposits occur in crystalline schist and quartzite, metamorphosed slates, argillaceous or sandy sediments, and volcanic rocks. Deposits are distributed mostly along the contacts of these rocks. The gangue consists of quartz, carbonates, and fluorite. The most common metal association is uranium-copper.

Deposits belonging to the vein deposit group include Papagallos and Soberania, in Mendoza and La Estela (La Marquesa) in San Luis; and Santa Brigida, San Victorio, and others, in the zone of Sanogasta, in La Rioja. Uranium-copper (low-vanadium) ore is present at Esperanza, in Salta, and at La Cieneguita in Catamarca. Uranium-nickel ore is found in La Rioja, and at La Niquelina, in Salta.

Deposits due to circulating solutions in continental sediments, and somewhat similar to the deposits of uranium and copper of the Colorado Plateau (United States), include the deposits of southern Mendoza, namely Cerro Huemul, Agua Botada, Cerro Mirano, and Pampa Amarilla.

Bodies and veins of asphaltite, the ash of which contains up to 1 percent U_3O_8, occur in Mendoza and Neuquén.

1–6.6 Sweden. The only known commercial source of uranium in Sweden at present is in certain alum shales. Uranium in the alum shales (in concentrations of 0.01 percent or more) is found in upper

Cambrian strata [28].   Districts of special interest are the Billingen-Falbygden, Vastergotland Province, and the province of Narke, where the uranium content ranges from 0.02 to 0.04 percent and higher. Strata richest in uranium also contain a coallike substance, "kolm," forming lenses or layers in the shale. The uranium content of about 0.3 percent makes up about 5 percent of the total uranium content of the highest-yielding part of this zone.

The uraniferous shale district of Billingen-Falbygden has been thoroughly investigated by core drilling.   This district covers a triangular area of about 500 square kilometers.   The uranium-rich layer averages about 3 meters thick and has an average uranium content of about 0.03 percent.   Uranium reserves in the Billingen-Falbygden district can thus be estimated at about 1 million tons, much of which can apparently be mined.

The province of Narke has not yet been fully investigated.   With information collected from the Kvarntorp district, where the uranium-rich layer is about 5 or 6 meters thick and the uranium content about 0.02 percent, and from the distribution of alum shale in other districts of this province, reserves are roughly estimated to be about 100,000 tons, including the uranium content of "kolm."

It is an important economic fact that much of the uranium-rich zone of shale in the province of Narke can be open-pit mined, and that it covers another shale layer that yields about 5 percent oil.   Narke already has a large-scale production of shale oil.   The uranium shale in the district of Billingen, however, is mined mainly underground, and the potential oil recovery from it and from surrounding layers of shales in this district is only about 1 percent.

1–6.7 Spain. Several hydrothermal pitchblende-bearing veins have been developed during the past few years in the Sierra Morena of south-central Spain. The Sierra Morena region is underlain by a massif consisting largely of biotite granite. Fractures in the granite are filled by various veins of hydrothermal origin in which occur such minerals as white barren quartz, quartz with chalcopyrite and pyrite, calcite, quartz, and hematite [29]. Radioactive minerals that have been identified are torbernite, autunite, and radioactive ochers. At depth are primary uranium oxide minerals.

REFERENCES

1. V. E. MCKELVEY et al., Origin of Uranium Deposits, *Econ. Geol.* **50,** 464–533 (1955).

2. D. L. EVERHART and R. J. WRIGHT, The Geologic Character of Typical Pitchblende Veins, *Econ. Geol.* **48,** 77–95 (1953).

3. HENRY BELL III et al., Lithologic and Structural Control of Uranium Deposition in the Southern Black Hills, South Dakota, in *U. S. Geological Survey Professional Paper* No. 300. Washington, D. C.: U. S. Government Printing Office, 1956. (pp. 345–349)

4. V. C. KELLEY, Influence of Regional Structure and Tectonic History on the Origin and Distribution of Uranium on the Colorado Plateau, in *U. S. Geological Survey Professional Paper* No. 300. Washington, D. C.: U. S. Government Printing Office, 1956. (pp. 171–178)

5. Y. W. ISACHSEN and C. G. EVENSEN, Geology of Uranium Deposits of the Shinarump and Chinle Formations on the Colorado Plateau, in *U. S. Geological Survey Professional Paper* No. 300. Washington, D. C.: U. S. Government Printing Office, 1956. (pp. 273–275)

6. L. S. HILPERT and V. L. FREEMAN, Guides to Uranium Deposits in the Morrison Formation, Gallup-Laguna Area, New Mexico, in *U. S. Geological Survey Professional Paper* No. 300. Washington, D. C.: U. S. Government Printing Office, 1956. (pp. 299–302)

7. J. W. GABLEMAN et al., *Ambrosia Lake—New Mexico's Newest Uranium Bonanza*, paper presented at the Colorado Mining Association Meeting, Denver, Colorado, Feb. 4, 1956.

8. E. W. GRUTT, Uranium Deposits in Tertiary Sedimentary Rocks in Wyoming and Northern Colorado, in *U. S. Geological Survey Professional Paper* No. 300. Washington, D. C.: U. S. Government Printing Office, 1956. (pp. 361–370)

9. W. I. FINCH, Uranium in Terrestrial Sedimentary Rocks in the United States Exclusive of the Colorado Plateau, in *U. S. Geological Survey Professional Paper* No. 300. Washington, D. C.: U. S. Government Printing Office, 1956. (pp. 324–327)

10. G. W. WALKER and F. W. OSTERWALD, Relation of Secondary Uranium Minerals to Pitchblende-Bearing Veins at Marysvale, Piute County, Utah, in *U. S. Geological Survey Professional Paper* No. 300. Washington, D. C.: U. S. Government Printing Office, 1956. (p. 123)

11. E. E. THURLOW, Uranium Deposits at the Contact Metamorphosed Sedimentary Rocks and Granitic Intrusive Rocks in Western United States, in *U. S. Geological Survey Professional Paper* No. 300. Washington, D. C.: U. S. Government Printing Office, 1956. (pp. 85–88)

12. R. C. DERZAY, Geology of the Los Ochos Uranium Deposit, Saguache County, Colorado, in *U. S. Geological Survey Professional Paper* No. 300. Washington, D. C.: U. S. Government Printing Office, 1956. (pp. 137–141)

13. J. D. SCHLOTTMAN and A. V. GREEN, Denver Area Office, AEC, 1957. Unpublished.

14. B. A. MACPHERSON, Division of Raw Materials, AEC. (In preparation)

15. A. C. WATERS, U. S. Geological Survey, 1955. Unpublished.

16. J. W. KING, *Uraniferous Lignites in the Western Dakotas*, paper presented at the Colorado Mining Association Meeting, Denver, Colorado, Feb. 3, 1956.

17. J. D. VINE, Uranium-Bearing Coal in the United States, in *U. S. Geological Survey Professional Paper* No. 300. Washington, D. C.: U. S. Government Printing Office, 1956. (p. 405)

18. E. V. McKELVEY, Uranium in Phosphate Rock, in *U. S. Geological Survey Professional Paper* No. 300. Washington, D. C.: U. S. Government Printing Office, 1956. (p. 477)

19. V. E. SWANSON, Uranium in Marine Black Shales of the United States, in *U. S. Geological Survey Professional Paper* No. 300. Washington, D. C.: U. S. Government Printing Office, 1956. (p. 451)

20. A. H. LANG, Canadian Deposits of Uranium and Thorium, *Can. Dept. Mines and Tech. Surveys, Geol. Survey Can., Econ. Geol. Ser.* **16,** 46–47, 71–75 (1952).

21. S. C. ROBINSON, Mineralogy of Uranium Deposits, Goldfields, Saskatchewan, *Can. Dept. Mines and Tech. Surveys, Geol. Survey Can., Geol. Survey Bull.* **31,** 32-33 (1955).

22. F. R. JOUBIN, Uranium Deposits of the Algoma District, Ontario, *Trans. Geol. Assn. Canada* **57,** 431–437 (1954).

23. Uranium Soars to Prominence in South Africa's Gold Fields, *Eng. Mining J.* **154,** No. 5, 72–76 (1953).

24. P. L. MERRITT, Pitchblende—The Primary Source of Uranium, in *Proceedings of the Upper Peninsular of Michigan Mining Industries Conference on Radioactive Ores*, Houghton, Mich.: Michigan College of Mining and Technology, 1949. (pp. 8–12)

25. The Natural Occurrence of Uranium and Thorium in Australia, in *Proceedings of the International Conference on the Peaceful Uses of Atomic Energy*, Vol. 6. New York: United Nations, 1956. (P/1071, p. 91)

26. ROGERIO CAVACA, Uranium Prospecting in Portugal, in *Proceedings of the International Conference on the Peaceful Uses of Atomic Energy*, Vol. 6. New York: United Nations, 1956. (P/968, p. 183)

27. VICTORIO ANGELELLI, Distribution and Characteristics of the Uranium Deposits and Occurrences in the Argentine Republic, in *Proceedings of the International Conference on the Peaceful Uses of Atomic Energy*, Vol. 6. New York: United Nations, 1956. (P/999, p. 63)

28. ERIC SVENKE, The Occurrence of Uranium and Thorium in Sweden, in *Proceedings of the International Conference on the Peaceful Uses of Atomic Energy*, Vol. 6. New York: United Nations, 1956. (P/782, p. 198)

29. MANUEL ALIA, Radioactive Deposits and Possibilities in Spain, in *Proceedings of the International Conference on the Peaceful Uses of Atomic Energy*, Vol. 6. New York: United Nations, 1956. (P/1122, p. 196)

CHAPTER 2

URANIUM EXPLORATION AND MINING*

Uranium is found in a variety of host rocks: igneous, metamorphic, and sedimentary. Sedimentary host rocks may be of any age from Pre-Cambrian to Quaternary. For each type of occurrence there may be variations in exploration and mining techniques; the following discussion defines general principles that apply in most cases.

2-1. RADIATION DETECTION EQUIPMENT

Nuclear radiation, consisting of alpha particles, beta particles, and gamma rays, is a universal property of uranium deposits. Since exploration makes wide use of this property, it is important to understand the equipment used to measure radiation. Two kinds of radiation detectors, Geiger and scintillation counters, are used.

2-1.1 Geiger counters. The detecting element of this counter is the Geiger-Mueller tube, which commonly consists of a metal or glass shell with a wire throughout its length, insulated from the shell. The shell is very thin and contains gases such as helium, argon, or krypton. In operation, a positive charge of about 1000 volts is applied to the center wire. "A radioactive element, such as uranium, emits either alpha or beta particles and may emit gamma rays as well. When a Geiger counter is placed near such an element, the tube is struck by the radioactive emissions. Alpha particles are stopped by the tube wall. Beta particles have greater penetrating power, and some of these enter the tube and are recorded. Most gamma rays, which are still more penetrating, pass completely through the tube with no effect; however a few gamma rays, about 0.5 percent, enter the tube and interact with a molecule of the enclosed gas to produce electrons. These negative electrons are attracted toward the positively charged center wire and produce a negative electrical pulse as they collect on the wire." [1] Suitable amplifying circuits then magnify the pulses enough to operate a meter, neon bulb, or headphones; the

---

* Sections 2–1 and 2–2 of this chapter were prepared by Merle E. Crew, U. S. Atomic Energy Commission, and Section 2–3 by Gordon B. Peck, also of the Commission.

intensity of the radiation is shown directly on the meter or is indicated by the frequency of the neon light flashes or the clicking in the head-phones.

There are many possible arrangements of the tubes and associated amplifying circuits of a counter. In some the metal case for the circuitry also contains the tubes; in others the tube is attached to the case by a flexible lead; some use a number of tubes. There are counters small enough to be carried easily with other field equipment and others, used in logging drill holes, so large and complex that they must be mounted in a vehicle.

2–1.2 Scintillation counters. "A scintillation counter, like the Geiger counter, also measures gamma and beta rays, but its operation depends upon another property of radiation—the ability of gamma (and beta) rays to produce tiny, momentary flecks of light (scintillations) in crystals of certain compounds, such as sodium iodide and potassium iodide.

"The chief advantage of a scintillation counter is that it responds to a large proportion of the gamma rays that penetrate the crystal. In contrast, most Geiger tubes are discharged by less than 1 percent of the gamma rays which penetrate them." [1] Thus the scintillation counter is more sensitive.

The scintillations are detected individually and converted to electric pulses by a photomultiplier tube. These pulses then are amplified and fed to a suitable indicator, usually a meter calibrated in equivalent milli-roentgens per hour, as in a Geiger counter.

Because of its greater sensitivity, the scintillation counter is far superior to a Geiger counter for aerial prospecting and generally is considered best for surface prospecting. For the same reason, it is inferior to a Geiger counter for use in mines, where the radiation level is relatively high. A scintillation counter costs 3 to 5 times as much as a Geiger counter.

2–1.3 Factors affecting use of counters. The use of counters in measuring radioactivity of a hand specimen, outcrop, mine face, or soil cover, as well as for aerial measurements, requires an understanding of some of the common complicating factors. Since field counters detect mainly gamma rays, the properties of gamma rays are of principal concern. Gamma rays are not affected by electric or magnetic fields, travel in straight lines at the speed of light, produce scintillations in certain crystals, have neither mass nor electric charge, blacken photographic film, penetrate matter, and ionize gases.

The extent to which gamma rays are absorbed by any material depends on its density. Since all gamma rays do not have the same energy, some penetrate a greater thickness of a given material than others. The radiations emitted by the most radioactive products of uranium disintegration are largely absorbed by 3 inches of lead, 1 foot of rock, $2\frac{1}{2}$ feet of water, or several hundred feet of air. Hence a counter is ineffective for indicating gamma rays from a source beneath more than one foot of rock cover, an important point to remember. It is possible, however, in the case of uranium deposits that are not buried deeply, for radioactive daughter products to have been separated from the parent uranium and transported by natural processes to, or near enough to, the surface for ready detection by a counter.

When a counter of any type is used, it is important to remember that it will indicate a small amount of radiation in any location. This is known as "background count" and is caused partly by cosmic rays and partly by the small amount of radioactive material present in all rocks. Therefore, it is necessary to make periodic determinations of background count away from any more intense radioactive source. Different geologic formations have different background counts. Granites are normally the highest, followed by shales, sandstones, and limestones, in decreasing order. In prospecting, the significant counter reading is the amount above background, rather than the total reading. This is usually expressed as a multiple of the background count. Sampling a prospective ore for chemical assay is usually considered worth while when the count exceeds 10 times normal background.

Equilibrium of the deposit is another factor that must be understood if a counter is to be used to best advantage as a prospecting tool. Uranium is one of the few naturally occurring elements that are unstable and undergo spontaneous radioactive decay. Some of the daughter products that result from the decay are also radioactive. Uranium itself emits only alpha particles, which cannot be detected by an ordinary Geiger or scintillation counter, but various daughter products emit beta and gamma rays which can be detected.

About 1,000,000 years are required for newly purified uranium to reach equilibrium with all its daughter products. If the uranium has been separated from some of its daughter products within the last million years, through any of many geologic processes, it is out of equilibrium, and a counter reading of the uranium-rich portion normally will be lower than a similar reading for a sample of like size and grade that is in equilibrium. Conversely, if a radiometric assay is made of a sample enriched in daughter products, it will indicate a much higher radiometric equivalent than chemical assay. Both of these examples would be deposits "out of equilibrium." The equilibrium conditions may vary widely from sample to sample and, therefore, counter readings can be quite inaccurate.

Comparison of chemical and radiometric assays is the most common method for determining equilibrium. By this method it usually is possible to determine the equilibrium conditions in any particular area and to formulate a calibration curve by means of which counter readings can be interpreted more reliably.

Radiation exerts a mass effect on a counter because a large specimen gives off more gamma rays than a small specimen of the same grade and composition. Thus, a small specimen from a rock outcrop containing uniformly disseminated radioactive material always will give a lower reading than the parent outcrop. Likewise, a small specimen of high-grade ore may give the same counter reading as a larger specimen of lower-grade material.

2–2. EXPLORATION

A well-planned exploration program normally will consist of three phases: (1) preliminary reconnaissance, (2) detailed geologic studies, and (3) physical exploration. Areas comprising tens of thousands of square miles should be evaluated to select large sections worthy of reconnaissance. This evaluation is based on the knowledge of geology of existing ore districts, the extent of favorable formations, geologic structures, and other pertinent geologic factors.

2–2.1 Preliminary reconnaissance. The first step in preliminary reconnaissance should always be a literature study. Important information about rock formations, mode of occurrence of mineral deposits in or adjacent to the area, geologic structure, presence and degree of metamorphism, and many other important factors usually can be obtained more rapidly from the literature than from independent field observation.

If aerial photographs are available, a study of these should be made with a stereoscope. All sedimentary and tectonic features visible on the photographs should be traced on the photographs or on an overlay drawing. The use and study of aerial photographs should continue throughout the reconnaissance and detailed study phases, and new information should be added to the photographs or overlay as it becomes available.

The second step in preliminary reconnaissance is ground examination, often supplemented by aerial observation. The preliminary ground examination will indicate the presence or absence of rock types or geologic structures favorable for uranium deposition. Aerial observation gives a much quicker coverage of regional geology, often revealing geologic detail that might be difficult to recognize on the ground, such as subtle color changes indicating alteration associated with mine mineralizing solutions. Radiation detection instruments should be used in both ground and aerial reconnaissance.

2–2.2 Detailed geologic studies. Favorable indications from reconnaissance will warrant the second phase of exploration, detailed geologic studies. This phase includes detailed surface mapping, sampling, and preparing subsurface maps by projection of surface, drill-hole, and mine data. Geochemical, geophysical, or further surface and aerial radiation surveys may be made.

Detailed geologic studies have been described by Isachsen, Mitchum, and Wright [2]:

"Final maps which result from thorough work in all phases should show:

"1. Positions and shapes of all known ore bodies and mineralized areas, as well as areas drilled and found to be barren. As a result, an ore trend may become recognizable. Such information would be of immediate application in planning future exploration.

"2. Detailed geologic maps and profiles of selected mines; knowledge of the shape, size, and habit of local ore bodies are essential in looking for new deposits.

"3. Alteration, e.g., limonite intensity, bleaching, and other discolorations, both within the ore zone and in the rocks above and below.

"4. Distribution of critical rock units, particularly those which are ore-bearing.

"5. Structures, e.g., attitude of bedding, faults, joints, and other fractures, and fold axes.

"6. Sedimentary structures (lineations, cross-bedding, ripple marks, festoon bedding, intraformational scours, fossil logs, channels), which may suggest sedimentation directions in the ore-bearing rock.

"7. Sedimentary features such as lithologic variations, changes in color, changes in thickness, etc.; measured sections are necessary.

"8. Gamma radiation intensity; this is shown by an isoradiometric map of the ground surface.

"9. Approximate surface contour maps or surface profiles as well as structure contour maps, to serve as a basis for estimating drilling depths.

"The above information should be plotted on as few maps as is consistent with clear presentation."

2–2.3 Physical exploration. A careful analysis and interpretation of all geologic and economic data will determine whether the third phase, physical exploration, is warranted. Depending upon local conditions, physical exploration may be by trenching, stripping, mine openings, or drilling.

Physical conditions such as topography, elevation, climate, availability of water, and the geologic situation must be considered in deciding the type and extent of exploration, and the cost of the project must be weighed against the possible returns. The probable size, grade, and value of any orebody likely to be discovered must be estimated to determine how much can be spent on exploration, development, and mining. Development and mining costs can usually be estimated closely and may be used in arriving at permissible exploration costs for an orebody of a given size and grade at a given depth.

Trenching and stripping. Trenching, to expose a fresh outcrop for sampling, may be done with pick and shovel or, on a larger scale, with a bulldozer or other heavy equipment to obtain more information on the habit of the ore. Rim stripping is much the same as trenching and consists of moving overburden or talus to expose underlying bedrock.

Mine openings. Mine openings include adits, inclines, shafts, and workings driven from these openings. Mine openings are made by the usual processes of drilling, blasting, and removing broken rock. Although they are the most costly type of exploration, they yield maximum information from the ground penetrated. Mine openings expose three dimensions of ore and provide excellent samples. Stripping and trenching, on the other hand, permit direct observations in only two dimensions, and drilling requires intepretation to arrive at the horizontal dimensions. Mine openings are normally given most consideration when they can be started from an outcrop of ore-grade material, because they then offer the possibility of recovering at least a part of their cost by the sale of ore.

Drilling. Among many basic types of drilling, the most common are core, rotary, pneumatic percussion, and churn drilling. Relative cost, type of rock, depth to deposit, angle of holes, and surface accessibility are among the factors to be considered in selecting drilling equipment.

Core drilling. Core drilling is the most costly type of drilling, but it also provides the most information. Prices range from $1.75 to $5.00 per foot for coring to 500 feet in Colorado Plateau sandstone formations, and from $8.00 to $14.00 for similar depths in harder rock. The basic design of the core drill has changed little in the past 50 years, but recent trends in mounting the drills on motor trucks, together with the necessary power units, hydraulic pressure pumps, pumps for circulating fluid, and drilling-water storage tanks, have made the core drill a much more useful tool because of greater mobility. Modern truck-mounted units have hydraulically raised masts high enough to permit 20- to 60-foot pulls of drill rod. The rate of coring will vary from 20 to 100 feet per 8-hour shift, depending on type of rock formation, angle, and depth of hole.

A new development in core-drilling technique is the "wire line core barrel," which permits the inner tube of the core barrel, containing the core sample, to be hoisted to the surface (without removing the drill rods from the hole) by a wire cable operated inside the rods. This is especially useful in deep holes, where 50 percent or more of the operating time may be spent raising and lowering drill rods to remove cores.

Rotary drilling. A rotary drill, designed and developed for seismic exploration, is widely used for uranium exploration in sedimentary rocks. This drill makes rapid progress in soft formations. It is usually designed with a rotary tri-cone bit, without provision for recovering cores. However, the rotary bit may be replaced with a core barrel and coring bit for taking core samples. Water, drilling mud, or air can be employed as the circulating fluid to cool the drill and carry away the debris. In the past few years, air has commonly been used on the Colorado Plateau. Air gives a rapid penetration and is invaluable in desert regions where drilling water is scarce. The use of air is generally limited to drilling in dry formations. In some cases, however, an air-water mixture can be utilized to penetrate wet ground, with a considerable saving of drill water. Prices for rotary drilling range from $.50 to $3.00 per foot, to a depth of 1000 feet.

When air is used as the drilling fluid, a cyclone dust collector gathers samples for lithologic study and assay. Dust samples are not as reliable as core samples because (1) they are broken to individual-component grain size, (2) they are subject to dilution by material abraded from the drill-hole wall above the interval being drilled, and (3) some of the finest material, often quite rich in uranium, will pass through the dust collector.

Wagon drilling. Pneumatic percussion drilling, commonly referred to as wagon drilling, utilizes a drifter (sinker) percussion air drill mounted on a suitable guide. Drilling is accomplished by impact transmitted through the drill rods. Compressed air is used both as power for the drill and as a circulating medium for removing the cuttings from the drill hole. Percussion is the cheapest method of drilling in dry formations to depths of 200 to 300 feet. Prices range from $.50 to $1.50 per foot. A dust collector of the type used on rotary drills can be employed for collecting samples. Although applicable in any type of rock, percussion drilling is most efficacious in hard, brittle rocks.

Churn drilling. Churn drilling is percussion or impact drilling accomplished by a heavy chopping bit suspended on a cable and given an up-and-down motion by an eccentric drive which imparts a jerking motion to the cable. Drilling is accomplished with water or mud in the hole. The bit is removed periodically and the cuttings are bailed out of the hole. Churn drilling is especially efficient and economical for penetrating loose, unconsolidated overburden. It is seldom used in exploration on the Colorado Plateau for penetrating the prospective ore horizon because of the difficulty of handling the samples and the risk of sample contamination.

Underground drilling. Underground exploration drilling from existing mine workings is commonly performed with either core drills designed for such work, or conventional air percussion sinkers or drifters for "long holes." For this work the drill rods must be in short lengths because of space limitations; otherwise, techniques are essentially the same as for surface drilling. These holes may be drilled at any angle, but normally do not exceed 100 feet in length.

Drilling patterns. Drill-hole pattern and spacing will depend on the geologic environment and habit of the orebodies in the area. For example, in exploring for a nearly vertical, vein-type deposit, a row of angle drill holes would be planned to intersect the vein at certain depths, as projected from its known exposures; in exploring the flat-lying formations a square- or diamond-shaped grid pattern would be used, to be followed by more closely spaced drilling around holes that penetrate mineralized ground.

Many uranium deposits of the Colorado Plateau occur in the sedimentary rocks filling ancient stream channels (paleochannels). In such places, according to Wood and Grundy [3], delineation of a channel should begin with a row (fence) of holes a short distance behind the outcrop and across the projected trend to determine the channel axis by an alignment of the lowest point on the rim with the lowest point as interpreted from drill holes. This first fence should consist of at least five holes spaced at intervals less than the width of the channel at the outcrop. After the completion of each hole, the altitude of the basal contact is corrected to the horizontal datum, the inferred contours are extended (or revised if necessary), and sites for additional holes are located.

If the last hole along a projected axis encounters the basal contact at a much higher corrected elevation than that predicted from the extended contours, it may have been drilled either on a flank near a change in channel trend or on a rise in the channel floor. The uncertainty of the interpretation is resolved by drilling a fence of at least three holes halfway between the last two holes and at right angles to the last known channel trend. If the results of any fence are inconclusive, the fence is extended on either end, or additional holes are drilled between the primary holes of the fence. Wherever the interpretation of subsurface data is in doubt, fences rather than single holes should be drilled.

In channels where ore most frequently occurs in troughs, the distance between single holes should not exceed the maximum size of anticipated orebodies. In areas where ore occurrences are known to be predominantly on the flanks of channels, it is necessary to test the flanks between fences with additional holes.

Drill-hole logging. Detailed lithologic logs should be made from each drill hole. These provide formational data for use in determining whether, when, and where further drilling in the area is likely to be most productive.

Complete and accurate information on sampled intervals is especially important because estimates of ore tonnage are based on these figures and on sample analyses. Since cuttings from rotary and percussion drilling are subject to contamination, a drilling program should include some core holes to provide reliable samples for assaying and for calibrating gamma-ray logging equipment. Samples are commonly assayed radiometrically, provided equilibrium has been established, because it is cheaper and faster. It is advisable, however, to make frequent chemical analyses as a check on equilibrium conditions.

Regardless of the type of drilling, gamma-ray logs should be made of the holes. The simplest but least reliable technique utilizes a portable Geiger counter equipped with an external probe on a long cable which can be lowered into the hole by hand. More elaborate devices using scintillation equipment mounted in trucks, complete with power winch, amplifying circuits, and recorders, are capable of giving much more complete and accurate data. The probes used with the various types of logging equipment range in diameter from $\frac{3}{4}$ inch to 2 inches. The diameter of the drill hole should be at least $\frac{1}{2}$ inch greater than the diameter of the probe to be lowered into it.

2–2.4 Ore reserve estimates.

Estimation of ore reserves is the final phase of exploration. Techniques for computing reserves vary from area to area, depending chiefly on the nature of the deposits. General knowledge of the habit and size of orebodies in the district is essential.

The reliability of the estimate is usually expressed by classification of reserves into such categories as *measured, indicated,* and *inferred.* Commonly used definitions of these classes are as follows:

Measured ore is ore for which tonnage is computed from dimensions revealed in outcrops, trenches, workings, and drill holes, and for which the grade is computed from detailed sampling. The sites for inspection, sampling, and measurement are so closely spaced and the geologic character is so well defined that the size, shape, and mineral content are well established. Computed tonnage and grade are judged to be accurate within limits which are stated, and no such limit is judged to differ from the computed tonnage or grade by more than 20 percent.

Indicated ore is ore for which tonnage and grade are computed partly from specific measurements, samples, or production data, and partly from projection for a reasonable distance on geologic evidence. Sites available for inspection, measurement, and sampling are too widely or otherwise inappropriately spaced to outline the ore completely or to establish its grade throughout.

Inferred ore is ore for which quantitative estimates are based largely on broad knowledge of the geologic character of the deposit and for which there are few, if any, samples or measurements. Estimates are based on an assumed continuity or repetition for which there is geologic evidence; this may include comparison with deposits of similar type. Bodies that

are completely concealed may be included if there is specific geologic
evidence of their presence. Estimates of inferred ore should include a
statement of the spatial limits within which it may lie.

Ore reserves are commonly computed by first plotting all information,
drawing the outline of the orebody, and measuring the area enclosed. This
area is then multiplied by the average thickness of the ore, to arrive at a
volume for the deposit. The volume is then divided by the average density,
or cubic feet per ton, which gives total tonnage for the deposit. The average grade is determined by weighting the assays of all samples.

At this point the job of exploration is completed. From the final ore
reserve calculations, costs of development and mining are estimated to
determine whether, and how, mining operations should be undertaken.

2–3. MINING

The methods used in mining uranium ore depend largely on the type of
deposit being exploited. The techniques vary considerably with the
depth, grade, and thickness of the orebody, the nature of the overburden,
and the terrain of the district. In this chapter, the discussion is limited
to the ore deposits in sandstone in the western United States, since these
comprise the bulk of the country's uranium ore reserves and since sandstone is an uncommon source of ore outside the uranium industry. These
deposits may be divided into three classes:

(1) The deep, regular deposits found in the lower Chinle formation
of the Big Indian Wash area, Utah, and in the Westwater Canyon sandstones of the Grants and Ambrosia Lake districts, New Mexico.

(2) The shallow, irregular occurrences such as are found in the Salt
Wash formation in the Uravan Mineral Belt, Colorado, and in the Shinarump "conglomerates" of the White Canyon district, Utah.

(3) The shallow occurrences, both regular and irregular, mined by
open pit methods in the Gas Hills area, Wyoming, the Grants district,
New Mexico, and the Cameron area, Arizona.

2–3.1 Deep deposits of Big Indian Wash. Large orebodies were first
developed and mined by underground methods in the lower Chinle formation of the Big Indian Wash-Lisbon Valley area near Moab, Utah. Until
recent discoveries in the Ambrosia Lake area, New Mexico, these deposits
were the largest known in the United States. The ore is flat-lying, with
thickness varying from 5 to 20 feet. The width of the deposits varies from
300 to 680 feet and the strike length from 1100 to 2400 feet. The depth of
cover ranges from 100 to 700 feet.

After the ore was delimited by drilling, the operator selected the mining
method for best grade control, highest extraction, and lowest costs. Three

different methods, room and pillar, longwall retreat, and panel mining, are employed successfully. Both track and trackless equipment is used, depending upon the thickness of the ore and the operator's preference.

Exemplifying the three methods are the Hecla Mining Company's Radon Mine, Homestake Mining Company's La Sal Mine, and Utex Exploration Company's Mi Vida Mine. Discussions of these and the Homestake-New Mexico Partners' Section 32 Mine, Ambrosia Lake, follow.

Radon Mine. The Hecla Company's Radon Mine works one of the highest-grade deposits of uranium ore on the Colorado Plateau. It averages 5 feet in thickness, 500 feet in width, and has a northwestward strike length of approximately 2200 feet. The average dip of ore is 7 degrees to the west. Depth of burial is approximately 600 feet.

To develop the orebody, a vertical shaft was sunk midway along the strike length. Two shaft stations were cut, one on the ore horizon to service the operation, and one 40 feet lower for sublevel haulage. From the upper shaft station an incline was driven across the ore, a distance of approximately 500 feet. Four strike drifts were advanced each way from

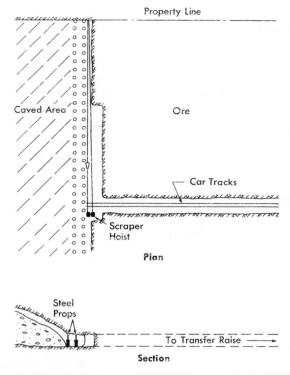

FIG. 2–1. Longwall retreat mining method, Radon Mine.

the incline, at 120-foot intervals, to the limits of the ore. These drifts were connected at the limits by inclines, in preparation for longwall retreat. From the haulage station a crosscut was made beneath the orebody at right angles to the strike, with four vertical raises at 120-foot intervals to connect with the strike drifts above. Each raise is timbered to provide an ore transfer and manway. Rail haulage is provided in all strike and haulage drifts.

Mining has been by retreat on a longwall system, followed by caving after removal of the ore. Application of this system at the Radon Mine is shown by the diagrams in Fig. 2–1.

The broken ore is dragged to the strike drift by electric slusher hoists, and loaded by a mucking machine into mine cars to be hauled to the transfer raises.

Two rows of retractable steel props are erected on 4-foot centers to provide ground support. As each cut is completed to the next strike drift, the outer row of steel props is removed and re-erected as the inner row. If the ground fails to cave, a row of holes previously drilled is loaded and blasted. Short retractable props are used to keep the roof low and avoid excessive dilution. This has been highly successful, as shown by the increase in grade after the completion of development work. The grade of the ore has been nearly doubled without appreciable increase in cost.

Surface installations consist of four buildings: a hoist and compressor building; a combination dry house, warehouse, and office building; a machine shop; and an oil house. All buildings are constructed of steel.

La Sal Mine. The La Sal Mine, owned by La Sal Mining and Development Company and operated by Homestake Mining Company, illustrates another highly successful approach to mining tabular uranium deposits, in this case by panel mining. The deposit has a northwestward strike length of 1200 feet, a width of 300 to 500 feet, and a thickness of from 5 to 20 feet. The thicker sections are on the up-dip side of the deposit, which has an average dip of 8 degrees to the southwest.

To develop the orebody, a three-compartment vertical shaft was sunk 520 feet to the ore horizon, where a shaft station and ore loading pocket were cut. Two drifts were advanced from the shaft station: one in the orebody along the strike to confirm the results of exploration drilling, and one nearly at right angles to the strike, for sublevel haulage. From the development drift, ore was systematically blocked out for mining by a series of inclines and strike drifts on 100-foot centers.

The mining method is to retreat on a panel system. The operation is shown in Fig. 2–2. A 12-foot room is started from the strike drift, at the extremity of the orebody, leaving a 6-foot pillar between the room and the outermost incline. As the first room is advanced, others are started, leaving pillars 6 feet wide and keeping the working faces staggered. When

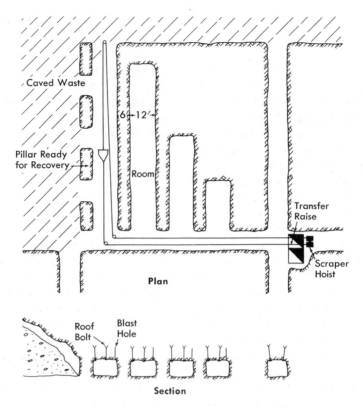

Fig. 2-2. Panel mining method, La Sal Mine.

the first room of the block is completed to the next drift, the work of extracting the pillar adjacent to the incline is started. Three or four windows are cut in the pillar, to recover approximately 40 percent of the ore. The remainder of the pillar is then drilled horizontally and blasted. If the roof fails to cave after the broken ore is removed, the previously drilled vertical blast holes are loaded and fired. The same procedure is followed to remove successive pillars.

Rail haulage is used only in the lower three strike drifts and the haulage drift. Electric slusher hoists installed in the strike drifts drag the broken ore from the rooms by lightweight welded scrapers. Ventilation is provided through a 36-inch diameter bore hole from the surface. Air is forced into the mine by a 30,000 cubic foot, 30-hp fan and exhausted through the shaft.

The ore is hoisted to the surface, dumped directly into trucks, hauled to the storage area, dumped, and then reloaded by a front-end loader for transport to the mill. There are four plant buildings: a hoist house; a combination dry house, office, and warehouse; a machine shop; and a power house. All buildings are constructed of steel.

Mi Vida Mine. The Mi Vida Mine, operated by Utex Exploration Company, is an outstanding example of underground mining with trackless equipment. The orebody has a northwest strike length of approximately 2400 feet, an average width of 600 feet, and dips 10 degrees to the west. Its average thickness of 16 feet makes possible the use of large trackless equipment.

The original entry for large tonnage extraction was through a 150-foot incline on the down-dip side of the orebody. It has a cross section of 15 feet by 12 feet to accommodate large haulage equipment. A new adit has been driven approximately 50 feet below the ore horizon to provide sublevel haulage. From the haulage level a series of vertical shafts to the orebody provide for ore storage and transfer. The broken ore is loaded by tractor front-end loaders into 8-ton diesel-powered dumptor trucks and hauled to the transfer raises. A trolley locomotive and ten 8-ton bottom-dump mine cars take the ore from the raises to the surface, where it is stored in two large steel bins.

Mining is by room and pillar, modified to a panel system at the northern end of the orebody. Rooms are approximately 20 feet wide, with heights from 12 to 20 feet, depending on the thickness of the ore. Pillars left to be recovered on retreat average 80 by 80 feet. At the northern end, where a panel system is employed, rooms are the same size but pillars between rooms average 20 feet in width. Inclines driven across the orebody connect the rooms at 100-foot intervals. Approximately 70 holes are required for each round blasted. The drill jumbo, shown in Fig. 2–3, consists of two hydraulic booms mounted on a diesel-driven tractor with two long drills mounted on the booms. Rods are of 11-foot mild carbon steel, with tungsten carbide bits. All controls are on the tractor, allowing one miner to operate both drifters. Using this equipment, the miner can drill 100 holes per shift. An average of 200 tons of ore is broken for each round blasted. Explosives consumption averages $1\frac{3}{4}$ pounds per ton. Roof bolting is required in all rooms.

A complete machine shop (Fig. 2–4) and a compressor room are underground near the center of the orebody. The machine shop is equipped to do all major repair work on the equipment. Two compressors provide 900 ft^3/min of air for drilling. Two 100,000 cubic foot fans provide ventilation, exhausting the air through two raises to the surface. Surface buildings include a garage, boarding house, two bunk houses, mine office, and dry building. Men are transported in and out of the mine by a converted army truck equipped with a diesel motor.

Section 32 Mine [4]. The Section 32 Mine in the Ambrosia Lake district, McKinley County, New Mexico, is operated by Homestake-New

FIG. 2–3. Tractor-mounted drill jumbo, Mi Vida Mine.

FIG. 2–4. Underground machine shop, Mi Vida Mine.

Mexico Partners. In Ambrosia, the ore lies in the water-saturated Morrison sandstone, 600 to 800 feet below the surface. The water in itself is not much of a problem, but it carries a great deal of silt and sand, causing undue wear on pumps. Some fourteen shafts are going down in the area (May 1958), and all but two will be under water.

In the Section 32 Mine, the orebody is 1500 to 2000 feet long and 50 to 60 feet wide. The mineable ore varies in thickness from 4 to 12 feet. The mine is being developed 20 to 30 feet below the ore bed to facilitate drainage. The mining system is not fully developed, but it will be similar to that of the La Sal Mine, described earlier. Preparations for panel mining are under way. Ore will be gathered by slusher scraping to chutes that lead to the haulage tunnel below.

Approximately 500 gal/min of water must be pumped from the mine sumps by a 125-hp Fairbanks-Morse turbine pump. The mine is ventilated through a 32-inch bore hole at the rate of 25,000 ft^3/min. No commercial power is available at the mine. Power supply depends on General Motors Model 567 C two-cycle engines operating on natural gas or diesel fuel. Direct power costs are estimated at 8 mills/kw·hr.

2–3.2 Shallow, irregular deposits. *Uravan mineral belt, Colorado.* The majority of the carnotite deposits in the Uravan mineral belt are shallow, thin, and irregular. The average deposit contains less than 2000 tons, and few deposits can be mined economically at depth. Only because access is comparatively easy, and by continuous exploration and development, have the operators been able to maintain fairly continuous production of a profitable grade of ore.

The type of entry is generally determined by the topography. Adits driven on the ore horizon are preferred. Low-gradient inclines and two-compartment vertical shafts are second and third choices. Adits are small, averaging 5 by 7 feet in cross section, and are equipped for rail haulage. Small electric or diesel locomotives with three or four small mine cars usually comprise the haulage equipment. Hand tramming is practiced extensively in smaller deposits.

Inclines are driven on as low gradients as practicable, 12 to 22 degrees. The cross section will average 8 by 9 feet, and rails are installed to allow use of large mine cars for hoisting. Small gasoline-driven hoists are installed on trestles located at the portal. The ore is hoisted onto the trestle, dumped into small bins or on the ground, and later reloaded into trucks for transportation to the mills. Unless the distance to ore is excessive, inclines have several advantages over vertical shafts. They are cheaper, and require little or no timbering or maintenance. Small hoists capable of handling loaded mine cars can be installed at less cost than those used on vertical shafts. At least one less man is needed.

Vertical two-compartment shafts are used only where the other two types of entry are not economical. The vertical shafts require a larger capital outlay, and maintenance costs are higher than for adits or inclines. Small wooden or steel headframes are erected. With the low mining rate, no high-speed hoisting is employed. Either framed timbering or cribbing is used in the shafts. Shaft pockets vary in size and layout, depending on ore storage requirements, but usually no more than fifty tons capacity is needed. A pillar may be left between the shaft and the pocket, or the shaft timber may be laced and the ground broken on a 60-degree slope from the shaft to form the storage area.

Development and mining are carried on simultaneously. Provided there has been adequate exploration drilling, development drifts are driven in the ore, as near the bottom as possible. As the drifts are advanced, crosscuts may be made to delimit the ore or explore favorable areas. Long-hole drilling of the walls, roof, and floor of the drifts has become one of the most effective methods of development. Using sectional steel and tungsten carbide bits, operators are able to explore favorable areas at a cost of $0.10 per foot, without drifting into the area. In many cases a systematic long-hole drilling program has more than doubled the known reserves of a mine.

Because the deposits are erratic, no uniform mining method is employed. The operator follows the ore by checking the working face daily with a Geiger counter. If the ore becomes thin, selective blasting is employed to reduce dilution. In the larger deposits, open stoping is used, with low grade or waste pillars left for roof support.

Mining equipment varies greatly. Light and easily transported jackleg drills are particularly adaptable, and are used extensively with alloy steel rods and tungsten carbide bits. The broken ore is hand-mucked or loaded by scrapers or mucking machines. Scrapers are used more extensively than mucking machines because they can be operated in lower headroom and are more maneuverable. The irregular lenticular nature of the deposits, which causes the ore to dip below the floor in some places and rise in others, precludes extensive use of trackless equipment.

In the Uravan mineral belt, mining costs are high because as much as 6 tons of waste may be moved for each ton of ore mined. Equipment maintenance costs and consumption of explosives are high because of the high ratio of waste to ore. Production per man-shift averages only 2 to 3 tons, making labor costs nearly twice as much as in other uranium mining areas. Total mining costs, exclusive of property acquisition or royalty, average $18 to $19 per ton.

White Canyon district, Utah. In the White Canyon district, ore occurs in channels and in scours within the channels. Three major deposits, each in excess of 100,000 tons, have been developed. Although the normal deposit, between 5000 and 10,000 tons, is somewhat larger than in the Uravan mineral belt, most deposits present mining problems similar to those in the Uravan belt. Entry is by adit or incline, depending on the topography. Inclines are similar to those in the Uravan mineral belt, except that trackless mining and haulage equipment are used in some of the larger deposits, thus eliminating the necessity for a hoist. In other installations, a hoist brings the ore to the surface after it has been mined with trackless equipment. Vertical shafts have not been used.

As in the Uravan belt, few deposits are regular enough for any uniform method of mining. The operator follows the channel, mining the ore pods by open stoping as they are encountered and maintaining a continuous development program. Frequent selective blasting in the thin ore horizons maintains a shipping grade of ore. Major deposits are being developed for mining by longwall retreat.

Trackless equipment is usually small. Shuttle cars are widely utilized. These diesel-powered trammers were designed originally for concrete transportation on construction work. Broken ore is loaded into the cars by hand-mucking, mucking machines, or front-end loaders. Ordinarily, thickness of ore controls the type of loading equipment.

Water for mining operations is a problem in this desert country. In many instances it must be hauled as far as 15 or 20 miles. Where feasible, a large storage tank is erected on the surface. Water is piped into the mine, if possible, but most operators use pressure tanks underground. These tanks may be permanent or mounted on trucks.

Surface equipment consists of one or two diesel-powered compressors, a small ore bin, and perhaps a small-machine repair shop. For the most part, the miners live in trailers.

Mining costs, exclusive of property acquisition and royalty, are somewhat lower than in the Uravan mineral belt, due in part to the slightly more regular ore occurrences.

2–3.3 Deposits of the Gas Hills and Grants areas.

In the Gas Hills area, Wyoming, and the limestones of the Grants district, New Mexico, deposits are mined by open-pit methods. This has several advantages where it can be employed. Complete extraction of the ore is possible, and grade can be controlled by selective mining and blending. Grade control is particularly important, since the majority of these deposits are low-grade.

The stripping ratios vary from 10:1 to 30:1. Little or no drilling and blasting is required to remove the loose or unconsolidated overburden. Rippers loosen the rock overburden, after which it may be loaded for removal from the pit by any of several methods. The most common method of transportation is the scraper-loader or "can."

Once the ore horizon is reached, the ore is drilled, blasted, and loaded with front-end loaders for removal from the pit. If the deposit is regular enough, scraper-loaders are also used in this operation. Rubber-tired equipment has been found most satisfactory because steel or cleated treads cause unnecessary dilution of the ore.

2–3.4 Mining costs. Mining costs vary over a wide range in the uranium industry. Each ore deposit has different mining problems, and only after careful study can probable costs be estimated. Some important factors that influence costs for any operation are (1) property acquisition costs or royalty, (2) size, altitude, thickness, and depth or burial of the ore, (3) type of entry, (4) mining method employed, and (5) type of equipment.

Costs for underground uranium mining are high in comparison with those of other metal mines. The irregular nature of the majority of the deposits now being mined and the comparatively small tonnages developed for each deposit cause a corresponding higher cost for exploration and mining. The type of equipment used for mining is also particularly important. A fairly low mining rate is necessary in the majority of the deposits to maintain grade, and this usually precludes the wholesale use of large-scale mechanized equipment.

Average costs can be misleading, since they vary within districts or areas. The typical costs presented in Table 2–1 are averages and may not be precise for any given deposit.

TABLE 2–1

UNDERGROUND OPERATIONS COST PER TON OF ORE MINED

	Big Indian Wash	White Canyon	Uravan
Exploration	$1.00	$2.00	$2.00
Amortization	2.00	1.00	2.00
Development	1.00	1.50	3.00
Direct mining			
Labor	3.50	5.00	6.50
Explosives	0.35	0.70	1.20
Bits and rods	0.20	0.40	0.40
Other	1.50	2.00	2.00
Indirect mining			
Mine overhead	0.50	0.50	0.50
Taxes	0.60	0.60	0.60
Total	$10.65	$13.70	$18.20

REFERENCES

1. R. J. WRIGHT, *Prospecting With a Counter,* U. S. Atomic Energy Commission. Washington, D. C.: U. S. Government Printing Office, 1954.

2. Y. W. ISACHSEN et al., *An Approach to Exploration for Uranium Ores,* USAEC Report RME-64, Grand Junction Operations Office, AEC, 1954.

3. H. B. WOOD and W. D. GRUNDY, Techniques and Guides for Exploration of Shinarump Channels on the Colorado Plateau, in *Proceedings of the International Conference on the Peaceful Uses of Atomic Energy,* Vol. 6. New York: United Nations, 1956. (P/517, p. 701)

4. R. J. STOEHR, personal communication.

CHAPTER 3

SAMPLING AND ANALYSIS

PART I. SAMPLING OF URANIUM ORES AND CONCENTRATES*

3–1. Introduction to Sampling

In July, 1948, the United States Atomic Energy Commission began purchasing uranium-bearing ores at Monticello, Utah. Previously, no United States ores had been sampled solely for their uranium content, although for some fifty years carnotite and roscoelite ores had been sampled for vanadium. When uranium sampling began, the methods were rather crude; very little effort had been put into modernizing procedures for sampling the small vanadium tonnages.

The Commission began its domestic uranium procurement program by purchasing only carnotite and roscoelite ores from the Colorado Plateau area. Shortly thereafter, ores with an asphaltic base from the Temple Mountain in Utah were included in this program. As new types of uranium-bearing ores were discovered, trial lots were purchased and tested for processing amenability. If tests proved favorable, ores were bought under special contracts by the Commission.

In the spring of 1948, preliminary sampling tests were made on a representative lot of carnotite ore at the Garfield Smelter of the American Smelting and Refining Company. Because of the relatively small amount of uranium contained in the Colorado Plateau ores and its spotty distribution, the preliminary procedure was patterned after standard methods for sampling gold ores. Results showed that this sandstone uranium ore could be accurately sampled by following standard practices.

Because of the 10-ton minimum lot size established by the AEC's published tariff and the small tonnages anticipated at that time, a capacity of 150 to 200 tons per 8-hour shift was chosen for a mechanical sampling plant (Fig. 3–1). Later, to increase the capacity, jaw-crushers were substituted for the rolls listed in the flowsheet.

At first a great number of the lots were small, ranging from 10 to 20 tons. To cope with this situation, sampling plants with a total capacity of 150 to 200 tons per 8-hour shift had to be designed to sample 10 to 20 lots per day. The average size of each lot during the first year of operations

---

* By Martin N. Gaines, Lucius Pitkin, Inc.

at Monticello was about 18 tons. Because such small lots created extra work both in sampling and assaying, and kept buying costs at a maximum, shippers were urged to deliver in larger lots. As the mines reached a firmer production basis, the operators themselves saw the advantages of making their lots as large as possible, and by 1957 the average lot size had been raised to 50 tons at the smaller stations and to 260 tons at the larger ones. The average lot size at the largest station (Moab) was about 350 tons. Sampling plants with a capacity of 75 to 100 tons per hour were designed for these large stations.

This increased lot size called for no basic change in the sample flow-sheet other than installing a larger primary jaw crusher. It was also found that three 10 percent cuts gave as accurate a sample as the three 20 percent cuts of the original flowsheet (see Fig. 3–1). The smaller cut reduced the amount of sample from the third cut, and thereby materially reduced the amount of handwork at this point, especially as the lot sizes were increased.

Early in 1952, the flowsheet for a permanent sampling plant, shown in Fig. 3–2, was designed. This design has been followed in all AEC sampling plants constructed in the area, with only minor changes for those plants handling smaller tonnages. The small sample mills were designed for use in out-of-the-way places and were semiportable. In some instances it was necessary to install a diesel generator to supply power. All buildings were of prefabricated steel, so that the plant could be easily dismantled and set up on a new site. Only the concrete in the scale pit, building foundations, and equipment bases would be lost.

3–2. Weighing Mine-Run Ore

Most uranium ore is delivered to the buying stations in trucks, and each truckload is weighed immediately upon arrival. Ore delivered in railroad cars is ordinarily transferred to trucks, and each truckload is weighed enroute to the sampling plant. Any standard truck scale having the desired capacity can be used. With trucks increasing in size and capacity, a 50-ton truck scale with a 50-foot platform is the minimum size now in use. At the newer mills, 60-ton scales with 60-foot platforms have recently been installed. Scales must be kept in accurate adjustment at all times, and are inspected semiannually by State inspectors.

3–3. Ore Sampling for Moisture Content

The haulage allowance for uranium ore is based on the gross wet weight, but the payment for U_3O_8 (and V_2O_5 where applicable) is based on the net dry weight. All uranium ores contain appreciable amounts of moisture, from 1 percent to more than 25 percent. This wide variation in

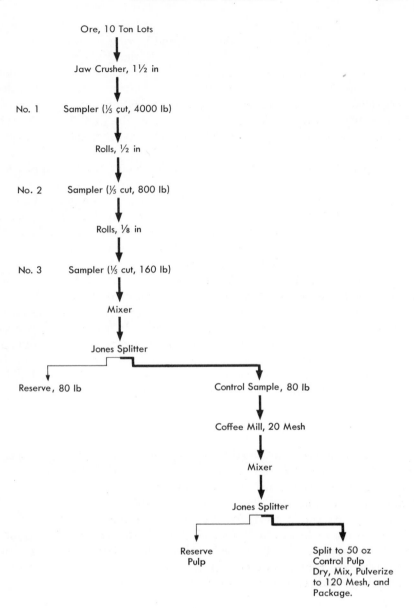

FIG. 3–1. Original sample mill flowsheet for Monticello, Utah, and Durango, Colorado.

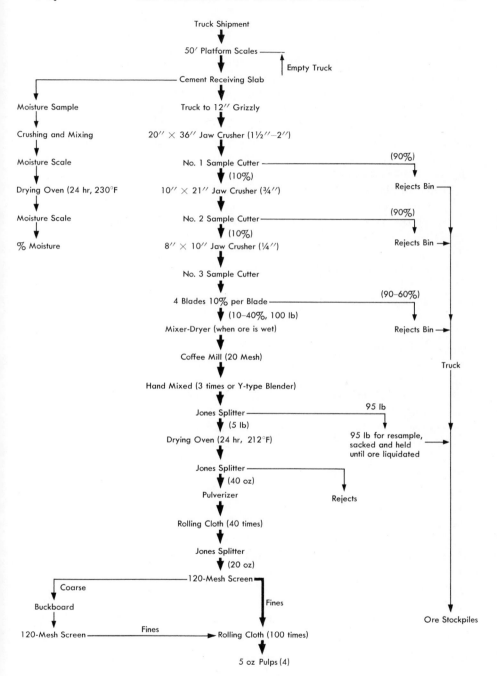

Fig. 3–2. Standard flowsheet for uranium ore sampling plant.

moisture content makes it necessary to take a moisture sample from each truckload of ore immediately after weighing, to prevent errors due to evaporation or wetting by rain or snow. Since the purchase specifications permit lumps as large as 12 inches, it is difficult to take an accurate moisture sample on mine-run ores containing a mixture of fines and lump. Common practice is to take a grab sample weighing 10 to 20 pounds from the truck and place it in a sample bucket with a tight top. The errors that result from this grab sampling are assumed to be less than those that could arise due from changes in storage conditions during the wait for the ore to start through the sampling plant.

Other methods of taking moisture samples would involve reweighing the ore somewhere along the sample flow, with expensive weighing installations, or the use of factors to compensate for moisture losses between the truck scale weight and the point at which the moisture sample is taken. The latter method is seldom acceptable to the ore seller.

In cutting grab samples of mine-run ore by shovel sampling, it would seem that the samples would yield an undue proportion of fines containing more moisture than coarse lumps. The apparent high moisture content would result, of course, in an error in favor of the ore buyer. Screen tests were made at various AEC installations, comparing the percentages of fines and lump in regular moisture samples with those obtained from screening several hundred pounds of the same ore. It was found that the small percentage of excess fines in the moisture sample is of little importance. The effect on the dry weight, and net payment for the ore, is negligible compared with the effect that could be produced by a 0.01 percent U_3O_8 variation in the assay of the ore.

Moisture samples are crushed to approximately $\frac{1}{2}$ inch and mixed before a 1 to 3-pound sample is weighed out for moisture determination. The sample can be crushed by hand, but it is better practice to run it through a 5 by 6-inch laboratory-type jaw crusher set at $\frac{1}{4}$ inch, and to mix it by hand on a steel-topped table before weighing out the sample to be dried. Moisture samples should be dried for about 24 hours at 230°F; higher temperatures produce a calcining effect and cause high moisture assays. Drying in an electric oven is the most practical method for determining moisture. However, gas-fired ovens with automatic temperature control are being used successfully at stations where 24-hour electric power is not available. Moisture balances which read directly in percent are normally used to weigh the moisture samples before and after drying.

3–4. Ore Sampling for Uranium Content

There are two general methods of sampling: hand sampling and mechanical sampling.

3–4.1 Hand sampling. Hand sampling is slow and expensive, and the personal element makes it difficult to obtain accurate results. Hand sampling of mine-run uranium ores, where a 12-inch lump is permitted, produces a bias in the sampling in favor of the ore seller. This was demonstrated at the one ore-buying station where only hand sampling was used. When hand-sampled ore was shipped out and sampled by a mechanical sampling plant, it was found that the results from hand sampling were 5 to 10 percent higher than those obtained mechanically. These percentages, changed into assay differences, amount to 0.01 percent and 0.02 percent on a 0.20 percent U_3O_8 assay and are not unusual except for the fact that the hand-sampling results are always higher. Similar differences in assay results occur between mechanical sampling plants, but they are plus-or-minus differences and produce no net bias.

For the above reasons, hand sampling of uranium ores should be avoided unless the expected tonnage does not justify the expense of installing an automatic mechanical sampling plant. If an ore-buying station in a new and isolated district must be started on a hand-sampling basis, a small portable automatic sample mill should be installed as soon as a regular tonnage of approximately 1000 tons per month develops.

Grab sampling. Ore to be hand-sampled is delivered in trucks and dumped on the ground. The grab-sampling procedure calls for taking random shovelfuls from around the pile and from top to bottom to obtain about 100 pounds of sample. The sample is then crushed by hand or in a small jaw crusher to reduce it to four 5-ounce pulps.

Grab sampling is a poor method because it takes samples only from the surface of the pile. It is difficult to get a representative sample, since the correct proportion of fines and lumps cannot be maintained in the shoveling. There is invariably a tendency on the part of the workman to get too large a proportion of fines which produces, in the case of uranium, samples assaying higher than a truely representative sample would assay. However, it is a quick and inexpensive method when only an approximate assay is required.

Trench sampling. The more common practice in hand-sampling uranium ore is trench sampling. This procedure yields a more representative product than grab sampling, since specimens are taken from a cross section of the pile or ore. A trench is cut through the pile just wide enough for the sampler to operate his shovel. As the trench is opened through the center of the pile, the sample is cut by taking every 10th, 15th, or 20th shovelful, depending on the size of the lot. Lots may contain more than one truckload. In actual practice as many as four truckloads are dumped in a windrow (elongated pile) which is trenched through lengthwise. The amount of sample obtained will weigh about 200 pounds per truckload of ore.

The entire sample is taken in wheelbarrows to a large steel plate, and the large lumps are broken by sledge. The sample is hand-mixed several times by coning and ringing and is cut down by split shoveling to about 100 pounds. This 100 pounds is then reduced to the requisite number of sample pulps by the usual procedure.

The trench sampling method was used at the Marysvale, Utah, ore-buying station because not enough tonnage developed in this area to warrant the expense of installing mechanical sampling. The flowsheet used is shown in Fig. 3–3.

Split-shoveling. Split-shovel sampling, the most accurate method of hand sampling, is not practicable in sampling uranium ores. It consists of taking every 2nd, 3rd, 4th, 5th, 10th, 15th or 20th shovelful as a sample during unloading of railroad cars by hand. Split-shovel sampling of truckloads requires the truckload of ore to be transferred to a new site by hand shoveling, which is slow and costly.

Coning and quartering. Coning and quartering was standard practice in the United States, Mexico, and South America before the start of mechanical sampling. Lot size was small, say 10 to 50 tons, and the ore was piled in cone shape. The top of the cone was raked down and the top of the pile was flattened and smoothed to obtain a uniform thickness. The pile was then divided into quarters, using the edge of the shovel to make two lines across the top of the pile through its center and at right angles to each other. Opposite quarters were taken as a sample, and the other two quarters were rejects. The sample was again piled in a cone by shoveling each shovelful onto the apex of the pile. The entire coning and quartering was repeated until the desired amount of sample was obtained. The specimen was then reduced by the usual methods to four or more sample pulps for assay.

3–4.2 Mechanical sampling. Either of two mechanical sampling systems is employed at the various ore-buying stations or mills: mine-run sampling or mill-run sampling. The American Smelting and Refining Company, through preliminary tests followed by actual sampling practice, established that mine-run sampling with three-stage crushing and a sample cutter after each crusher met both the theoretical and practical sampling requirements for uranium ore. The Colorado School of Mines Research Foundation, Inc., in its December 22, 1952, report to the U. S. Atomic Energy Commission [1] confirmed that a three-stage crushing flowsheet is typical of sound practice.

In mine-run sampling, mine-run ore is usually reduced to $1\frac{1}{2}$ to 2 inches in a primary crusher and a primary sample is taken. Secondary crushing reduces the sample from the primary sample cutter to $\frac{3}{4}$ inch, and tertiary

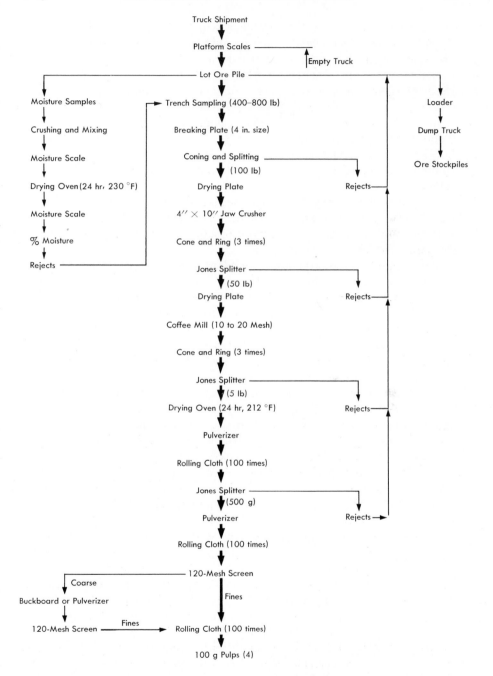

FIG. 3–3. Hand-sampling flowsheet used at Marysvale, Utah.

crushing further reduces the secondary sample to $\frac{1}{4}$ inch. The first and second sample cutters should each be able to cut 10 to 25 percent of the ore, and the third cutter 5 to 40 percent. This variance provides the flexibility necessary to obtain the desired amount of sample just before the final sample preparation. Four or more assay pulps, as needed, are then prepared for determining the U_3O_8 content in the lot of ore.

In mill-run sampling, two-stage crushing to $\frac{1}{2}$ to $\frac{3}{4}$ inch is carried out before the first sample cut is made. Rejects are sent directly to fine-ore bins at the mill, thus eliminating stockpile loss. The sample is subjected to further crushing, sample cutting, and pulp preparation, as in mine-run sampling.

Sampling plants may be either permanent or semiportable. Three-stage crushing (or four-stage crushing in the case of mill-run sampling), with three sample cutters, is standard practice in the uranium ore industry for permanent sample plants.

The portable automatic sampling plant was developed for temporary installation in out-of-the-way places. The first, with only two-stage crushing, was put in operation in White Canyon, Utah, in October, 1954. However, the secondary crushing produces minus $\frac{1}{2}$-inch material that has been well mixed and the method conforms to good practice in every way. Comparative sampling tests between this type of sample mill and the permanent, three-stage crushing mill checked closely, well within established tolerances.

Uranium ore-buying stations must often be set up in out-of-the-way places and operated for a considerable period in order to determine whether the district contains enough ore to warrant constructing a processing plant. Initial capital expenditure must be kept to a minimum, and difficulty in maintenance and repairs of heavy equipment must be considered in selecting equipment. Jaw crushers have become standard in uranium ore sampling plants. Gyratory crushers, cone crushers, or rolls would also serve, but they are higher priced, more complicated, easily clogged, and harder to clean.

Size reduction and sample cutting equipment. The capacity of a sampling plant is determined by the size of the primary crusher and its feeding equipment. Certain crusher sizes have become accepted as standard. As primary crushers in mills handling from 30 to 40 tons per hour of dry ore, 15 by 24-inch jaw crushers are used. Mills handling from 75 to 100 tons per hour require either an 18 by 36-inch or a 20 by 36-inch crusher. In all cases the jaws are set for $1\frac{1}{2}$ inches. Average uranium ores contain about 50 percent of $1\frac{1}{2}$-inch material, with some ores running as high as 90 percent. The processing of wet ore (10 percent or more of moisture) reduces the capacity of the crushing plant, sometimes by as much as one-half.

In the permanent plants, secondary crushing is accomplished by a 10 by 20-inch crusher with the jaws set at $\frac{3}{4}$ inch. The material from this unit is then fed to a third stage: an 8 by 10-inch crusher set at $\frac{1}{4}$ inch. The sample is then ready for final grinding and preparation of sample pulps.

In the semiportable plants, which use only two stages of crushing, the secondary, and final, crushing is accomplished in a small gravel crusher or scalping unit. Here the $1\frac{1}{2}$-inch material from the primary crusher is reduced to $\frac{1}{2}$ inch by a jaw crusher and a set of rolls mounted in closed circuit with two vibrating screens having $1\frac{1}{2}$ and $\frac{1}{2}$-inch openings, respectively. The jaw crusher reduces the oversize to $1\frac{1}{2}$ inch, and the rolls further reduce this material to $\frac{1}{2}$ inch. The sample then goes to the grinding and pulp preparation step.

In mechanical sampling plants, automatic sample cutters are placed after each of the crushing stages. Experiments have shown that the first sample cut on $1\frac{1}{2}$-inch material should be not less than 5000 pounds, even on the smallest lots. A 25 percent cut would be needed on the minimum ore lot of 10 tons to obtain the desired amount of sample. On large lots, a 10 percent first cut is acceptable. Second-stage samplers are also set to take cuts in the range of 10 to 20 percent, and the third-stage samplers cover a wider range of 5 to 40 percent, to permit greater latitude in selecting the final amount of sample to go to pulp preparation.

Throughout the crushing and sample-cutting procedure, the ore should be mixed wherever possible at likely points along the sample flow—this is one of the most important steps in sampling mine-run ores. The repeated handling to which the ore is subjected as it is unloaded, reloaded, and passed through various feeding devices provides rough mixing. However, there should be additional mixing, particularly ahead of the sample cutters, to prevent segregation of fines. Up to the point where pulp preparation starts, standard practice at AEC buying stations calls for the use of surge bins to obtain the necessary mixing. Revolving-drum mixers would give much better results, but would significantly increase the initial and operating costs of the mill. For this reason, they have not been used except after the last stage of crushing, where the importance of good mixing outweighs the additional costs involved. Experience has shown that passing the ore through a mixer-drier just before it goes to the pulp preparation step is one of the most important operations in the entire sampling scheme.

3–5. ACCESSORY OPERATIONS

3–5.1 Dust control. All states have strict health regulations requiring rigid control of dusting. For the large, permanent sampling plants the bag-house collector with tubular cloth bags is in standard use. The size of the collector is based on the tonnage of ore to be handled and the amount of dust in the ore. In most permanent buying stations the dust is effectively controlled by using a bag-house with an air capacity of 12,000 to 15,000 ft^3/min and with a cloth area of 4000 to 5000 square feet. All crushing equipment, sample cutters, and transfer points are enclosed and connected to the bag-house through a duct system. Suitable hoods are installed behind blenders, buckboards, and work tables and are connected to the duct system. Suction is produced in the ducts by an exhaust fan powered by a 30-horsepower motor capable of moving air at a rate of 13,000 to 16,000 ft^3/min against static pressure of 9 inches of water. Cyclone collectors are also being used successfully in some of the newer sample plants of the uranium industry.

Semiportable sampling plants do not require a dust-control system as elaborate as that of the permanent mills, since the primary and secondary crushing equipment is in the open air. Only a simple system of hoods and ducts is needed to collect the dust from the sample and pulp preparation rooms, where the samples are ground by hand with a buckboard and muller.

Even with proper dust control, workmen must wear respirators at all dusty spots to keep health hazards to a minimum. Respirator filter elements should be changed at least daily, or oftener if conditions warrant.

3–5.2 Conveying and feeding equipment. In addition to the crushing and sampling equipment used in sampling plants, a wide variety of accessory equipment is required for smooth, dependable operation. Probably most important in this category is the conveying and feeding equipment. Conveyor belts are standard for transporting the ore between crushers, sample cutters, feeders, and surge bins. Belts provide an inexpensive and quick method for continuous transportation of ore over relatively short distances, and they give long service. However, care must be taken to use the proper width, belt speeds, and inclination from the horizontal. A safe speed for all belts in a sampling plant is 120 feet per minute; faster belt speeds increase the velocity of the ore streams to the sample cutters, with consequent bad effect on cutter performance. Speeds faster than 120 feet per minute are therefore considered unsound practice, except for belts carrying main rejects, where speeds up to 150 feet per minute are used to prevent overloading. The maximum slope of belt conveyors should not exceed $3\frac{3}{4}$ inches per foot, or about 17 degrees.

Bucket elevators should never be used in sample mills because they are difficult to clean, are easily clogged by wet or sticky ore, and can cause salting of samples, that is, changing the analysis of a sample by adulteration with ore previously handled.

Various kinds of ore feeders and surge bins are used to provide the constant and uniform flow of ore essential for accurate mechanical sampling. The types of feeders commonly used in uranium mills are (1) reciprocating plate feeders, (2) apron feeders, and (3) vibrating feeders. Details of these machines may be found in standard references on ore dressing [2].

Moisture sampling is carried on separately from all other sampling procedures, and is largely done by hand. Aside from a small jaw crusher for reducing the sample to $\frac{1}{4}$ inch, the only items of equipment required are buckets and shovels for handling the sample and a small room fitted with the usual laboratory equipment for determining moisture.

All sampling plants require some mobile equipment; the amount and variety depend on the size and type of plant. Heavy-duty trucks are needed for stockpiling and moving ore outside the plant. Track or rubber-tired loaders, bulldozers, and trucks are necessary for blending separate truckloads of ore and for feeding ore to the primary crushing system. A sampling plant operating in an out-of-the-way place needs a repair shop and garage facilities.

3–5.3 Preparation of pulps. The preparation of pulps is the final step in reducing the 100 to 200-pound sample of minus $\frac{1}{4}$-inch ore to the minus-120 mesh pulps suitable for chemical analysis. The total sample at this point is thoroughly mixed in a twin-shell blender, split through a Jones splitter, and dried, if necessary, in a mixer-drier. The sample then is split to about 100 pounds and ground to minus-10 mesh in an Englebach, coffee-mill-type, No. 2 sample grinder. This is the most satisfactory sample grinder because of its low cost, speed, and ease of operation and maintenance. However, since the streams coming from the two spouts on the machine invariably differ in amount, grade, and size of product, this mill should not be used for splitting. The ground product from both spouts should be recombined to form one sample.

The combined sample is then reduced to 5 to 10 pounds in a Jones splitter, and the 90 to 95 pounds of rejects are sacked and stored for possible resampling until the lot of ore is disposed of. The 5 to 10-pound sample is then dried for 16 to 24 hours at 100°C, mixed in a blender, and split to about 40 ounces through a Jones splitter. The final grinding step is best effected in a disk pulverizer, where the ore is reduced to minus-120 mesh. The ore is mixed, split to 20 ounces, and then screened through a 120-mesh screen. The small amount of oversize is either reground or bucked down by hand with a buckboard and muller. The final product is mixed and packaged into four pulps: one for the buyer, one for the seller, and two held for reserve and umpire.

3–5.4 Check sampling. A program of regular check sampling was set up at each ore-buying station opened by the Atomic Energy Commission. A similar program was in effect at all buying stations operated by private industry. Individual lots from various producers were sampled for purchase and then resampled one or more times at each ore-buying station. Other representative lots were sampled for purchase at one station and hauled to another station for check sampling. A few lots of ore were sampled for purchase and then shipped by motor truck for resampling at all the automatic sampling plants in the area. A statistical study of the results showed that all sampling plants throughout the area were obtaining consistent results and were checking each other within the established limits of tolerance for all classes of ore.

Continuous check sampling is a "must" for uranium ores. The procedures followed for sampling gold and similar ores, including control sampling, have been found entirely satisfactory for uranium ores.

3–5.5 Stockpiling. Stockpiling requires careful consideration in the uranium industry not only to secure proper blending for the processing plants but also to keep stockpile losses by wind, rain, and leaching to a minimum. These problems arise because all AEC ore purchases are stored for lengthy periods of time before being milled. It was found that uranium ore should be handled in the same manner as other ores, such as copper, lead, and zinc. In other words, to keep fines and dust losses to a minimum, the ore should not be crushed any finer than is necessary to obtain good sampling. Therefore, the standard sample flowsheets were designed to have the primary crusher set to $1\frac{1}{2}$-inch minimum.

These stockpiles, on being milled, show no great differences between the purchase figures and the mill-feed figures, and over a period of time average out.

Stockpile areas should be paved to keep losses, particularly from leaching and run-off during heavy rains, to a minimum. Unpaved ore pads at Monticello showed that the first 12 inches of ground, after careful cleanup, contained 0.04 percent U_3O_8, and the second 12 inches, 0.01 percent U_3O_8. The value of this uranium, lost beyond recovery, would have paid for concrete or black-top paving of the stockpile area.

The most serious problem encountered in sampling uranium ores was the idea prevalent throughout the Plateau area that dust losses produced in the handling and sampling and the use of dust-control equipment would tend to downgrade the ore and cause the miners appreciable loss in their final settlements. It was found that the dust loss on average grade ore could not be measured with enough accuracy to have an appreciable affect on the chemical assay, whose limit of tolerance is about 0.01 percent U_3O_8 on 0.20 percent uranium ore.

3–5.6 Housekeeping. As in all sampling operations, good housekeeping in uranium ore sampling is most important. All bins and crushing and sampling equipment must be thoroughly cleaned by brushing and using compressed air after each lot is sampled. Vacuum cleaners are used to clean the sample preparation, moisture, and bucking rooms. Workmen must use dust respirators and goggles.

3–5.7 Operating costs. Table 3–1 shows the average operating cost under normal conditions of a number of sampling plants, including those shown in Figs. 3–1 through 3–3. In addition to the actual sampling costs, Table 3–1 shows the laboratory and administrative costs. These costs are only for sample plants operating with no associated processing mill.

3–6. Concentrate Sampling

3–6.1 General description. At the start of the AEC Domestic Uranium Procurement Program in 1948, there were only two processing plants in operation, whose major product was vanadium concentrates in the form of vanadium pentoxide, with a small amount of uranium concentrate as a byproduct. In 1949 the AEC uranium processing plant at Monticello, Utah, was started up and, as time went by, other uranium concentrators, owned and operated by private industry, came into operation. Today there are 18 uranium processing plants in operation in Colorado, Utah, South Dakota, Wyoming, New Mexico, Arizona, and Washington, with several more mills under construction.

During 1948 and 1949, the total production of uranium concentrates amounted to only a few tons a month. Today the production amounts to about 1000 tons of concentrates a month, containing an average of 75 to 85 percent U_3O_8. The total production of uranium concentrates in the western United States is purchased by the AEC at Grand Junction, Colorado. Concentrates are delivered at Grand Junction packaged in steel drums. At first 30-gallon drums were used, but these were later replaced by 55-gallon drums, since the larger drum could be handled more economically with the same equipment. These 55-gallon steel (18 gage minimum) open-head drums are equipped with a bolt locking ring closure and a rubber gasket to prevent spillage. They hold 300 to 1200 pounds of uranium concentrates, depending on the density of material, with an average weight of about 550 pounds.

At the start of the uranium concentrate procurement program, production was small and was sampled only every 2 or 3 months. Pipe samplers were used to cut a sample from each drum. When the material was so tightly packed that it was impossible to hammer the pipe sampler more than a few inches into the concentrates, the contents of the drum were

TABLE 3-1

URANIUM ORE BUYING COSTS

	Monti-cello	Moab	Edge-mont	White Canyon	Riverton	Globe*	Grants	Marys-vale†	All stations
Average monthly tonnage	16,500	27,200	3,200	6,450	8,400	1,300	5,600	1,670	70,320
Average size lot (tons)	115	190	50	85	95	40	130	40	93
				Cost per dry ton					
Ore yard cost	$0.66	$0.55	$1.60	$1.41	$0.82	$2.47	$1.40	$1.31	$0.90
Assaying	0.07	0.02	0.19	0.08	0.10	0.09	0.07	0.15	0.07
Administration	0.24	0.24	0.23	0.26	0.26	0.33	0.28	0.24	0.25
Total	$0.97	$0.81	$2.02	$1.75	$1.18	$2.89	$1.75	$1.70	$1.22

Note: Depreciation of plant and equipment is not included in the above costs. These costs may vary from 25 cents to 50 cents per ton at individual stations, depending upon tonnage and service life.

* High cost due to isolated location of station, necessitating living allowance, free trailer housing, extended work week, etc., for all employees.

† Hand sampling.

spilled on the floor, and a grab sample was taken with a long, narrow hand scoop. The sample from each drum was dried for a moisture determination and ground to 100 mesh. A composite sample was made from these samples, based on the dry weight of each drum in the lot. This composite sample pulp was assayed, and the result was used as the basis for payment.

In 1949, with production increasing to the point requiring continuous sampling, the American Smelting and Refining Company was retained by the AEC to design a sampling plant with improved procedures and sufficient capacity to sample the expected increased production.

Since concentrates are delivered in drums and must be shipped out in drums, a falling-stream type of automatic sampling plant was not practical because the drums would have to be emptied, the material run through the sample mill, and then re-drummed for shipment. It was decided, therefore, to continue sampling the concentrates in drums, cutting the sample with a ship's auger operated by a portable electric drill. This auger-sampling method had been successfully used for a great many years by the American Smelting and Refining Company to sample copper, lead, and zinc concentrates. Preliminary tests showed that the auger worked satisfactorily for both uranium and vanadium concentrates. A sampling plant was then designed to carry out the auger-sampling method, which has proven satisfactory throughout.

A building 80 by 60 by 16 feet was built to house the equipment. Open sheds, each 80 by 20 by 16 feet, were built on each side of the sampler building to serve as receiving docks for the concentrates. All areas were floored with concrete. The sample building was divided by a partition into two sections, one for uranium sampling and the other for vanadium.

Gasoline-driven fork lift trucks for barrels are used to handle the drummed material on the receiving docks. Monorail cranes with 1-ton electric hoists handle the drums inside the sampler building. The fork lift truck places the drums on a roller conveyor passing over a 1-ton platform scale, where each drum is weighed and then moved on to the end of the conveyor. The drums are picked up in pairs by the hoist and spotted for the auger drilling in front of dust hoods connected by ducts to a baghouse dust collector. The volume of air removed is controlled by individual dampers for each hood. Figure 3–4 shows a sample-cutting line with drums in place. The drill cart with auger is shown at right. The hood at left contains a funnel with vibrator to fill sample jars.

This original concentrate sampling plant was designed to receive and sample monthly 800 drums of uranium and 2000 drums of vanadium concentrates, in 30-gallon drums with an average weight of 300 pounds per drum. The continued rapid increase in production of uranium concentrates made it necessary to expand the capacity of the concentrate sample mill, and in 1957 additions to the sampler building and receiving docks

FIG. 3–4. View of sample-cutting line for uranium concentrates.

were made which doubled the total floor space. Another sample cutting line was installed, with provision for a third, when needed, with platform scales, roller conveyors, craneway and electric hoist. Mixing, drying, grinding, and dust collecting facilities were doubled. Arrangements were made with the producers to use 55-gallon drums, instead of the 30's, with an average weight of 500 to 550 pounds of material per drum, so that today the capacity of the sampling plant is 10,000 to 12,000 drums per month. By adding a third cutting line, for which floor space has been provided, the total sampling capacity can be increased another 1250 tons of concentrates per month.

3–6.2 Sampling Procedure A. Figure 3–5 outlines "Procedure A" used at Grand Junction, Colorado, for sampling uranium concentrates from new mills and material too wet to sample by "Procedure B," described in Article 3–6.3.

Concentrates arrive by truck and rail packaged in 55-gallon drums containing from 300 to 1300 pounds of material. A lot consists of from 10 to 75 drums, and has a wet weight of 4000 to 60,000 pounds. The drums are weighed, and the gross and tare weights are recorded. A 2000-pound platform scale is used for weighing, and weights are recorded to the nearest one-half pound. The drums are lined up in front of the sample-drilling hoods, and three auger samples are taken from each one with an electric drill driving a 36 by $1\frac{3}{16}$-inch ship's auger. The three auger samples from

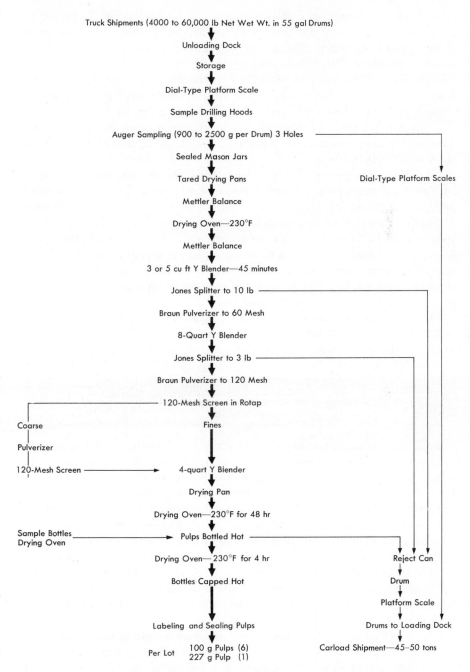

Fig. 3–5. Sampling flowsheet for wet concentrates, Procedure A.

each drum are caught in a stainless steel pan and immediately placed in a $\frac{1}{2}$-gallon Mason jar and sealed. The quantity of sample taken from each drum varies from 900 to 2500 grams, depending on concentrate density.

After sampling, the drums are reweighed and moved to the outdoor loading dock. The samples are taken to the weighing and drying room. Each sample is transferred to a tared, stainless steel drying pan, weighed immediately on a Mettler balance, and placed in a drying oven at 110°C. The samples are dried to constant weight, requiring from 48 to 120 hours. The percentage of moisture is reported for each drum, and an average for the whole lot is computed.

After the moisture samples have been dried, the samples are composited by emptying them into a 3- or 5-cubic-foot Patterson Kelly "Y" blender and mixing for 45 minutes. The composite is removed from the blender and split down to 7 to 10 pounds in a large Jones splitter. This sample is then ground to 60 mesh in a Braun pulverizer, mixed for 15 minutes in an 8-quart "Y" blender, and split to about 3 pounds in a Jones splitter. The sample is again ground in a Braun pulverizer to about 120 mesh, screened through 120 mesh in a Rotap, with the oversize being reground, and mixed in a 4-quart "Y" blender for 30 minutes.

The composite sample is next placed in a stainless steel drying pan and further dried at 110°C for 48 hours. Clean sample bottles are put into the drier and dried for about 4 hours. The sample is removed from the oven, and six 100-gram pulps and one 227-gram pulp are weighed into the sample bottles as rapidly as possible. The uncapped bottles are immediately replaced in the drying oven for 4 hours, and then capped hot, sealed, and labeled.

3–6.3 Sampling Procedure B. "Procedure B," outlined in Fig. 3–6, is used for sampling concentrates from all mills for which "Procedure A" is not used. The drums are auger-sampled as in Procedure A, but in Procedure B the individual drum samples are composited before a moisture sample is taken. The samples are quickly emptied into a 3- or 5-cubic-foot twin-shell blender with intensifier bar, and mixed for 1 hour. The blender is stopped in a vertical position, a large sample bucket is placed under the outlet, and the outlet gate is opened. Four blender samples of 2000 to 3000 grams each are taken with a scoop as quickly as possible from the falling stream. The bottom gate of the blender is kept closed between the taking of successive samples. The samples are sealed immediately in individual Mason jars.

The sealed samples are taken to the moisture weighing room, placed in tared drying pans, weighed, and dried to constant weight at 110°C. The percentage weight losses of the four samples are averaged and recorded as the lot moisture.

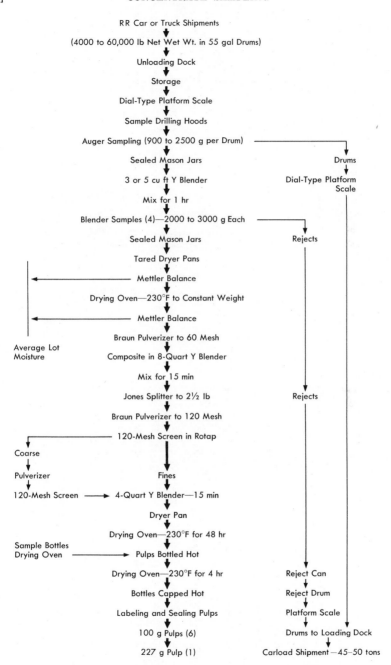

FIG. 3–6. Sampling flowsheet for concentrates, Procedure B.

TABLE 3–2

METHODS USED FOR THE DETERMINATION OF URANIUM IN U. S. MILLS

Name	Location	Volumetric	Fluorometric*	Spectrophotometric*
Anaconda Co.	Bluewater, N. M.	1a, 2	3	6
Climax Uranium Co.	Grand Junction, Colo.	1b	(3)	6
Kerr-McGee Oil Industries, Inc.	Shiprock, N. M.	1a, 2	(3)	(6)
Mines Development, Inc.	Edgemont, S. D.	1b	3	—
National Lead Co., Inc.	Monticello, Utah	1b	3	5
Rare Metals Corp. of America	Tuba City, Arizona	1a, 2	3	5
Union Carbide Nuclear Co.	Rifle, Colo.	1a, 1c	—	—
	Uravan, Colo.	1a, 1c	—	(5)
	Maybell, Colo.	1a, 1c	(3)	5
Uranium Reduction Co.	Moab, Utah	1a, 2	3	—
Vanadium Corp. of America	Durango, Colo.	1a, 1c	—	—
	Naturita, Colo.	1a, 1c	—	—
Vitro Uranium Co.	Salt Lake City, Utah	2	4	—
Texas Zinc Minerals Corp.	Mexican Hat, Utah	1a, 2	(3)	—

1. Volumetric: Jones reductor, aeration, titration with (a) dichromate, (b) ceric, or (c) permanganate. 2. Volumetric: Lead reductor, titration with ceric. 3. Fluorometric: Platinum dish method. 4. Fluorometric: Gold dish method. 5. Spectrophotometric: Thiocyanate. 6. Spectrophotometric: Dibenzoylmethane.

* Numbers in parentheses indicate that the method is being considered for use.

After drying, the four samples are taken to the bucking room, ground through a Braun pulverizer to about 60 mesh, combined and mixed for 15 minutes in an 8-quart twin-shell blender, split down to about $2\frac{1}{2}$ pounds in a Jones splitter, and again ground in a Braun pulverizer to 120 mesh. The sample is screened through 120-mesh screen in a Rotap, with the oversize being reground, and then mixed for 15 minutes in a 4-quart twin-shell blender. The blended sample is placed in a drier pan and dried 48 hours at 110°C. The sample is removed from the oven and six 100-gram pulps and one 227-gram pulp are weighed into clean sample bottles that have been predried as in Procedure A. The uncapped bottles are replaced in the oven for 4 hours, then capped hot, sealed, and labeled.

3–6.4 Control sampling. A continuous program of evaluation of the auger method of sampling uranium and vanadium concentrates has been carried on since the start of operations. It provides a continuous check and statistical evaluation of the sampling method. Frequent comparisons of purchase and check sampling results have proved this sampling procedure to be accurate. Weight losses by handling and dusting have been reduced to a negligible quantity.

PART II. ANALYSIS OF URANIUM ORES*

3–7. INTRODUCTION TO ANALYSIS

Many methods for determination of uranium have been developed during the past 10 to 15 years as a result of the needs of various countries in their atomic energy programs. Most techniques of classical and instrumental analysis have been used to solve specific problems. Yet only a few of these methods have been culled for use in the uranium ore processing industry. A total of six methods for uranium analysis are used by the uranium mills now operating in the United States, as shown in Table 3–2. These methods comprise two versions each of the following analysis types: volumetric, fluorometric, and spectrophotometric. The six, along with their recently reported variations, will be outlined and discussed here and newer methods that may eventually prove acceptable for use in the mills will also be evaluated.

3–8. VOLUMETRIC METHODS

A survey by this author revealed that in 1957 most mills in the United States were using some version of the procedure involving oxidimetric titration of uranium +4. The general procedure involves dissolving the

---

* By Michael A. DeSesa, AEC Raw Materials Development Laboratory, National Lead Company, Inc.

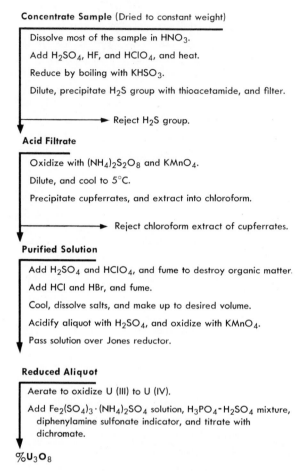

Concentrate Sample (Dried to constant weight)

Dissolve most of the sample in HNO_3.

Add H_2SO_4, HF, and $HClO_4$, and heat.

Reduce by boiling with $KHSO_3$.

Dilute, precipitate H_2S group with thioacetamide, and filter.

→ Reject H_2S group.

Acid Filtrate

Oxidize with $(NH_4)_2S_2O_8$ and $KMnO_4$.

Dilute, and cool to 5°C.

Precipitate cupferrates, and extract into chloroform.

→ Reject chloroform extract of cupferrates.

Purified Solution

Add H_2SO_4 and $HClO_4$, and fume to destroy organic matter.

Add HCl and HBr, and fume.

Cool, dissolve salts, and make up to desired volume.

Acidify aliquot with H_2SO_4, and oxidize with $KMnO_4$.

Pass solution over Jones reductor.

Reduced Aliquot

Aerate to oxidize U (III) to U (IV).

Add $Fe_2(SO_4)_3 \cdot (NH_4)_2SO_4$ solution, H_3PO_4-H_2SO_4 mixture, diphenylamine sulfonate indicator, and titrate with dichromate.

$\%U_3O_8$

FIG. 3-7. Volumetric Method 1 for concentrates.

sample, separating interferences, reducing the uranium to the +4 valence state, and titrating with standard oxidizing solution to the +6 valence state.

Two versions of the oxidimetric procedure are in common use. These procedures, as now used at Lucius Pitkin, Inc. [3], are outlined in Figs. 3-7 and 3-8. The first is based on the procedure described in detail by Rodden and Tregoning [4], and is generally used for the analysis of uranium concentrates and for referee analyses. The distinguishing features of this method are the reduction of uranium in a zinc amalgam column, aeration of the reduced solution to oxidize any uranium +3 to uranium +4, and titration of the uranium +4 with dichromate. This method has been dis-

Ore Sample (Dried)

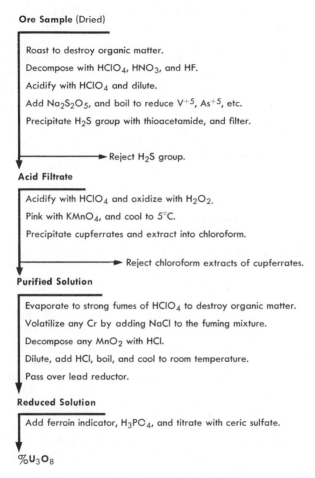

Roast to destroy organic matter.

Decompose with $HClO_4$, HNO_3, and HF.

Acidify with $HClO_4$ and dilute.

Add $Na_2S_2O_5$, and boil to reduce V^{+5}, As^{+5}, etc.

Precipitate H_2S group with thioacetamide, and filter.

→ Reject H_2S group.

Acid Filtrate

Acidify with $HClO_4$ and oxidize with H_2O_2.

Pink with $KMnO_4$, and cool to 5°C.

Precipitate cupferrates and extract into chloroform.

→ Reject chloroform extracts of cupferrates.

Purified Solution

Evaporate to strong fumes of $HClO_4$ to destroy organic matter.

Volatilize any Cr by adding NaCl to the fuming mixture.

Decompose any MnO_2 with HCl.

Dilute, add HCl, boil, and cool to room temperature.

Pass over lead reductor.

Reduced Solution

Add ferroin indicator, H_3PO_4, and titrate with ceric sulfate.

%U_3O_8

Fig. 3–8. Volumetric Method 2 for ores.

cussed thoroughly in the early literature of the atomic energy program [5]. Detailed information on several sources of error and how they are produced has been reported by Rodden [5], Sill and Peterson [6], and Patterson [7], and need not be repeated here.

One peculiar effect, reported by Rabbitts [8] of the Canadian Bureau of Mines and by Valent et al. [9] of the Feed Materials Production Center in this country, has received insufficient attention. These workers found it necessary to standardize the dichromate solution against various quantities of standard U_3O_8, because the apparent titer of the dichromate solution, in terms of milligrams of uranium per milliliter of $K_2Cr_2O_7$, varied with the amount of uranium determined. This effect may be due to the behavior described by Lingane [10], who pointed out that the equivalence point in a titration will be at a more positive value if the oxidized form of the ion being titrated is present in the solution. In the method under discussion, excess ferric ion is added to the solution containing uranium and an equivalent amount of ferrous ion is produced to be titrated with dichromate. At the beginning of the titration, the solution already contains an amount of ferric ion that varies inversely with the amount of reduced uranium originally present. The smaller the concentration of uranium taken for analysis, the greater the resulting concentration of ferric ion. The equivalence potential therefore shifts towards the formal potential of the dichromate-chromic couple and away from the formal potential of the diphenylamine indicator, producing a greater tendency to overtitrate the solution. Thus, the factor mg U/ml Cr_2O_7 becomes smaller as less dichromate is used in the titration, which corresponds to the behavior observed by Valent.

Such difficulty evidently has not been experienced at the mills using this procedure for concentrate analysis, possibly because the accepted procedure [3] has been slightly modified by adding only half the excess ferric ion recommended in the original procedure by the New Brunswick Laboratory [4]. Also, the samples taken for analysis may contain sufficient uranium to be in the optimum range. When this method is used, the dichromate solution should be standardized against various amounts of standard U_3O_8, as recommended by Valent [9], to establish optimum range and to prepare an empirical calibration curve that can be used for analyses falling outside the optimum range.

The second volumetric method, Fig. 3–8, widely used for ore analysis in the United States, is based on the original excellent work of Sill and Peterson [6] of the Bureau of Mines. The distinguishing features of this procedure are the reduction of the uranium in hydrochloric acid solution in a lead reductor [11], the use of ferroin as indicator, and the use of sulfatoceric acid as the titrant in the presence of a small concentration of ferric sulfate or phosphoric acid. The detailed method of analysis may be obtained by referring to the original article of Sill and Peterson and to various handbooks [3,4,12].

The lead reductor method has several important advantages over that of the classical Jones reductor. Perchloric acid is substituted for sulfuric acid in the decomposition of the ore and no precipitation problems are encountered with high-lime ores. Uranium +3 is not formed in the reduction step, avoiding the aeration step and the precautions that must go with it to avoid oxidation of uranium +4. The lead reductor is easily prepared, and amalgamation is not necessary since the reaction between lead and nonoxidizing acids is slow. Some of the elements that interfere with the use of zinc amalgam have no effect on the lead reductor. The use of ferroin as the indicator produces a sharper color change, more reproducible blanks, and independence of volume in comparison with diphenylamine sulfonic acid. The use of small amounts of ferric sulfate or phosphoric acid [13] to promote the rate of titration allows the titration to be made with sulfatoceric acid at room temperature in an essentially colorless solution.

The main advances in volumetric methods up to 1953 were reviewed by Rodden [14], and most procedures were concerned with methods of reduction. The only one of these which was widely accepted was the lead reductor method. Main [15] has since reported that uranium may be reduced rapidly with stannous chloride by adding iron as a catalyst. The reduction is quantitative in the presence of orthophosphate. The procedure involves reduction of uranium with stannous chloride, oxidation of excess stannous chloride with mercuric chloride, and titration of uranium with dichromate. Titanous sulfate has again been proposed [16,17] as a reductant for uranium prior to oxidimetric titration. Since neither of these reductants offers any increase in accuracy over the column reductor methods, they do not seem destined for wide acceptance.

3–9. FLUOROMETRIC METHODS

The fluorometric method of analysis, widely used for the rapid analysis of samples low in uranium content, has been adopted in about half the uranium mills in the United States for the analysis of ores, residues, and solutions containing less than about 1 gram of U_3O_8 per liter. Use of this method increased analytical capacity tenfold during the early years of the Atomic Energy Commission Raw Materials Development Laboratory [18]. The fluorometric method still serves as the most useful analytical tool of the Raw Materials Development Laboratory, the Grand Junction Pilot Plant, and other AEC and private groups.

In brief, the fluorometric method consists of fusing a small aliquot of a uraniferous liquor with a sodium fluoride flux in a platinum or gold dish, irradiating the resultant disk or button with ultraviolet light of a suitable wavelength, and measuring the emitted fluorescence in a fluorometer.

The fluorescent property of trace concentrations in sodium fluoride is specific for uranium except for a few rare elements, so direct interference from other ions is not a problem. However, several elements can quench the fluorescence of uranium. To avoid the interference of quenchers, two techniques can be used: the dilution technique, in which the sample is diluted to such an extent that the concentration of any quencher is too small to be harmful, and the extraction technique, in which uranium is separated from quenching materials by selective solvent extraction, and a portion of the organic extract is used for the fluoride fusion. Anions that form complexes with uranium hinder the extraction and must be rendered inactive by complex ion formation.

The literature on the fluorometric determination of uranium is voluminous. Early information may be covered by reading the reviews by Rodden [14,19,20] and the comprehensive article by Price et al. [21].

The "platinum dish" method, which evolved during many years of practical experience at the Raw Materials Development Laboratory, has recently been adopted by most mills employing the fluorometric method of analysis. This procedure has been reported by Centanni et al. [22] in sufficient detail to enable any newcomer in the field to use it. A combination of dilution and solvent extraction is used to separate the uranium from possible interferences and quenchers. An aliquot of a liquid sample or of a solid sample solution is diluted and acidified so that the diluted sample contains approximately 0.01 mg U_3O_8/ml in a 5 percent nitric acid solution. One milliliter of the diluted sample is "salted" with saturated aluminum nitrate solution, and the uranium is extracted into 10 milliliters of ethyl acetate. Aliquots of 0.1 milliliter are removed and transferred onto pellets of 2 percent lithium fluoride—98 percent sodium fluoride flux in platinum dishes. The pellets are dried, fused, and allowed to cool, forming buttons which slide easily from the dish. The fluorescence of the fluoride button is measured in a Galvanek-Morrison reflectance fluorometer (commercially available from the Jarrell-Ash Co., Newtonville, Massachusetts, and the Engineering Equipment Co., Boynton Beach, Florida).

Many chemical compounds and mixtures have been used as the flux in the fluorometric determination of uranium. Selection is complicated by the many properties required of an acceptable flux. Fluxes currently in use may be placed in the following two categories:

(1) High-carbonate fluxes: low-melting (approximately 600°C) materials which, after fusion and solidification, are readily removed from the dish in a single button.

(2) High-fluoride fluxes: high-melting (approximately 1000°C) materials which, after fusion and solidification, cannot be removed from the dish without fracturing the button.

High-carbonate fluxes are exemplified by sodium fluoride-sodium carbonate-potassium carbonate mixtures containing 1 to 10 percent sodium fluoride. In practice, the amount of this flux used per sample is 2 to 3 grams, with the fusion performed in a gold [4] or platinum [23] dish. These fluxes have the advantage that the fusion dish plays no part in the measurement of the fluorescence intensity of the button. All buttons are removed from the fusion dishes and their intensities are measured in a holder that reflects a minimum of the ultraviolet light. High-carbonate fluxes have the additional advantage of being usable in fluorometers employing either the reflection or the transmission principle.

Unfortunately, however, in reflection-type fluorometers, uranium fluorescence is lower in high-carbonate fluxes than in high-fluoride fluxes. Also, with high-carbonate fluxes there are variations between daily batches prepared from the same reagent lots, and moisture control is required because of the hygroscopic nature of the button. In addition, the presence of impurities in the sample being analyzed often causes more interference in high-carbonate fluxes than in high-fluoride fluxes [21]. Cadmium, for example, fluoresces only in the former. Also, quenching of uranium fluorescence is often more pronounced in high-carbonate fluxes.

High-fluoride fluxes are exemplified by pure sodium fluoride. In practice, the amount of sodium fluoride flux used is approximately 0.4 gram, with the fusion performed in a platinum dish. This type of flux has the advantage of maximum enhancement of uranium fluorescence; therefore, it provides greater sensitivity than that afforded by other fluxes. Because of their smaller size, sodium fluoride pellets can be fused efficiently in 20-pellet lots. On the other hand, the larger pellets of the high-carbonate fluxes are handled only 4 to 6 at one time. Thus, more uranium determinations can be performed per man-day by using a high-fluoride flux.

The principal limitation of the sodium fluoride flux is the necessity for careful control of the temperature and atmosphere during fusion in order to obtain analytical reproducibility. Another important limitation is the influence of the fusion dish on the fluorescence measurement. Since the button is not easily removed from the dish, the fluorescence of each button must be measured in its dish, and accordingly the reflectivity of the dish affects the amount of light reaching the radiation detector. This reflectivity varies markedly from dish to dish, and constitutes an important source of error. The principal source of this variation is the presence of brown stains on the fusion dish, presumably formed by the high-temperature reaction between the flux, the dish, and the atmosphere. To minimize these reflectivity differences, it is necessary after each use to clean and, where necessary, polish each dish by a tedious and detailed procedure.

The method used by the Raw Materials Development Laboratory embodies a flux offering all the advantages of both types and none of the disadvantages. This flux is composed of sodium fluoride into which have been admixed small amounts of lithium fluoride. Although it has previously been reported [21] that fluxes containing lithium attack the platinum dishes, this chemical attack presumably takes place only with high-lithium fluxes, because it is neither observed with low-lithium fluxes such as employed in the recommended procedure nor with fluxes containing as much as 10 percent lithium fluoride. It was found that for measurements in the Galvanek-Morrison fluorometer with the recommended optics [24] flux compositions containing between 1 and 3 percent added lithium fluoride provide optimum performance. When the flux contains less than 1 percent lithium fluoride, the button is not readily removed from its dish, and at concentrations higher than 3 percent lithium fluoride, the fluorescence per unit weight of uranium is inferior. Accordingly, a mixture of 2 percent lithium fluoride and 98 percent sodium fluoride was selected as the flux composition.

A temperature of 850 to 900°C was found adequate for fusing the mixed-fluoride flux. The resultant button is readily removed from its dish, so that the fluorescence of each button measured in the same holder and variations in reflectivity are eliminated. A polished aluminum receptacle has been built into the fluorometer slide to hold the button during fluorescence measurements. The aluminum receptacle has two primary functions. First, it acts as a reflector of induced radiation, increasing the sensitivity of the analytical method by the additional fluorescence reflected into the radiation detector. Second, it provides a fixed and uniform amount of reflection of the ultraviolet light used to induce uranium fluorescence, thereby providing a constant background.

Since the mixed-fluoride flux allows all fluorescence measurements to be made without the fusion dish, carefully controlled cleaning and polishing is eliminated. The dishes are simply rinsed thoroughly in water and reused. Even after a fluoride button containing as much as 10 micrograms of U_3O_8 has been prepared in a dish, no contamination of the dish has been noted after a thorough washing with water. After two or three months of use, the dishes may be given a thorough polishing to extend the life of the platinum.

Good precision and accuracy can be obtained by this fluorometric procedure, and recently there has been reported [25] an automatic fusion burner unit, which minimizes the atmosphere-temperature fluctuations and makes possible better reproducibility and greater accuracy in the uranium determination. Also, eliminating the reference standard in the Galvanek-Morrison fluorometer has further improved the operating stability and simplified the operation of this excellent instrument [25].

Several interesting developments have been reported recently in the field of fluorometric analysis. In keeping with the tendency for most workers in the field to design their own instruments, several new fluorometers and modifications of older models have been described [26–33], both in this country and abroad. Although several of these instruments are well designed, all are custom built and not commercially available. However, the Mount Sopris Instrument Corp., Boulder, Colorado, has recently made available a transmission-type fluorometer. This instrument should bring about an increasing interest in the procedures which have been recommended [23,34] by the laboratories of the U. S. Geological Survey, where transmission fluorometers with very high sensitivity and precision have been used for several years for measuring uranium in alkali carbonate-fluoride melts.

The critical factors in preparing the fluoride melt have been examined by Michelson [35], and a machine for preparing the fluoride phosphors has been described [36]. The use of aluminum nitrate as the salting agent for the separation of uranium by extraction into ethyl acetate, as first introduced by Grimaldi and Levine [37], has been widely adopted [38–41]. Trialkyl phosphine oxides have been reported [42] to be excellent extractants for uranium prior to fluorometric determination. These reagents have the advantage of quantitatively extracting uranium from samples that are as concentrated as 12 M with respect to such acids as sulfuric, phosphoric, and hydrochloric. The extraction is also quantitative in the presence of anions that form strong complexes with uranyl ion in solution, such as citrate, oxalate, and tartrate. A detailed procedure has been presented [42] for preparing tri-n-octylphosphine oxide, but the reagent is now commercially available.

3–10. Spectrophotometric Methods

Colorimetric and spectrophotometric methods for uranium determination have been applied to solve many analytical problems when a sensitive, rapid, and reasonably accurate method is required. As with the fluorometric method, this technique has been adopted in about half the mills in operation, and is used mainly for analyzing solutions containing more than 1 gram U_3O_8 per liter.

3–10.1 Thiocyanate. Various modifications of the spectrophotometric determination of uranium with thiocyanate have been proposed. Currah and Beamish [43] first used thiocyanate as a colorimetric reagent for determining uranium. The yellow uranyl thiocyanate color was developed in an aqueous solution, and stannous chloride was recommended to prevent the interference of iron +3. Nelson and Hume [44] examined the procedure with respect to errors inherent in the analytical method and possible interferences. As a result of this study, a more reproducible and sensitive method was developed. Henicksman [45] thoroughly investigated interferences and first recognized the serious interference of vanadium.

Although the method may be applied to the analysis of certain materials without preliminary separation of the uranium (to monazite concentrates [46] for example) most of the recent papers dealing with this method have been concerned with removing anionic and cationic interferences. Crouthamel and Johnson [47] found that the stannous chloride reductant generated an interference peak around 375 millimicrons when in the presence of uranium and ammonium thiocyanate in aqueous solution. This interference became more serious as the thiocyanate solution aged. By developing the color in an acetone-water solvent, Crouthamel and Johnson were able to inhibit this attack of thiocyanate by stannous chloride. The use of an acetone-water solvent eliminated the majority of the anionic interferences in the aqueous thiocyanate method, increased the sensitivity, enhanced the stability of color, and made the correct color development independent of pH in the acid region. However, several elements, such as vanadium and titanium, cannot be tolerated when using the acetone-water solvent.

Extraction of the colored uranyl thiocyanate complex into amyl alcohol or ether to eliminate some interferences was recommended by Gerhold and Hecht [48], and dibutoxytetraethylene glycol has recently been used in a similar manner [49]. Ethyl acetate extraction of uranium from a nitrate solution has been utilized in several procedures involving recovery of the uranium from the ethyl acetate phase and determination with thiocyanate in water [50, 51], or in an acetone medium [52].

A method was reported [53,40] from the AEC Raw Materials Development Laboratory for analyzing uraniferous ores and leach liquors. The procedure consists of extracting the uranium from an aluminum nitrate solution into ethyl acetate, followed by color development in a portion of the ethyl acetate extract with a solution of ammonium thiocyanate and stannous chloride in an acetone-water solvent. This method offers several advantages over the other reported modifications of the determination of uranium with thiocyanate. By the preliminary separation of uranium, interferences are eliminated more efficiently than by extraction of uranyl thiocyanate after the color development. Since the color is developed directly on the extract, less time is required than for procedures involving a preliminary extraction separation. Also, higher sensitivity is obtained in the acetone-ethyl acetate-water solvent. A slightly modified version of this method has been used at the Oak Ridge National Laboratory [54]. From the University of Utah it was reported [55] that "highly accurate results may be quickly obtained by this procedure." However, the method does have several limitations. The chromogenic reagent is stable for only 3 hours and is usually prepared no more than 1 hour before use. The yellow color of the uranyl thiocyanate complex is stable for only 10 minutes, and then becomes more intense on standing. While the increase amounts only to 3 percent after 1 hour, this behavior limits the number of samples that can be prepared at one time. The procedure is not applicable when the sample aliquot contains more than 2 milligrams of vanadium, this quantity being the tolerable limit of the element. Most alkaline leach liquors require an initial neutralization with nitric acid in order to obtain a quantitative extraction of uranium into ethyl acetate. Also, the acetone-ethyl acetate-water solution of ammonium thiocyanate tends to creep in the absorption cells and volatilizes to leave a residue of ammonium thiocyanate around the edges.

Russian workers [56] reported a similar procedure in which the uranium is extracted into methylethyl ketone and the color developed by mixing the organic phase with a solution of ammonium thiocyanate and ascorbic acid in acetone. However, in this procedure, two extractions are required, and it is advisable to measure the color intensity before 30 minutes have elapsed. Vanadium, titanium, bismuth, and molybdenum are extracted by methylethyl ketone and must be specially separated to prevent interference.

Another version of the thiocyanate method, in which all the previous difficulties are eliminated, has been reported [57]. Substituting butyl Cellosolve for acetone in the chromogenic reagent reduces the volatility of the colored solution and eliminates the creeping of solution in the absorption cells. Instead of stannous chloride, ascorbic acid is used as the reducing agent. As a result of using a milder reducing agent, the chromogenic reagent and the colored solutions do not deteriorate for at least 48 hours. Also, the tolerable limit of vanadium is greatly increased, since the seriously interfering vanadium +3 species is not formed in the colored solution. The use of methylisobutyl ketone as the extractant for uranium results in a more selective separation from other cations and makes it possible to analyze alkaline leach liquors directly without prior neutralization.

In this method, the solution to be analyzed is diluted to a concentration of 0.2 to 2.0 grams of U_3O_8 per liter if absorbance measurement is to be made at 375 millimicrons. It is analyzed without dilution if the adsorbance is to be measured at longer wavelengths. An aliquot of the sample (no more than 3 milliliters) is transferred into a 40-milliliter vial. If the sample is strongly acid or alkaline, or if the sample is in a concentrated buffer solution, especially carbonate-bicarbonate, the pH is adjusted to 0 to 3 by the dropwise addition of nitric acid or concentrated sodium hydroxide. Approximately 15 milliliters of aluminum nitrate reagent are added, followed by exactly 20 milliliters of methylisobutyl ketone. The vial is capped and shaken for 2 minutes. The organic and aqueous phases are completely separated by centrifugation. Ten milliliters of the organic phase are transferred by pipet into another vial, and 15 milliliters of the chromogenic reagent are added. The vial is capped and the solution is mixed well. A reagent blank is prepared in the same manner as the samples. The absorbance is measured against the reagent blank at 375 millimicrons or, if the absorbance is greater than 1.0, at 420 millimicrons.

The yellow uranyl thiocyanate complex forms immediately, and the color is stable for at least 48 hours. Very good precision and accuracy approaching that of the volumetric methods can be obtained. Titanium is the only serious interference, but procedures are given that make it possible to analyze samples containing as much as 5 milligrams of titanium in the sample aliquot. The procedure can be geared to production work by performing the solvent extraction in small vials, using automatic pipets for delivery of reagents, and pipeting out unvarying amounts of solvent and color developing reagent to avoid diluting to volume. Using this procedure, two analysts can turn out about 75 analyses in an 8-hour day. By 1957, this procedure had been adopted at two of the uranium mills now in operation in the United States.

One other similar thiocyanate procedure has been proposed for the determination of uranium [58]. The uranium is separated from possible interferences by solvent extraction into a solution of tri-n-butyl phosphate (TBP) in carbon tetrachloride. The color is developed on a portion of the organic extract with a solution of ammonium thiocyanate in ethanol. Antimony and vanadium are the most serious interferences. Although this procedure was designed for the analysis of solutions in the processing of spent reactor fuel elements, it probably could be adapted to leach solutions. However, this procedure seems to offer no particular advantage over the thiocyanate method previously described.

3–10.2 Dibenzoylmethane. In 1953, 1, 3-diphenyl-1, 3-propanedione, or dibenzoylmethane, was proposed [59] as a colorimetric reagent for uranium. This compound was found to be slightly more sensitive for uranium than other colorimetric reagents which have been proposed. Pribil and Jelinek [60] used a solution of dibenzoylmethane in ethyl acetate to extract uranium from aqueous solution and combined the extracts for color development. They recommended using ethylenediamine tetraacetic acid to complex possible interferences in the solution and prevent their extraction. Adams and Maeck [38] used dibenzoylmethane in the analysis of uranium ores. After separating the uranium from possible interferences by solvent extraction with ethyl acetate, they developed the color on a portion of the ethyl acetate extract with an alcoholic solution of dibenzoylmethane. Lerner and Eberle [61] recommended extracting the uranium from a 5 N nitric acid solution of the sample into a 70:30 mixture of TBP and ethyl acetate. After neutralizing the acid in the organic extract, the color was developed. As interferences, zirconium, thorium, and molybdenum were found to be the most serious. Procedures for eliminating the interference of zirconium and thorium were outlined.

A detailed investigation into potential applications of the dibenzoylmethane method was reported by Francois [62]. The uranium is separated from contaminants by extracting from an aluminum nitrate solution with TBP dissolved in 2, 2, 4-trimethylpentane (isooctane). Color is developed by introducing an aliquot of the TBP-isooctane mixture into an acetone-water solution of dibenzoylmethane with pyridine for buffering action. Common cations do not interfere, except for thorium in a concentration exceeding ten times that of the uranyl ion. The color develops immediately and is stable for at least 24 hours. By using only 3 milliliters of organic solution for the extraction and taking 2 milliliters of this solution for the final color development in a solution of 25 milliliters, it is possible to determine as little as 0.05 milligrams of uranium.

3–10.3 Peroxide.   Until recent years, the most popular inorganic reagent for the colorimetric determination of uranium was alkaline sodium peroxide [5], but at the time of this writing the method had been largely replaced because of its relatively low sensitivity and poor selectivity.

In general, the uranium is separated from possible interferences in the sample by solvent extraction or precipitation. The purified uranium solution is neutralized with sodium hydroxide, and sodium peroxide is added to develop the color. The procedure recommended by Rodden and Tregoning [4] involves separating the uranium by extraction from a nitrate solution of the R_2O_3 group precipitate in a continuous ether extractor. The color is measured at 425 millimicrons, where there is the least interference from the color of sodium peroxide and other materials.

Later work reported on the use of the peroxide color method was concerned with various means of separating uranium prior to analysis. Vita et al. [63] recommended chelating the interfering cations with ethylenediamine tetraacetic acid or its derivatives and precipitating the uranium selectively with diammonium phosphate. The precipitated uranium may be separated in a centrifuge and determined colorimetrically by the alkaline peroxide method. Guest and Zimmerman [64] separated the uranium in high-grade materials by means of an ethyl acetate extraction using aluminum nitrate as salting agent, then stripped the uranium from the ethyl acetate layer with water, and developed the uranium peroxide color.

Three similar procedures have recently been reported [65–67] for the separation of uranium by adsorption as a sulfate complex on quaternary ammonium anion-exchange resin. In the procedure of Fisher and Kunin, interference of such ions as iron +3 and vanadium +5 is avoided by their preferential reduction with sulfurous acid so that they, as well as other cations, are not retained by the resin. After elution of the uranium with dilute perchloric or hydrochloric acid, the analysis is completed by the alkaline peroxide method. This ion-exchange method of separation has been successfully applied to the routine determination of uranium in ores and solutions. According to workers at the University of Nevada [67], about 20 analyses can be made per man per day with a minimum of equipment and at relatively low cost. However, solvent extraction is more rapid and the equipment is no more expensive.

Finally, Cheng and Lott [68] have developed a method for the spectrophotometric determination of uranium in the presence of other metals by using a mixture of nitrilotriacetic acid (NTA), hydrogen peroxide, and ammonium hydroxide. The NTA is believed to complex most interfering metals, but the method needs to be investigated in detail before being applied to routine analysis of ores and leach liquors.

3–10.4 Other methods. Many other methods have been suggested for the spectrophotometric determination of small amounts of uranium in the presence of foreign elements [69,70]. Three recent publications are worthy of mention in connection with the determination of uranium in leach solutions, ores, and concentrates.

Canning and Dixon [71] described a method for the direct spectrophotometric determination of uranium in leach liquors. A two-component procedure was utilized after reducing uranium and vanadium by ferrous sulfate in 40 volume percent phosphoric acid. The method is not simple to use, since a blank must be prepared for each sample and the calculations involve solving simultaneous equations, but it may find application when a simultaneous determination of uranium and vanadium is desired.

Paige et al. reported [72] an ultraviolet spectrophotometric method based on the absorbance of the complex of uranium with TBP. The complex is formed by extracting uranium from an aqueous 6 M sodium nitrate solution into a 25 percent solution of TBP in an inert diluent. This extraction also separates uranium from many interfering impurities. The method is attractive because of its sensitivity and simplicity, but has not been proved on complex samples such as leach liquors. Also, the necessity of using an ultraviolet spectrophotometer requires a much larger initial capital outlay than that required for methods based on absorbing visible light.

Another method [73] for determining high concentrations of uranium is based on the yellow color produced in TBP when uranium is extracted from an aqueous solution. The uranium is extracted from a solution 5 N in nitric acid by 100 percent TBP, and the color is measured at 420 millimicrons for solutions containing 0.1 to 20 grams of uranium per liter. Although molybdenum is a serious interference, this procedure could find a useful application in the rapid analysis of concentrate samples.

3–11. POLAROGRAPHIC METHODS

The polarographic method of analysis has not been used in any of the mills in the United States, but various procedures have been recommended from laboratories in this country and abroad for using it to determine uranium in ores and leach liquors.

The uranium content of dissolved ores has been determined [74] by extracting the uranium into an isopropyl ether solution of TBP, diluting the organic solvent with glacial acetic acid, adding lithium perchlorate as a supporting electrolyte, and determining the polarographic wave. In a similar procedure [73], the uranium was separated by extraction from 5 N nitric acid with 100 percent TBP, the TBP extract was diluted with at least 4 parts of glacial acetic acid containing 2 percent water, ammonium acetate was added as supporting electrolyte, and the polarographic wave was determined.

Wild [75] has separated uranium by extraction into ether from nitric acid on a cellulose column, evaporating off the ether, concentrating the uranium in perchloric acid, and determining the uranium polarographically, using a medium of sulfuric acid and tartrate originally recommended by Lewis and Overton [76] and modified by Shalgosky [77]. Legge [78] also used column chromatography for the separation, and determined uranium in a supporting electrolyte of oxalic and sulfuric acids.

While some degree of separation generally has been necessary for an accurate polarographic determination of uranium in ores, it has been claimed that the direct analysis of ore solutions is possible in supporting electrolytes of acid and alkaline ascorbic acid [79,80], hydrazine sulfate [81], and lactic acid [81]. However, very few data are available to substantiate the validity of these claims.

The Russians have stated that vanadium offers the greatest difficulty in the polarographic determination of uranium [81], and several other investigators have attempted to cope with the problem of vanadium interference. Ordinarily, polarographic interferences may be divided into two categories. Some elements are reduced before the ion which is being determined, and thus contribute to a high background current. Other elements are reduced at approximately the same half-wave potential as the element being determined, and thus produce a direct interference by contributing to the total current. However, it has been found by DeSesa and Nietzel that vanadium interferes in both ways, since vanadium $+5$ is reduced at zero applied voltage and at the same time enhances the uranium wave.

This phenomenon is illustrated by the four polarograms in Fig. 3–9. Curve 1 is a blank run on the supporting electrolyte consisting of sufficient dissolved magnesium sulfate to give a sulfate concentration of 30 g/liter and enough sulfuric acid to adjust the pH to 1.5. Curve 2 is the polarogram for a 1.0 mM vanadium $+5$ solution, and illustrates the normal reduction waves for vanadium in this medium from the $+5$ valence state to the $+4$ at positive potentials and from $+4$ to $+2$ at a half-wave potential of -0.96 volt. Curve 3 is the reduction wave for 1.1 mM uranyl ion illustrating the reduction from the $+6$ valence state to $+5$ at -0.23 volt and the consecutive reduction from $+5$ to $+4$ and $+3$ at -0.98 and -1.06

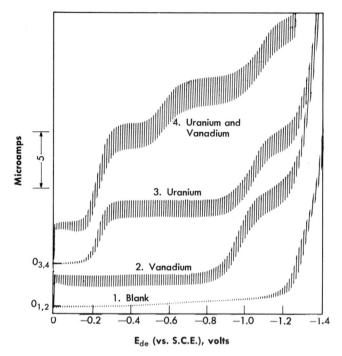

Fig. 3–9. Polarogram showing enhancement of the uranium wave in the presence of vanadium.

volt. Curve 4 is the polarogram for a mixture of 1.1 mM uranyl ion and 1.0 mM vanadium $+5$ in the same supporting electrolyte. In this case, the wave for the reduction of uranium $+6$ to uranium $+5$ has a height of 9.1 microamperes as compared with 5.8 microamperes in the absence of vanadium $+5$. Also a new wave has occurred at a half-wave potential of -0.58 volt. This wave is believed to be due to the reduction of vanadium $+3$ to vanadium $+2$, which has been reported [82] to occur at -0.51 volt in 0.5 M sulfuric acid.

The enhancement of the uranium wave in the presence of vanadium and sulfate is believed to be the result of an oxidation-reduction reaction between the uranium $+5$ and vanadium $+4$ ions produced during the electrode reduction reactions,

$$UO_2^+ + VO^{++} + 2H^+ = UO_2^{++} + V^{+++} + H_2O.$$

The uranyl ion formed at the surface of the drop by this reaction is then reduced to account for the increased wave height.

It is unlikely that polarography will be adopted as an analytical method to determine uranium, at least in United States mills, for the following reasons: the special interference problem of vanadium, which commonly occurs in uraniferous ores of the United States; the complicated polarographic procedures that have been used to determine uranium in ores; and the general difficulties associated with polarographic analysis.

3–12. COULOMETRIC METHODS

A few applications of the coulometric method of analysis to the determination of uranium have appeared in the literature. Two are adaptations of the conventional volumetric procedure in which electrolytically generated cerium +4 [83] or bromine [84] is used to oxidize the uranium after it has been separated from interferences and reduced in a column reductor. Lingane and Iwamoto [85] found that in citrate medium of pH 0.5 to 1.5, uranyl ion could be titrated to the +4 state with titanous ion generated by reduction of +4 titanium at a mercury cathode. By titrating at 85°C, equilibrium was established quickly, and the equivalence point was precisely determined by the usual potentiometric technique. Using a strictly constant generation current, and measuring the time to the endpoint, the average error of 19 titrations of 28 to 112-milligram quantities of uranium was 0.02 percent.

Booman has described [86] an instrument for controlled potential electrolysis and precision coulometric integration. This apparatus was used [87] at the Idaho Chemical Processing Plant to analyze nitric acid solutions from the processing of spent fuel elements from nuclear reactors. Uranium +6 was reduced to uranium +4 at a controlled-potential mercury cathode, in a potassium citrate-aluminum sulfate or a sulfuric acid electrolyte. Essentially complete reduction was accomplished in 5 to 10 minutes at room temperature by using an electrolysis cell of 5-milliliter capacity. The method can tolerate mercury +2, copper +2, iron +3, and large amounts of nitric acid, and is capable of giving results reliable to less than 0.1 percent standard deviation in the range from 0.75 to 75 milligrams of uranium.

The inherent accuracy of the coulometric method may lead to the adoption of this technique for ore and concentrate analysis when the highest precision is desired.

3–13. X-RAY SPECTROCHEMICAL METHODS

An increasing interest is being shown in the determination of uranium by x-ray spectrochemical analysis. In this technique, a liquid or solid sample is bombarded with primary x-rays, and fluorescent x-rays characteristic of the elements in the sample are emitted. The x-ray spectrum may be separated into its different lines by diffraction on the natural cleavage faces of a crystal. Qualitative and quantitative spectrochemical analysis, using the emission spectra in the x-ray wavelength region, have been employed successfully during the past decade.

Several applications of this method to the analysis of solutions have been reported. Birks and Brooks [88] evaporated a 1-milliliter sample of an aqueous uranium solution in a shallow cup and analyzed the residue. Pish and Huffman [89] have described an x-ray spectrometric method for analyzing thorium and uranium-bearing aqueous and organic solutions by using strontium and bromobenzene, respectively, as the internal standard. Solutions containing from 0.1 to 5.0 grams of uranium per liter were analyzed with an accuracy of 1.0 percent. Kehl and Russell [90] precipitated uranium from solution, and analyzed the ashed precipitate by fluorescent x-ray spectrography. Solution samples from separation processes for nuclear reactor fuels were analyzed for uranium in the concentration range 3 to 5×10^{-3} M (about 1 g U_3O_8/liter) with a precision of 2 percent at the 95 percent confidence level by using a special glass sample cell and stabilized current to the x-ray tube [91]. Wilson and Wheeler [92] determined 0.2 to 2.0 grams of uranium per liter in nitric acid solution with a precision of 1 percent by modifying the commercial equipment and using a scintillation counter and pulse-height analyzer in the detection circuit. Using the adsorption edge technique, Wright and Barringer [93] were able to analyze aqueous samples with about the same precision and sensitivity.

A combined radiometric and fluorescent x-ray spectrographic method has been used [94] to determine uranium and thorium in ores with an accuracy of 10 percent of the amount present in samples containing more than 0.5 percent of these elements. The lower limit of detection in this method was reported to be 0.01 to 0.03 percent of either element. Cope [94] has described a procedure in which 1 gram of minus-100 mesh sample is mixed for 20 minutes or more with 1 milliliter of a solution of yttrium nitrate in ethanol in an automatic mortar, the sample is packed in a sample holder, and the intensity ratio of the uranium and yttrium lines is determined. From a calibration curve covering the range 0.01 to 20 percent U_3O_8, the percentage of uranium in the sample was then determined. The accuracy of the analysis decreased from 1 percent to about 10 percent as the percentage of U_3O_8 in the ore decreased from 5 percent to 0.05 percent.

Although major advances have been made in the field of x-ray analysis in recent years, it seems that the method is not yet ready for routine mill application. Samples may be analyzed by the existing fluorometric and spectrophotometric methods more rapidly, with greater sensitivity, and with equal accuracy.

3–14. ANALYSIS FOR OTHER ELEMENTS

A variety of other determinations are needed in the efficient operation of a uranium mill or a research group investigating uranium ore processing. It is impossible within the scope of this chapter to discuss in detail the non-uranium analyses. The details of most other analyses that may be required are available in handbooks such as *Analytical Procedures Used by the Grand Junction Laboratory*, Lucius Pitkin, Inc. [3] and *Raw Materials Development Laboratory Handbook of Analytical Methods* [12]. In most cases, the procedures of analysis available in standard textbooks and the published literature have been adapted for use in the analysis of uranium ores.

REFERENCES

1. *Survey of Sampling Procedures at Various Main Ore Buying Stations in the Colorado Plateau Area*, USAEC Report M-5203, Colorado School of Mines Research Foundation, Inc., Dec. 22, 1952.

2. A. F. TAGGART, *Handbook of Mineral Dressing, Ores and Industrial Minerals.* New York: John Wiley & Sons, Inc., 1945.

3. R. W. LAUDRIDGE, *Analytical Procedures Used by the Grand Junction Laboratory*, Western Uranium Project, Lucius Pitkin, Inc., Grand Junction, Colorado, 1957. (p. 1)

4. C. J. RODDEN and J. J. TREGONING, *Manual of Analytical Methods for the Determination of Uranium and Thorium in Their Ores.* Washington, D. C.: U. S. Government Printing Office, 1955.

5. C. J. RODDEN (Ed.), *Analytical Chemistry of the Manhattan Project*, National Nuclear Energy Series, Division VIII, Volume 1. New York: McGraw-Hill Book Co., Inc., 1950. (p. 54)

6. C. W. SILL and H. E. PETERSON, Volumetric Determination of Milligram Quantities of Uranium, *Anal. Chem.* **24**, 1175 (1952).

7. J. H. PATTERSON et al., *Manual of Special Materials Analytical Laboratory Procedures*, USAEC Report ANL-5410, Argonne National Laboratory, March 1955.

8. F. T. RABBITTS, *Can. Dept. Mines and Tech. Surveys, Mines Branch, Mem. Ser.* No. 103 (1949).

9. G. VALENT et al., paper presented at Annual Analytical and Physical Testing Symposium of the National Lead Co., New York, 1955.

10. J. J. LINGANE, *Electroanalytical Chemistry.* New York: Interscience Publishers, Inc., 1953. (p. 113)

11. W. D. COOKE et al., Application of the Lead Reductor to Determination of Uranium, *Anal. Chem.* **22**, 654 (1950).

12. M. A. DeSESA, *Raw Materials Development Laboratory Handbook of Analytical Methods*, USAEC Report TID-7002, National Lead Co., Inc., Mar. 30, 1956.

13. N. BERNBAUM and S. M. EDMONDS, New Applications of the Silver Reductor (Determination of Uranium and Copper), *Ind. Eng. Chem., Anal. Ed.* **12**, 155 (1940).

14. C. J. RODDEN, Analytical Chemistry of Uranium, *Anal. Chem.* **25**, 1598 (1953).

15. A. R. MAIN, Determination of Uranium by Reduction with Stannous Chloride, *Anal. Chem.* **26**, 1507 (1954).

16. R. J. GUEST and C. R. LALONDE, The Determination of Uranium in High-Grade Uranium Products—Use of Titanous Sulfate as a Reductant, *Can. Dept. Mines and Tech. Surveys, Mines Branch, Radioactivity Div. Topical Rept.* No. TR-135/56 (1956).

17. J. S. WAHLBERG et al., Volumetric Determination of Uranium; Titanous Sulfate as Reductant Before Oxidimetric Titration, *Anal. Chem.* **29**(6), 954 (1957).

18. A. M. GAUDIN, Massachusetts Institute of Technology, 1951. Unpublished.

19. C. J. RODDEN, Determination of Naturally Occurring Radioactive Elements, *Anal. Chem.* **21**, 327 (1949).

20. C. J. RODDEN (Ed.), *Analytical Chemistry of the Manhattan Project*, National Nuclear Energy Series, Division VIII, Volume 1. New York: McGraw-Hill Book Co., Inc., 1950. (p. 565)

21. G. R. PRICE et al., Fluorophotometric Determination of Uranium, *Anal. Chem.* **25**, 322 (1953).

22. F. A. CENTANNI et al., Fluorometric Determination of Uranium, *Anal. Chem.* **28**, 1651 (1956).

23. F. S. GRIMALDI et al., Fluorometric Methods of Uranium Analysis, in *U. S. Geol. Survey Circ.* No. 199. Washington, D. C.: U. S. Government Printing Office, 1952.

24. P. GALVANEK, JR., and T. J. MORRISON, JR., *A New Fluorimeter for the Determination of Uranium*, USAEC Report ACCO-47, American Cyanamid Company, May 27, 1954.

25. F. A. CENTANNI and T. J. MORRISON, JR., *Improvements in the Fluorometric Determination of Uranium*, USAEC Report WIN-63, National Lead Co., Inc., Apr. 3, 1957.

26. H. J. DiGIOVANNI et al., *Photofluorimeters for Determination of Uranium and Beryllium Concentrations*, USAEC Report NYO-4508, New York Operations Office, AEC, Aug. 18, 1954.

27. I. DRAGANIC, Fluorimetric Determination of Uranium in Ores, *Rec. trav. inst. recherches structure matière (Belgrade)* **1**, 89 (1952).

28. C. D. FLORIDA and C. N. DAVEY, A Sensitive Photometer Using Modulated Light and Its Applications in a Uranium Fluorimeter, *J. Sci. Instr.* **30**, 409 (1953).

29. L. R. FORTNER, paper presented at the American Chemical Society Conference on Analytical Chemistry and Applied Spectroscopy, Pittsburgh, Pa., March 1956. (Paper 99)

30. M. T. KELLEY et al., *An Improved Fluorophotometer for Determination of Uranium in Fused Sodium Fluoride Pellets*, USAEC Report ORNL-1445, Oak Ridge National Laboratory, Feb. 8, 1954.

31. C. A. KINSER, The Model VI Transmission Fluorimeter for the Determination of Uranium, in *U. S. Geol. Survey Circ.* No. 330. Washington, D. C.: U. S. Government Printing Office, 1954.

32. L. KOSTA, Determination of Uranium in Low-Grade Siliceous Material, *Bull. sci. Conseil acad. RPF Yougoslavie* 1(2), 41 (1953).

33. F. J. LYNCH and J. B. BAUMGARDNER, New Fluorescence Photometer, *Rev. Sci. Instr.* 26, 435 (1955).

34. F. S. GRIMALDI et al., Collected Papers on Methods of Analysis for Uranium and Thorium, *U. S. Geol. Survey Bull.* No. 1006, Parts 8 and 11–13. Washington, D. C.: U. S. Government Printing Office, 1954.

35. C. E. MICHELSON, *The Preparation of Fluoride Melts for Use in the Fluorimetric Method of Uranium Analysis*, USAEC Report HW-36831, Hanford Atomic Products Operation, July 11, 1955.

36. R. E. STEVENS et al., paper presented at the American Chemical Society Conference on Analytical Chemistry and Applied Spectroscopy, Pittsburgh, Pa., March 1956. (Paper 98)

37. F. S. GRIMALDI and H. LEVINE, *The Rapid Fluorimetric Determination of Uranium in Low-grade Ores: A Preliminary Report*, USAEC Report AECD-2824, U. S. Geological Survey, April 1948.

38. J. A. S. ADAMS and W. J. MAECK, Fluorometric and Colorimetric Microdetermination of Uranium in Rocks and Minerals, *Anal. Chem.* 26, 1635 (1954).

39. M. D. HASSIALIS and R. C. MUSA, The Analysis of Low-Grade Uranium Ores and Their Products, in *Proceedings of the International Conference on the Peaceful Uses of Atomic Energy*, Vol. 8. New York: United Nations, 1956. (P/116, p. 216)

40. O. A. NIETZEL and M. A. DeSESA, Spectrophotometric Determination of Uranium with Thiocyanate in Acetone-Ethyl Acetate-Water Medium, in *Proceedings of the International Conference on the Peaceful Uses of Atomic Energy*, Vol. 8. New York: United Nations, 1956. (P/532, p. 320)

41. J. B. ZIMMERMAN et al., Determination of Uranium in Concentrates by the Fluorophotometric Method, *Can. Dept. Mines and Tech. Surveys, Mines Branch, Tech. Paper* No. 6 (1953).

42. J. C. WHITE, *The Use of Trialkyl Phosphine Oxides as Extractants in the Fluorometric Determination of Uranium*, USAEC Report ORNL-2161, Oak Ridge National Laboratory, Nov. 1, 1956.

43. J. E. CURRAH and F. E. BEAMISH, Colorimetric Determination of Uranium with Thiocyanate, *Anal. Chem.* 19, 609 (1947).

44. C. M. NELSON and D. N. HUME, *Spectrophotometric Determination of Microgram Amounts of Uranium by Means of Ammonium Thiocyanate*, USAEC Report Mon-C-28, Oak Ridge National Laboratory, Nov. 1, 1945.

45. A. L. HENICKSMAN, *The Spectrophotometric Determination of Uranium*, USAEC Report LA-1394, Los Alamos Scientific Laboratory, Nov. 7, 1955.

46. M. M. TILLU et al., Colorimetric Estimation of Uranium with Ammonium Thiocyanate and Its Application to Determination of Uranium in Minerals, Particularly Monazite Concentrates, *Proc. Indian Acad. Sci.* 42A 28 (1955).

47. C. E. CROUTHAMEL and C. E. JOHNSON, Spectrophotometric Determination of Uranium by Thiocyanate Method in Acetone Medium, *Anal. Chem.* **24,** 1780 (1952).

48. M. GERHOLD and F. HECHT, Photometric Determination of Small Quantities of Uranium with Potassium Thiocyanate, *Mikrochemie ver Mikrochim. Acta 36/37,* 1100 (1951).

49. L. SILVERMAN and L. MOUDY, Photometric Determination of Uranium in Thorium, *Nucleonics* **12**(9), 61 (Sept. 1954).

50. C. J. RODDEN, Analysis of Uranium and Thorium Raw Materials, in *Proceedings of the International Conference on the Peaceful Uses of Atomic Energy,* Vol. 8. New York: United Nations, 1956. (P/952, p. 197).

51. R. J. GUEST, Determination of Small Quantities of Uranium in Ores and Solutions with Tributyl Phosphate and Ethyl Acetate, *Can. Dept. Mines and Tech. Surveys, Mines Branch, Radioactivity Div. Topical Rept.* No. TR-128/55 (1955).

52. H. I. FERNSTEIN, *The Determination of Uranium in Ores: Separation by Ethyl Acetate Extraction and Spectrophotometric Determination by the Thiocyanate Method in Acetone-Water Medium,* USAEC Report TEI-555, U. S. Geological Survey, September 1955.

53. M. A. DESESA and O. A. NIETZEL, *Spectrophotometric Determination of Uranium with Thiocyanate,* USAEC Report ACCO-54, American Cyanamid Company, July 19, 1954.

54. C. D. SUSANO and L. J. BRADY, *Some Selected Methods for Determining Uranium and Vanadium in the Presence of Each Other,* USAEC Report CF-55-1-77, Oak Ridge National Laboratory, Jan. 12, 1955.

55. R. L. PEARSON et al., *Equipment and Preliminary Results for the Leaching of UO₂ in a Basic Carbonate Circuit.* Technical Report No. VIII, USAEC Report AECU-3051, University of Utah, May 15, 1955.

56. P. N. PALEY, Determination of Small Quantities of Uranium in Ores, in *Proceedings of the International Conference on the Peaceful Uses of Atomic Energy,* Vol. 8. New York: United Nations, 1956. (P/629, p. 225)

57. O. A. NIETZEL and M. A. DESESA, Spectrophotometric Determination of Uranium with Thiocyanate in Butyl Cellosolve-Methyl Isobutyl Ketone-Water Medium, *Anal. Chem.* **29,** 756 (1957).

58. R. B. KIMBALL and J. E. REIN, *Spectrophotometric Determination of Uranium in Highly Impure Solutions,* USAEC Report IDO-14380, Phillips Petroleum Company, July 13, 1956.

59. J. H. YOE et al., Colorimetric Determination of Uranium with Dibenzoyl-Methane, *Anal. Chem.* **25,** 1200 (1953).

60. R. PRIBIL and M. JELINEK, Use of Complexon in Chemical Analysis. XLI. Colorimetric Determination of Uranium Using Dibenzoylmethane, *Chem. listy* **47,** 1326 (1953).

61. C. J. RODDEN, Semiannual Progress Report for the Period July 1955 Through December 1955, USAEC Report NBL-127, New Brunswick Laboratory, AEC, May 1956.

62. C. A. FRANCOIS, Rapid Spectrophotometric Determination of Submilligram Quantities of Uranium, *Anal. Chem.* **30,** 50 (1958).

63. O. A. Vita et al., *Purification and Determination of Uranium in Impure Solutions Using Versene*, USAEC Report GAT-186, Goodyear Atomic Corporation, July 6, 1956.

64. R. J. Guest and J. B. Zimmerman, Determination of Uranium in Uranium Concentrates, *Anal. Chem.* **27,** 931 (1955).

65. A. L. Arnfelt, A Rapid Method for the Determination of Uranium, *Acta Chem. Scand.* **9,** 1484 (1955).

66. S. Fisher and R. Kunin, Use of Ion Exchange Resins for Determination of Uranium in Ores and Solutions, *Anal. Chem.* **29,** 400 (1957).

67. H. J. Seim et al., Rapid Method for Determination of Uranium in Ores, *Anal. Chem.* **29,** 443 (1957).

68. K. L. Cheng and P. F. Lott, Reaction of Hydrogen Peroxide with Complexes of (Ethylenedinitrilo)-tetraacetic Acid and Nitrilotriacetic Acid, *Anal. Chem.* **28,** 462 (1956).

69. E. B. Sandell, *Colorimetric Determination of Traces of Metals.* New York: Interscience Publishers, Inc., 1950.

70. L. Silverman et al., Small Amounts of Uranium in the Presence of Iron (Colorimetric Determination with 8-Quinolinol), *Anal. Chem.* **25,** 1369 (1953).

71. R. G. Canning and P. Dixon, Direct Spectrophotometric Determination of Uranium in Aqueous Solutions, *Anal. Chem.* **27,** 877 (1955).

72. B. E. Paige et al., Ultraviolet Spectrophotometric Determination of Uranium, *Anal. Chem.* **29,** 1029 (1957).

73. R. J. LeStrange et al., *Rapid Methods for Uranium Determination*, USAEC Report M-5495, New Brunswick Laboratory, AEC, February 1954.

74. D. J. Fisher and P. F. Thomason, Rapid Polarographic Determination of Uranium in Nonaqueous Solvents, *Anal. Chem.* **28,** 1285 (1956).

75. F. E. Wild, *The Determination of Uranium in Low Grade Ores*, Report AERE-C/R-1868, Gt. Brit. Atomic Energy Research Establishment, March 1956.

76. J. A. Lewis and K. C. Overton, *A New Method for the Polarographic Determination of Uranium in the Presence of Other Metals*, Report CRL-AE-41, Gt. Brit. Chemical Research Laboratory, Teddington, October 1949.

77. H. I. Shalgosky, The Polarographic Determination of Uranium, *Analyst* **81,** 512 (Sept. 1956).

78. D. I. Legge, Polarographic Determination of Uranium, *Anal. Chem.* **26,** 1617 (1954).

79. M. V. Susic, Polarography of Uranium: Polarographic Determination of Uranium in Ores Without Preliminary Chemical Separation, in *Proceedings of the International Conference on the Peaceful Uses of Atomic Energy*, Vol. 8. New York: United Nations, 1956. (P/964, p. 254)

80. M. Susic et al., Polarographic Determination of Uranium in Ores in Ascorbic Acid Supporting Electrolyte, *Anal. Chim. Acta* **11,** 586 (1954).

81. A. P. Vinogradov, Physico-Chemical Methods of Uranium Production Control, in *Proceedings of the International Conference on the Peaceful Uses of Atomic Energy*, Vol. 8. New York: United Nations, 1956. (P/627, p. 206)

82. I. M. Kolthoff and J. J. Lingane, *Polarography.* 2nd ed. New York: Interscience Publishers, Inc., 1952. (p. 450)

83. N. H. FURMAN, Titration of Uranium(IV) by Electrolytically Generated Ceric Ion, *Anal. Chem.* **25**, 482 (1953).

84. W. N. CARSON, JR., Coulometric Determination of Uranium, *Anal. Chem.* **25**, 466 (1953).

85. J. J. LINGANE and R. T. IWAMOTO, Coulometric Titrations of Uranium with Electrogenerated Titanous Ions, *Anal. Chim. Acta* **13**, 465 (1955).

86. G. L. BOOMAN, Instrument for Controlled Potential Electrolysis and Precision Coulometric Integration, *Anal. Chem.* **29**, 213 (1957).

87. G. L. BOOMAN et al., Coulometric Determination of Uranium(VI) at Controlled Potential, *Anal. Chem.* **29**, 219 (1957).

88. L. S. BIRKS and E. J. BROOKS, Analysis of Uranium Solutions by X-ray Fluorescence, *Anal. Chem.* **23**, 707 (1951).

89. G. PISH and A. A. HUFFMAN, Quantitative Determination of Thorium and Uranium in Solutions by Fluorescent X-ray Spectrometry, *Anal. Chem.* **27**, 1875 (1955).

90. W. L. KEHL and R. G. RUSSELL, Fluorescent X-ray Spectrographic Determination of Uranium in Waters and Brines, *Anal. Chem.* **28**, 1350 (1956).

91. D. S. FLIKKEMA et al., *The X-ray Spectrometric Determination of Uranium in Solution*, USAEC Report ANL-5641, Argonne National Laboratory, November 1956.

92. H. M. WILSON and G. V. WHEELER, *Determination of Uranium in Solution by X-ray Spectrometry*, USAEC Report IDO-14393, Phillips Petroleum Company, Jan. 30, 1957.

93. W. B. WRIGHT, JR., and R. E. BARRINGER, *Uranium Analysis by Monochromatic X-ray Absorption*, USAEC Report Y-1095, Oak Ridge National Laboratory, Aug. 26, 1955.

94. W. J. CAMPBELL and H. F. CARL, Combined Radiometric and Fluorescent X-ray Spectrographic Method of Analyzing for Uranium and Thorium, *Anal. Chem.* **27**, 1884 (1955).

95. J. H. COPE, *Norelco Reptr. III*, 41 (1956).

CHAPTER 4

MINERALOGY OF URANIUM AS IT RELATES TO HYDROMETALLURGICAL PROCESSING*

4-1. INTRODUCTION

Uranium is ordinarily recovered from ores by hydrometallurgical processing, i.e., leaching with sulfuric acid or sodium carbonate solutions. There are a few exceptional cases in which other techniques are used, notably at plants in the Belgian Congo and at Port Radium in northwest Canada, where a declining production of relatively rich uranium concentrates still depends on physical concentration procedures. The widespread use of hydrometallurgical processing is easily explained; few ores have been found which yield their uranium with an acceptable efficiency by physical concentration methods.

The choice of leaching reagents, either acid or alkaline, is determined largely by the over-all composition of the ore and its effect on reagent cost. The extent and ease with which uranium can be extracted depends upon the composition of the uranium-bearing constituents in the ore and how intimately they are associated with the gangue minerals. This chapter discusses the general mineralogy of uranium and its relationship to hydrometallurgical processing.

4-2. URANIUM MINERALS

Detailed descriptions of more than 100 minerals containing uranium, with their chemical and physical properties, are to be found in a number of standard references and special reports [1,2,3]. Fewer than 10 are of major economic significance. Chemically, the uranium minerals may be classified into five distinct types: (1) simple oxides, (2) simple silicates, (3) multiple oxides, (4) hydrated oxides, and (5) hydrated uranyl salts.

4-2.1 Simple oxides. *Uraninite (pitchblende).* Uraninite is essentially a mixture of UO_2 and UO_3. The uranium content, expressed as U_3O_8, ranges from 60 to 90 percent. Originally, all the uranium probably was present as UO_2 but, as a result of oxidation, varying amounts of UO_3 are always found. Other constituents include lead (of radiogenic origin),

---

* By D. R. George, AEC Raw Materials Development Laboratory, National Lead Company, Inc.

the rare earths, and, commonly, thorium. The words *uraninite* and *pitch-blende* are synonymous; by popular usage, however, the name uraninite is generally applied to disseminated crystals, and pitchblende to the massive form as it occurs in veins. Pitchblende commonly contains only insignificant quantities of the rare earths or of thorium.

4–2.2 Simple silicates. Coffinite and uranothorite are the only simple silicates known that contain uranium as a major constituent. Their compositions are usually given as

$$\text{Coffinite: } U(SiO_4)_{(1-x)}(OH)_{4x},$$

$$\text{Uranothorite: } Th_{(1-x)}U_xSiO_4,$$

where x is less than 1. Both minerals are orthosilicates and have a crystal structure like that of zircon. In coffinite, hydroxyl substitutes for SiO_4. Thorogummite or uranoan thorogummite are varieties of thorite in which hydroxyl is also found in substitution for SiO_4 groups [4].

The uranium content of coffinite, expressed as U_3O_8, is approximately 72 percent. The uranium content of uranothorite is variable, but generally is less than 10 percent. In both minerals the uranium is in the tetravalent form.

4–2.3 Multiple oxides. According to Dana [5], the multiple oxides are those minerals with a composition expressed by the general formula $A_mB_nO_x$, where $m:n$ is 1:1 to 1:2 and A represents the rare earths, uranium, thorium, calcium, ferrous iron, manganese, zirconium, etc., and B represents columbium, tantalum, titanium, ferric iron, tin, tungsten, and possibly zirconium. The uranium content of these minerals varies from less than 1 percent to nearly 50 percent.

Approximately 20 different minerals of this type are known. The following classification shows the general composition of some of the more common varieties. In each case the minerals bracketed under a particular type form a solid solution series, with more or less continuous variation from one to the other as the proportion of the underlined elements in column A or B varies.

Type $A_2B_2O_6(O, OH, F)$

	A	B
$\left\{\begin{array}{l}\text{Microlite}\\ \\ \text{Pyrochlore}\end{array}\right.$	$\left\{\begin{array}{l}\text{Na, Ca, K, Mg, Mn, Ce, Fe}^{++},\\ \text{La, Di, Er, Y, Th, U, Zr}\end{array}\right\}$	Cb, Ta, Ti, Fe^{+++}, W Ta, Cb, Ti, Fe^{+++}, W

Type ABO_4

	A	B
$\begin{cases}\text{Fergusonite} \\ \\ \text{Formanite}\end{cases}$	$\left\{\begin{array}{l}\text{Y, Er, (Ce, La, Di), Fe}^{++}\text{, U,} \\ \quad\text{Zr, Th, Ca} \\ \\ \end{array}\right\}$	Cb, Ta, Ti, Sn, W Ta, Cb, Ti, Sn, W

Type $A_mB_nO_p(m\!:\!n = 2\!:\!3 \text{ to } 3\!:\!5)$

	A	B
$\begin{cases}\text{Brannerite} \\ \\ \text{Absite}\end{cases}$	U, Ca, Fe, Y, Th Th, U, Ca, Fe, Y	$\left\{\text{Ti}\right\}$

Type AB_2O_6

	A	B
$\begin{cases}\text{Euxenite} \\ \\ \text{Polycrase}\end{cases}$	$\left\{\text{Y, Ca, Ce, U, Th}\right\}$	Cb, Ta, Ti Ti, Cb, Ta, Fe^{+++}
$\begin{cases}\text{Eschynite} \\ \\ \text{Priorite}\end{cases}$	Ce, Ca, Fe^{++}, U, Th Y, Er, Ca, Fe, Th, U	$\left\{\text{Ti, Cb, Ta}\right\}$
Samarskite	Y, Er, Ce, La, U, Ca, Fe, Pb, Th	Cb, Ta, Ti, Sn, W, Zr(?)

Type $A_mB_nO_p(m\!:\!n = 1\!:\!3)$ [2]

	A	B
Davidite	Fe^{++}(Rare earths, U^{+6}, Ca, Zr, Th)	Ti(Fe^{+++}, V, Cr)

4–2.4 Hydrated oxides and uranyl salts. The largest groups of uranium minerals are the hydrated oxides, uranates, and uranyl salts. Many of them are of secondary origin and are formed by the direct alteration of previously existing primary minerals such as pitchblende or uraninite. Most of the minerals of this type (described through 1957) are listed as follows:

Hydrated oxides

Gummite	$UO_3 \cdot nH_2O$
Epiianthinite	$UO_3 \cdot 2H_2O$
Becquerelite	$2UO_3 \cdot 3H_2O$
Schoepite	$4UO_3 \cdot 9H_2O$
Ianthinite	$2UO_2 \cdot 7H_2O$
Fourmarierite	$PbO \cdot 4UO_3 \cdot 5H_2O$
Curite	$2PbO \cdot 5UO_3 \cdot 4H_2O$
Uranosphaerite	$Bi_2O_3 \cdot 2UO_3 \cdot 3H_2O$
Vandenbrandite	$CuO \cdot UO_3 \cdot 2H_2O$

Hydrated phosphates

(Meta) Autunite	$CaO \cdot 2UO_3 \cdot P_2O_5 \cdot 8H_2O$
Saleite	$MgO \cdot 2UO_3 \cdot P_2O_5 \cdot 8H_2O$
Uranocircite	$BaO \cdot 2UO_3 \cdot P_2O_5 \cdot 8H_2O$
(Meta) Torbernite	$CuO \cdot 2UO_3 \cdot P_2O_5 \cdot 8H_2O$
Phosphuranylite	$3UO_3 \cdot P_2O_5 \cdot 8H_2O$
Sabugalite	$HAlO_2 \cdot 4UO_3 \cdot 2P_2O_5 \cdot 16H_2O$
Parsonsite	$2PbO \cdot UO_3 \cdot P_2O_5 \cdot 8H_2O$
Renardite	$PbO \cdot 4UO_3 \cdot P_2O_5 \cdot 9H_2O$
Dumontite	$2PbO \cdot 3UO_3 \cdot P_2O_5 \cdot 5H_2O$
Dewindite	$3PbO \cdot 5UO_3 \cdot P_2O_5 \cdot 12H_2O$

Hydrated arsenates

(Meta) Zeunerite	$CuO \cdot 2UO_3 \cdot As_2O_5 \cdot 8H_2O$
Uranospinite	$CaO \cdot 2UO_3 \cdot As_2O_5 \cdot 8H_2O$
Abernathyite	$K_2O \cdot 2UO_3 \cdot As_2O_5 \cdot 8H_2O$
Troegerite	$3UO_3 \cdot As_2O_5 \cdot 12H_2O$
Novacekite	$MgO \cdot 2UO_3 \cdot As_2O_5 \cdot nH_2O$
Walpurgite	$3UO_3 \cdot 5Bi_2O_3 \cdot 2As_2O_5 \cdot 12H_2O$

Hydrated vanadates

Carnotite	$K_2O \cdot 2UO_3 \cdot V_2O_5 \cdot 3H_2O$
Tyuyamunite	$CaO \cdot 2UO_3 \cdot V_2O_5 \cdot 8H_2O$
Sengierite	$2CuO \cdot 2UO_3 \cdot V_2O_5 \cdot 10H_2O$
Uvanite	$2UO_3 \cdot 3V_2O_5 \cdot 15H_2O$
Ferghanite	$UO_3 \cdot V_2O_5 \cdot 6H_2O$
Rauvite	$CaO \cdot 2UO_3 \cdot 6V_2O_5 \cdot 20H_2O$

Hydrated molybdate

Umohoite	$UO_3 \cdot MoO_4 \cdot 4H_2O$

Hydrated sulfates

Zippeite	$2UO_3 \cdot SO_3 \cdot nH_2O$
Uranopilite	$6UO_3 \cdot SO_3 \cdot nH_2O$
Johannite	$CuO \cdot 2UO_3 \cdot 2SO_3 \cdot 7H_2O$

Hydrated carbonates

Liebigite	$2CaO \cdot UO_2 \cdot 2CO_2 \cdot 10H_2O$
Bayleyite	$MgO \cdot UO_3 \cdot 3CO_2 \cdot 18H_2O$
Andersonite	$Na_2O \cdot CaO \cdot UO_3 \cdot 3CO_2 \cdot 6H_2O$
Swartzite	$CaO \cdot MgO \cdot UO_3 \cdot 3CO_2 \cdot 12H_2O$
Rabbittite	$3CaO \cdot 3MgO \cdot 2UO_3 \cdot 6CO_2 \cdot 20H_2O$
Voglite	$2CaO \cdot CuO \cdot UO_3 \cdot 6CO_2 \cdot 7H_2O$
Rutherfordine	$UO_2 \cdot CO_3$
Schroeckingerite	$3CaO \cdot Na_2O \cdot UO_3 \cdot CO_2 \cdot SO_3 \cdot F \cdot 10H_2O$

Hydrated silicates

Uranophane	$CaO \cdot 2UO_3 \cdot 2SiO_2 \cdot 6H_2O$
Beta-uranotil	$CaO \cdot 2UO_3 \cdot 2SiO_2 \cdot 6H_2O$
Sklodowskite	$MgO \cdot 2UO_3 \cdot 2SiO_2 \cdot 6H_2O$
Cuprosklodowskite	$CuO \cdot 2UO_3 \cdot 2SiO_2 \cdot 6H_2O$
Soddyite	$5UO_3 \cdot 2SiO_2 \cdot 6H_2O$
Kasolite	$PbO \cdot UO_3 \cdot SiO_2 \cdot 6H_2O$
Boltwoodite	$K_2O \cdot 2UO_3 \cdot 2SiO_2 \cdot 6H_2O$

4–3 METALLURGICAL CLASSIFICATION OF URANIUM ORES

The preceding mineralogical classification is strictly chemical. From the point of view of metallurgical processing, uranium ores may be grouped into five general mineralogical classes based on the chemical nature of the uranium minerals and their response to leaching or on physico-chemical associations of the uranium and their effect on treatment procedures. The five general classes are (1) ores containing tetravalent uranium, (2) ores containing hexavalent uranium, (3) refractory uranium minerals, (4) associations of uranium and carbon, and (5) phosphates and miscellaneous. This classification is not rigid; more than one type of mineralization usually is encountered in an ore.

4–3.1 Ores containing tetravalent uranium. Most of the world's important uranium deposits contain a significant portion of their uranium in the tetravalent form. The most common mineral containing tetravalent uranium is uraninite, or pitchblende. However, the mineral coffinite

$(U(SiO_4)_{(1-x)}(OH)_{4x})$ has been found with increasing frequency in many major ore deposits in Utah, New Mexico, Colorado, and Wyoming, and is reported to represent a major fraction of the uranium in these ores [6]. In the Bancroft area of Canada, a portion of the uranium in the ores is present in the tetravalent form in the mineral uranothorite [7].

When uraninite, coffinite, or uranothorite occurs in an ore an oxidizing condition must be maintained during leaching since, in the absence of an oxidant, tetravalent uranium is essentially insoluble in dilute sulfuric acid and in sodium carbonate solutions.

Uraninite, or pitchblende, occurs in a variety of forms. In some ores, for example those at Great Bear Lake and in the Belgian Congo, it occurs in relatively large masses and is in part recoverable as a shipping-grade concentrate by hand sorting or gravity concentration. In other ores, such as those in the Lake Athabasca district of Canada, much of it is extremely finely disseminated. In the western United States, uraninite is the major source of uranium in the White Canyon and Big Indian Wash districts of Utah and probably accounts for a large portion of the uranium in the Jackpile ores of New Mexico. (Only coffinite has been reported in the Ambrosia Lake district ores.) Uraninite occurs as a soft cementing constituent of the sandstones and as a replacement of calcite, quartz, and organic material. In the ores from the Witwatsrrand district in South Africa, the source of the uranium is also uraninite. It occurs in part as minute rounded grains in the matrix of the conglomerates and as minute inclusions in a carbonaceous material commonly referred to as "thucholite." Photomicrographs of some typical occurrences of uraninite and pitchblende are shown in Figs. 4–1, 4–2, 4–3, and 4–4.

The response of ores containing uraninite, or pitchblende, to leaching is variable. An oxidant is required, and fine grinding may be essential to ensure that the uraninite is exposed to the leaching solution. This is particularly important with carbonate leaching, because there is essentially no attack on the gangue minerals that often enclose the uraninite. On the other hand, many gangue minerals, and notably the carbonates with which the uraninite is commonly intimately associated, are dissolved by the acid, thus exposing the uraninite to the leaching solution. Fine grinding is also needed to provide reasonable dissolution rates during carbonate leaching, since the rate of dissolution of uraninite in this medium is much slower than in an acid system. This is particularly true of the hard, dense varieties of uraninite.

Little is known about the solubility of the mineral coffinite under normal leaching conditions, since the pure mineral has not been isolated. On the basis of its reported composition and structure, a refractory behavior might be predicted. However, the ores reported to contain major amounts of uranium as coffinite, such as those from the Ambrosia Lake district in

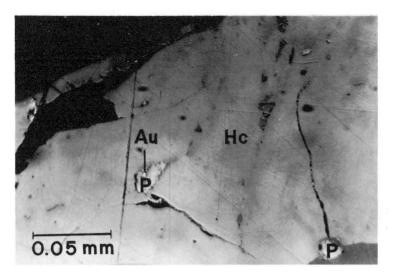

FIG. 4–1. Pitchblende inclusions in hydrocarbon (thucholite), Blyvooruitzicht Mine, South Africa. P = pitchblende, Hc = hydrocarbon, Au = gold.

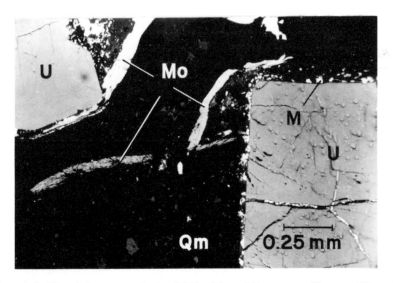

FIG. 4–2. Uraninite crystals in Little Man Mine near Hanna, Wyoming. U = uraninite, Qm = quartz ground mass, Mo = molybdenite, M = sulfides, including marcasite and galena.

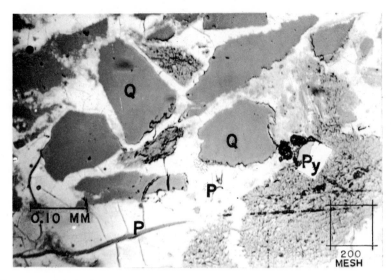

FIG. 4–3. Pitchblende filling voids between grains in sandstone ore, Mi Vida Mine, Utah. P = pitchblende, Q = quartz, Py = pyrite.

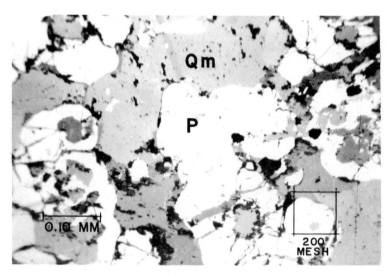

FIG. 4–4. Pitchblende, Eldorado Mine, Port Radium, NWT, Canada. P = pitchblende, Qm = quartz ground mass.

New Mexico and the Big Indian Wash in Utah, all yield satisfactory uranium extractions in 0.1 N H_2SO_4 or 0.5 M Na_2CO_3-$NaHCO_3$ solutions in the presence of an oxidant.

Uranothorite, a variety of thorite in which tetravalent uranium substitutes for thorium, accounts for an undisclosed portion of the uranium in the pegmatite type ores of the Bancroft district of Halliburton County, Ontario, Canada [7]. The principal ore mineral is uraninite. Thorite is chemically refractory; however, in view of the very mild acid leaching conditions in use in the mills in the Bancroft district, it is assumed that the uranothorite is of the more soluble variety of thorogummite or that it does not account for a significant portion of the uranium in these ores.

Tetravalent uranium is also a primary constituent in the multiple oxide minerals. These minerals present special problems in processing which are not related to the oxidation of the uranium and which will be discussed separately.

4–3.2 Ores containing hexavalent uranium. Next to uraninite, minerals which contain uranium in the hexavalent form are the most common source of uranium in ores. Most of these are considered to be secondary.

Although more than 50 different species are known, the most important from a production viewpoint are carnotite, tyuyamunite, autunite, torbernite, and uranophane. In the Colorado Plateau, carnotite accounts for most of the uranium in the low-lime, uranium-vanadium ores that are characteristic of the Salt Wash formation. Tyuyamunite is more prevalent in ores of higher lime content and probably accounts for a major portion of the secondary uranium in the Todilto limestone ores near Grants, New Mexico, and in the ores from the Big Indian Wash district of Utah. Torbernite, although not common in the western United States, occurs in at least trace amounts in the White Canyon district of Utah. In the Belgian Congo, torbernite and various hydrated oxides and silicates are a major source of the uranium in the upper zones of the orebodies. Autunite, perhaps the most common of all the secondary uranium minerals, is most often encountered in the oxidized zones of pitchblende deposits containing phosphate minerals such as apatite. Autunite is not a significant source of uranium in the United States, although it is fairly common in the ores from Marysvale, Utah; Spokane, Washington; and Riverton, Wyoming. In Australia, saleite, the magnesian equivalent of autunite, accounts for a major portion of the uranium in the Dyson's mine near Rum Jungle. Uranospinite and abernathyite are prominent sources of uranium in the arsenical ores of Lake County, Oregon.

Many of the other secondary uranium minerals occur in at least trace amounts in the oxidized portions of pitchblende deposits, and the ores of the Belgian Congo are notable for their variety of secondary uranium minerals. In the United States, the Happy Jack and other mines in the White Canyon area of Utah contain a large number of rare species, including zippeite, johannite, uranopilite, schoepite, schroeckingerite, and zeunerite [8].

So far as is known, all secondary uranium minerals are rapidly soluble in dilute acid or carbonate solutions and some of them, particularly the carbonates, are appreciably soluble in water.

4–3.3 Refractory uranium minerals. The refractory uranium minerals, as defined here, are the multiple oxides previously described. They occur characteristically in pegmatites and pegmatite-type deposits, in placers derived from the weathering of pegmatites, and, occasionally, as disseminated constituents in granitic ores. The uranium in these minerals probably was present originally in the tetravalent form, but now in most of them there probably are also significant amounts of hexavalent uranium, produced by weathering.

The term "refractory uranium minerals" is used to denote their resistance to chemical dissolution. In the absence of alteration by weathering or other natural processes, all the multiple oxides are chemically refractory. Specific information on the rate of dissolution in acid of the different minerals is limited, but it appears that their refractoriness increases with increasing columbium and tantalum content and decreases with increasing titanium, iron, and uranium content.

The two principal sources of uranium from ores or minerals of this type are the davidite deposits of Radium Hill in South Australia, and the brannerite and uraninite ores of the Blind River (Elliott Lake) district of Ontario, Canada.

Davidite is essentially $FeTi_3O_7$ in which uranium (3 to 7 percent) probably substitutes for iron. Other constituents include the rare earths, vanadium, and thorium. Davidite resembles ilmenite in chemical behavior; digestion in hot, strong sulfuric acid is required. The Radium Hill ores contain about 0.2 percent uranium. Leaching the whole ore in 30 percent sulfuric acid is not economic; the actual leaching operation at Port Pirie, therefore, is preceded by gravity concentration and flotation. This concentrate contains 15 to 25 percent davidite, or about 1 percent U_3O_8, the remainder being largely ilmenite, rutile, magnetite, biotite, and quartz.

Brannerite is a uranium-titanium oxide containing minor amounts of iron, calcium, the rare earths, and thorium. The pure mineral contains 30 to 40 percent TiO_2 and 40 to 50 percent uranium oxide as both tetravalent and hexavalent uranium. Unaltered brannerite is refractory. Leaching tests [9] on an impure concentrate from Climax, Colorado, showed that only 13 percent of the uranium was extracted by leaching for 64 hours at room temperature with 10 percent sulfuric acid. Boiling in 40 percent sulfuric or nitric acid yielded extractions of 25 to 50 percent, respectively. Ninety-seven percent of the uranium was extracted by fuming the concentrate with 1 gram of concentrated sulfuric acid per gram of concentrate and digesting the sulfated residue with water.

In the ores from the Blind River district, brannerite occurs in quartzite conglomerates as altered grains composed of a mixture of anatase and uranium oxide. X-ray patterns of the altered mineral give only the pattern of anatase but, on heating, the mixture recrystallizes and yields the pattern of brannerite [10]. The altered material is difficultly soluble, and high uranium extraction necessitates fine grinding followed by leaching for 48 hours at 120°F in a solution containing about 50 grams of free sulfuric acid per liter [11]. A high-thorium variety of brannerite, called absite, occurs in granitic rock at Crockers Wells, near Radium Hill, in South Australia; it is readily recovered by flotation.

Most other refractory minerals are of mineralogical interest only, although a small production of euxenite is reported from dredging operations in Idaho.

The data in Table 4–1 on the solubility of euxenite and priorite, containing 14.3 and 3.5 percent U_3O_8, respectively, were obtained on minus-100 mesh euxenite and priorite from Norway.

Extensive deposits of pyrochlore in massive carbonate rocks, granites, or syenites are known [12,13] in the Lake Nipissing district of Canada and in Nigeria, Africa. The pure Nigerian pyrochlore mineral contains 41.1 percent $Cb_2O_5 + Ta_2O_5$, 3.1 percent U_3O_8, and 3.3 percent ThO_2. The ore, however, contains only about 1 percent pyrochlore. The Canadian deposits are of similar grade. It is probable that production of uranium will be possible only if the deposits can be worked for columbium.

TABLE 4–1

SOLUBILITY OF EUXENITE AND PRIORITE

Test conditions	Uranium extraction, %	
	Priorite	Euxenite
Leach 1 g 48 hr at 25°C in 100 ml 10% H_2SO_4-0.5% $NaClO_3$	19	12
Leach 1 g 4 hr at 75°C in 100 ml 25% HNO_3	34	18
Leach 1 g 4 hr at 75°C in 100 ml 25% H_2SO_4-0.5% $NaClO_3$	60	48

4–3.4 Associations of uranium and carbon. Associations of uranium and carbonaceous material can be found in most of the uranium deposits in the United States and in South Africa. These associations are of two general types: (1) associations of uraninite or other uranium minerals with fossil organic matter, and (2) associations of uranium with organic matter presumably as an organo-uranium complex.

The first presents no particular problem in processing, although fine grinding may be required if the association is extremely intimate. In the western United States, uraninite and coffinite commonly are found replacing organic matter. Among the ores containing such occurrences are those from the Big Indian Wash and the southern part of the Ambrosia Lake district. All these ores respond satisfactorily to conventional acid or carbonate leaching.

In South Africa, many of the ores from the Witwatersrand district contain a considerable proportion of their uranium as minute inclusions of uraninite in a hydrocarbon, called thucholite. Figure 4–1 shows the occurrence of uraninite and gold in thucholite. Extremely fine grinding is necessary to achieve high extractions of uranium and gold.

In the second type of occurrence of uranium with carbon, no discrete uranium minerals are recognizable, and it is postulated that the uranium occurs as an organo-uranium complex. In the Temple Mountain district of Utah, over 60 percent of the uranium in some of the ores is associated with a black, vitreous hydrocarbon commonly called asphaltite. High recoveries of uranium are obtained only after roasting the asphaltite or by grinding it to an extremely fine grain size and then leaching with strong sulfuric acid.

In North and South Dakota, extensive deposits of uraniferous lignite have been found, and consideration is being given to processing them for the recovery of uranium. In several of these deposits, the uranium content averages as much as 0.25 percent U_3O_8, and local concentrations of 1 to 5 percent have been encountered. Where the lignite beds are extensively weathered, autunite, carnotite, and other secondary uranium minerals are found, but in most of the uraniferous lignites, the uranium is in an adsorbed form. Breger [14] reports that the uranium occurs as an organo-uranium complex, probably a uranyl humate.

The uranium in lignite is readily extracted, or desorbed, from raw lignite by acid or alkaline carbonate solutions. In some lignites, particularly those which contain a large quantity of water-soluble organic material and give an acid reaction (pH 4 to 5), appreciable uranium is extracted when the lignite is ground in water. For various processing reasons, however, it is preferable to destroy the carbon by roasting before leaching.

Molybdenum also occurs in the uraniferous lignites in about the same concentrations as uranium. Like the uranium, it is extracted by acid or alkaline carbonate solutions.

Perhaps the most noted occurrences of uranium with organic matter are the "kolm," or organic shale deposits, of Sweden and the black shales of the Chattanooga formation in Tennessee. The Swedish shales, now being processed on a semicommercial scale, contain approximately 0.03 percent U_3O_8. The Tennessee black shales average about 0.006 percent U_3O_8. Estimates of the uranium content of the Swedish deposits are in excess of 100,000 tons; of the Tennessee shales, more than 500,000 tons. The uranium in both shales is associated with a kerogenous hydrocarbon.

4–3.5 Phosphates and miscellaneous. Uranium is a common trace constituent in phosphate minerals, principally apatite, $Ca_5(PO_4)_3(F, Cl, OH)$, and crandallite, $CaAl_3(PO_4)_2(OH)_5H_2O$. It is present in the tetravalent form in ionic substitution for calcium; it can be recovered only by completely dissolving the minerals in acid.

Although apatite is a common accessory mineral in uranium deposits, particularly the vein-type occurrence of pitchblende, in these deposits it is quantitatively unimportant as a source of uranium. The major occurrences of uranium in phosphate minerals are the phosphate rock deposits of marine origin of Florida and Idaho. The uranium content of these deposits ranges from 0.006 to 0.035 percent U_3O_8, and it has been estimated that their total uranium content is in excess of 600,000 tons at an average grade of 0.012 percent U_3O_8. Hence, they constitute a potential future reserve. Limited production of uranium is being obtained from wet-process phosphoric acid, an intermediate product in the manufacture of fertilizers and phosphate chemicals.

Small amounts of uranium are known to be present in ionic substitution in a number of other minerals. Among those sometimes encountered in uranium ores are fluorite, zircon, and uraniferous hydrated silica, such as opal or hyalite. Since all are chemically refractory, it is fortunate that they do not account for an appreciable amount of uranium in commercial ores.

4–3.6 Vanadium. Vanadium is ubiquitous in the ores of the western United States. It occurs in these ores primarily as a silicate or as an oxide. It can be found in the minerals carnotite and tyuyamunite in very small amounts. Roscoelite and hydromicas are the chief source of the vanadium in those ores processed for its recovery. These include the ores from the Entrada formation in the vicinity of Rifle and Placerville, Colorado, and typical carnotite ores from the Salt Wash formation, the principal uranium-producing horizon in the Uravan mineral belt.

The principal vanadium oxides are montroseite (VO[OH]) and paramontroseite (VO_2). These minerals occur in the ores in the Chinle formation in the Big Indian Wash or Lisbon Valley district of Utah.

Vanadium silicates and oxides are partially soluble in dilute sulfuric acid or sodium carbonate solutions. In general, approximately 20 percent of the vanadium is extracted from the roscoelite ores by acid leaching at ambient temperature, and somewhat less by hot carbonate solutions. Under the same conditions, the solubilization of vanadium oxides ranges up to 40 percent. Vanadium solubilization in excess of 90 percent may be accomplished by leaching at 75°C or higher with a large excess of sulfuric acid, or by pugging the dampened ore with concentrated sulfuric acid, curing the mix at elevated temperature, and then leaching the sulfated mass with water.

REFERENCES

1. CHARLES PALACHE et al., *Dana's System of Mineralogy.* 7th ed. New York: John Wiley & Sons, Inc., 1951. (Vols. I and II)

2. J. W. FRONDEL and M. FLEISCHER, *A Glossary of Uranium and Thorium Bearing Minerals,* U. S. Geological Survey Bulletin No. 1009-F, Washington, D. C.: U. S. Government Printing Office, 1955.

3. D. R. GEORGE, *Mineralogy of Uranium and Thorium Bearing Minerals,* USAEC Report RMO-563, Division of Raw Materials, AEC, 1949.

4. CLIFFORD FRONDEL, Hydroxyl Substitution in Thorite and Zircon, *American Mineralogist* **38,** 1007 (1953).

5. CHARLES PALACHE et al., *Dana's System of Mineralogy.* 7th ed. New York: John Wiley & Sons, Inc., 1951. (Vol. 1, p. 745)

6. R. A. LAVERTY and E. G. GROSS, Paragenetic Studies of Uranium Deposits of the Colorado Plateau, in *Proceedings of the International Conference on the Peaceful Uses of Atomic Energy,* Vol. 6, New York: United Nations, 1956. (P/297, p. 533)

7. L. KELLEY, The Bancroft Pegmatites, *Can. Mining J.* **77,** No. 6, 157-158 (1956).

8. J. W. GRUNER and L. GARDNER, *Mineral Associations in the Uranium Deposits of the Colorado Plateau, and Adjacent Regions with Special Emphasis on Those in the Shinarump Formation. Part III. Annual Report for July 1, 1951 to June 30, 1952,* USAEC Report RMO-566, University of Minnesota, 1952.

9. D. R. GEORGE, *Recovery of Uranium From Climax Brannerite Concentrate-C-7,* USAEC Report MITG-231, Massachusetts Institute of Technology, 1950.

10. R. J. TRAIL, A Preliminary Account of the Mineralogy of Radioactive Conglomerates in the Blind River Region, Ontario, *Can. Mining J.* **75,** 63–68 (1954).

11. Personal communication.

12. R. B. ROWE, Notes on the Geology and Mineralogy of the Newman Columbian-Uranium Deposits, Lake Nipissing, Ontario, *Can. Dept. Mines and Tech. Surveys, Geol. Survey, Can. Paper 54–5* (1954).

13. C. F. DAVIDSON, Radioactive Minerals in the British Colonies, in *Proceedings of the International Conference on the Peaceful Uses of Atomic Energy.* Vol. 6. New York: United Nations, 1956. (P/761, p. 210)

14. I. A. BREGER et al., Geochemistry and Mineralogy of a Uraniferous Lignite, *Econ. Geol.* **50,** 206–226 (1955).

CHAPTER 5

PRELIMINARY ORE TREATMENT*

5-1. Roasting of Uranium Ores

5-1.1 Introduction. Roasting techniques in the treatment of uranium ores are used primarily to (1) form soluble vanadium and uranium compounds by salt roasting carnotite ores, (2) remove carbonaceous matter from ores before leaching, and (3) roast ores containing large amounts of clay minerals to improve their settling and filtering characteristics.

The use of heat to promote chemical reactions between gases and solids, such as chlorination procedures, is not considered a simple roasting procedure and will not be discussed here.

5-1.2 Salt roasting of carnotite ores. The salt-roasting process [1] was devised to extract vanadium from oxidized carnotite ores; as a result, much of its chemistry is as concerned with vanadium as with uranium. Salt roasting does not improve the extraction of uranium from carnotite ores over that which can be obtained from a sodium carbonate-sodium bicarbonate leaching of the unroasted ore, as Fig. 5-1 shows, but it improves vanadium extraction materially. In fact, poor temperature control during roasting may result in extraction inferior to that from leaching the unroasted ore. This results from the fact that, in salt roasting, apparently three distinct physical or chemical changes occur as a function of temperature. For example, with carnotite these are:

(1) *Temperature range to* 350°C. The mineral carnotite is stable and remains soluble in Na_2CO_3-$NaHCO_3$ solutions.

(2) *Temperature range of* 350 *to* 660°C. The mineral carnotite loses its water of hydration or decomposes to form a uranium complex that is insoluble in Na_2CO_3-$NaHCO_3$ solutions.

(3) *Temperature range of* 600 *to* 850°C. Sodium chloride reacts with vanadium minerals to form sodium vanadates. Sodium vanadates react with uranium compounds to form sodium uranyl vanadates which are soluble in Na_2CO_3-$NaHCO_3$ solutions.

Because the third reaction is reversible, the roasted ore must be quenched as rapidly as possible to prevent the sodium uranyl vanadate from revert-

---

* Section 5-1 of this chapter was prepared by F. M. Stephens, Jr., of Battelle Memorial Institute, and Section 5-2 by O. F. Tangel, also of Battelle.

103

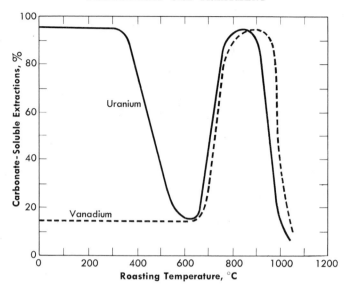

FIG. 5–1. The effect of salt-roasting temperature on extraction of uranium and vanadium in sodium carbonate-bicarbonate solution.

ing to a sodium vanadate and an insoluble uranium complex. Similar reactions occur with other uranium minerals and compounds.

The soluble uranium compound formed in the salt-roasting step is a complex vanadate. Therefore, salt roasting is not successful in converting uranium minerals to the carbonate-soluble form unless there is enough vanadium in the ore to form the sodium uranyl vanadate.

In salt roasting ores high in calcium carbonate, calcium uranates tend to form in preference to sodium uranyl vanadates. Because these calcium uranates are not soluble in Na_2CO_3-$NaHCO_3$ solutions, it is not possible to extract uranium efficiently from high-lime ores after a normal salt roast. This difficulty can be overcome, in part, by adding enough excess vanadium in the form of V_2O_5 to react with the calcium carbonate to form soda-soluble calcium vanadate in preference to insoluble calcium uranates.

The flowsheet for the salt roasting process used with carbonate leaching at the AEC Mill, Monticello, Utah, when high-vanadium ores were being processed is shown in Article 7–3.1. The Climax Uranium Company, Grand Junction, Colorado, uses salt roasting with acid leaching to produce both uranium and vanadium. A flowsheet for this operation is shown in Article 6–4.6.

5–1.3 Removal of carbonaceous material. Uranium compounds quite commonly occur with carbonaceous materials. Notable examples are the

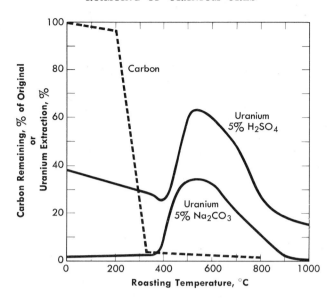

FIG. 5–2. Extraction of uranium from shale as a function of roasting temperature.

shales, lignites, and asphaltic carnotite ores. The uranium values present are usually soluble in either acid or alkaline leach solutions, but to obtain reasonably high extractions with acceptable reagent concentrations, the carbonaceous material must first be removed from the ore. This material can be removed by low-temperature roasting in an excess of air.

As with salt roasting of carnotite ores, temperature is important in roasting carbonaceous materials. Hassialis and Musa [2] cite the data in Fig. 5–2 to show that in roasting a shale, maximum extraction is obtained from ores processed at 500 to 600°C (932 to 1112°F). Above and below this range, extraction drops off markedly. They attribute poor extractions below 500°C to incomplete removal of carbon, with subsequent low porosity, and the poor extractions above 600°C to a sintering effect that also decreases porosity.

Much the same reactions hold true for lignites. It has been demonstrated that roasting the lignite at temperatures between 500 and 600°C produces an ash from which acid leaching can extract the major portion of the uranium. Lower temperatures do not remove carbon completely, and higher temperatures convert the uranium to an insoluble form.

It is interesting to note that higher uranium extraction can be obtained from the raw carbonaceous ore than from an ore in which 40 to 80 percent of the carbon has been removed. Probably this is due to activation of the residual carbon during roasting, allowing it to absorb uranium selectively from the leach solution.

In the asphaltic carnotite ores, the carbon is automatically removed during roasting. To date, this is the only practical method for treating such ores.

In methods most commonly proposed to treat shale [3], two separate heating steps are employed. The first is a retorting, carried out under an inert atmosphere to distill off volatile organic matter. The second is a low-temperature roast (not to exceed 600°C) carried out under oxidizing conditions to remove the balance of the carbon by converting it to CO_2. The residual calcine is then used as feed to a conventional leaching plant.

For treating uranium-bearing lignites, the same general procedure was investigated, that is, a low-temperature roast (max 600°C), with or without a preliminary retorting to recover tar. Again, the carbon-free ash is used as feed to a conventional leaching circuit. There were insufficient recoverable values to justify the retorting.

5–1.4 Roasting to improve settling and filtering.

Many of the uranium ores in sedimentary formations are associated with considerable amounts of finely divided clay minerals which hamper liquid-solids separation steps, such as thickening or filtering. Moreover, the clay is chemically attacked fairly rapidly, particularly in alkaline circuits, where it forms sodium silicate. In severe cases, the sodium silicate can impart a gel-like consistency to the leach solutions, making it impossible to filter, settle, or pump them.

It has been demonstrated that a low-temperature roast [4] can dehydrate the clays and alter their physical properties so that settling and filtration characteristics are markedly improved. Here again, however, consideration must be given to the effect of roasting temperature on the subsequent solubility of the uranium compounds. Much laboratory work has shown that again roasting temperature must not exceed 600°C. This is unfortunate, because the settling and filtering characteristics of these ores continue to improve at roasting temperatures above 600°C.

Typical data for ores containing large amounts of clay minerals are shown in Figs. 5–3 and 5–4. In Fig. 5–3, comparative settling rates of the raw and roasted ore are compared. These data show that the roasted ore settled to its terminal density in one hour, but the raw ore required 21 hours to reach the same density. Figure 5–4 shows comparative data for raw and roasted ore in a standard filtration test where filter-cake weight is plotted against cake-forming time. This curve shows that the roasted ore can be filtered at approximately twice the rate for the raw ore.

This method of roasting ores high in clay content to improve physical characteristics is obviously useful, but in the past few years it has been largely abandoned unless roasting is required for another reason, such as carbon removal. Meanwhile, other techniques were developed, such as

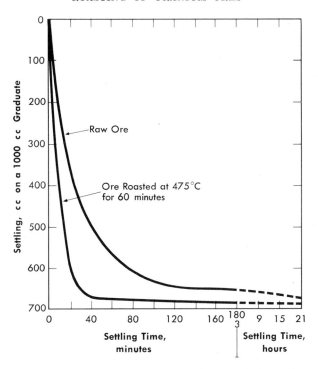

FIG. 5–3. The effect of roasting on settling characteristics. Test used 200 g of −100 mesh ore and 800-ml leach solution at room temperature.

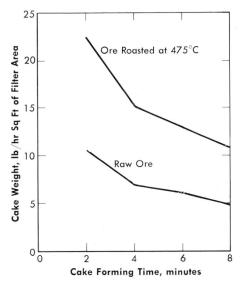

FIG. 5–4. The effect of roasting on filterability. Test was run at 50% solids.

use of flocculating agents (synthetic polyacrylamides, certain vegetable gums, etc.) that are both effective in handling the clay minerals and can be employed with less expense in both operating and capital costs.

5–2. Physical Concentration of Uranium Ores

There has been only limited commercial application of physical concentration to uranium ores. Physical beneficiation was early used at the Eldorado Mine, Port Radium, Northwest Territories, Canada, and at the Shinkolobwe mine, Belgian Congo. In both instances, the ore is high grade, and uranium-bearing minerals are liberated at sizes coarse enough to permit gravity concentration. More recently, physical beneficiation processes have been used successfully with much lower-grade ores at Radium Hill, South Australia, and in several South African operations.

5–2.1 Eldorado Mine. The history of Eldorado's gravity plant has been reviewed by R. L. Behan [5]. Ore from the coarse bin passes over a grizzly with $1\frac{1}{2}$-inch openings. The oversize is fed to a sorting belt, washed by sprays, and then hand-sorted for the removal of waste. A Geiger counter, actuating a signal light, indicates when the waste exceeds the allowable limit. In addition to eliminating waste, the hand-sorting separates out a high-grade pitchblende concentrate.

Further crushing and screening before the fine-ore bin is reached produces a minus $\frac{3}{8}$-inch product with about 90 percent by weight plus-10 mesh. A magnetic head pulley on the plus $\frac{3}{8}$-inch circuit removes tramp iron and some magnetite. The magnetite contains no appreciable amount of pitchblende and is discarded.

Ore from the fine-ore bins is screened to produce three size fractions; plus-4 mesh, minus-4 plus-8 mesh, and minus-8 mesh. The two coarser sizes are treated in a circuit that produces a jig concentrate for shipment, and magnetic waste. In this circuit James jigs separate the gravity concentrate which, after drying, is conveyed over a permanent-magnet head pulley for removal of the magnetite waste. Tailings from the rougher and cleaner jigs are dewatered in a drag classifier, ground in a rod mill, and returned to the screens following the fine-ore bin.

The circuit treating the minus-8 mesh ore produces a jig concentrate for shipment, waste copper flotation concentrate, and the feed to the leach plant. In this circuit the minus-8 mesh ore is treated in a bowl classifier that separates sand and an overflow product. Sizing the sand in a hydraulic classifier gives three products for further treatment: coarse spigots, 1, 2, 3, and 4; fine spigots 5 and 6; and a classifier overflow. The coarse spigots are sent to jigs which produce a finished concentrate. The jig tailing is dewatered in a drag classifier, ground in a 4 by 6-foot ball mill and returned to the bowl classifier. The hydraulic-classifier overflow is fed to a 6-foot hydroclassifier. The hydroclassifier underflow is treated in flotation cells, where a copper sulfide concentrate is removed as waste. The feed to the leach plant is a combination of four products from the gravity plant and a tailings reclamation plant. The bowl classifier overflow is combined with the 6-foot hydroclassifier overflow before thickening in a 40-foot, double-tray thickener. The thickener underflow is combined with the flotation tails and spigot products 5 and 6 to become feed to the leach plant.

In the Eldorado operation, advantage is taken of the relatively coarse-size liberation of pitchblende and its high specific gravity to permit gravity separation of uranium concentrates. Other heavy minerals, such as magnetite and sulfides, concentrate with the pitchblende in the gravity processes. Magnetic separation and sulfide flotation assist in removing these minerals from the pitchblende.

These procedures are not novel, and may be compared with tin-milling practices in Bolivia for the recovery of cassiterite. Pitchblende, like cassiterite, is friable and tends to slime. It is necessary, therefore, to take precautions during size-reduction operations to minimize slime production. Because both pitchblende and cassiterite have high specific gravity, they can be treated by relatively low-cost gravity processes, provided liberation is obtained at a reasonably coarse size. The cassiterite ores normally in sulfide minerals are removed by flotation. At Eldorado it was found that gravity concentration of disseminated pitchblende ore, as with tin ores, gave good recovery only at the expense of grade.

After the leaching plant began operating at Eldorado, recovery of concentrates in the gravity plant became relatively unimportant. The gravity plant has two basic purposes: (a) removal of massive pitchblende that otherwise might result in high losses in the leach plant, and (b) removal of heavy minerals by gravity concentration and flotation, thus saving reagent costs in the leach plant.

5–2.2 **Radium Hill concentrator.** The ore mined at Radium Hill, South Australia, contains uranium in the mineral davidite. Associated gangue minerals are largely ilmenite, rutile, hematite, magnetite, biotite, and quartz. The ore, as mined, contains about 0.2 percent U_3O_8. It is processed at the mine by heavy media separation and flotation to produce a concentrate containing about 1 percent U_3O_8, which is shipped by rail to Port Pirie for chemical treatment. Capacity of the Radium Hill concentrator is approximately 600 tons per day, or about 100 tons of flotation concentrates. A schematic flowsheet of the Radium Hill concentrator is shown in Fig. 5–5.

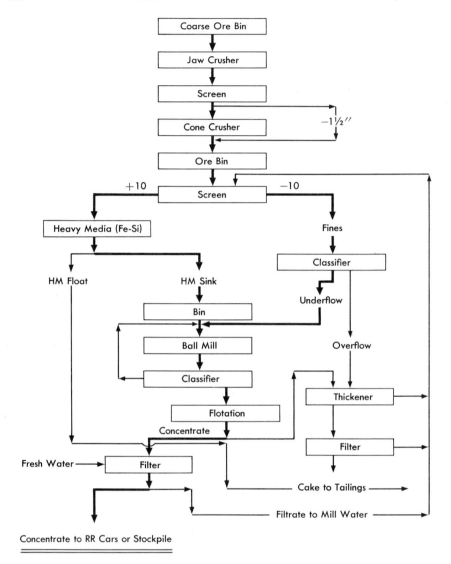

Fig. 5–5. Flowsheet of Radium Hill concentrator.

5–2.3 South African mines. In the early work on uranium recovery from South African gold mill tailings, it was found possible to concentrate uranium by flotation at much lower cost per pound than by directly leaching the gold tailings [6]. However, flotation would have reduced the total output by about 60 percent, because recoveries of only 40 to 50 percent were obtained. Since maximum output was the overriding consideration, it was decided to treat all the ore possible by acid leach under oxidizing conditions.

As the uranium industry developed, the demand for sulfuric acid increased greatly. The sulfur for acid plants is provided by flotation of pyrite from gold tailings, ordinarily after the uranium leaching step. Since uranium can also be concentrated by the sulfide flotation process, in a number of instances uranium production is being increased by leaching pyrite concentrates followed by reclaiming pyrite through a second flotation.

The operation of such a pair of flotation plants at Vogelstruisbult Gold Mining Areas Limited has been described by Read et al. [7]. Main Reef slime from current gold extraction and slime reclaimed from an old slime dam are treated by flotation. This produces a concentrate amounting to about 6 percent of the feed with recovery of 90 percent of the sulfur and 40 percent of the uranium. The concentrate is then mixed with Kimberley Reef slime and acid-leached to recover uranium. The leach residue is treated in a second, separate, flotation plant to recover pyrite.

At Daggafontein, two orebodies are being mined. After gold is extracted from the ores, they are treated together in a uranium-leaching plant. At the South Reduction Plant, current and old Main Reef slimes containing about 0.007 percent U_3O_8, are treated by flotation. Uranium recovery averages 50 percent. The pyrite concentrate, containing about 0.06 percent U_3O_8, is pumped to the North Reduction Plant, where it is mixed with cyanided residue and old slimes containing about 0.025 percent U_3O_8. The combined pulp is acid-leached, after which the pyrite is refloated. Pyrite production is about 225 tons per day. The pyrite flotation circuit and reagents are described in Section 11–7.

5–2.4 Radioactive sorting. In physical concentration, minerals are separated by utilizing differences in their natural or induced properties. Radioactivity is the unique property of uranium-bearing minerals employed to separate them from nonradioactive minerals. For example, the Lapointe Picker [8] originally passed the ore on a conveyor belt under a detector. Later, to make the unit more sensitive, a scintillation detector was placed under the conveyor belt. This permitted the bulk of each piece of ore to be close to the gamma-ray detector. The signal from the detector operates a gate, shunting low- and high-grade pieces to separate bins. The limitations of the unit confine its use to relatively coarse (plus $1\frac{1}{2}$-inch) pieces of ore. Consequently, the ore requires screening into size ranges before treatment. The following summary of laboratory results was reported by Bettens and Lapointe on plus $1\frac{1}{2}$-inch mine ore from the Beaverlodge area, Saskatchewan:

Calculated heads	0.045 to 0.08% U_3O_8
Recovery	75 to 80%
Weight rejected	70 to 75%
Grade of concentrate	0.15 to 0.22% U_3O_8
Grade of rejects	0.01 to 0.02% U_3O_8

In the period 1947–1950, the Lapointe picker was used at Eldorado to clean coarse jig concentrates [5].

5–2.5 Sand-slime separation. This method is employed on sandstone ores found in the western United States. The hard sand grains of these ores are usually barren; the cementing material contains the uranium. In the wet method, the ore is ground to liberate the sand grains, mechanical classifiers separate the coarse sand from the slimes, and wet cyclones wash the sand before discarding it. Sand-slime separation for upgrading ore before leaching is employed, for example, by the Vanadium Corporation of America at its Monument No. 2 mine, Monument Valley, Arizona [9]. Considerable attention has been given to dry methods for sand-slime separations for use in arid areas in the western United States.

5–2.6 Summary. The preceding paragraphs have reported current commercial-scale methods—in brief, hand-sorting, jigs for gravity concentration, magnetic concentration to remove magnetite, and flotation to remove sulfides and uranium.

Flotation has been extensively investigated in the laboratory, both for removal of reagent consumers, such as lime in ores to be treated by an acid leach, and for flotation of uranium minerals. Some of these processes have also been studied in extensive large-scale pilot-plant operations [11]. Presumably, various gravity and flotation methods have shown sufficient promise on relatively low-grade ores to warrant pilot-plant studies. In many instances, the investigators have reported interesting results [12–15].

Pilot plants employing flotation and tabling have operated in France. Flotation is used at Lâchaux (Puy-de-Donne) [16]. An ore concentration plant at Guengnon (Saône-et-Loire) has an annual capacity of 50,000 tons of ore, ranging from 1 to 8 percent in grade. Two other plants are under construction, one at Ecapière to treat 1.1 to 1.5 percent ore at the rate of 300,000 tons a year, the other at Bessines (Haute-Vienne) to treat 1.1 to 2.5 percent ore at the rate of 200,000 tons a year.

If it were possible to concentrate or upgrade low-grade uranium ore by physical methods, the size and cost of leaching plants could be reduced. In addition, in many instances it would be possible to treat ore at the mine by physical methods and to reduce the cost of shipping to distant chemical plants. Investigators have been aware of these facts, and operators also recognize the need for preconcentration to allow use of lower-grade ores [17,18]. The question arises, why are physical concentration methods not more common in commercial plants? The answer is as much a matter of economics and demand for maximum recovery as of technology.

Although physical concentration is now little used, it is reasonable to assume that it will play a more important role in the future as the price of uranium decreases and lower-grade ores are exploited in larger tonnages. It is to be expected that a method that combines physical concentration and leaching will result in lower percentages on over-all uranium extraction from a particular ore than would come from direct leaching. Exceptions may occur when the uranium is associated with several mineral constituents which can be separated for treatment by two distinct leaching methods. Excluding such exceptions, a satisfactory commercial physical concentration procedure must meet three conditions:

(1) High ratio of concentration to reduce shipping costs (if any) to the leach plant and to reduce capital investment and maintenance costs of the leach plant.

(2) Removal of nonuranium-bearing minerals that are costly reagent consumers.

(3) High uranium recovery, to the extent that the additional loss incurred by the combination concentration-leach process is more than offset by reducing shipping costs and reagent consumption.

References

1. A. C. RICHARDSON et al., *The Recovery of Uranium from Carnotite Ores*, USAEC Report BMI-JDS-195, Battelle Memorial Institute, June 30, 1949.

2. M. D. HASSIALIS and R. C. MUSA, Some Unusual Problems Met in the Recovery of Uranium from a Very Low-grade Ore, in *Proceedings of the International Conference on the Peaceful Uses of Atomic Energy*, Vol. 8. New York: United Nations, 1956. (P/521, p. 13)

3. R. Q. WILSON et al., *The Recovery of Uranium from Chattanooga Shales*, USAEC Report BMI-274, Battelle Memorial Institute, Jan. 14, 1954.

4. C. M. WHEELER et al., *The Alkaline Leaching of Uranium Ores Proposed as Feed to the Pilot Plant at Grand Junction, Colorado: Progress Report [No. 1 for the Period March 24 to August 6, 1954]*, USAEC Report AECU-2946, Battelle Memorial Institute, Aug. 20, 1954.

5. R. L. BEHAN, The Eldorado Gravity Plant, Port Radium, N. W. T., *Trans. Can. Inst. Mining Met.* **59,** 154-161 (1956).

6. Record of Proceedings of Session 14B, in *Proceedings of the International Conference on the Peaceful Uses of Atomic Energy*, Vol. 8. New York: United Nations, 1956. (p. 140)

7. F. O. READ et al., Flotation of Uranium and Pyrite at Vogelstruisbult, in *Uranium in South Africa 1946–1956*, Vol. 2. Johannesburg: The Associated Scientific and Technical Societies of South Africa, 1957. (p. 208)

8. P. Maris, Discussion of Flotation of Uranium and Pyrite at Vogelstruisbult, in *Uranium in South Africa 1946–1956*, Vol. 2. Johannesburg: The Associated Scientific and Technical Societies of South Africa, 1957. (p. 41)

9. A. H. Bettens and C. M. Lapointe, Electronic Concentration of Low-grade Ores with the Lapointe Picker, *Can. Dept. Mines and Tech. Surveys*, Paper 10 (1955).

10. F. A. Brinker, *Concentration of Vanadium and Uranium Ore at Monument No. 2 Mine of Vanadium Corporation of America*, paper presented at the Western Mining Conference, Denver, Colorado, Feb. 3, 1956.

11. S. Dayton, U_3O_8 Processing Made More Efficient by Plant Controls at Edgemont Mill, *Mining World* **18,** 36 (January 1957).

12. A. Ginocchio, Two Instances of Physical Uranium Ore Dressing, in *Proceedings of the International Conference on the Peaceful Uses of Atomic Energy*, Vol. 8. New York: United Nations, 1956. (P/340, p. 133)

13. B. C. Mariacher, Preconcentration of Primary Uranium Ores by Flotation, *Mining Eng.* **8,** 1006 (October 1956).

14. T. V. Lord and D. E. Light, The Flotation of Radioactive Minerals *Trans. Can. Inst. Mining Met.* **59,** 53 (1956).

15. A. B. Van Cleave, Beneficiation of Low-grade Pegmatitic Uranium Ores, *Trans. Can. Inst. Mining Met.* **59,** 433 (1956).

16. J. B. Rosenbaum et al., *Innovations in Processing Uranium Ores*, U. S. Bureau of Mines, Research Report No. 46.1. Washington, D. C.: U. S. Government Printing Office, September 1956.

17. J. Grinrod, Uranium in France, *Mining J.* (*London*) **248,** No. 6356, 752 (June 14, 1957).

18. E. B. Hotchkiss, *The Preconcentration of Uranium Ores*, paper presented at the Western Mining Conference, Denver, Colorado, Feb. 8, 1957.

19. The Growing Trend to Uranium Up-grading Revives an Old Concentration Method, *Mining World* **18,** 9 (March 1957).

CHAPTER 6

ACID LEACHING OF URANIUM ORES*

6-1. Introduction

The most widely used process for producing uranium concentrates is dilute aqueous leaching with sulfuric acid and, if necessary, an oxidant. Total milling capacity in 1957, in existing plants and in plants under construction in the United States, Canada, Africa, and Australia, was in excess of 100,000 tons per day, over 90 percent by acid leaching.

This chapter discusses acid leaching by agitation under the following main topics: (1) factors affecting reaction rates and extraction, (2) leaching methods, and (3) plant practice.

The history of extracting uranium from its ores by an oxidizing leach with dilute sulfuric acid dates only from 1944. That year the Massachusetts Institute of Technology, under contract to the United States Government, began a project to study the treatment of low-grade uranium ores. First samples studied were from the Belgian Congo, and this district became the first major producer of uranium concentrates by ambient-temperature leaching with dilute sulfuric acid.

Investigation of the South African Ores [1–4] was begun in 1946 at the following laboratories: the Government Metallurgical Laboratory, Johannesburg, South Africa; Massachusetts Institute of Technology, Cambridge, Massachusetts; Mines Branch, Canada Department of Mines and Technical Surveys, Ottawa, Canada; and the Chemical Research Laboratory, Teddington, England. The cooperative efforts of these groups culminated in an agreement in 1950 that South Africa would produce uranium concentrates for sale to the Combined Development Agency of the United States and United Kingdom. The 1950 agreement called for four plants (increased by subsequent agreements to fifteen), to be supplied with cyanide residues by 26 gold producers in the Rand and Orange Free State.

The Canadians [5] began developing an acid-leaching method for treating the tailings from the gravity concentration plant at Port Radium at about the same time the work was started on the South African ores. The Canadian group at Ottawa, working on the Port Radium Project, closely cooperated with similar groups working on extractive metallurgy of uranium in the United States and Great Britain.

---

* By R. J. Woody and D. R. George, AEC Raw Materials Development Laboratory, National Lead Co., Inc.

Early in the testing programs it became apparent that pitchblende and uraninite, which contain tetravalent uranium, dissolved at satisfactory rates under mildly acidic conditions in the presence of an oxidant such as ferric iron. Addition of a chemical oxidant such as manganese dioxide or sodium chlorate was often required to maintain the concentration of ferric iron at the proper level. United States patents on acid leaching were obtained by Gaudin and Schuhmann [6] and Gaudin [7].

Data from early laboratory and pilot-plant work were applied to the study of treatment methods for the many ore deposits developed as the search for uranium was intensified. As indicated in Chapter 4, each new ore type required modification of the leaching conditions for optimum recovery.

For security reasons, information on the extraction of uranium was withheld from the public for many years. Among the first papers published on the subject were those by Macdonald [8] and Thunaes [9] in 1954. Subsequently, at the Geneva Conference on the Peaceful Uses of Atomic Energy in August 1955, many authors presented papers [10–16] on extracting uranium with sulfuric acid. Some of these articles were general; others dealt with specific raw materials and special methods.

In most uranium ores, part of the uranium is tied up in minerals that are more refractory to alkaline than to acidic leaching solutions. As a consequence, in most cases acid leaching will yield a somewhat higher over-all extraction. From the standpoint of recovery and costs, alkaline and acid processes are competitive at several of the ore deposits in the western United States and perhaps in the Beaverlodge area of Canada. In ores containing little or no refractory uranium mineralization, and moderate to low lime, both processes are applicable. Advantages of acid leaching are:

    (1) Relatively coarse preparatory grinding.

    (2) Comparatively mild reagent concentration.

    (3) Shorter leaching time.

    (4) Ambient-temperature rather than high-temperature leaching.

Furthermore, either ion exchange or solvent extraction can reliably recover the uranium and produce a nearly completely barren solution. Acid leaching and either ion exchange or solvent extraction are complementary processes operable over an extremely wide range of solution composition. Acid-leaching efficiency need not be impaired in order to prepare a more suitable feed for the subsequent processes.

6–2. LEACHING CONDITIONS

The rate and degree of extraction of uranium from its ores by acid leaching depend upon a number of variables: (1) acid concentration, (2) degree of oxidation, (3) leaching temperature, (4) particle size, and

(5) the extent to which the uranium minerals are locked or bound by gangue minerals. These factors are closely interrelated. For many ores comparable extractions and extraction rates may be achieved under a variety of leaching conditions. Optimum conditions are seldom easy to select.

Each ore presents its own leaching problems, most of which affect the extraction rate. A knowledge of the ore type, including the uranium minerals, is very important to the selection of optimum leaching conditions and is discussed in Chapter 4. Differences in extraction of 1 or 2 percent may be economically significant and should be carefully weighed in determining the optimum leaching conditions and over-all flowsheet.

6–2.1 Acid concentration. In acid leaching, sulfuric acid is universally used because of its low cost. The uranium is taken into solution as the uranyl ion, and the acidity must be maintained high enough to prevent reprecipitation of the dissolved uranium, not only during leaching, but also during the subsequent uranium recovery steps.

The pH range for precipitating hexavalent uranium from sulfate solutions in the presence of various anions at ambient temperature is shown in Table 6–1. The pH of precipitation, however, is affected by the alkali used, the temperature, the concentration of uranium, and the extent and nature of other impurities. In general, the pH of precipitation decreases with increasing temperature. The presence of other constituents such as ferric iron, which precipitates at a lower pH than uranium, causes the loss of uranium by occlusion. If phosphate and arsenate are present, however, excess ferric iron is desirable, since it forms a strong complex with these constituents and retards the precipitation of uranyl phosphate or arsenate. A suitable acidity for leaching pitchblende and the oxidized uranium minerals is in the range of 3 to 7 grams of free acid per liter, or a pH of 1.0 to 2.0. On the other hand, some of the refractory minerals, such as davidite and brannerite, may require concentrations of free acid in excess of 50 grams per liter.

TABLE 6–1

RANGES OF pH FOR PRECIPITATION OF URANIUM
FROM SULFATE SOLUTIONS

Hydroxide	Carbonate	Phosphate	Arsenate
3.8–6.0	3.5–6.0	1.9–2.5	1.3–1.7

With most nonrefractory uranium ores, acid consumption during leaching depends primarily on the carbonate content, principally calcite but also including dolomite, magnesite, and siderite. These minerals consume approximately 1 pound of sulfuric acid per pound of calcium carbonate or its equivalent. Other minerals in the ore also contribute to acid consumption. For example, when high acid concentrations or elevated temperatures must be used, such relatively insoluble gangue minerals as clays, micas, phosphates, fluorides, sulfides, and oxides are attacked, and the consumption of acid is increased.

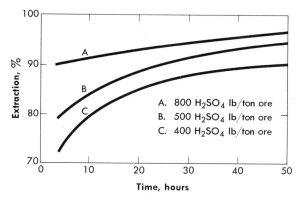

FIG. 6–1. Effect of acid concentration on rate of extraction from pitchblende ore. Shown are three leaches on a single ore at 50% pulp density.

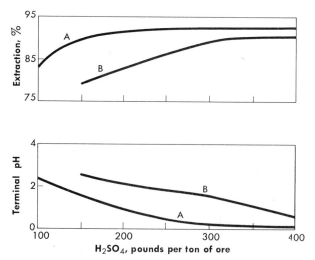

FIG. 6–2. Effect of acid concentration on extraction from two pitchblende ores. Leaching time was 16 hr.

The effect of increased acid concentration is twofold:

(1) It increases the rate of dissolution of the uranium minerals. This is a particularly useful effect when processing refractory ores, many of which do not have a practical dissolution rate in dilute acid.

(2) It dissolves coatings of minerals which would otherwise enclose the uranium minerals and limit access of the leaching solution.

Figure 6–1 illustrates the effect of acid concentration on the rate of uranium extraction from a pitchblende ore having an acid consumption of approximately 400 lb/ton. Figure 6–2 shows the effect of acid concentration on two other pitchblende ores at a fixed leaching time of 16 hours.

6–2.2 Oxidation. As discussed in Chapter 4, a portion of the uranium in such minerals as uraninite, pitchblende, and coffinite is present in the tetravalent form, which is essentially insoluble in dilute sulfuric acid in the absence of an oxidant. Figure 6–3 shows the rates of dissolution of pure UO_2 and of pitchblende in sulfuric acid at pH 1.5. One of the most effective oxidants for UO_2 in sulfuric acid is ferric iron. The reaction is

$$UO_2 + 2Fe^{+++} \rightarrow UO_2^{++} + 2Fe^{++}.$$

For efficient oxidation of UO_2 by ferric iron, the ratio of ferric iron to ferrous iron in solution must be in excess of 1:1. Figure 6–4 shows the effect of the ferric-ferrous ratio on the dissolution of UO_2 in dilute sulfuric acid at pH 1.0. In these tests the ferric iron concentration was held at about 2 g/liter, while the ferrous iron was varied from 1 to 12 g/liter. As the graph shows, the dissolution rates improved as the ferrous iron was decreased. The absolute concentration of ferric iron, as shown in Fig. 6–5,

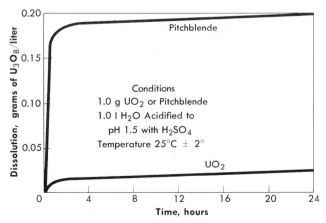

FIG. 6–3. Dissolution of UO_2 and pitchblende in H_2SO_4 solution.

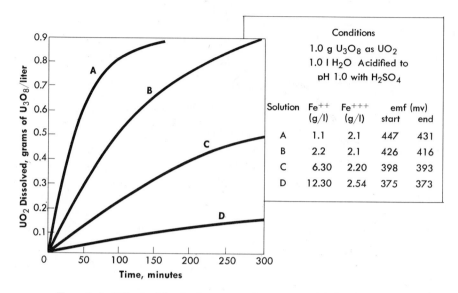

Conditions

1.0 g U_3O_8 as UO_2
1.0 l H_2O Acidified to
pH 1.0 with H_2SO_4

Solution	Fe^{++} (g/l)	Fe^{+++} (g/l)	emf (mv) start	end
A	1.1	2.1	447	431
B	2.2	2.1	426	416
C	6.30	2.20	398	393
D	12.30	2.54	375	373

Fig. 6–4. Effect of ferric-ferrous ratio on rate of UO_2 dissolution.

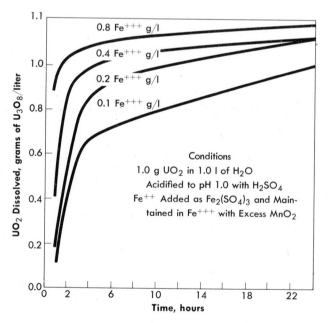

Conditions

1.0 g UO_2 in 1.0 l of H_2O
Acidified to pH 1.0 with H_2SO_4
Fe^{++} Added as $Fe_2(SO_4)_3$ and Main-
tained in Fe^{+++} with Excess MnO_2

Fig. 6–5. Effect of ferric iron concentration on the dissolution rate of UO_2 in the absence of ferrous iron.

is of less importance. In this series of tests, UO_2 was contacted with pH 1.0 sulfuric acid containing 0.1 to 0.8 g/liter of ferric iron. No ferrous iron was present, since an excess of manganese dioxide was added to ensure that all the iron was maintained in the ferric form.

In ore leaching, sufficient iron for leaching is usually taken into solution from iron-bearing minerals and from the metallic iron abraded during crushing and grinding. However, since most of the iron is dissolved in the ferrous state and is not readily oxidized by oxygen in acid solutions at atmospheric pressure, it is necessary to add an oxidant. The most suitable oxidants are manganese dioxide and sodium chlorate, which react as follows to oxidize the iron:

$$2Fe^{++} + MnO_2 + 4H^+ \rightarrow 2Fe^{+++} + Mn^{++} + 2H_2O$$

and

$$6Fe^{++} + ClO_3^- + 6H^+ \rightarrow 6Fe^{+++} + Cl^- + 3H_2O.$$

In the absence of iron, neither manganese dioxide nor sodium chlorate is an effective oxidant for UO_2. Figures 6–4 and 6–5 show that satisfactory uranium dissolution rates are achieved when the ferric-ferrous ratio is about 1:1, and when the total quantity of ferric iron is between 0.5 to 2.0 g/liter. The rate of oxidant addition may be controlled by analyzing for ferric and ferrous iron or, more conveniently, by measuring the redox potential.

Figure 6–6 shows the course of a potentiometric titration of a sulfuric acid solution of iron, vanadium, and uranium with permanganate [17]. At −300 millivolts, essentially all the iron is in the ferrous state. At about −430 millivolts, at least half the iron is in the ferric form, and above −600

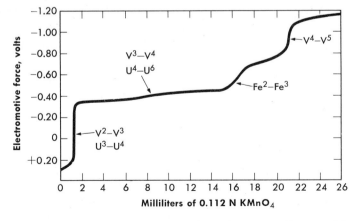

Fig. 6–6. Potentiometric titration of uranium, vanadium, and iron.

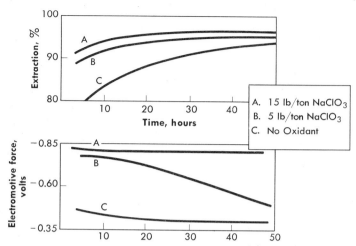

Fig. 6–7. Effect of oxidant (and emf) on uranium extraction from pitch-blende ore.

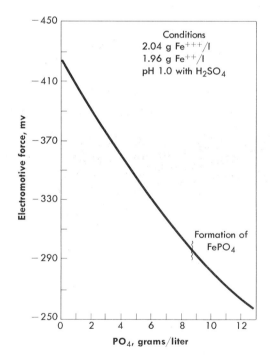

Fig. 6–8. Effect of phosphate ion concentration on emf of $Fe^{++} - Fe^{+++}$ solution.

millivolts, all the iron is in the ferric form. Therefore a minimum emf of −430 millivolts in the circuit will, in most cases, result in a desirable ferric-ferrous ratio. In some instances, however, extraction rates may be improved significantly by maintaining more negative emf values. Figure 6–7 illustrates the effect of oxidant and the emf on the leaching of a pitchblende ore.

In the control of oxidation in leaching circuits, it is important to remember that it is the ratio of free ferric iron to ferrous iron that determines the oxidizing power of the solution. In the presence of phosphate, arsenate, or fluoride, a portion of the ferric iron is complexed, so that for a given total ferric-ferrous ratio, lower redox potentials are obtained. Figure 6–8 shows the adverse effect of phosphate on the emf of a solution containing 2 grams each of ferric and ferrous iron. This adverse effect was further demonstrated by leaching about 1 gram of UO_2 at pH 1.0 in a liter of solution containing 2 grams of ferric iron, 2 grams of ferrous iron, and 8.75 grams of PO_4. At the resulting emf of −305 millivolts, the extraction of uranium was less than 1 percent after 6 hours. Thus it is evident that larger quantities of oxidant are required for leaching ores containing detrimental amounts of phosphate, arsenate, or fluoride. When solutions are deficient in iron, extra iron may sometimes be added to obtain a suitable emf and free ferric iron concentration. Some of the practical aspects of the role of "free" ferric iron in the presence of phosphate and arsenate are discussed by Thunaes [5].

In order to dissolve the uranium rapidly, the oxidant is often added at the start of leaching, but in pulps containing excessive quantities of metallic iron, oxidant consumption can sometimes be significantly reduced by withholding it until the metallic iron has been dissolved. In the absence of ferric iron, the metallic iron is oxidized to ferrous iron and dissolved by reducing the acid, with resulting evolution of hydrogen. In the presence of ferric iron, the metallic iron dissolves much more rapidly because of oxidation by the ferric iron, but this more rapid dissolution is obtained at the expense of an amount of oxidant equivalent to the amount of ferric iron reduced.

6–2.3 **Effect of temperature.** As with most chemical reactions, the rate of dissolution of uranium is increased by increasing the temperature. Figure 6–9 shows the effect of temperature on the dissolution rate of UO_2 in the presence of approximately 1 gram each of ferric and ferrous iron; the rate of dissolution was increased approximately threefold by increasing the temperature from 26 to 40°C. A comparable increase in extraction rate for a pitchblende ore is shown in Fig. 6–10, where approximately 93 percent extraction was obtained in 4 hours at 40°C and in 12 hours at 25°C.

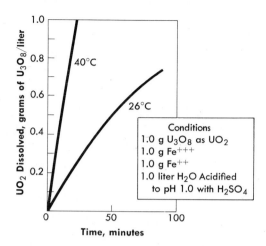

FIG. 6–9. Effect of temperature on the dissolution rate of UO$_2$.

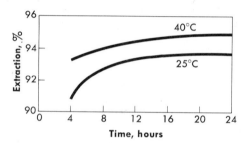

FIG. 6–10. The effect of temperature on the extraction of a pitchblende ore.

For ores containing difficultly soluble minerals, the improvement in extraction at elevated temperatures may be very marked, particularly at temperatures higher than 50°C. However, as mentioned earlier, the increased extraction is usually obtained at the expense of higher acid and oxidant consumption due to increased solubilization of silicates, sulfides, phosphates, and other minerals in the ores. Although corrosion of equipment also becomes an increasingly important economic factor at higher temperatures, the beneficial effects should not be overlooked in selecting optimum operating conditions.

6–2.4 Effect of grind. The fineness of grind is one of the most important variables affecting uranium extraction. The effect is twofold: (1) overall extraction is increased as a result of improved liberation, and (2) the rate of extraction is improved as a result of increased surface area of the exposed uranium minerals. For many ores, particularly those from the western United States, uranium minerals are not significantly locked within insoluble minerals, and satisfactory extractions may be obtained from particles as coarse as 10 mesh. A minus-28 mesh grind, however, is generally required to facilitate agitation and materials handling. Other ores may require extremely fine grinding to liberate or expose the uranium minerals effectively.

6–3. LEACHING METHODS AND EQUIPMENT

Five methods are available for extracting uranium from ores by acid treatment: (1) aqueous leaching with agitation, (2) percolation, (3) hot digestion, (4) acid curing at a high percentage of solids, and (5) pressure leaching. Only the first three methods are in use today, and of these the aqueous leach with agitation accounts for most uranium concentrate production.

6–3.1 Aqueous leaching with agitation. The leaching section is the heart of the ore processing plant, and a large portion of production cost must be allocated to it. Operating costs as well as recovery of uranium depend on the choice of leaching methods and, to some extent, on the selection of equipment for leaching. As a general rule, the operations ahead of the leaching circuit should be designed to produce leach feed of optimum grain size and pulp density, and the operations following it should be designed to handle whatever product results from optimum leaching conditions.

Pulps for acid leaching are generally prepared by grinding in water in a closed circuit, to produce the optimum particle size for leaching and materials handling. This procedure also improves efficiency without increasing the volume of the pregnant solution. It is advantageous to maintain the solids content of the pulp at or near the maximum consistent with good mixing in the agitators; a reduction in the ratio of liquid to solid cuts down on the size of the leaching equipment and also saves acid. A partial dewatering of the classifier overflow can be accomplished by means of thickeners or filters. In the Canadian mills multicompartment tray thickeners are standard equipment, and some plants filter all or part of the thickened pulp to obtain a maximum-density feed for agitation leaching. Pulp densities vary from about 40 percent solids for agitation of ores with high clay content to 65 percent solids, for pulp of relatively low viscosity. If ore particles as coarse as 28 to 35 mesh can be leached, the classifier overflow may be passed directly to the agitation circuit at 50 to 55 percent solids. Currently, this is standard practice in the acid-RIP* plants, since it is desirable to keep the content of slimes in the pulp to a minimum.

---

* RIP = Resin in Pulp. See Section 9–4.

Agitation equipment. The choice of agitation equipment is wide. Both air and mechanical agitation give satisfactory results. The Pachuca tank is universally used for acid leaching in South Africa, and is also used in Canada and Australia. The South African tanks are rubber-lined steel, 22.5 ft in diameter and 45 ft high, with a 60-degree conical bottom [18]. Center airlifts are not employed in South African uranium plants. Air pressures are 35 to 42 psi in agitating pulps of 65 percent solids. A typical installation to service 10 Pachuca tanks consists of four compressors, each rated at 1035 ft^3/min and powered by 130-hp motors. In the Bancroft Area of Canada, 220 ft^3/min at 40 psi are used in each 18 by 45 ft Pachuca tank. These tanks are constructed of wood staves and have a 12-in. by 12-ft lift column in the 60-degree cone at the bottom. All of the air can be used in the short center lift, or part of it may be introduced elsewhere near the bottom of the cone. The advantages of air agitation in acid leaching are low maintenance and low first cost per unit of tank volume. Power costs are also low compared with most purely mechanical installations.

The combination air and slow-sweep mechanical agitation typified by the Dorr agitator is employed in the Blind River and Lake Athabasca districts of Canada [19,20]. At the Rare Metals Corporation in Tuba City, Arizona, both Dorr and straight-blade turbine agitators are used. The Dorr agitators are preferred for the highly thixotropic pulps from the Arrowhead ores, but the extremely sandy ores of the Blind River Area of Canada were hard to handle in the 32 by 30-ft Dorr machines. Even though the pulps were finely ground and near terminal density, both rake speed and air input had to be increased to prevent settling of the sand. Addition of glue to the leaching circuits, which increased the viscosity of the pulps, also helped to suspend the sands.

Mechanical agitation with ship-type or turbine impellers singly in baffled tanks, or with several units per tank, is widely practiced in the uranium mills of the United States. This preference for strictly mechanical agitation probably arises from the coarse grind commonly employed for the sandstone ores. The resulting pulps often contain sand grains as coarse as 20 mesh and usually contain more water than would a normal thickener underflow. Since the coarse material is unsupported by thickened slimes, positive and rather violent agitation is required to keep it in suspension during leaching. Many operators also feel that mechanical agitation gives greater assurance of rapid reaction between the acid and carbonate minerals. The Uranium Reduction Company at Moab, Utah, uses ten tanks, 24 by 14 ft, for leaching 1500 to 1800 tons of ore per day. Each tank is equipped with three curved-blade turbines 54 inches diameter, powered by 30-hp drives.

Bench-scale tests at the Winchester Laboratory comparing agitation by air, by slow-speed mechanical agitation, and by high-speed mechanical agitation showed that the last resulted in a greater rate and magnitude of uranium extraction [21]. Side effects observed were greater acid consumption, finer grinding of ore particles during agitation, and higher pulp temperatures caused by increased energy input. Further testing indicated that these effects were the cause of improved uranium extraction. The effects of grinding and supplying heat in bench-scale air-agitation leaching tests on a sample of Big Indian Wash ore are depicted in Fig. 6–11, along with the extraction curve obtained by leaching a similar charge with high-speed agitation.

Harrison [22] studied the effects of different impeller speeds on the extraction of uranium by acid leaching. He noted that the extraction rate of uranium and iron was higher at the faster impeller speeds. A temperature rise caused by increased energy input was also noted, and more acid was consumed. Measured power inputs per unit of pulp volume were high compared with plant practice in treating similar ore pulps with agitators that combined air and mechanical mixing.

The choice of leaching equipment is not critical. Laboratory and pilot-plant studies show that the prime function of the agitator is to keep the heaviest and coarsest mineral particles suspended while maintaining reagent concentrations at reactive levels at the mineral surfaces. There is no evidence to show that any one method of agitation excels in extraction results. Means other than high-speed agitation, however, should be sought for comminution or for supplying heat when finer grinding or increased temperature is beneficial. The horsepower requirements for leaching uranium ores with various types of agitation equipment fall within the ranges shown in Table 6–2.

Continuous versus batch leaching. Leaching may be either batchwise or continuous, but there are few proponents of batch leaching of ores

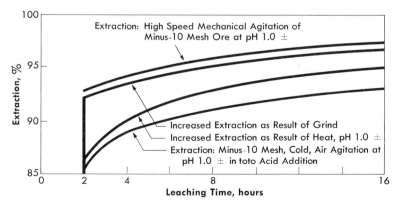

FIG. 6–11. Cumulative effect of agitation, heating, and grinding on uranium extraction.

TABLE 6-2

POWER REQUIRED FOR AGITATION

Method of agitation	Horsepower per 1000 ft^3 of pulp
Air only (Pachuca tank)	2 to 4
Mechanical (propeller or turbine)	4 to 15
Combination (slow sweep plus central or side airlifts)	0.5 to 1.5

today. Several of the earlier plants in South Africa which were originally designed for batch leaching have been converted to continuous operation. These include the Anglo-American plants at Daggafontein and Western Reefs. Among the advantages of continuous leaching cited by Pinkney [18] are lower costs for installation, operation, and maintenance, and greater ease and improved consistency of control of the critical leaching variables.

Continuous leaching circuits are laid out with several tanks in series. The pulp flows by gravity from one tank to the next, and some of the ore particles remain in a given tank for much shorter than the average time. Increasing the number of tanks in series for agitating a given volume of pulp lowers the amount of bypassing of incompletely leached solids through the circuit. In practice, the minimum number of tanks in series for leaching is four, and as many as fourteen are used.

Two-stage countercurrent leaching. Most uranium plants employ a single-stage leach and make no attempt to recover unused leaching reagents. However, methods are available that promise substantial reagent savings or improved recovery. Figure 6-12 is a schematic flow diagram of the most important of these methods, the two-stage countercurrent leach. The leaching reagents (acid and, if necessary, an oxidant) are added to the strong-acid leaching stage. The strong leach solution containing the dissolved uranium and unused reagents is recovered in the subsequent washing circuit, and is advanced to the neutralizing stage of leaching. In the neutralizing leach, the excess reagents in the strong leach liquor react with the readily soluble reagent consumers in the ore. Furthermore, since strongly oxidizing conditions are not generally required in the neutralizing stage, the removal of a pregnant solution containing a high ratio of ferrous to ferric iron considerably reduces the amount of chemical oxidant required for maximum uranium extraction. Consequently, the reagents added to the strong leaching stage are essentially "free" to attack the more

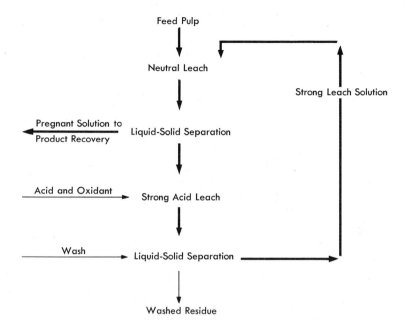

FIG. 6–12. Flowsheet for two-stage leach.

refractory uranium minerals. The principal advantages to be gained by leaching countercurrently are, therefore:

(1) Reduction of chemical costs for leaching and waste disposal.
(2) Improved extraction.
(3) Partial purification of pregnant solution.

When barren liquors must be neutralized before disposal, a saving in alkali is also realized. More important is the possibility of realizing either a substantial saving of leaching reagents or a significant increase in extraction. Typical laboratory results for single-stage versus two-stage leaching of samples of various ore types are presented in Table 6–3.

In many cases the two-stage countercurrent leach can partially purify the pregnant solution. Often the pH of the neutralizing stage can be carried high enough to virtually eliminate bisulfate and molybdenum. Moreover, the natural reducing constituents in the pulp make unnecessary the use of metallic iron or ferrous sulfate for emf adjustment prior to ion exchange or solvent extraction. Increased pH of the pregnant solution and lower redox potential give improved loadings and faster throughput rates in recovery by ion exchange and solvent extraction and thus lower chemical and capital costs.

Two-stage leaching was tried in both the laboratory and on a pilot-plant scale [4] on the Rand cyanide residues, with one stage of filtration

TABLE 6–3

COMPARISON OF SINGLE-STAGE AND TWO-STAGE LEACHING

Ore type	Single-stage leach				Two-stage leach			
	H_2SO_4 lb/ton	$NaClO_3$ lb/ton	Preg., pH	U_3O_8 Extr., %	H_2SO_4 lb/ton	$NaClO_3$ lb/ton	Preg., pH	U_3O_8 Extr., %
Primary	500	5	0.5	94	400	0.5	1.5	98
Oxidized	70	0	1.5	97	50	0	2.3	98
Lignite ash	700	0	0.5	95	550	0	2.7	95

following each leaching step. Less acid was required than for single-stage leaching, but the recovery of the dissolved uranium by filtration was adversely affected. These ores, with few exceptions, are leachable at low concentrations of free acid, and actual acid consumption by the ore minerals is low. Consequently, the plants were built for single-stage leaching followed by two stages of filtration.

Stanley [23] reported excellent results in countercurrent leaching of Big Indian Wash ore in the laboratory. The comparison with single-stage leaching at room temperature and equivalent oxidizing conditions indicated a saving of over 100 pounds of acid per ton of ore and an increase of about four percentage points in extraction.

Lignite ash has been treated by two-stage leaching at the pilot scale after extensive laboratory studies [24] had indicated that very substantial reagent savings and improved recovery could be achieved. Under certain conditions much of the troublesome molybdenum was rejected without loss of uranium. (Further discussion of the treatment of lignites is presented in Section 12–4.)

Although two-stage countercurrent leaching yields its maximum benefits in treating ores that are heavy acid consumers and also require a high concentration of free acid for maximum uranium extraction, the possibilities for savings in treating readily leachable ores should not be overlooked. Almost invariably the acid concentration required to dissolve uranium is greater than that necessary to retain it in solution. Consequently, partial neutralization with ore will conserve both acid required for leaching and alkali required for tailing neutralization.

Equipment for two-stage leaching may be arranged in several ways. A liquid-solids separation step is required between leaching stages, the solution must be recovered, and the residue must be washed after the strong-acid leach. Liquid-solids separation equipment may consist of thickeners, filters, or a combination of both. If extraction in the neutralizing stage is high, the first stage of liquid-solids separation may replace one washing stage on the final residue.

The flowsheet shown in Fig. 6–13 is particularly suitable for sandstone-type ores since the coarse sands, which might present agitation difficulties in the dilute pulp of the neutralizing stage, are treated only at high pulp density in the strong-acid stage. Most of the acid-consuming constituents in a ground ore pulp normally accompany the slimes. Consequently, nearly full realization of the acid neutralizing power of the ore is obtained by subjecting only the slimes to the neutralizing leach. Furthermore, should an ore contain coarse carbonate minerals, the danger of continuing reaction with acid in the neutral-stage thickener is minimized.

Single-stage leach with pregnant solution recycle. The system of recycling pregnant solution employed in the Blind River area of Canada* is

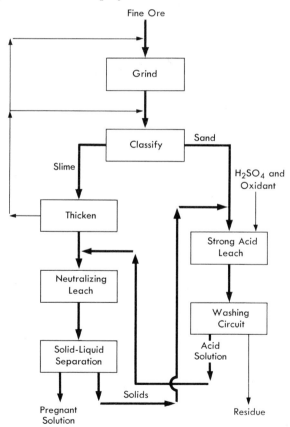

FIG. 6–13. Flowsheet for two-stage leach of sandy ores.

---

* Detailed flowsheets are shown in Section 11–2.

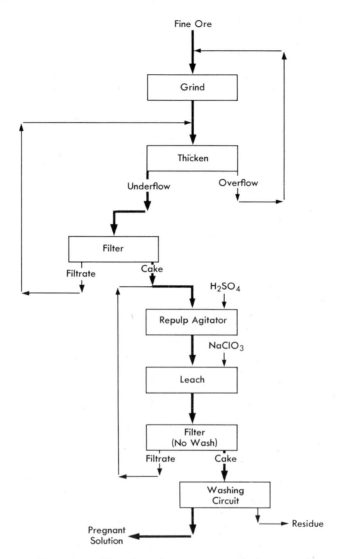

Fig. 6–14. Flowsheet for pregnant solution recycle.

notable among alternatives to the two-stage countercurrent leaching system for conserving leaching reagents. A typical schematic flowsheet is
shown in Fig. 6–14. This type of single-stage leaching with reagent recovery applies particularly to ores that consume little acid but require a
high acid concentration for good extraction. In this system a fixed proportion of the pregnant solution available at the end of the leach is removed
from the circuit as filter-cake moisture; the remainder is returned as fil-

trate to the head of the leaching circuit at the proper concentration for leaching. Unlike the two-stage countercurrent leach, the acid saving is not limited to that which can be consumed by the ore. The single-stage cyclic method is characterized by a buildup of in-process inventory of valuable product and impurities, while the two-stage method removes the readily soluble uranium and other constituents from the circuit more quickly.

A similar system of reagent recovery for recycle may be laid out with thickeners. One of the present authors proposed such a solution-recovery system for a carbonate RIP process in which two stages of thickening are used. Reagent recoveries of over 70 percent were demonstrated on the pilot scale, and it appears probable that this process can be used commercially.

Neutralizing excess acid with a less refractory ore. Occasionally a mill may have to treat a refractory ore together with one that responds to very mild leaching conditions. In this case it is possible to grind separately, leach the refractory ore with excess acid, and add the unleached amenable ore to the highly acidic pulp. This practice is followed at Randfontein Estates [4] by treating the more refractory cyanide residue from East Champ d'Or in a separate leaching circuit before blending with the more readily amenable Randfontein Estates material to secure maximum utilization of the acid.

6–3.2 Percolation leaching. Leaching by percolation of the lixiviant through a fixed bed of ore in filter-bottom tanks has found a very limited application in the treatment of uranium ores. A small plant in Sweden [15] treats a heavy-media concentrate by percolation with dilute sulfuric acid. The ore is a low-grade shale, and the uranium is concentrated in a lightweight carbon fraction. The heavy-media sink product is discarded.

Percolation rates are generally unsatisfactory on unroasted ores if any slimes are present. Climax Uranium Company treats unroasted sands in its Grand Junction Mill by percolation with hot, strong solutions of sulfuric acid and sodium chlorate to extract both uranium and vanadium. The sands are washed essentially free of slimes before being introduced to the filter-bottom tanks for percolation. The ores treated are mostly carnotites, and recovery of vanadium is economically significant. Since only the slimes are salt-roasted, about two-thirds of the ore feed bypasses this step. Originally the salt-roasted slimes at the Climax mill were first leached with water to extract the sodium vanadate and then leached by percolation with sulfuric acid solution to recover the uranium and some residual vanadium. This is no longer practiced. The water-leached vanadium residue is now acid-leached by agitation, and the uranium solution is recovered by stagewise filtration on rotary drum filters.

Except for treatment of salt-roasted material, whole ores are not being treated by percolation. The Anaconda Company performed extensive pilot-plant tests on percolation leaching of sandstone ores from the Jackpile deposit, but rejected the method in favor of agitation leaching. Extraction rates are comparatively slow under the near static conditions of percolation leaching, and it is difficult to maintain the concentration of leaching reagent at an active level at the mineral surfaces. Bypassing or channeling of solutions is also frequently difficult in percolation leaching. However, when percolation is feasible it minimizes water consumption, produces a high-grade pregnant solution, and eliminates expensive thickeners or filters. Percolation of washed sands undoubtedly will play an important part in chemical upgrading of ores in remote areas where the operator is willing to sacrifice recovery to save on freight.

A typical upgrading process for a sandstone ore might consist of grinding the ore to its natural grain size, followed by sand-slime separation and acid percolation leaching of the sand. The resulting leach liquor would be neutralized on the ore slimes, precipitating the uranium values. The slimes would then be dewatered, partially dried, and shipped to a uranium mill for processing to yellow cake.

6–3.3 Hot digestion. The method of hot digestion requires a very high concentration of free acid, with agitation at or near the boiling point. This extremely rigorous treatment is required for some of the more refractory uranium minerals. The one commercial application of the method is at Port Pirie in South Australia, where davidite concentrates from the Radium Hill mine are treated batchwise in brick-lined digesters. The charge to the digester consists of 10 tons of concentrate, 12,500 pounds of water and 7500 pounds of H_2SO_4. Digestion time is about 10 hours at 220 to 230°F and atmospheric pressure. A more complete description of the Port Pirie operation is presented in Article 6–4.4.

Fortunately, few of the major uranium deposits require such rigorous treatment. A high-grade feed is necessary, since both the operating costs and the capital outlay for leaching equipment are high.

6–3.4 Acid curing at high solids. In the acid-cure process the ore is ground dry to at least minus-10 mesh and dampened with water to about 10 percent moisture. Concentrated sulfuric acid is then mixed with the damp ore (pugging), after which the material is cured in bins or piles. Curing time varies with different ores, ranging from 1 to 24 hours. The cured material is pulped with water and, if necessary, subjected to an oxidizing aqueous leach. The pregnant solution containing uranium (and vanadium) is separated from the residue by filtration or countercurrent decantation.

An alternative method of recovering the solubilized uranium from the acid-cured material is to apply solvent extraction directly to pugged material. This process has been described by Galvanek [25]. Its principal advantages are the high purity of the uranium product, the possible saving of water, and the elimination of settling or filtration problems. Acid-curing followed by direct extraction into a nonaqueous medium has not been applied commercially.

The Kerr-McGee plant at Shiprock, New Mexico, originally used the method of pugging and curing, followed by a very short aqueous leach. After two years of operation, however, the pugging step was discontinued in favor of direct aqueous leaching with agitation. A primary reason for acid curing at this plant was the intent to recover vanadium. Vanadium extraction is seldom greater than 50 percent in the dilute leach at room temperature, and pugging usually solubilizes over 90 percent. However, the increase in vanadium extraction requires 100 to 200 pounds more acid than is required to extract the uranium. Some of this excess remains in the solution as "free" acid, and the expense encountered in neutralizing it is also chargeable to vanadium recovery.

As an alternative to the simple acid cure followed by an aqueous leach, a two-stage countercurrent pugging and leaching process has been laboratory tested. It substantially reduces the quantity of acid and alkali required for leaching, the necessity for pH adjustment, and problems of tailing disposal.

The flowsheet of Fig. 6–15 is similar to that for the two-stage leaching process shown in Fig. 6–13, with the exception that a pugging step is incorporated between the neutral- and strong-acid leaching steps. This requires filtration of the residue from the neutral leach, and possibly a partial drying operation. Table 6–4 shows the effect of various treatment

TABLE 6–4

TREATMENT OF HIGH-LIME ORE

Leaching method	H_2SO_4, lb/ton	$NaClO_3$, lb/ton	$CaCO_3$, lb/ton	Preg. soln., pH	Extraction, %	
					U_3O_8	V_2O_5
Simple leach	500	5	60	1.3	94	48
Two-stage countercurrent	400	5	0	1.5	98	49
Simple pug	700	5	246	1.3	94	89
Two-stage pug leach	575	5	0	2.0	97	97

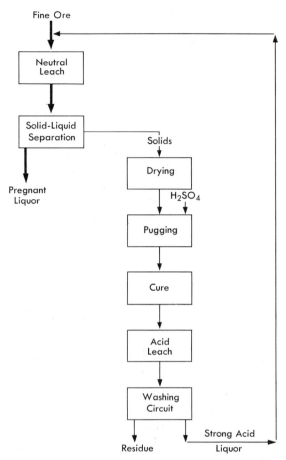

FIG. 6–15. Flowsheet for two-stage pug leach.

procedures on uranium and vanadium extraction, and the consumption of reagents on a high-lime (17.3 percent $CaCO_3$), high-vanadium ore from the Big Indian Wash district.

6–3.5 Acid leaching under pressure. Forward and Halpern [26] were first to report on the leaching of uranium ores at elevated temperatures and pressures, during which sulfuric acid for leaching is autogenously generated by oxidation of sulfide minerals in the ore and by the hydrolysis of ferric sulfate. The reactions involved are reported as follows:

$$2FeS_2 + 7\tfrac{1}{2}O_2 + H_2O \rightarrow Fe_2(SO_4)_3 + H_2SO_4$$

and

$$Fe_2(SO_4)_3 + (3 + x)H_2O \rightarrow Fe_2O_3 \cdot x\,H_2O + 3H_2SO_4$$

or

$$Fe_2(SO_4)_3 + (2 + 2x)H_2O \rightarrow 2Fe(OH)SO_4 \cdot x\ H_2O + H_2SO_4.$$

In the above reactions, pyrite is the source of the sulfur, but other sulfide minerals or elemental sulfur can be oxidized in a similar manner. Suitable operating temperatures for pyrite ores are in the range of 130 to 150°C (266 to 302°F) and partial oxygen pressures of 10 to 15 psi. The rate of reaction is favored by increasing temperatures. Partial oxygen pressures in excess of 15 psi have little effect.

In the acid pressure leach, the sulfuric acid generated dissolves the uranium minerals. Obviously, however, the ore must contain enough sulfides to generate sufficient acid to neutralize the acid-consuming minerals in the ore. In the absence of sufficient sulfides, sulfur in some form, or sulfuric acid, must be added. Gray [13] studied pressure leaching of non-sulfide-bearing Australian davidite concentrates by adding sulfuric acid and obtained equivalent extractions with half the acid required in the hot-digestion process at atmospheric pressure. The resulting liquors were also much lower in iron and titanium. Data are given in Table 6–5.

Aside from the ability to make the acid necessary for leaching directly from sulfide minerals or sulfur, pressure leaching has the advantage of not requiring a chemical oxidant. This is particularly important in acid-leaching ores or concentrates containing large quantities of sulfide minerals which, under normal leaching conditions, result in strong reducing conditions and thereby prevent efficient oxidation and dissolution of tetravalent uranium. For example, a sample of uranium-bearing copper sulfide concentrate yielded a 77 percent uranium extraction when leached at atmospheric pressure for six hours at 95°C with 400 pounds of sulfuric acid plus 150 pounds of manganese dioxide per ton. The same material

TABLE 6–5

ACID-LEACHING OF RADIUM HILL CONCENTRATES

H_2SO_4, lb/ton	Time, hr	Temp., °C	Pressure, total psig	Extraction, % U_3O_8	Solution, g/liter	
					Fe_2O_3	TiO_2
610	8	100	0	89.5	50	0.37
765	8	100	0	91.2	50	0.66
920	8	100	0	92.3	50	1.06
205	6	150	100	73.6	0.6	0.05
306	6	150	100	92.5	3.0	0.05

yielded a 99.4 percent uranium extraction when leached with water for six hours at 200°C with a partial oxygen pressure of approximately 10 psi.

Other advantages of the pressure leach are purification of the solution by hydrolysis of ferric iron, molybdenum, titanium, and other metals. However, the process is not likely to be widely adopted for processing run-of-mine uranium ores. Its inherent corrosion problems are severe, and capital outlay for handling large throughput tonnages are heavy.

6–4. Milling Practice

With the exception of the RIP plants in the United States, all existing acid-leaching plants recover dissolved uranium from the leached pulp by filtration or countercurrent decantation, followed by ion exchange or solvent extraction. The choice of equipment for the processing steps is determined to a large extent by the physical and chemical character of the ores. Milling practice is also influenced by the background of ore-treatment practice of a particular area or country.

The following descriptions of operating plants illustrate variations in milling practices and give some details on equipment and operating data.

6–4.1 Blind River area, Ontario, Canada.* The ores of the Blind River (Elliot Lake) area of Ontario, Canada, are extremely hard, coarse conglomerates in which the uranium minerals are brannerite and uraninite. The average assay is approximately 0.1 percent U_3O_8. About 34,500 tons of ore per day are mined and milled in eleven acid leaching plants. All the mills employ essentially the same leaching conditions:

(1) Fine grinding—65 to 70 percent minus-200 mesh.
(2) Long agitation—48 hours.
(3) High pulp density—67 percent solids.
(4) High free acid concentration—40 to 50 grams of H_2SO_4 per liter.
(5) Elevated temperature—104 to 122°F.
(6) Chemical oxidant—2 pounds of $NaClO_3$ per ton.
(7) Addition of glue to the leaching circuit to increase pulp viscosity.

Acid consumption by the ore minerals under the above conditions ranges from 20 to 40 lb/ton of ore, but the acid requirement is about 100 lb/ton to maintain free acid concentration during leaching. To reduce acid consumption, part of the strongly acidic pregnant solution is recycled to the leaching circuit. (How this is accomplished is illustrated in Fig. 6–15.) Otherwise, most of the free acid in the leached pulp would have to be neu-

---

* A more detailed discussion of Blind River milling practice is given in Section 11–2.

tralized by agitation with lime before making the liquid-solids separation, and lime consumption would be high, since the liquor at the end of the leach contains about 50 grams of free H_2SO_4 per liter. Disk filters are used to recover solution for recycle.

Crushing and grinding the abrasive quartz conglomerate introduces about 4 pounds of metallic iron per ton of ore to the leach feed. Classifier overflow is thickened in 2-tray, 3-compartment thickeners and filtered on disk filters before leaching. The reason for filtration here is to maintain high solids in the agitators and allow for recycle of strongly acidic solution. The sodium chlorate is added to the second agitator of the series to prevent consumption of the oxidant by direct reaction with metallic iron; it is dissolved in water before it is fed into the leaching circuit. Agitation is in 32 by 30-ft Dorr agitators. It was found necessary to increase the speed of the agitators and to triple the recommended air flow to maintain agitation.

At Pronto the recovery of solution from the partially neutralized pulp was initially accomplished by two stages of rotary drum filtration, using water for washing and repulping between stages. Soluble losses were high, and a washing thickener was installed ahead of the filters. All the filtrates are combined for ion-exchange feed. About 1.75 tons of pregnant solution is produced per ton of ore treated.

Algom-Nordic uses one stage of thickening and two stages of filtration to recover dissolved uranium. Filtrate from both stages is returned to the thickener from which the unclarified pregnant solution is obtained. Residues at Consolidated Dennison are also washed by drum filters after a preliminary stage of washing in thickeners. The filters are of the Fraser and Chalmers design developed in South Africa. They differ from the ordinary drum in that the division strips between panels are angled up and down across the face of the drum rather than being straight and horizontal. This allows the filtrate to flow to a suction port at the vertex of a triangle whether the panel motion is upward or downward. The blowback of solution with cake discharge is thereby greatly reduced.

Five stages of continuous countercurrent decantation (CCD) are employed at Algom-Quirke to recover uranium-pregnant solution. The tanks are in the open and are not covered. Pregnant solution volume is about 1.75 tons per ton of ore. Although fine grinding is employed, the pulps are granular, and thickener rakes frequently stick. Since the rakes can be freed only by sluicing out the tank, there have been difficult problems, especially in winter.

The Blind River plants use precoated vacuum leaf filters for clarification, and ion-exchange columns to recover uranium. A detailed description of their operation is given in Section 11–2.

6–4.2 South Africa.* In South Africa [2,4,18], the uranium leaching plants treat ores that have already been leached for gold with cyanide solutions. Both current cyanide residues and reclaimed tailings are treated. The grinding for liberation of gold is considered to be more than ample for uranium leaching. The material enters the acid plant as a thick slurry carrying a small amount of soluble cyanide compounds in solution. Certain reduced sulfur compounds, such as tetrathionate, are also encountered in the uranium leach liquors, presumably as a result of the oxidation of pyrite before treatment with acid. At any rate, it was found beneficial to filter and wash the ore before leaching with acid. This is the primary filtration step indicated at the top of Fig. 6–16. The filtrates from the primary filter contain some gold and are returned to the gold plant.

The washed cyanide residue is repulped to 60 percent solids with filtrate from the last-stage (tertiary) filters and leached in 22.5 by 45-ft Pachucas with sulfuric acid and manganese dioxide. Two stages of rotary drum filtration (secondary and tertiary) are used to recover the uranium solution. A customary water balance, as indicated in Fig. 6–16, produces about 0.75 ton of pregnant solution per ton of ore. Column ion exchange is used to recover the uranium from solution. The tertiary filtrate is split between the primary repulpers ahead of leaching and the washing sprays on the secondary drum filters. Plants in other areas treating higher grade materials include the filtrate from the last stage of washing as part of the pregnant to reduce loss of dissolved uranium.

General practice in the continuous leaching circuits is to add all required acid to the first leaching tank and to add most of the manganese dioxide to the second and third. Reagent consumption per ton of ore averages about 50 pounds of sulfuric acid and 10 pounds of manganese dioxide.

The source of manganese dioxide is low-grade (40 percent MnO_2) pyrolusite ore from the Union of South Africa. This is delivered as minus one-inch material which is ground to 75 percent minus-200 mesh, thickened, and pumped to storage tanks from which it is fed as a thick slurry to the leaching circuit. This oxidant is cheap enough that manganese recovery circuits built at many plants are not being operated.

Control of oxidant is by determination of ferric and ferrous iron, with more than half the total iron held in the ferric state to the end of the leach. Acidity is controlled by titration for "free" acid rather than by pH measurement. Glue for flocculation is added to the transfer sumps just before pumping to the filters.

Heating to the temperature range 40 to 50°C (104 to 122°F) during leaching improves the extraction of uranium from most South African

---

* A more detailed discussion of South African milling practice is given in Section 11–2.

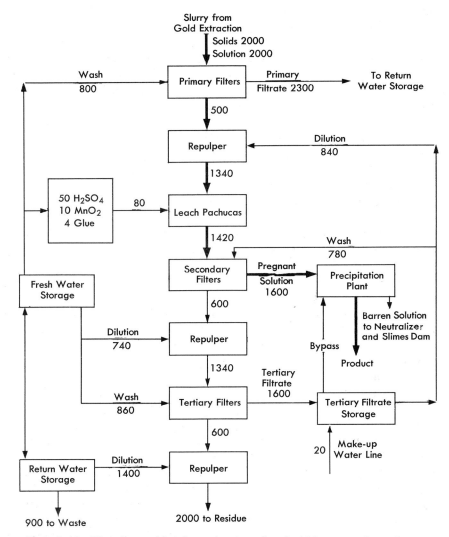

FIG. 6–16. Flowsheet of leach section in a South African uranium plant.

ores, and its cost is justified on some of the higher grade materials. At Vaal Reefs, live steam is used at the rate of 18,000 lb/hr at 150 psi in treating 100 tons of dry solids per hour.

Lime is employed at several points in the uranium milling plants, e.g., for (1) neutralization of eluate to precipitate iron and sulfate ahead of uranium, (2) neutralization of waste solutions, and (3) pH control for flotation of pyrite for sulfuric acid manufacture. Local industry supplies lump lime (to 2 inches in bulk), which is ground in a closed circuit and pumped as a slurry (about 20 percent solids) to various storage tanks.

Most sulfuric acid used for uranium recovery is made from pyrite recovered by flotation from acid-leached residues. Forty percent sulfur concentrates are produced (sometimes from a feed of less than 1 percent) and are fed as a wet slurry to the Fluosolids reactors for burning to sulfur dioxide and iron oxides. The sulfur dioxide is converted by the contact process.

Ammonium nitrate and nitric acid are used to elute the uranium from the ion-exchange columns. In the two-stage precipitation technique, lime is used to destroy most of the free acid and to reduce the sulfate in the eluate to 10 to 15 g/liter. Ammonia is used for the final pH adjustment to bring down the iron cake and to precipitate uranium from the resulting filtrate. Nitric acid is employed to replenish the nitrate and the acid in the uranium-barren eluate before reuse as fresh eluant. The iron precipitate from the first precipitation stage is returned to the head of the leaching circuit. A troublesome buildup of ferric iron is not encountered, since only a small proportion of the total iron in the leach liquor is taken up by the resin.

The final yellow cake is thickened and filtered on candle-type vacuum filters. Centrifuges are also employed in a number of plants for this purpose. The product from all the leaching plants is shipped as a thick slurry to a central plant for sampling and drying.

6–4.3 Bancroft area, Ontario. Two mills operating in the Bancroft district in Halliburton and Hastings Counties, Ontario, produce uranium from pegmatitelike ore [27,28]. These mills are owned by Bicroft Uranium Mines, Ltd. and Faraday Uranium Mines, Ltd. Each mill has a capacity of from 1000 to 1200 tons a day. The highly siliceous ores contain about 0.1 percent U_3O_8 in the form of uraninite and uranothorite. The mills, designed by Kilborn Engineering, Toronto, are almost identical except for the washing circuits. A flowsheet of the Bicroft mill is shown in Fig. 6–17.

At both installations, ore is ground to about 55 percent minus-200 mesh. The classifier overflow is thickened to 55 to 58 percent solids in double compartment tray thickeners and is leached in a series of Pachucas with sulfuric acid and sodium chlorate.

The Pachucas are 18 by 45-ft wood-stave tanks with 12-ft conical bottoms and 1 by 12-ft polyvinyl chloride center lift columns. Air requirement per tank is 200 ft^3/min at 40 psig. Total leaching time is approximately 40 hours at 28°C (82°F) and a constant pH of 1.8. Reagent consumption is approximately 90 pounds of sulfuric acid and 1.5 to 2 pounds of sodium chlorate per ton. The low sodium chlorate consumption is due to the low metallic iron content of the feed, as a result of pebble mill grinding.

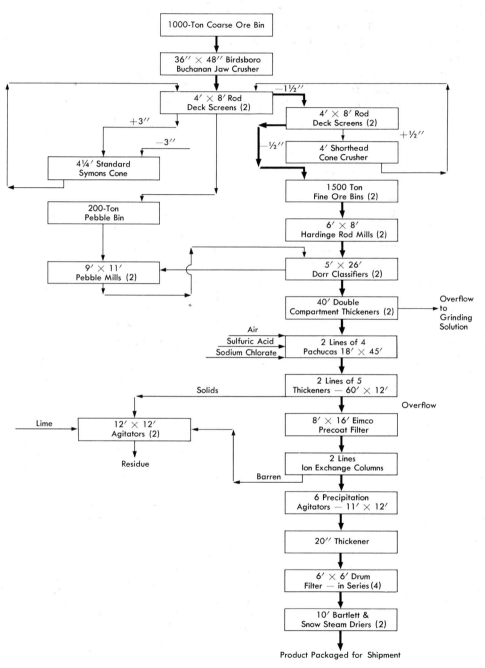

Fɪɢ. 6–17. Flowsheet of Bicroft Uranium Mines, Ltd.

At the Bicroft mill, five stages of CCD in two parallel circuits of 60 by 12-ft wooden thickeners are used for solution recovery. The Faraday mill employs two stages of filtration with string discharge drum filters in two parallel circuits. Both mills use a mixture of guar gum or glue and a synthetic polymer for flocculation. The volume of pregnant solution is 1.75 to 1.8 tons/ton of feed and is clarified with precoat drum filters.

Both plants employ ion-exchange columns to recover uranium. At Bicroft, two sets of four 8 by 16-ft columns are used, and Faraday employs one set of four 9 by 16-ft columns, the largest in use in the uranium industry. Elution is with a solution of salt and sulfuric acid, followed by single-stage precipitation with magnesia. At Faraday, the yellow cake is filtered and washed in plate-and-frame presses; four stages of drum filtration are used at Bicroft. In both plants the yellow cake is dried in steam-heated Bartlett-Snow driers.

6–4.4 South Australia. Uranium production in South Australia is of particular interest in that gravity concentration and flotation are employed prior to acid leaching for recovery of uranium. In addition, the uranium mineral is refractory, requiring drastic chemical treatment to dissolve it.

At Radium Hill a concentrate containing about 1 percent U_3O_8 is produced by heavy media separation and flotation. This concentrate is shipped to Port Pirie for chemical treatment.

The flowsheet employed at Port Pirie is shown in Fig. 6–18. The concentrates, which are minus-100 mesh, are fed to a mixing tank or repulper. The concentrates are treated in lots of 10 tons. Each batch is mixed with 1250 imperial gallons of dechloridized water, produced by ion exchange, and the pulp is pumped into one of six mechanically agitated digesters. The digesters are of the vertical type, with domed covers and a shallow cone bottom. The construction is mild steel, clad with lead or stainless steel, followed by a course of acid-proof brick for erosion protection. Submerged stainless steel steam coils supply heat. Seven hundred and fifty pounds of acid per ton of concentrate are added to the digesters, and the pulps are digested for 10 to 12 hours at or near the boiling point, which, because of the high concentration of dissolved salts, ranges up to 230°F at atmospheric pressure.

During digestion, 90 to 95 percent of the uranium is solubilized. The thick, viscous pulp is then discharged by gravity to a dilution tank containing overflow from the CCD circuit. Lime amounting to about 115 lb/ton is then added to adjust the pH, and the diluted pulp is pumped to the first of a four-stage CCD circuit consisting of two 100-ft and two 80-ft-diameter rubber-lined steel thickeners. Glue is used to flocculate the pulps. Pregnant solution from the first thickener is clarified with a pre-

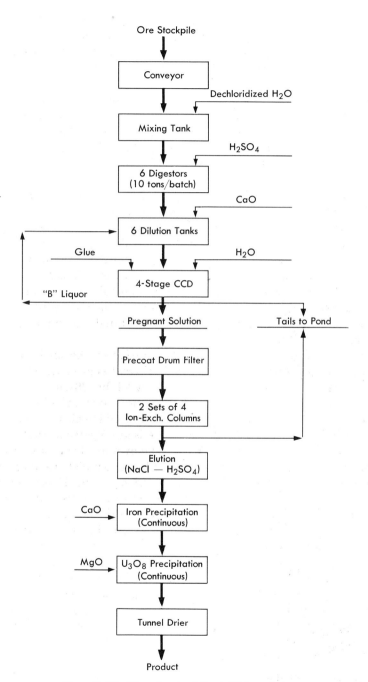

Fɪɢ. 6–18. Flowsheet of Port Pirie refinery.

coat drum filter and is pumped through ion-exchange columns. A four-column automatic system, employing British Permutit Deacidite F. F. resin, is used. Three columns are used on exhaustion while the fourth is being eluted. Operation on loading is to break-through on the second column.

Uranium is eluted with one-molar sodium chloride acidified with sulfuric acid. The 50–50 split elution technique is used, and the pregnant eluates are precipitated continuously in two stages using lime (for precipitation of iron) and magnesia (for precipitation of uranium). The final product is dried in a steam-heated tunnel of local design.

6–4.5 Uranium Reduction Company, Moab, Utah.*

The Uranium Reduction Mill at Moab, Utah, treats ores from a number of mines, a majority of which lie in the Big Indian Wash district of Southern Utah. Design capacity of this plant is 1650 tons per day.

The Big Indian Ores are sandstones of intermediate to fairly high lime content. Uraninite is the principal uranium carrier. Vanadium is present in moderate amounts, principally in oxide minerals, and is not being recovered. Extraction of vanadium is not high in the ambient-temperature leach, and that which does dissolve is precipitated and impounded with the leached residue.

The Moab Mill flowsheet, shown in Fig. 6–19, uses the single-stage leach followed by sand-slime separation and RIP treatment of the slimes. The ore is crushed to pass a 1-inch screen by a 24 by 36-inch Traylor jaw crusher and a $5\frac{1}{2}$-ft Symons Shorthead cone. Wet grinding is in two parallel circuits, each containing a 7 by 7-ft ball mill in closed circuit with a 78-inch spiral classifier. Ball mill discharge is at 65 percent solids, and the classifier overflow at 50 percent solids. The overflow from both classifiers is pumped to a blending agitator and split to the parallel leaching circuits.

Leach feed contains about 3 percent plus-28 mesh and 25 percent minus-325 mesh material. The two leaching sections each consist of five 24 by 14-ft tanks equipped with three 30-hp Turbo-Mixers. The impellers are 54 inch-diameter turbines containing six curved blades. Construction is mild steel, neoprene covered (replacements will be covered with gum rubber). Tanks are rubber-lined, with acid-proof brick in the bottom.

All the acid is added to the No. 1 agitators, and enough is used to maintain as nearly as possible a pH of 1.5 in the ion-exchange feed. Measurements of pH for control purposes are made at agitators 1, 3, and 5. A chemical oxidant is necessary, and current practice is to add enough 85 percent manganese dioxide to one of the grinding circuit classifiers to

---

* The Uranium Reduction Company mill is discussed in more detail in Section 11–6.

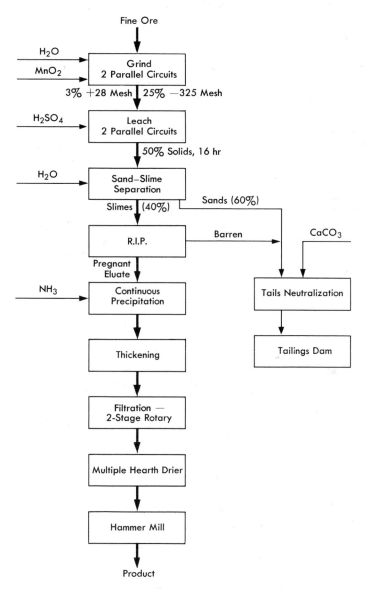

Fig. 6–19. Flowsheet of Uranium Reduction Company, Moab, Utah.

maintain an emf (Pt vs. Standard Calomel Electrode) of −400 mv at No. 5 agitator.

Chemical and mechanical action in the leaching and sand-slime circuits increases the proportion of minus-325 mesh to about 40 percent of the total dry solids in the final residue. Drag classifiers and cyclones prepare the fine slimes for RIP. Particularly noteworthy is the practice of joining cyclone underflows and classifier overflows in cyclone feed sumps rather than returning cyclone underflows to classifiers. Details of this operation are shown in Section 11–6. The specific gravity of the slime feed to RIP is held at about 1.06. The total water used per ton of ore is about 5 tons, of which 4.8 passes through the RIP circuit.

The RIP section consists of two parallel circuits of 14 banks, each bank contains four 6 by 6 by 6-foot baskets. Both circuits are operated with 10 banks on exhaustion and four banks on elution. Each basket contains 35 to 40 cubic feet of coarse-bead (plus-20 mesh) resin. Changeover time is set in accordance with the feed and residue assays of the previous cycle and the flow rate. In other words, changeover is based on a given uranium throughput.

Elution is essentially batchwise, with an eluate volume of 4 to $4\frac{1}{2}$ times the wet settled resin volume going to precipitation. The only reagents for precipitation and eluate makeup are ammonia and nitric acid. Eluate from the resin circuit is pumped to a surge tank ahead of the continuous precipitation circuit.

Continuous precipitation is accomplished at 50°C (122°F) with three tanks in series, and contact times of 20 to 35 minutes in each tank. Enough gaseous ammonia is added to each tank to maintain pH's of 3, 5, and 7. The slurry is thickened and filtered by two stages of rotary filters; repulping between stages is with water. The thickener overflow is clarified in a plate-and-frame press, and nitric acid is added for makeup nitrate and acidity. About 2.8 pounds of nitric acid is used per pound of U_3O_8 produced.

The final filter cake is repulped with little or no water and pumped with a Moyno pump at 1.7 to 1.8 specific gravity to the drier. The drier is a multiple-hearth unit 6 feet in diameter, with 6 hearths. Air temperature is held to a maximum of 900°F. A small hammer mill attached to the discharge of the drier discharges directly into the shipping drums.

6–4.6 Climax Uranium Company. The Climax Uranium Company's mill at Grand Junction, Colorado, produces both uranium and vanadium. Compared with the straightforward aqueous leaching and solution recovery methods that have proved to be most economical for uranium recovery, the processing steps indicated in the Climax flowsheet (Fig. 6–20)

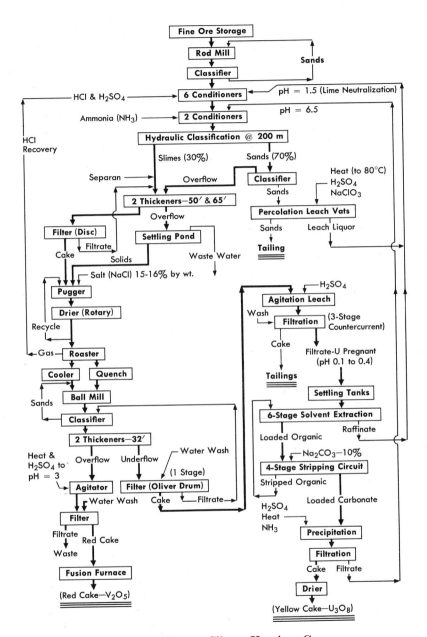

Fig. 6–20. Flowsheet of Climax Uranium Company.

become quite complicated when both uranium and vanadium are recovered.

The ore is ground in a rod mill and treated first with acid to destroy the
carbonates. The acid conditioning utilizes HCl scrubbed from the salt
roaster gases, raffinate from the solvent extraction step, and pregnant sulfuric acid liquor from the sand percolation leach. Part of the calcium occurring as carbonate in the ore is converted to the soluble chloride and the
remainder to calcium sulfate. Neither interferes with the conversion of the
vanadium to the soluble sodium vanadate in the subsequent salt-roasting
operation. Undecomposed calcium carbonate in the salt-roaster feed
would interfere with vanadium recovery. The acid slurry is neutralized
to precipitate uranium and vanadium compounds, and the solids are
classified at 200 mesh into sands and slimes. The sands are leached by
percolation in filter-bottom tanks with hot (to 170°F) solutions of sulfuric
acid and sodium chlorate.

The slimes, consisting of chemical precipitates as well as ore particles,
are thickened, filtered, mixed with salt, dried, and roasted. The thickener
overflow generally carries an appreciable amount of valuable metals as
chemical precipitate, and these are recovered by impounding in shallow
ponds where the slimes are settled and sufficiently dried that they can be
fed back to the slimes stream ahead of the roaster. The salt-roasted
slimes are leached with water to extract sodium vanadate. The vanadium
leaching circuit consists of a ball mill and classifier in a closed circuit, followed by thickening and one stage of filtration. The thickener overflow
constitutes the pregnant vanadium solution, which is heated, acidified to
pH 3, and oxidized to precipitate the vanadium as the polyvanadate or
"red cake." When red-cake production is properly carried out, the resulting product is a coarse crystalline material that can be readily drained
and washed in filter-bottom tanks. The filtrate is rejected as waste, and
the washed red cake is fused and marketed as a high-grade V_2O_5 product.

After the salt-roasted material has been water-leached for vanadium, it
is leached for uranium by agitation with dilute sulfuric acid, and the pregnant solution is recovered by three countercurrent stages of rotary filtration. The pregnant solution is highly oxidized and quite strongly acidic
(pH 0.1 to 0.4). The U_3O_8 content ranges from 7 to 10 g/liter. The vanadium assay is comparable to the uranium assay and the total salt content
of the liquor is quite high, with sulfates approximating 100 g/liter.

Originally, the Climax Mill employed the uranous phosphate method of
precipitation of uranium recovery. This method utilized iron turnings for
reduction and orthophosphoric acid for the required phosphate addition.
Conversion to solvent extraction as a uranium recovery procedure has
eliminated several troublesome processing steps. Solvent extraction is
accomplished in six stages of mixer-settlers with 0.07 to 0.08-molar EHPA

(di-2-ethylhexyl phosphoric acid) plus 0.07 to 0.08-molar TBP (tributyl phosphate) in kerosene. Uranium loading in the organic is about 4 grams of U_3O_8 per liter in extracting over 99 percent from the pregnant solution. The free acid in the uranium barren raffinate is utilized in the "lime kill" step at the start of the ore treatment operations.

Stripping is accomplished with 10 percent Na_2CO_3. The pregnant carbonate solution is acidified with H_2SO_4 and heated to drive off CO_2. Gaseous ammonia is then added to precipitate the uranium "yellow cake," which is filtered in plate-and-frame presses.

References

1. L. TAVERNER, An Historical Review of the Events and Developments Culminating in the Construction of Plants for the Recovery of Uranium from Gold Ore Residues, *J. S. African Inst. Mining Met.* 57(4), **125** (1956).

2. A. M. GAUDIN et al., Development of the Extraction Process for Uranium from South African Gold Uranium Ores, *J. S. African Inst. Mining Met.* 57(5), **287** (1956).

3. C. S. McLEAN and T. K. PRENTICE, The South African Uranium Industry, in *Proceedings of the International Conference on the Peaceful Uses of Atomic Energy*, Vol. 8. New York: United Nations, 1955. (P/997, p. 100)

4. P. A. LAXEN and M. G. ATMORE, The Development of the Acid Leaching Process for the Extraction and Recovery of Uranium from Rand Cyanide Residues, *J. S. African Inst. Mining Met.* 57(6), **359** (1957).

5. A. THUNAES et al., Development of the Port Radium Leaching Process for the Recovery of Uranium, *Can. Dept. Mines and Tech. Surveys*, Paper 13 (1955).

6. A. M. GAUDIN and R. SCHUHMANN, *Process for Extracting Uranium from Its Ores*, U. S. Patent 2,736,634 (Feb. 28, 1956).

7. A. M. GAUDIN, *Recovery of Uranium from Gold Ore Leached Residues*, U. S. Patent 2,737,438 (Mar. 6, 1956).

8. R. D. MACDONALD, The Extractive Metallurgy of Uranium, *Chem. Eng. Prog. Symposium Series 50(11)*, **69** (1954).

9. A. THUNAES, Recovery of Uranium from Canadian Ores, *Trans. Can. Inst. Mining Met.* **57,** 60 (1954).

10. A. M. GAUDIN, Principles and New Developments in Uranium Leaching, in *Proceedings of the International Conference on the Peaceful Uses of Atomic Energy*, Vol. 8. New York: United Nations, 1955. (P/529, p. 8)

11. A. THUNAES, Canadian Practice in Ore Dressing and Extractive Metallurgy of Uranium, in *Proceedings of the International Conference on the Peaceful Uses of Atomic Energy*, Vol. 8. New York: United Nations, 1955. (P/2, p. 81)

12. G. G. MARVIN et al., Recovery of Uranium from Its Ores, in *Proceedings of the International Conference on the Peaceful Uses of Atomic Energy*, Vol. 8. New York: United Nations, 1955. (P/519, p. 3)

13. P. M. J. GRAY, Acid Pressure Leaching of Uranium, in *Proceedings of International Conference on the Peaceful Uses of Atomic Energy*, Vol. 8. New York: United Nations, 1955. (P/986, p. 96)

14. M. D. HASSIALIS and R. C. MUSA, Some Unusual Problems Met in the Recovery of Uranium from a Very Low Grade Ore, in *Proceedings of the International Conference on the Peaceful Uses of Atomic Energy*, Vol. 8. New York: United Nations, 1955. (P/521, p. 13)

15. E. SVENKE, Recovery of Uranium from Uranium Bearing Alum Shale, in *Proceedings of the International Conference on the Peaceful Uses of Atomic Energy*, Vol. 8. New York: United Nations, 1955. (P/784, p. 90)

16. F. J. MAFFEI et al., Chemical Aspects of the Uraniferous Zirconium Ores of Poços de Caldas, Brazil, in *Proceedings of the International Conference on the Peaceful Uses of Atomic Energy*, Vol. 8. New York: United Nations, 1955. (P/134, p. 116)

17. J. TOOHEY and D. KAUFMAN, *The Relationship Between Oxidation Reduction Potential and Valence State of Iron, Vanadium and Uranium in Sulfuric Acid Leach Liquors*, USAEC Report ACCO-60, American Cyanamid Co., July 1954.

18. E. T. PINKNEY, A Review of Uranium Leaching Practice in South Africa, *J. S. African Inst. Mining Met.* **57**(6), 386 (1956).

19. R. H. LIGHT, Milling at Gunnar Mines, *Can. Mining J.* **77**(6), 141 (1956).

20. RADIOACTIVITY DIVISION, MINES BRANCH, OTTAWA, Processing the Blind River Ores, *Can. Mining J.* **77**(6), 145 (1956).

21. P. N. THOMAS, *Studies of the Effects of Various Types of Agitation on the Extraction of Uranium from a Sample of Utex Ore*, USAEC Report WIN-29, National Lead Company, Inc., Dec. 1, 1955.

22. V. F. HARRISON, A Study of the Effect of Different Impeller Speeds on the Extraction of Uranium in 65 Per Cent Solids Acid Leach Pulp, *Can. Dept. Mines and Tech. Surveys, Mines Branch, Spec. Rept.*, SR-332/55 (May 1955).

23. A. STANLEY et al., *Two Stage Leaching Tests on Utex Ore*, USAEC Report ACCO-52, American Cyanamid Co., July 22, 1954.

24. R. J. WOODY et al., *Laboratory Investigation of Dakota Lignites*, USAEC Report WIN-54, National Lead Company, Inc., Apr. 1, 1957.

25. P. GALVANEK, *A Solvent Leaching Process for the Production of High-purity Uranium Products Directly from Low-grade Ores*, USAEC Report WIN-31, National Lead Company, Inc., Dec. 9, 1955.

26. F. FORWARD and J. HALPERN, Acid Pressure Leaching of Uranium Ores, *J. Metals* **7**(3), 463 (1955).

27. J. R. ROACH, Faraday's Milling Plans, *Can. Mining J.* **77**(6), 149 (1956).

28. Bicroft Uranium Mines, *Can. Mining J.* **78**(8), (1957).

CHAPTER 7

CARBONATE LEACHING OF URANIUM ORES*

7-1. INTRODUCTION

Alkaline carbonate leach solutions are frequently used to recover uranium from its ores. The process takes advantage of a very stable complex that exists between uranyl and carbonate ions, i.e., that many uranium minerals will react with carbonate solutions, under proper conditions, to produce the soluble uranyl carbonate complex. Carbonate leaching has been applied to both primary and secondary mineral deposits. It has found particular use with ores of high carbonate content, for which the use of acid leach solutions is costly.

Carbonate leach solutions have several important advantages over acid leach solutions, including noncorrosive properties, and relatively specific solvent ability for uranium and vanadium. Few ore components other than uranium and vanadium minerals and some silicates are attacked by the reagent. Thus, comparatively pure solutions are readily obtained, and the consumption of the reagent by the ore is low. The uranium can be recovered readily from the leach liquors, and the carbonate solutions can be regenerated for further leaching use.

However, there are also limitations to the use of carbonate leaching. Some uranium minerals are not solubilized by carbonate leach solutions, and many uranates that tend to form during the roasting of ores will not dissolve in them. The selective attack of the carbonate leaching agent on the ore components necessitates a much finer grinding of some ores for carbonate leaching than for acid leaching. Such grinding is necessary if the ores are to be opened sufficiently for the uranium mineral to come in contact with the leach solution. In some ores, attack on gangue components by carbonate leach solutions may be serious. Carbonate can be consumed by the following reactions:

$$CaSO_4 + CO_3^= \rightarrow CaCO_3 + SO_4^=,$$

$$SiO_2 + H_2O + 2CO_3^= \rightarrow SiO_3^= + 2HCO_3^-,$$

$$2FeS_2 + 7O_2 + 8CO_3^= + 6H_2O \rightarrow 2Fe(OH)_2 + 4SO_4^= + 8HCO_3^-.$$

---

* By L. A. McClaine, Arthur D. Little, Inc.

153

The attack of carbonate on silica and silicates becomes appreciable only at the higher temperatures that usually exist only when leaching is carried out at pressures greater than atmospheric.

7–2. Chemistry of Carbonate Dissolution

The discussion of the dissolution process can be divided into two sections: (1) the chemical behavior of uranium in carbonate solutions, and (2) the extent and rate of the removal of uranium from ore into leach solution.

7–2.1 Chemistry of uranium in carbonate solution. The uranium species soluble in carbonate leach solutions is the uranyl tricarbonate ion. The formation of this ion by the solubilization of a hexavalent uranium mineral such as carnotite, or a quadrivalent uranium mineral such as uraninite, may be represented by the following reactions:

$$K_2(UO_2)_2(VO_4)_2 \cdot 3H_2O + 6CO_3^= \rightarrow 2K^+ + 2UO_2(CO_3)_3^{-4}$$
$$+ 2VO_3^- + 4OH^- + H_2O,$$

$$2UO_2 + 6CO_3^= + O_2 + 2H_2O \rightarrow 2UO_2(CO_3)_3^{-4} + 4OH^-.$$

These reactions show hydroxyl ion formed in the dissolution. Uranates will precipitate when the hydroxyl ion concentration becomes sufficiently high, according to the reaction

$$2UO_2(CO_3)_3^{-4} + 6OH^- + 2Na^+ \rightarrow Na_2U_2O_7 + 6CO_3^= + 3H_2O.$$

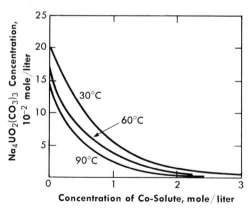

Fig. 7–1. Solubility of $Na_4UO_2(CO_3)_3$ in sodium salt solutions at 30, 60, and 90°C.

Some bicarbonate or other acid cation, therefore, is required in a leach solution, to neutralize this ion and prevent uranate formation. A complex between +4 uranium and carbonate ion exists [1], but it appears to be unstable in hot carbonate solutions and thus to play no part in leaching.

The solubility of sodium uranyl tricarbonate has been investigated by various workers. Bunce et al. [2] measured the solubility of sodium uranyl tricarbonate in sodium bicarbonate, sodium carbonate, and sodium sulfate solutions at 30, 60, and 90°C. They demonstrated that the solubility of sodium uranyl tricarbonate is decreased by an increase in either temperature or ionic strength. Their data are shown in Fig. 7–1. Brown and Schmitt [3] investigated the solubility of sodium uranyl tricarbonate as a function of ionic strength in the solutions of various sodium salts. They found that this solubility at room temperature (26 to 30°C) can be expressed quite well by the equation

$$\log_{10} K_{SP} = 1.25\sqrt{\mu} - 2.2,$$

where μ is the molal ionic strength, $\frac{1}{2}\Sigma(m_i z_i^2)$, and K_{SP} is the molal solubility product of $Na_4UO_2(CO_3)_3$.

The stable uranium complex in hot carbonate solution is that of hexavalent uranium. Thus, if uranium minerals containing quadrivalent uranium are to be solubilized, or if reducing materials exist in the ore or are produced in the leaching operation, an oxidizing agent must be present in the leach solution. The oxidation potentials for UO_2 and U_3O_8 in carbonate solutions have been estimated [1] to be

$$UO_2(s) + 3CO_3^= \rightarrow UO_2(CO_3)_3^{-4} + 2e, \qquad E° = 0.32 \text{ v},$$

$$U_3O_8(s) + 2H_2O + 9CO_3^= \rightarrow 3UO_2(CO_3)_3^{-4} + 4OH^- + 2e,$$
$$E° = 0.35 \text{ v}.$$

On the basis of these potential estimates, oxygen can be used for the oxidation of UO_2 and its dissolution in carbonate leach solutions. The maintenance of sufficiently oxidizing conditions during the leaching operation is extremely important. It has been shown [4] that if aeration is not maintained during the leaching operation, or the solution is not otherwise oxidized, iron picked up during grinding will reduce the uranium and decrease the amount of uranium extracted.

In practice, uranium is recovered most frequently from carbonate solutions by precipitation with sodium hydroxide and the formation of sodium diuranate. Uranium also can be precipitated by neutralizing the carbonate leach solution to a pH of about 6. This procedure decomposes the carbonate solution and thus prevents its reuse. When the uranium is recovered by diuranate precipitation, the carbonate leach solution can be regenerated by adding CO_2 or bicarbonate, and can then be recycled for further leaching use.

Many other methods of recovering uranium from carbonate leach solutions have been investigated. They are primarily based upon reducing uranium and precipitating the lower valent hydroxide. The reduction processes studied include the use of hydrogen [5], the mercury-cathode cell [6], and sodium amalgam [7]. Any vanadium present is removed at the same time as an insoluble hydroxide of +3 vanadium. Procedures have also been investigated for the separate precipitation of vanadium as either lead or iron vanadate [8,9]. The uranium is subsequently recovered by precipitation.

The uranyl tricarbonate anion can be adsorbed by anion-exchange resins [10]. Investigations on a RIP process for carbonate leach systems have been reported [11].* The only processes utilized in practice, however, are caustic-soda precipitation if uranium alone is to be recovered, and neutralization of the carbonate with acid when both vanadium and uranium are to be recovered. After the uranium is precipitated from carbonate leach solutions as a diuranate, in practice the solutions are usually regenerated by being passed through absorption towers countercurrent to CO_2 obtained from boiler-stack gases.

7–2.2 Factors affecting leaching efficiency.

The factors that affect leaching efficiency are divided for discussion into two categories: (1) those related to the structure of the ore, and (2) those related to the rate of extraction of a given uranium mineral.

Structure of the ore. The factors related to the structure of the ore that are of importance to uranium extraction are (a) the uranium minerals present, (b) their dissemination in the ore, and (c) the other minerals associated with uranium.

It is necessary to know the reactivity of the uranium minerals with carbonate leach solution. Only limited information has been reported in the literature. From a chemical standpoint, the uranium minerals have been classified [12] as arsenates, carbonates, molybdates, niobates-tantalates-titanates, oxides, phosphates, silicates, sulfates, and vanadates.† It may be stated generally [13] that the simple and complex arsenate, carbonate, molybdate, phosphate, sulfate, and vanadate minerals of hexavalent uranium are all readily soluble in carbonate solutions. The silicate minerals, however, because of their complex polymeric nature, can be expected to dissolve with difficulty. Their dissolution would be favored by high pH and temperature—conditions that promote the depolymeriza-

---

* See Section 9–4 for descriptions of resin-in-pulp recovery.
  † See Section 4–2.

tion and solubility of silicates. Limited studies on uranophane indicate that it dissolves slowly, and apparently incompletely, in carbonate leach solutions. The presence of oxidants is not beneficial. Coffinite, a basic uranous silicate, has also been studied. With the use of oxidants this mineral can be dissolved in carbonate leach solution.

The simple oxide minerals of hexavalent uranium are readily soluble in carbonate solutions. The quadrivalent oxides and mixed oxides can be dissolved completely only with the use of oxidants. The rate of solution of these reduced oxides in the presence of oxidants appears to be greater for uraninite samples from the Colorado Plateau ores than for uraninite samples from vein deposits in Canada [13]. In view of the known variation in reactivity of the uranium oxides with the method and conditions of their preparation [14], this difference in rate is not surprising. Reactivity can be expected to vary to some extent for each individual ore deposit, and similar differences can be expected for minerals other than the oxides.

No studies have been reported on mineral specimens identified as uranates or on ores reported to contain them. However, the uranates of several metals have been made in the laboratory [13], and many of these fail to dissolve in carbonate leach solution. Sometimes the refractory uranates could be solubilized by adding to the leach solution a reagent that would solubilize the cation; for example, lead uranate was essentially insoluble until ethylenediamine tetraacetic acid was added. This behavior may indicate that an insoluble lead carbonate film has formed on the surface of the compound and retarded its solution. Since uranates generally cannot be directly precipitated from carbonate leach solutions, the failure of the uranates to dissolve may be caused by some such rate-inhibiting factor as an insoluble surface film.

The complex niobates-tantalates-titanates might be expected to be more refractory than silicates in carbonate solutions. These minerals, most frequently found in pegmatite ores, are of little importance at present as a source of uranium, and no experience with the carbonate leaching of them has been reported.

Carbonate solutions attack very few ore components other than the uranium minerals; any uranium surrounded by gangue minerals in the ore will not be leached. If a carbonate leach is used, therefore, the ore must be so ground that the uranium minerals will be available to solution. The grind required varies with the ore. Some of the Colorado Plateau ores, which are sandstones in which the uranium minerals are found with the materials cementing the sand grains, need be ground only to the size of the sand grain. At the opposite extreme are limestone ores, in which the uranium minerals are present as intergrowths and inclusions with calcite and fluorite. In these ores, the finer the grind (even to micron size), the greater the extraction possible [15].

UO_2 and UO_3 react readily at relatively low temperatures with basic oxides and some of their salts to form uranates [14]. Undoubtedly, many of the complex uranium minerals will react in the same manner. Thus, the formation of uranates, which are frequently insoluble or difficult to dissolve in carbonate solution, may account for the resistance of many uranium ores to carbonate leaching after roasting.

With uraninite specimens analyzing 4.5 to 60 percent U_3O_8, it was observed [15] that uranium extractions after roasting at 500°C in air are slightly higher than those before roasting. After such roasting, however, the total extractions obtained with the use of an oxidant are not as great as those obtained from the unroasted ore. After an air roast at 850°C the extractions are very low, and oxidants cannot increase them. The only exceptions to these results were cases in which a large quantity of vanadium was closely associated with the uranium; the roasted minerals were then readily soluble in carbonate solution.* Titrations of acid solutions of the roasted samples indicate that only hexavalent uranium is present. Thus the uraninite reacts during the roast with other components of the ores, probably to form uranates, and to form soluble uranyl vanadates in samples with a high vanadium content. Workers at Battelle Memorial Institute [16] have demonstrated that the use of V_2O_5 during roasting improves the subsequent uranium extraction, and that other acidic oxides, such as P_2O_5, are equally beneficial.

The foregoing comments emphasize the need for considering the chemical nature of the uranium minerals and the associated minerals in processing the ore prior to carbonate leaching.

Rate of extraction. Dissolution of a mineral is a heterogeneous reaction. For such reactions the leaching rate of the minerals is proportional to the mineral surface exposed, which in turn is determined by the grind of the ore and the dissemination of the mineral in the ore.

Very few kinetic studies of uranium minerals or compounds have been made that prove any quantitative relationship between the rate of solution and the variables controlling the rate. Most of the work reported has compared the effect of various oxidants on the extraction, in a given period, from ores containing reduced uranium minerals.

McGlone [17] and Miller [18] have reported studies on the factors controlling the solution of UO_2, UO_3, U_3O_8, copper uranyl phosphate, and pitchblende. In their work they compared the effectiveness on the reduced oxides of the oxidants Na_2O_2, H_2O_2, $(NH_4)_2S_2O_8$, and $Na_2S_2O_8$. In a given period they obtained the greatest extraction by using $Na_2S_2O_8$, and they demonstrated that dissolution increases with temperature.

---

* See Section 5–1.

The temperatures at which the studies were carried out were limited by the decomposition of $Na_2S_2O_8$ above 60°C. They showed that the rate of dissolution for pitchblende increased with an increasing carbonate concentration and with increasing carbonate-bicarbonate ratio, but no quantitative dependency was worked out. The rate of dissolution of UO_3 increased with a decreasing carbonate-bicarbonate ratio, an effect opposite to that observed for pitchblende.

Some work on the leaching of ores in open and pressurized vessels, with air or $KMnO_4$ as the oxidants, has been carried out at the Canadian Bureau of Mines [19]. A great number of oxidants, including Na_2O_2, $KClO_3$, $CaCl(ClO)$, KNO_3, $NaBO_3$, H_2O_2, $K_2Cr_2O_7$, and $KMnO_4$, were compared. It was concluded that $KMnO_4$ was the most effective oxidant, possibly because the MnO_2 formed in the reaction may affect the over-all leaching rate in a catalytic manner. Details of the studies on atmospheric and pressure leaching are not available. Apparently, quantitative relationships between the rate of solution and the variables concerned were not derived.

Some work has been carried out at the Raw Materials Development Laboratory, Winchester, Massachusetts, on the leaching of specific ores and the variables affecting extractions from them [22]. The work, conducted on Rand cyanide ore residues, compared the effectiveness of several oxidants: $Ca(ClO)_2$, $CaCl(ClO)$, Cl_2, $K_2S_2O_8$, $K_2Cr_2O_7$, and $KMnO_4$. $KMnO_4$ proved most effective, and the $KMnO_4$ oxidation process was studied in more detail. At low $KMnO_4$ concentration, temperatures greater than 100°C (provided by pressure leaching) gave a higher leaching rate. However, if the $KMnO_4$ concentration was increased threefold, no appreciable increase in leaching rate was observed at temperatures higher than 95°C.

One of the quantitative kinetic studies reported in the literature was carried out at the University of British Columbia by Forward et al. [5] on the air oxidation of pitchblende. Their studies may be summarized by the expression

$$\text{Rate} = \alpha A[O_2]^{1/2} e^{-12,300/1.987T},$$

where α is a proportionality constant, A is the area of ore surface exposed, and $[O_2]$ is the partial pressure of oxygen. They concluded that varying the carbonate concentration or the carbonate-bicarbonate ratio had no direct effect on the rate of solution of the pitchblende (these conclusions do not agree with those of the British). Forward et al. state that for best results leaching should be carried out at between 80 and 115°C with an oxygen partial pressure of 1 to 2 atmospheres. They feel that the optimum reagent concentration is 50 g/liter of sodium carbonate, plus some bicarbonate. In their studies on ores they found that an adequate rate was obtained by a grind of 70 percent minus-200 mesh, and that the rate was increased by finer grinding. The leaching process required a closed system at superatmospheric pressure.

Workers at the University of Utah have reported [20] kinetic studies on the dissolution of UO_2 in carbonate solutions. Their studies were made in a temperature range of 125 to 200°C and at oxygen pressures up to 800 psi. They report that the rate may be represented by

$$\text{Rate} = \frac{A[O_2]^{1/2}}{1 + B[O_2]^{1/2}},$$

where A and B are constants. They found that a maximum existed in the curves for the rate versus the ratio of carbonate to bicarbonate, and that the height of the maxima decreased with lower temperatures. They pointed out that at sufficiently low temperatures the rate may appear to be independent of the carbonate concentration or the carbonate-bicarbonate ratio, as Forward et al. had observed in their work on pitchblende. They concluded that the dissolution of UO_2 in carbonate solutions involves a process of competitive adsorption between oxygen and undissociated H_2CO_3, and they presented a possible sequence of reactions for the dissolution.

More recently, Schortmann and DeSesa [21] have examined the kinetics of the dissolution of powdered UO_2 samples in sodium carbonate-sodium bicarbonate solutions. They propose a mechanism consisting essentially of two consecutive reactions at steady state: the oxidation of U^{+4} to U^{+6}, and the subsequent formation of uranyl dicarbonate by reaction of the hexavalent uranium oxide with either the carbonate or bicarbonate ions. It is postulated that the rate of oxidation is governed by the rate of dissociation of adsorbed oxygen, and that uranyl dicarbonate converts to uranyl tricarbonate very rapidly. A rate expression for this mechanism was derived and shown to be consistent with experimental information obtained at temperatures of 60 to 100°C and oxygen pressures of 0.5 to 13.5 atm:

$$\frac{d(\text{UTC})}{dt} = \frac{k_1 k_2 K (S_T/L) P_{O_2}{}^{1/2} C_r^2 e^{-E_{a1}/RT} e^{-E_{a2}/RT}}{k_1 P_{O_2}{}^{1/2} e^{-E_{a1}/RT} + k_2 C_r^2 e^{-E_{a2}/RT}},$$

where (UTC) = concentration of uranyl tricarbonate ion, t = time, k_1 = rate constant for oxidation, k_2 = rate constant for dicarbonate formation, K = constant stating weight of UTC produced from a unit of UO_2 surface area, S_T = total surface area, L = volume of solution, P_{O_2} = oxygen partial pressure, C_r = total reagent molar concentration,

E_{a1} = activation energy for the oxidation = 13 kcal/mole, E_{a2} = activation energy for the dicarbonate formation = 14 kcal/mole, R = gas constant, and T = absolute temperature.

Workers at Arthur D. Little, Inc. [23] attempted to find a catalyst for the oxidation of reduced uranium compounds by oxygen. It was thought that the use of atmospheric air oxidation in the presence of catalysts might prove more economical than the use of large quantities of $KMnO_4$ in atmospheric leaching, or the use of pressure equipment to obtain the temperatures and the oxygen partial pressure necessary for reasonable rates of oxidation with oxygen. It was found that the addition of thallous nitrate, cobaltous chloride, cuprous oxide, or manganous sulfate increased the rate of oxidation by air, and that the most effective catalyst for increasing the rate appeared to be copper. Copper salts at 25 milligrams of copper per liter (especially in the presence of ammonium ion) increased the rate of air oxidation by factors ranging up to about 10 for U_3O_8 and about 3 for UO_2. When used on various ores (at an ore pulp density equivalent to a concentration of 1 g/liter of U_3O_8), copper plus aeration proved substantially superior to aeration alone for two ores and of no advantage for two others. Copper ion in the presence of ammonia plus aeration was superior to copper plus aeration in all cases, and appeared equal to or better than the use of $KMnO_4$ plus aeration. Copper salts also appeared to catalyze the hypochlorite oxidation of reduced uranium compounds.

The use of copper and ammonia plus aeration has recently been again recommended [24] as an efficient and economical means of providing oxidant during carbonate leaching. On the basis of this new laboratory demonstration of the copper-ammonia catalysis for air oxidation, pilot-plant tests were conducted at the AEC Raw Materials Pilot Plant in Grand Junction, Colorado.

The results obtained from parallel leach tests on La Sal ore from Monticello, Utah, illustrated the superiority of this system of oxidation. The following 24-hour-average residue analyses were obtained: air alone, 0.037 percent U_3O_8; air plus 7.5 pounds $KMnO_4$ per ton, 0.028 percent U_3O_8; and air plus 4.0 pounds $CuSO_4 \cdot 5H_2O$ and 6.5 pounds NH_3 per ton, 0.015 percent U_3O_8. Based on a 24-hour residence time, the addition of copper and ammonia when compared with air alone recovered an additional 0.44 pounds of U_3O_8 per ton of ore at a reagent cost of $0.85 per ton. At a price of $8.00/lb of U_3O_8 the net value gained would be $2.67 per ton. The use of 7.5 pounds of $KMnO_4$ per ton, when compared with air alone, recovered only 0.18 pound of U_3O_8 per ton at a reagent cost of $1.95, which actually amounted to a loss of $0.51 per ton. (These cost figures are based on $CuSO_4 \cdot 5H_2O$ at $261, NH_3 at $102, and $KMnO_4$ at $520 per ton.)

After the pilot plant had demonstrated the practicality of the use of copper and ammonia in the catalysis of air oxidation, this system was adopted at the AEC Monticello mill early in December of 1957. During the first five weeks that copper and ammonia were used in place of permanganate, a steady increase in carbonate plant recoveries from 86 to 91 percent was obtained, and during this time copper usage was decreased from 3 to 2 pounds per ton and ammonia from 5 to 3.3 pounds per ton of ore. The reagent cost for oxidation was $1.75 to $3.50 per ton when permanganate was used; now higher extractions are obtained for $0.40 to $0.60 per ton of ore.

Summary. The following conditions are necessary to obtain maximum uranium extractions from ores by carbonate leaching:

(1) The uranium mineral must be soluble in carbonate solution or through the addition of oxidants.

(2) Sufficient bicarbonate must be maintained in the leach solution to counteract the formation of hydroxide in the leaching operation.

(3) Oxidants must be added when substances present in the ore or introduced during processing would reduce the uranium (present in solution as a uranyl tricarbonate complex) to an insoluble uranous oxide.

(4) Roasting operations in which uranates or other uranium compounds insoluble in carbonate leach solution will be formed should be avoided.

(5) The ore must be ground finely enough to make the uranium accessible to the carbonate leach.

If oxidation is required to solubilize the uranium mineral or to overcome reducing agents present in the leaching operation, many different oxidants can be used.

7–3. Methods of Dissolution

This section will present typical flow sheets for carbonate leaching and discuss variations that have been proposed.

7–3.1 Salt-roast carbonate leach on high-vanadium carnotite ores [25]. A flowsheet for the salt-roasting process operated at the Monticello, Utah, mill of the U. S. Atomic Energy Commission is given in Fig. 7–2.* In the Monticello salt-roast process, the minus-10 mesh ore, with 6 to 9 percent sodium chloride and sufficient V_2O_5 to maintain a 10:1 V_2O_5-U_3O_8 ratio,

---

* See Article 5–1.2 for further discussion of salt roasting. The salt-roast process is no longer employed at Monticello; the plant has been converted to a raw-ore carbonate leaching process.

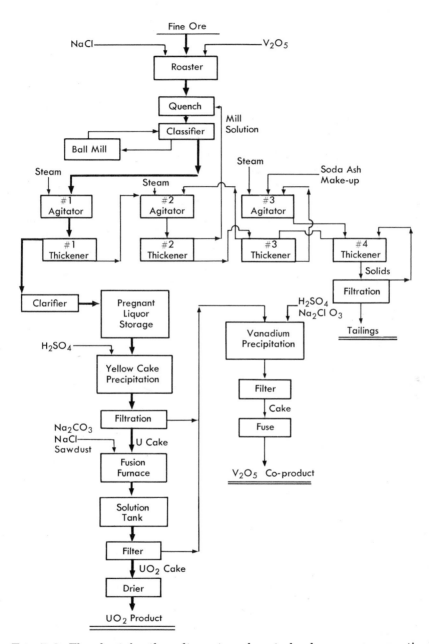

FIG. 7–2. Flowsheet for the salt-roast, carbonate leach process as practiced at the U. S. Atomic Energy Commission mill at Monticello, Utah, until early 1955.

was fed to the roaster. The roaster operated at a maximum temperature of 1562°F, and the ore was retained for 55 minutes at a temperature ranging from 1500 to 1550°F. As it left the roaster, the ore was quenched in a stream of 3 to 5 percent sodium carbonate solution. The resulting slurry was given a light grind in the ball mill to about 60 percent minus-100 mesh, to free the natural sand grains from cementing material. The ball mill operated in a closed circuit with a classifier. The classifier overflow was maintained at 30 percent solids, and went to three agitator tanks operating at about 170°F. The slurry underwent a liquid-solids separation step involving a four-stage countercurrent decantation in thickeners with intermediate agitation and·heating, followed by a final filtration step. The carbonate leach solution remained in contact with the sands for 8 to 9 hours, when the pregnant liquor went to the clarification and precipitation steps. In the precipitation step, the uranium was precipitated as a yellow cake (artificial carnotite) by the adjustment of the pH of the solution to 6, with sulfuric acid. The yellow cake was then filtered out in plate-and-frame presses, was refined further by fusion with sodium carbonate, salt, and sawdust to form UO_2 and water-soluble vanadium, which was removed by leaching. The uranium-free liquor was treated for vanadium recovery by adjusting the pH with sulfuric acid to a value of 2.5. At this point the vanadium precipitated as red cake (V_2O_5), which was filtered out and fused to give the final product, a black V_2O_5. In this process there is no opportunity to recycle the carbonate leach solution, since it is destroyed in precipitating the yellow cake. In proposed variations of the process, the carbonate leach solution would be recycled after uranium and vanadium were removed by a reduction process. No such variation has been practiced.

7–3.2 Raw-ore carbonate leach of high-lime ores. The carbonate leach circuits in the Bluewater plant of The Anaconda Company [26–28] were designed to recover uranium from ores with a high limestone content, specifically the Todilto limestone ores, which are from 75 to 80 percent calcium carbonate. The limestone ores contain uranium as the minerals carnotite [$K_2(UO_2)_2(VO_4)_2 \cdot 3H_2O$] and tyuyamunite [$Ca(UO_2)_2(VO_4)_2 \cdot nH_2O$], as well as in the form of the reduced mineral, uraninite. The uranium minerals are found along cracks and fissures, and are sometimes finely dispersed throughout the calcite matrix. Thus fine grinding (to make the uranium mineral accessible) and oxidant (to oxidize any reduced uranium mineral present) is required in the leaching process.

The ore is ground in hot recycle carbonate-bicarbonate solution to 5 percent plus-65 mesh and 69 percent minus-200 mesh in a rod mill in open circuit followed by a ball mill in closed circuit with a cyclone. The ore is leached in either of two circuits consisting of 6 sweep-agitated autoclaves in series. Leaching takes place at 250°F and 30 psig. One pound of $KMnO_4$ per ton of ore is added as oxidant when uraninite is present in the ore. Calcined brucite (MgO) is added to the pulp to adsorb organic matter.

Hot, leached pulp is flashed to atmospheric pressure in airlift agitator tanks from which pumps deliver the pulp batchwise to five 5 by 40-ft Burt pressure filters and continuously to three $11\frac{1}{2}$ by 18-ft vacuum drum filters operating in series. Conventional three-stage washing with recycle filtrate, barren leach solution, and hot water is practiced. Tailings are repulped in water for disposal. "Separan"* solution is added as a flocculant to Burt filter feed, to the pulp feed of No. 1 drum filter, to the repulper of No. 1, and a small amount to the repulper of No. 2 filter.

With the two types of filters almost any ore can be treated. Difficult filtering ores can be forced through the Burt filters, which can also filter pulp too coarse to be picked up on the drum filters.

Insoluble sodium uranate is precipitated from clarified solution in a steam-heated tank by adding NaOH. The sodium uranate is recovered by filtration in a plate-and-frame filter, and the carbonate solution flows through a carbonation tower, with CO_2 flowing countercurrent to the solution. The regenerated leaching solution is returned for further process use. Liquors used in the plant are a mixture of 10 percent sodium carbonate and 1 percent sodium bicarbonate.

7–3.3 Raw-ore leach with sodium carbonate-bicarbonate solutions. A pressure-leaching process utilized at the Beaverlodge property of Eldorado Mining and Refining, Ltd., in Saskatchewan, Canada [29], is discussed in detail in Section 11–2. Briefly, the uranium mineral is principally uraninite, occurring as thin seams and as coatings on other minerals. The ore is ground to 78 percent minus-200 mesh in carbonate solution. In one circuit leaching takes place in horizontal autoclaves, which operate at 230°F and 80 to 90 psi. Each autoclave is equipped with three Turbo-Mixers: the center mixer is used to mix air thoroughly with the pulp and the two end mixers are used to keep the pulp in suspension. The pulp from the autoclaves passes through heat exchangers, so that its heat will be conserved. After thickening and clarification, uranium is precipitated with sodium hydroxide. The barren carbonate solution is carbonated with boiler flue gases in an absorption tower, and is then recirculated to the leaching process.

In recent major expansions of the Beaverlodge mill, the flowsheet has been modified [30].with the installation of a second leach circuit using an atmospheric-pressure leach in Pachuca tanks. The Pachuca tanks are

---

* A synthetic polyacrylamide manufactured by the Dow Chemical Co.

cylinders 18 feet in diameter and 34 feet high, with 18-inch diameter air-lifts in the center to provide for pulp agitation. Air for oxidation is introduced through twenty 1-inch pipes extending vertically from the top of the tank and spaced equally over the tank area. The pulp is heated by steampipes immersed in pulp. Provision is made for recovering heat carried by the Pachuca exit gases.

Leaching is carried out at 55 to 60 percent solids in a solution containing about 30 grams of Na_2CO_3 and 20 grams of $NaHCO_3$ per liter at 170°F. Retention times of 96 to 100 hours are required in the Pachucas to obtain the same uranium extractions that can be obtained in 16 hours in the autoclaves.

In a recent review of this atmospheric-leach process Hannay [30] summarized the desirable features of using Pachuca tanks as follows:

The Pachucas at Beaverlodge have been under test for about one and one-half years and, compared with other leaching methods, some operation features are worthy of mention:

(1) There are no moving parts in the pulp stream.

(2) At pulp densities of 55 to 60 percent solids there is no sanding out of coarse ore fractions.

(3) Very high pulp circulating rates (1000 gal/min) can be maintained by the airlifts without further degradation of the ore particles.

(4) There is less tendency to dissolve silica and sulfur (sulfur is the major consumer of reagents).

7–3.4 Pilot-plant studies on leaching at high temperatures and pressures. Pilot-plant studies at the Grand Junction, Colorado, pilot plant of the Atomic Energy Commission on leaching at high temperatures and pressures have recently been reported [31]. The leaching was carried out in either four 4 by 47-ft Pachuca tanks in series, or a $4\frac{1}{2}$ by 12-ft horizontal autoclave.

Each Pachuca had a 3-inch internal airlift for pulp circulation, two $\frac{1}{4}$-inch pipes in the cone for adding aeration air, and four 1-inch steam-pipes to maintain the desired pulp temperatures (Fig. 7–3). The 45-ft elevation to the discharge level provided a pressure of approximately 30 psig in the bottom of the tank when it was filled with a 50 percent solids pulp. The provision for operating under a pressure of up to 20 psig at the top resulted in a pressure of 50 psig at the bottom.

The horizontal autoclave (Fig. 7–4) was divided into three sections by baffle plates. Pulp entered at one end and discharged at the other after passing through each section. Each section was agitated with a 5-hp turbine-type agitator equipped with a 5-blade 16-inch turbine. Air was added through a $\frac{1}{2}$-inch line discharging beneath each agitator. In the

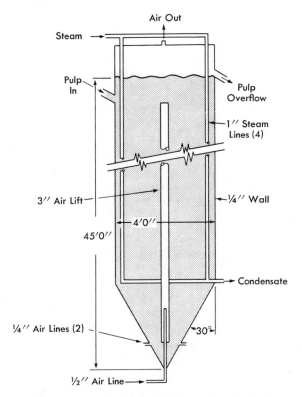

FIG. 7–3. Diagram of Pachuca tank used in U. S. Atomic Energy Commission pilot-plant studies at Grand Junction, Colorado.

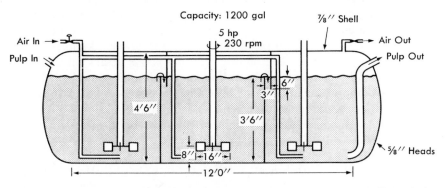

FIG. 7–4. Diagram of autoclave used in U. S. Atomic Energy Commission pilot-plant studies at Grand Junction, Colorado.

studies the autoclave was operated at pressures to 70 psig and temperatures to 275°F.

It was observed that under all variations in pressure and temperature, approximately the same extraction from a given ore was obtained, provided the leach time was long enough. Higher pressures permitted higher temperatures of leaching and resulted in shorter extraction times. The authors have summarized and compared their studies to date as follows:

"To summarize the advantages of pressure leaching over leaching at atmospheric pressure, higher pressures permit operation at higher temperatures, which reduce the leach contact time required and the size of the vessels. It appears that temperature is the major factor as long as oxidation is adequate. When the pressure is increased from atmospheric to 20 psig and the temperature from 180 to 220°F in Pachuca tanks, leach retention times are roughly cut in half. At higher levels, in the range of 50 psig and 250°F and with mechanical agitation in an autoclave, retention time is cut to a tenth or a twentieth of that required at atmospheric pressure. Less air is required for oxidation. Steam and power costs are lower, and space requirements are less. Autoclave pressure leaching is more versatile, permitting a range of operating conditions which best suit the ore.

"Disadvantages of leaching under pressure are the increased cost of building a pressure vessel, somewhat more instrumentation, and the use of more complex mechanical equipment, such as agitator shaft seals for an autoclave. Sodium carbonate consumption may be higher if appreciable amounts of sulfides are present in the ore. The presence of sulfides also may present a corrosion problem which should be considered in the design of the vessel."

7–3.5 Pilot-plant studies on the ammonium carbonate pressure leaching of uranium ores [32].

This process utilizes ammonium carbonate instead of sodium carbonate to leach uranium ores. The chemistry of the extraction process is unchanged. Because of the lower alkalinity of the ammonium carbonate solution, however, there is less attack on silica and silicate minerals, and possibly on alumina. This difference in behavior might prove important in the leaching of some ores.

The ammonium carbonate solution and the uranium-carbonate complex are readily decomposed at atmospheric pressure by heating to 212°F, according to the following reactions:

$$(NH_4)_2CO_3(aq) + heat = 2NH_3(g) + CO_2(g) + H_2O(l),$$

$$(NH_4)_4UO_2(CO_3)_3(aq) + heat = 4NH_3(g) + CO_2(g) + UO_3 \cdot 2H_2O(s).$$

The process takes advantage of this behavior to precipitate the uranium by steam-stripping the pregnant leach solution. The ammonia and carbon dioxide expelled are recovered by absorption and subsequently returned to the leaching system. The fact that the solutions decompose on heating necessitates operation under pressure. Studies have been made up to pressures of 90 psig and temperatures of 250°F.

When this process was evaluated at the AEC Raw Materials Development Laboratory it was found that the ammonium carbonate leach resulted in poorer extractions than were obtained with sodium carbonate on ores in which the uranium was associated with vanadium in the mineral [33].

REFERENCES

1. L. A. McClaine et al., The Carbonate Chemistry of Uranium: Theory and Applications, in *Proceedings of the International Conference on the Peaceful Uses of Atomic Energy*, Vol. 8. New York: United Nations, 1956. (P/525, p. 26)

2. W. E. Bunce et al., *The Solubility of Sodium Uranyl Carbonate in Water and in Solutions of Various Salts*, USAEC Report M-4238, Princeton University, May 1947.

3. K. B. Brown and J. B. Schmitt, *Studies in the Carbonate-Uranium System; Part II. The Solubility of Sodium Uranyl Tricarbonate in Solutions of Certain Sodium Salts*, USAEC Report AECD-3229, Oak Ridge National Laboratory, Oct. 20, 1950.

4. C. J. Hoffman et al., *A Study of the Factors Affecting the Efficiency of Carbonate Leaching*, USAEC Report RMO-2617, Arthur D. Little, Inc., Mar. 31, 1955.

5. F. A. Forward et al., Studies in the Carbonate Leaching of Uranium Ores, *Trans. Can. Inst. Mining Met.* **56**, 344 (1953).

6. J. C. Huggins, *Mercury Cathode Cell Reduction of Carbonate Solutions*, USAEC Report RMO-2618, Arthur D. Little, Inc., March 1955.

7. L. A. McClaine and B. L. Mahan, *A Preliminary Economic Analysis of the Sodium-Amalgam Process*, USAEC Report RMO-2609, The Merrill Company, Nov. 1, 1952.

8. W. E. Clifford and J. C. Huggins, *The Lead Vanadate Precipitation Method for the Recovery of Vanadium from Carbonate Leach Solutions*, USAEC Report RMO-2619, Arthur D. Little, Inc., June 1955.

9. J. Halpern, University of British Columbia, 1952. Unpublished.

10. C. S. Abrams, *Ion-exchange Studies on Carbonate Leach Liquors from Grants, N. M., Ores*, USAEC Report ACCO-8, American Cyanamid Co., Oct. 30, 1951.

11. J. Q. Jones et al., *Alkaline Resin-in-pulp Process for the Recovery of Uranium from Its Ores*, USAEC Report WIN-39, National Lead Co., Inc., Jan. 19, 1956.

12. J. W. FRONDEL and M. FLEISCHER, Glossary of Uranium and Thorium Bearing Minerals, *U. S. Geological Survey Bulletin 1009F*, Washington, D. C.: U. S. Government Printing Office, 1955.

13. W. I. WATSON et al., *Studies on the Chemical Behavior of Uranium Minerals and Compounds*, USAEC Report RMO-2620, Arthur D. Little, Inc., July 1955.

14. J. J. KATZ and W. RABINOWITCH, Eds. *The Chemistry of Uranium*, National Nuclear Energy Series, Division VIII, Volume 5. New York: McGraw-Hill Book Co., Inc., 1951.

15. C. J. HOFFMAN et al., *A Study of the Factors Affecting the Efficiency of Carbonate Leaching*, USAEC Report RMO-2617, Arthur D. Little, Inc., Mar. 31, 1955.

16. A. C. RICHARDSON et al., *The Recovery of Uranium from Carnotite Ores*, USAEC Report BMI-JDS-195, Battelle Memorial Institute, June 30, 1949.

17. PATRICIA McGLONE, *Factors Influencing the Extraction of Uranium from Minerals and Ores; Part II. Studies on the Solutions of Uranium Dioxide in Sodium Carbonate Solution in the Presence of Oxidizing Agents*, Report CRL/AE-59, Gt. Brit. Chemical Research Laboratory, Teddington, April 1950.

18. R. P. MILLER et al., *Factors Influencing the Extraction of Uranium from Minerals and Ores; Part 5. Studies on the Extraction of Uranium from Pitchblende with Sodium Carbonate Solutions in the Presence of Oxidizing Agents*, Report CRL/AE-68, Gt. Brit. Chemical Research Laboratory, Teddington, October 1950.

19. F. T. RABBITTS, Alkaline Carbonate Leaching of Uranium Ores, *Can. Dept. Mines and Tech. Surveys, Mines Branch, Topical Report* No. TR-67/50 (Nov. 13, 1950).

20. R. L. PEARSON and M. E. WADSWORTH, *A Kinetic Study of the Dissolution of UO_2 in Carbonate Solutions*, paper presented at the annual meeting of the American Institute of Mechanical Engineers, New Orleans, February 1957.

21. W. E. SCHORTMANN and M. A. DeSESA, *Kinetics of the Dissolution of Uranium Dioxide in Carbonate-Bicarbonate Solutions*, USAEC Report WIN-89, National Lead Co., Inc., Mar. 12, 1958.

22. E. G. BROWN, *Preliminary Investigation of Carbonate Leaching*, USAEC Report ACCO-36, American Cyanamid Co., Oct. 15, 1953.

23. W. E. CLIFFORD et al., *Catalysis of Air and Hypochlorite Oxidation of Uranium Compounds in Carbonate Leach Slurries*, USAEC Report RMO-2621, Arthur D. Little, Inc., June 1956.

24. P. J. MAGNO and M. A. DeSESA, *Oxidants in Carbonate Leaching of Uraniferous Ores*, USAEC Report WIN-86, National Lead Co., Inc., Aug. 23, 1957.

25. J. A. BUTLER, Utah's New Uranium Mill, *Eng. Mining J.* **152,** No. 3, 56 (March 1951).

26. J. B. HUTTL, New Mexico Uranium, *Eng. Mining J.* **155,** No. 8, 96 (August 1954).

27. E. C. PETERSON and D. C. MATTHEWS, Uranium Milling at the Bluewater Plant, *Mining Congr. J.* **43,** 58–59, 66 (January 1957).

28. G. O. ARGALL, Jr., How Anaconda Recovers U_3O_8 from Sandstone Ore at Bluewater Mill, *Mining World* **18,** 47 (October 1956).

29. R. W. MANCANTELLI and J. R. WOODWARD, The Beaverlodge Hydrometallurgical Plant, *Trans. Am. Inst. Mining Met. Engrs.* **203,** 751 (1955).

30. R. L. HANNAY, Milling at Beaverlodge, *Can. Mining J.* **77,** No. 6, 135 (June 1956).

31. R. G. BEVERLY et al., Atmospheric vs. Pressure Leaching, *Mining Eng.* **9,** 982 (September 1957).

32. B. G. LANGSTON et al., Ammonium Carbonate Pressure Leaching of Uranium Ores, *J. Metals* **9,** 752 (1957).

33. E. T. HOLLIS, *Semi-pilot Operation of the Ammonium Carbonate Leaching Process,* USAEC Report WIN-37, National Lead Co., Inc., Feb. 27, 1956.

CHAPTER 8

LIQUID-SOLIDS SEPARATIONS*

8-1. INTRODUCTION

Separating liquids from solids is a unit operation common to all milling and hydrometallurgical processes. The liquid-solids separation problem may well dictate the choice of the treatment method. Regardless of metallurgy, inability to handle a product at some step in the recovery flowsheet often makes the difference between economic success and failure.

A common liquid-solids separation problem arises in thickening or filtration of leached uranium ore slurry. Since the loss of weight in leaching is usually small, virtually all of the ore must be handled by a multistage process to recover a pregnant solution of suitable uranium content while making a throw-away tailing product. Preroasting the ores and using common flocculating agents such as starches and glues have helped to accelerate the thickening and filtering of some ores, but have shown little benefit for others. A search for better flocculants revealed that certain polysaccharides, such as locust bean gum, guar gum, and cactus extract, were decidedly more powerful than the glues and starches. Intensified industrial interest subsequently led to the development of synthetic polymers better in some ways than the natural products [1].

The introduction of vegetable gums and synthetic polymers as aids in liquid-solids separations was a turning point in uranium ore processing, but ores containing a large proportion of slime materials were heavy consumers of the flocculants. Therefore, to avoid the expense of a liquid-solids separation from slime-laden pulps, ion-exchange procedures [2] were developed to recover the uranium from a slime slurry.

Solids and liquids are separated at one or more points in the flowsheets of all uranium ore processing plants. However, equipment and methods vary even in plants employing the same general process; a multiplicity of types of liquid-solids separations and techniques for performing the operation are used. Since, with few exceptions, thickening and filtering processes call for a flocculating agent, this chapter includes a discussion of the criteria developed in the laboratory for evaluating different flocculants to be used with uranium plant leach pulps. Industrial practice in percolation leaching, sand-slime separations, countercurrent decantation washing in classifiers and thickeners, and filtration are reviewed separately for alkaline and acid systems.

---

* By J. B. Rosenbaum and J. B. Clemmer, U. S. Bureau of Mines.

8–2. Developments in Use of Flocculants

Early in 1953 at the Salt Lake City station of the U. S. Bureau of Mines, research was initiated to find more versatile flocculants than glue and starches, customarily employed for accelerating liquid-solids separations in uranium ore processes. The research was sponsored by the Raw Materials Division of the United States Atomic Energy Commission.

8–2.1 Exploratory screening tests. Several hundred potential flocculants, including inorganic chemicals, gum, glues, starches, and other carbohydrates, as well as synthetic polymers, were tested during the study. The researchers observed the effect of the reagents on the settling rates of carbonate and acid leach slurries for a moderately slimy ore from the Colorado Plateau. The outstandingly effective reagents were found to be locust bean gum, guar gum, pear cactus extract, and a commercially available polyacrylamide.*

To determine the broad ranges of applicability of the more promising reagents, cactus extract, guar gum, and the polyacrylamide were systematically tested on five Colorado Plateau ores with different handling characteristics. Glue was also included in the study because of its use in some segments of the industry. The scope of the study included thickening and filtering tests on pulps from acid leaching the ores at ambient temperature and 90°C, and from sodium carbonate leaching at 90°C. The leaching procedures gave uranium extractions similar to those obtained in commercial practice. The terminal pH after acid leaching was 0.5 to 1.0; alkaline leaching with a solution containing 5 percent Na_2CO_3 and 2 percent $NaHCO_3$ gave a terminal pH of 10.2.

All reagents except the cactus extract were used as 0.5 percent solutions. Guar gum was prepared by slowly sifting the powder into vigorously agitated water of 80°C. After cooling, 1 ml of 37 percent formaldehyde was added per liter of solution as a preservative. The cactus extract was prepared by grinding the prickly pear cactus nodes in a meat chopper and then agitating 100 grams of the pulp in a liter of water for 1 hour. The fibrous material was filtered out and discarded.

Preliminary settling tests were made visually, to determine the quantity of reagent necessary for maximum flocculation of the leach slurry. Then quantitative thickening tests were made with this reagent added. The leach slurry in a 1-liter graduate was diluted to 25 percent solids by adding dilute acid (pH 1.5) or carbonate leach solution. The flocculant was

---

* Dow Chemical Co., "Separan" 2610. Subsequently, several producers have made similar products available: Monsanto Chemical Co., Union Carbide Chemical Co., Rohm & Haas Co., American Cyanamid Co., General Mills, Inc., Stein, Hall & Co., etc.

TABLE 8–1

INFLUENCE OF FLOCCULANTS ON THICKENING AND FILTERING SLICK
ROCK LEACH SLURRIES.

PRELIMINARY SCREENING WITH EXCESS REAGENT

Type of leach	Flocculant		Thickening data		Filtering data	
	Name	Quantity, lb/ton	ft²/ton per day	Terminal density, % solids	Filter time, min	Filter cake, % solids
Cold acid	None	—	12.1	41.3	20.0	71.9
	Cactus	16.7	0.4	59.4	21.0	81.7
	Hide glue	2.0	3.7	41.6	6.0	75.0
	Guar gum	0.5	0.9	59.3	3.7	75.8
	Separan	0.5	0.4	57.4	1.5	76.3
Hot acid	None	—	5.3	44.3	17.5	73.3
	Cactus	7.5	0.4	57.8	6.2	76.2
	Hide glue	1.0	2.6	47.5	7.6	70.1
	Guar gum	1.0	0.7	56.0	2.6	73.7
	Separan	0.5	0.4	53.7	0.8	77.7
Carbonate	None	—	20.8	45.4	6.2	75.0
	Cactus	8.3	0.4	59.8	1.2	75.3
	Hide glue	1.0	6.9	47.8	9.7	79.3
	Guar gum	1.0	0.5	60.2	0.4	76.2
	Separan	0.5	0.3	61.1	0.3	77.1

then added and mixed with the solution by inverting the cylinder three
times. The thickener area was calculated according to the Coe and
Clevenger [3] method from the single-zone settling rate; three-zone settling tests appeared incompatible with the preliminary nature of the
study. After settling at room temperature for 19 hours, the supernatant
liquor was decanted and the thickened pulp was filtered on an 18-cm
Büchner funnel through Reeves-Angel No. 202 paper under a vacuum of
16 to 18 inches of mercury. The time of filtration to a dry top, plus a
75-ml displacement wash, was used as an index of filterability.

With minor variations, all the ores behaved in a similar manner. The
results on Slick Rock, Colorado, ore (given in Table 8–1) illustrate the
typical improvement in thickening and filtering from the use of flocculating agents.

8–2.2 Influence of slurry dilution on effectiveness of flocculants. Flocculation tests were made on both acid and carbonate leach slurries of Slick

TABLE 8–2

EFFECT OF LEACH SLURRY DILUTION ON REAGENT PERFORMANCE

Reagent	Initial density, % solids	Initial settling rate, ft/hr	Terminal density, % solids	Thickener area, ft^2/ton per day	Filtrate, ml/min
Acid slurries					
No reagent	25	0.2	43.4	14.5	55
	33	0.1	47.2	15.1	45
	50	0.1	63.8	6.3	88
0.2 lb guar gum	25	3.9	55.4	0.8	220
	33	1.2	55.7	1.4	110
	50	0.3	65.2	2.3	850
0.4 lb guar gum	25	4.1	54.2	0.7	271
	33	2.3	55.4	0.7	235
	50	1.6	62.0	0.3	1140
0.2 lb Separan	25	2.9	54.8	1.0	142
	33	1.0	54.5	1.6	127
0.4 lb Separan	25	8.4	49.3	0.3	400
	33	3.5	53.6	0.5	244
	50	0.2	61.0	2.5	215
18 lb cactus	25	3.1	51.7	0.9	150
	33	0.2	50.4	7.2	84
36 lb cactus	25	99.0	57.8	<0.1	1400
	33	2.1	55.7	0.9	212
	50	0.3	60.8	2.1	205
Carbonate slurries					
No reagent	25	0.2	47.0	12.0	88
	33	0.1	49.4	10.8	77
	50	0.1	60.7	3.4	133
0.2 lb guar gum	25	10.1	52.3	0.3	244
	33	2.9	53.6	0.5	238
	50	6.4	60.7	0.1	450
0.4 lb guar gum	25	14.9	50.8	0.2	440
	33	5.1	54.8	0.3	390
	50	9.2	59.8	0.1	675

(*continued*)

TABLE 8–2 (*Continued*)

Reagent	Initial density, % solids	Initial settling rate, ft/hr	Terminal density, % solids	Thickener area, ft²/ton per day	Filtrate, ml/min
0.2 lb Separan	25	79.0	59.4	<0.1	650
	33	15.8	56.4	0.1	567
0.4 lb Separan	25	188.0	60.1	<0.1	1300
	50	0.9	64.0	0.6	275
18 lb cactus	24	105.0	62.0	<0.1	1250
	33	22.9	59.3	<0.1	450
36 lb cactus	25	317.0	58.6	<0.1	1350
	33	159.0	58.2	<0.1	1350
	50	12.8	62.0	<0.1	500

Rock ore at 50 percent solids and after dilution to 33 and 25 percent solids to observe the effect of slurry dilution on reagent performance. All leaches were at 50 percent solids for 6 hours on 300-gram charges of ore dry-ground through 65 mesh. Sufficient acid was used in the ambient-temperature leach to give a terminal pH of 0.5 to 1.0. A solution containing 5 percent Na_2CO_3 and 2 percent $NaHCO_3$ was used in carbonate leaching at 90°C.

The leach slurries were transferred to 1-liter graduates and diluted with dilute acid (pH 1.5) or carbonate solution to the desired pulp density. Guar gum and Separan were added as 0.5 percent solutions, and the cactus as a 10 percent solution, based on weight of the original cactus nodes. Thickening and filtering test procedures have already been described.

The data in Table 8–2 show that guar gum was affected only slightly by changes in pulp density, but Separan and cactus extracts were much less effective in thick slurries than in thin ones. Although 0.1 pound of Separan accelerates thickening and filtering of thin acid slurries, 0.4 lb/ton was barely adequate on a thick slurry. Cactus extract behaved similarly, with twice the quantity being required to flocculate a thick slurry. As with acid slurries, larger quantities of Separan and cactus extract were needed to flocculate thick carbonate leach slurries effectively.

A possible explanation for the relative inefficiency of Separan and cactus in thick slurries is that these reagents are adsorbed and firmly bound on the first particles encountered, so that the reagent is not disseminated adequately through the thick pulp. The effect of reagent dilution, which bears on this same problem, is taken up in the following paragraphs.

8–2.3 Effect of reagent dilution on behavior of flocculants. The effect of flocculant dilution on acid and carbonate leach slurries of Slick Rock ore was studied. The customary 0.5 percent solutions of guar gum and Separan, and 10 percent solution of cactus, were diluted to the desired concentration with dilute acid (pH 1.5) or carbonate solution. The diluted flocculant was used for final adjustment of the solids content to 33 and 25 percent. Slurry and reagent were mixed by inverting the graduate three times.

There was no significant difference in the behavior of guar gum over the dilution range investigated. Thickening and filtering rates were about the same with solutions containing 0.5, 0.1, and 0.01 percent of the gum.

Selected data from tests made at 25 percent solids (given in Table 8–3) show that the effectiveness of Separan and cactus extract improved with increasing dilution in both acid and carbonate pulps.

Other tests were made to ascertain whether the use of recycled pregnant solution for diluting the reagent (to eliminate introduction of extraneous water) would have deleterious effects on flocculation. Pregnant solutions from both acid and carbonate leaching proved satisfactory.

8–2.4 Influence of slurry pH on effectiveness of guar gum and Separan. The effect of pH on flocculation with guar gum and Separan was examined by adjusting the pH of acid and carbonate leach slurries with H_2SO_4 or NaOH, as required. The leach slurries were diluted to 33 percent solids with dilute acid (pH 1.5) or carbonate solution before finally adjusting the pH and adding the flocculant as a 0.5 percent solution. The maximum permissible pH for acid slurries was about 3.0, and for carbonate slurries, 10.6, because precipitation occurring at higher pH's vitiated the test data.

Guar gum and Separan proved to be better in alkaline than in acid slurries. Except for this, the results (summarized in Table 8–4) indicate that, within the ranges studied, pH does not markedly influence the performance of the reagents.

8–2.5 Guides for the use of flocculants. The laboratory research, complemented by continuous tests in a small pilot plant, developed a number of criteria for the use of flocculants. The most important are maximum dilution of the flocculant and optimum agitation for mixing to disperse the flocculant throughout the slurry without degrading the floccules. The more pertinent factors governing application of flocculants for accelerating thickening and filtering of uranium pulps are discussed in the following sections.

TABLE 8–3

EFFECT OF REAGENT DILUTION ON PERFORMANCE OF SEPARAN AND CACTUS EXTRACT

Reagent	Reagent solution strength, %	Initial settling rate, ft/hr	Terminal density, % solids	Thickener area, ft²/ton per day	Filtrate, ml/min
Acid slurry					
No reagent		0.2	43.4	14.5	55
0.2 lb Separan	0.5	2.9	54.8	1.0	142
	0.1	1.7	50.8	1.5	220
	0.05	1.6	49.6	1.6	180
	0.01	3.5	50.5	0.8	150
	0.005	19.0	54.5	0.1	925
18 lb cactus	10.0	3.1	51.7	0.9	150
	2.0	8.8	57.9	0.3	258
	1.0	41.0	62.4	<0.1	287
4 lb cactus	0.25	2.2	55.0	1.3	138
9 lb cactus	0.1	23.7	56.4	0.1	235
Carbonate slurry					
No reagent		0.2	47.0	12.0	88
0.2 lb Separan	0.5	79.0	59.4	<0.1	650
	0.1	151.0	60.0	<0.1	1500
	0.05	178.0	60.1	<0.1	1500
	0.01	227.0	59.2	<0.1	1500
18 lb cactus	10.0	105.0	62.0	<0.1	1250
	2.0	240.0	59.2	<0.1	1250
	1.0	200.0	59.5	<0.1	1250
4 lb cactus	0.25	9.8	57.0	0.3	160
9 lb cactus	0.1	97.0	61.0	<0.1	1250

TABLE 8–4

INFLUENCE OF SLURRY pH ON PERFORMANCE OF GUAR GUM AND
SEPARAN

Reagent	Slurry pH	Initial settling rate, ft/hr	Terminal density, % solids	Thickener area, ft^2/ton per day	Filtrate, ml/min
Acid slurries					
No reagent	1.0	0.1	47.2	15.1	45
0.6 lb guar gum	1.0	2.4	51.6	0.6	525
	2.0	5.8	54.0	0.3	900
0.6 lb Separan	1.0	10.7	55.9	0.1	1000
	2.1	8.8	57.7	0.2	725
	2.9	9.9	49.6	0.2	717
Carbonate slurries					
No reagent	10.2	0.1	49.4	10.8	77
0.6 lb guar gum	10.2	12.2	55.4	0.1	583
	9.0	9.4	54.7	0.2	600
	8.0	7.4	53.7	0.2	500
	7.1	9.0	55.3	0.2	172
0.6 lb Separan	10.2	51.2	58.8	<0.1	1400
	9.0	98.6	58.8	<0.1	1400
	8.1	81.5	59.1	<0.1	1400
	6.8	33.5	58.0	<0.1	1400

Reagent storage and preparation. No particular storage or solution-preparation problems were encountered with the synthetic polymers. The vegetable gums, however, must be stored in a dry place, and to ensure a smooth, lump-free reagent, care must be taken in preparing the water sols. The 0.5 percent solutions convenient for laboratory work can be readily prepared by slowly sifting 5 grams of the powdered gum into a liter of vigorously agitated water at 80°C. A few minutes suffice for adding the powder, and agitation is continued for about 15 minutes without additional heating. A preservative such as formaldehyde should be added to inhibit fermentation. Natural gum and glue solutions prepared in this manner showed no noticeable deterioration after several days at room temperature.

Reagent dilution. Separan and cactus extract are much more effective flocculants when they are used as dilute solutions. To avoid excessive dilution, the use of recycled pregnant solution or advancing wash solution as a reagent diluent was beneficial. Pregnant liquor from either acid or carbonate processes proved satisfactory for diluting the reagents. In treating slimy ores by countercurrent decantation, recycling the solution within each thickener to dilute the flocculant and the thickener feed markedly improved the thickening operation. Since filtration rates usually drop off with increasing pulp dilution, only limited dilution can be tolerated in filtration.

Slurry dilution is so closely related to reagent dilution that both must be considered together. Although it would seem that diluting the slurry should give the same over-all effect as diluting the reagent, indications are that diluting the reagent is more beneficial.

Method of adding flocculant to slurry. The method of adding the flocculant to the pulp is an important factor in the effectiveness of the reagent. The flocculant must be disseminated uniformly throughout the slurry without degrading the floccules. Intense agitation to distribute the reagent for maximum effectiveness degrades the fragile floccules, and thus defeats its own purpose. Data on several ores show that flocculant requirements increase with intensity and time of agitation.

Dilute pulps are much easier to flocculate than thick slurries. However, the nature of the solids influences the flocculating characteristics, so that a dilute slime pulp may be more difficult to flocculate than a dense granular pulp. In tests on dilute pulps in graduated cylinders, the reagent and pulp were satisfactorily mixed by inverting the cyclinder three or four times. For thicker slurries, reproducible results were obtained by simultaneously pouring the slurry and reagent into a container and then further blending by pouring the mixture back and forth into a second container three or four times. Adding the flocculant by stages was frequently beneficial. A satisfactory pilot-plant procedure was to introduce the reagent in stages from finger troughs discharging into the slurry launder (trough) at 12-inch intervals. A few feet of launder, with or without a baffle, ahead of the discharge into the thickener well or filter boot, usually suffices for adequate mixing.

Reagent quantity. The optimum quantity of flocculant for a specific application depends upon several technical and economic factors. Properly adding a small quantity of reagent gives better flocculation than improperly adding a large quantity.

Thickening usually requires less flocculant than does filtration. The larger quantity required for filtering can be attributed in part to poor dissemination of the reagent in the thick pulp. Use of more reagent than needed for thickening may improve subsequent filtration of the thickened pulp.

The degree of flocculation and the speed of settling can be varied within wide limits by regulating the reagent quantity. With guar gum, the increase in thickening rate is almost linear until a plateau is reached; then it regresses upon further addition. The plateau may be reached with as little as 0.8 or as much as 20 lb/ton of solids, depending on the slime content of the slurry. The plateau and regression observed for guar and similar natural gums were not observed for Separan or cactus extract. Flocculation of primary ore slimes and chemical precipitates may require inordinately large quantities of reagent.

A combination of guar gum, glue, and Separan was more effective on some ores than a costwise equivalent quantity of the separate reagents.

In handling pulps by multiple-stage countercurrent decantation, or by filtering and repulping, supplemental additions of reagent are usually needed ahead of each stage. The quantity required is related to the amount of degradation of the floccules upon mixing with the advancing wash solution.

Physical and chemical nature of the solids. The particle size of the solids plays a critical role in accelerated thickening and filtering. Primary slime in the submicron range and amorphous precipitates (owing to the enormous surfaces presented) are avid consumers of flocculants. Large quantities of slime, even in dilute slurries, complicate the problem of adequately disseminating the reagent for effective use. Although quantitative data are incomplete, indications are that the chemical nature of the solids also affects reagent performance.

Single-zone settling tests on slimy materials are likely to be misleading. Differences in the deportment of slime pulps are so pronounced that generalizations regarding their treatment are difficult. In some instances, large reagent additions were ineffective either for thickening or filtering. Sometimes only a specific reagent was effective, for example, small quantities of Separan were very effective in settling slimes from phosphoric acid liquor.

Composition of the pregnant liquor. Little is known about the effect of cations and anions in the pregnant liquor on the performance of flocculants. In at least one instance, however, the response to guar gum was improved markedly when molybdenum and copper were precipitated before the flocculant was added. A high concentration of salts in the pregnant solution often slows both thickening and filtering.

Clarity of pregnant solution. Supernatant liquors and filtrates from thickening and filtering are not always sparkling clear. Specific particle sizes or specific minerals may resist flocculation. However, in most instances it has been possible to select a flocculant or combination of flocculants that will produce clear liquors. A small amount of gelatin or glue in conjunction with the primary flocculant has been helpful on many pulps. On some leach slurries the order of reagent addition is critical; on others the reagents can be added together [4]. The clarity of the liquor can often be improved by some sacrifice in thickening rate.

In plant practice, requisite clarity is obtained by batch settling or by "polishing" in Moore-type leaf filters or on precoated filter presses or drum filters. Sand filters are also used for clarifying pregnant solutions.

Washing of thickener underflows and filter cakes. In pilot-plant studies on countercurrent decantation (CCD) for washing intensely flocculated pulps in classifiers or thickeners, it was necessary to install mixing tanks to blend the thickened pulp and advance the wash solution. Partial destruction of the floccules was necessary for high washing efficiency. Supplementary reagent was added to the overflow of the mixer to re-flocculate the pulp for the next washing stage. A convenient and effective technique was to divert about 10 percent of the advancing wash solution for diluting the flocculant.

In existing CCD operations the flocculant is usually added to the advancing wash solution before it is mixed with the thickened pulp. The acceptable results obtained by this procedure can probably be attributed to light flocculation of the material being processed. Existing thickener installations, in general, have not been designed to take full advantage of the flocculants. An intensely flocculated slurry settles to a viscous pulp with sluggish flow characteristics. Overstrength rakes and oversize pumps are necessary to handle such thickener underflows.

Although good displacement washing of filter cakes was obtained in the laboratory batch tests, effective washing in continuous practice usually requires repulping. The full possibilities of displacement washing of heavily flocculated filter cakes remain to be explored.

Scale-up of laboratory results. Pilot-plant and commercial thickening of leach slurries have shown that thickener-area requirements cannot be accurately predicted from static settling tests. Periodic or continuous slow stirring to simulate the action of thickener rakes will increase the terminal densities in batch tests to near those obtained in a thickener. A batch thickening test that will give results extrapolative to continuous plant operation needs to be developed. Papers by Roberts [5], Kynch [6], and Talmadge and Fitch [7] are an excellent starting point for a further study of thickening.

8–3. LIQUID-SOLIDS SEPARATIONS IN ALKALINE SYSTEMS

The sodium carbonate-bicarbonate solutions for leaching uranium ores do not severely attack the rock matrix. Therefore, less secondary slime is formed than in acid leaching. Filtration aids in minimizing dilution of the leach liquor. Dilution is undesirable where the uranium is recovered by direct precipitation or where the leach liquor is regenerated and recycled. Because of the noncorrosive nature of carbonate leach pulps corrosion-resistant filters are not required, and there is little cost advantage for countercurrent decantation.

Percolation leaching combines the leaching and liquid-solids separation steps in a single operation. Its applicability to carbonate circuits is limited to the treatment of calcines from salt roasting certain Colorado Plateau ores for recovery of both uranium and vanadium. A sand-slime separation for carbonate leach pulps was tested in the AEC's Grand Junction, Colorado, pilot plant in conjunction with studies on the carbonate RIP recovery process. This procedure is analogous to that described later in the section on acid systems.

8–3.1 Filtration. Carbonate leach pulps generally are processed directly by multiple-stage filtration, although thickening may precede the filtration step. Wire-wound or panel-type drum filters are ordinarily used, and the liquor is hot. A flocculating agent is added to the filter feed, which averages 50 percent solids. A synthetic polymer in amounts ranging from 0.2 to 1.0 lb/ton of ore is most often used. As much wash solution as possible is sprayed on the filter for displacement washing, but most of the washing is obtained by repulping and refiltering the cake twice. The filter cakes are about $\frac{3}{8}$ inch thick and average 75 to 80 percent solids. Blowing facilitates cake removal, although string discharge filters have been found essential in a Canadian plant for satisfactory cake discharge. A vacuum capacity of about 1 ft^3/min per square foot of filter area is required. Loss of soluble uranium in the washed filter cake ranges from 0.5 to 2 percent, depending on the number of stages and the permeability of the cake.

One of the newer filter installations uses three drums, 11.5 feet in diameter and 16 feet long, for three-stage filtration of 440 tons of ore per day. This is equivalent to 1.4 ft^2/ton day per stage. Nylon filter cloths, specially woven to resist blinding, are replaced at about 40-day intervals. In other plants, similar filter cloths are used for 6 months or more. Carbonate plants treating ores of less favorable filtration characteristics require from 1.5 to 4.0 ft^2/ton day per filter stage.

Burt-type pressure filters 5 feet in diameter by 40 feet long, with 720 square feet of filter area, are being used in one carbonate leach plant.

Each filter handles 80 tons of feed per day in a three-cycle operation. This is equivalent to 3.0 ft^2/ton day per stage. Pressure filters have higher operating and maintenance costs than drum filters, but can handle a coarser feed.

8–3.2 Countercurrent decantation washing in thickeners. Washing thickeners preceded filters in the Atomic Energy Commission's carbonate leach plant at Monticello, Utah, and in the old carbonate plant at Beaverlodge, Canada. At Monticello, pulp from the atmospheric-pressure leach at 50 percent solids was processed in four 30 by 8-foot CCD thickeners followed by two stages of filtration. Approximately 1 ton of wash solution per ton of ore advanced through the thickeners, giving a feed pulp containing about 33 percent solids. A flocculating agent was added to the advancing wash solution before mixing with the thickener underflows, which averaged 50 percent solids. The uranium concentration ranged from 2.5 to 3 g/liter in the first thickener to about 1.0 g/liter in the last thickener. The 30-foot thickeners provided about 4 square feet of thickener area per ton day per stage.

8–3.3 Percolation leaching. For percolation leaching wooden vats about 30 feet in diameter by 10 feet deep are ordinarily used. A false bottom is covered with coconut matting which is protected from abrasion and held in place by wooden slats. The salt-roast calcine is quenched in carbonate-bicarbonate solution to give a slurry of 30 to 40 percent solids, and sluiced to the percolation leach vats. The vat is filled in 24 hours to a depth of 9 feet with about 250 tons of calcine. Another 24 hours are needed for washing, first with carbonate solution and then with water. The area required is 4 to 6 ft^2/ton day of calcine. The coconut matting is replaced at about 6-month intervals.

8–3.4 Clarifying pregnant solutions from carbonate leaching. To clarify solution, the Colorado Plateau uranium plants use filter presses with either open or closed discharge. One of the plants formerly used filter-sock clarifiers, and a Canadian plant currently employs leaf clarifiers of the Moore type.

The AEC plant at Monticello, Utah, clarifies 200 tons of solution per day through a 42 by 42-inch 30-frame open-discharge press. The press is precoated with about 10 pounds of diatomaceous-earth filter aid, and additional filter aid is added as needed; about 160 pounds are used in a 2 to 3-week campaign before the press is cleaned. The feed-pump pressure reaches 40 to 50 pounds as the press becomes filled.

Nylon filter cloths on the presses at Monticello are not covered, although at other installations a kraft paper covering is customary. The 760-square-foot area of the press is equivalent to about 4 ft^2/ton of solution per day. The area requirement of leaf filters in the Canadian plant are given as 6.5 ft^2/ton day of liquid [8].

8–3.5 Filtering the uranium concentrate.

Uranium is recovered from sodium carbonate solution as sodium diuranate by precipitation with caustic soda. All carbonate plants use plate-and-frame filter presses to separate the uranium concentrate from the stripped solution. The two precipitate presses at Monticello are 42 by 42 inches, with thirty 2-inch frames. A 60-ton batch of precipitated solution can be filtered in 3 hours. This is equivalent to 1.6 square feet of filter area per ton of solution per day. In practice, each press is unloaded at 5-day intervals after filtering 400 to 500 tons of solution to yield 3000 pounds of concentrate. The filter cake, containing about 50 percent solids, is repulped for continuous drying on a steam-heated drum drier. The feed to the drier is often diluted to as low as 35 percent solids to facilitate handling the slurry and forming the thin film of product required for proper drying on the steam-heated drums. The Canadian plant dries its product in a steam-heated twin-screen Holoflite drier.

8–4. LIQUID-SOLIDS SEPARATION IN ACID SYSTEMS

Acid leach pulps are usually handled by conventional countercurrent decantation in thickeners or multiple-stage filtration on drum filters. Some CCD systems have a separate circuit for handling the sands in classifiers. Thickeners or filters may be used in the grinding and leaching circuits to control dilution, to save acid, and to yield richer pregnant solutions.

8–4.1 Countercurrent decantation.

In a few CCD plants, the sand component of the leach pulp is handled separately in classifiers. The split is made at 65 to 150 mesh in plants that produce clear liquor in thickeners. There are contradictory schools of thought as to the desirability of separately washing sands and slimes. One group holds that sands are best handled in classifiers to avoid raking and pumping troubles in thickeners. The contrary view is that, with the advent of powerful flocculants, the sands assist the settling of the slime component and get a "free ride" through the thickeners.

Kerr-McGee's mill at Shiprock, New Mexico, discussed in Section 11–5, is a good example of separate handling of sands and slimes by countercurrent decantation. Originally, 6-mesh ore was acid-cured to solubilize both uranium and vanadium, and the extreme coarseness of the leached ore made separate washing mandatory. Currently the ore is ground to about 20 mesh for agitation leaching, but the dual system with an unusual interlocked washing arrangement continues in use. The acid-cure process appeared to dehydrate some of the clay minerals in the ore, resulting in a pulp that settled better than the agitation-leach pulp. The change from acid-curing resulted in a thickening problem; however, this was solved by recycling pregnant solution to the thickeners to increase the feed dilution and give better flocculation.

The initial sand-slime split of the leach pulp is made at about 65 mesh in two 6-inch cyclones. The sand fraction, about 60 percent, is washed in four 2 by 12-foot spiral classifiers. The slime fraction, about 40 percent, is thickened and washed in four 40-foot thickeners; the area requirements are 6 to 7 square feet per ton of slime or 2 to 3 square feet per ton of original feed. Wash water equivalent to 2.2 tons per ton of ore enters the last thickener and classifier and advances alternately between classifiers and thickeners. A part of each thickener overflow is recycled to dilute the thickener feed to 10 percent solids. The synthetic polymer used to flocculate the thickener feed is prepared as a 0.3 percent solution and further diluted about tenfold with wash solution for use. A total of 0.1 to 0.2 pound of flocculant per ton of ore is added to the four thickeners. Thickener underflows average 40 percent solids, compared with 75 to 80 percent solids in the classifier sands.

8–4.2 Countercurrent washing in classifiers and cyclones. Hydraulic cyclones have gained popular acceptance for a wide range of applications. They are used for removing tramp oversize from slime pulps, for removing slime from sand slurries, and for separations between these extremes. The cyclones are almost always used in conjunction with rake, drag, or spiral classifiers, and are interlocked with the classifiers in different ways.

Plants that recover uranium from a slime slurry by RIP use diverse arrangements of cyclones and classifiers for making a sand-free slime product and for countercurrent washing of the sands. The proportions of slime range from less than 20 to more than 50 percent, and since feed of 1.08 specific gravity or less is requisite for the RIP reciprocating-basket cell now in use, the quantity of wash water is varied within wide limits. The classifier rake products contain from 75 to 80 percent solids. Loss of soluble uranium in the sands ranges from 0.1 to 0.5 percent.

Duplex rake classifiers are used at the Anaconda plant, Bluewater, New Mexico. Each classifier overflows to a corresponding cyclone in a parallel cyclone circuit. Instead of returning to the classifier circuit, the cyclone underflows are advanced for washing within the cyclone circuit.

The unusual expedient of adding flocculants to a RIP circuit was adopted by Rare Metals Corporation at Tuba City, Arizona, to inhibit the buildup of a circulating load of fine sand in the cyclone-classifier circuit. Care is exercised to avoid too much flocculant, which might cause trouble by flocculating the slime in the resin baskets. The synthetic polymer as a 0.1 percent solution is added to all but the first classifier at the edge of the classifier pool. Only 5 to 10 pounds of flocculant are used in processing about 300 tons of ore per day.

8–4.3 Countercurrent washing in thickeners. Although four or five thickeners comprise the usual installation, as many as eight thickeners may be found in a single circuit. The thickeners range in size from 30 to 120 feet. Underflow densities range from 30 to 40 percent solids on slime feeds and from 50 to 60 percent solids on unclassified leach pulps. Thickener operation customarily is controlled by regulating the addition of flocculant to maintain 2 to 3 feet of clear liquor in each thickener. About two-thirds of the flocculant is added to the first thickener, and the rest is distributed to the washing thickeners. Thickener areas range between 2 and 6 ft^2/ton of ore per day. The quantity of wash solution varies from about 1.5 to 3 tons per ton of ore and is a compromise between maintaining a high-grade pregnant solution and minimizing the soluble uranium loss. The loss may range from less than 0.5 up to 3 percent in the different plants, depending upon the design and operation of the plant.

Thickeners for dewatering neutral pulps in the grinding circuits of several of the Canadian acid-leach plants provide 5 to 12 square feet of thickener area per ton day.

The Vitro Uranium Company mill, described in Section 11–4, processes 600 to 650 tons of ore per day in four 70-foot thickeners, which is equivalent to about 6 ft^2/ton of ore per day per stage. Before the advent of the new flocculants, less than half the current tonnage in this plant could have been handled, even with two stages of filtration following the thickener circuit. From 0.2 to 0.3 pound of flocculant per ton of ore is added as a 1 percent solution to the advancing wash water. About three-fourths of the flocculant is added to the first thickener, and the remainder is divided among the other thickeners. The clear-liquor depth in the thickeners is held at 30 inches by regulating the amount of flocculant. Underflows average 50 percent solids. Ore ground to about 28 mesh is leached at 60 percent solids, and 2.5 tons of water per ton of ore are used for washing, resulting in a soluble uranium loss of 0.5 to 1 percent.

8–4.4 Filtering acid-leach pulps. Most of the South African and several of the Canadian plants handle the leach pulp by two-stage drum filtration. Plants in the Blind River district of Canada recycle pregnant solution to the leaching step and, to reduce soluble losses, use one stage of washing thickeners ahead of 2-stage filtration. One plant with favorable terrain uses 5-stage countercurrent decantation instead of thickening and filtration. Dynel filter cloths, 2 by 2 twill, are in general use and last 2 to

3 months. Flocculation of the pulp with glue is a prerequisite for filtration rates of 1.5 to 3 ft^2/ton day per stage. The filters are designed to obtain maximum effectiveness from displacement washing. String filters are used in some of the Canadian mills to minimize soluble loss resulting from solution blowback during cake discharge. Wash volumes are 0.25 to 0.4 ton per ton of ore, resulting in a ratio of pregnant solution to ore of 1.6 to 1.8. Soluble uranium loss is 0.5 to 1 percent [8]. The filter cakes average $\frac{1}{2}$ inch thick and are unusually dry, containing only about 20 percent moisture.

8–4.5 Percolation leaching. The plants that salt roast use combinations of percolation leach vats, hydraulic classifiers, cyclones, thickeners, and assorted filters to recover both uranium and vanadium. Typical of a salt-roast flowsheet employing a variety of liquid-solids separations is that used by the Climax Uranium Company at Grand Junction, Colorado [9], discussed in Article 6–4.6. An initial neutralizing leach that utilizes waste acid solutions for converting calcium carbonate in the ore to calcium chloride and sulfate is followed by a sand-slime separation in a hydraulic sizer. The separation at about 150 mesh concentrates 70 to 80 percent of the values in the slime fraction, which represents one-third of the total weight. The plus-150 mesh sands are dewatered to 75 percent solids in a rake classifier and then sluiced to percolation tanks for acid leaching.

The percolation leach tanks are 11 feet in diameter by 18 feet deep. A false bottom of wood grid construction is covered with Saran-screen filter media. Fifty tons of sands, which fill a tank to a depth of 15 feet, are percolation-leached, washed, and discharged in a 24-hour cycle. This is equivalent to 2 ft^2/ton of sand per day.

The slimes from the hydraulic sizer, at 6 to 8 percent solids, are flocculated by adding 0.2 pound of a synthetic polymer per ton of original ore and thickening to 30 to 40 percent solids. The thickener area is 11 to 13 ft^2/ton of original ore. Before the new flocculants became available, submerged disk filters were used to dewater the slime. The thickener underflow is filtered on standard disk filters, and then salt-roasted. After cooling, the calcine is ground and water-leached for vanadium. The vanadium pregnant solution and water-leach tails are separated in a thickener, and the tails are washed on a drum filter and then acid-agitation leached to dissolve the uranium. Next, the slime tailing is filtered and washed in three stages, using 8 by 11-foot drum filters. The cake is $\frac{1}{4}$ inch thick and contains about 70 percent solids. Filter area for the slime tails is 2 ft^2/ton of slimes per day per stage, but the filters could handle more tonnage. Uranium is recovered from the acid leach liquors by solvent extraction [10], and the final yellow cake is separated from the stripped solution in a plate-and-frame filter press.

8–4.6 Clarifying pregnant solutions from acid processes. Batch settling, sand filters, plate-and-frame presses, sock filters, and leaf filters are employed on the Colorado Plateau by various mills to clarify pregnant solutions before ion exchange or solvent extraction. Loaded ion-exchange eluate and loaded solvent extraction strip solution are clarified in plate-and-frame presses. Clarification of ion-exchange eluates is sometimes combined with sulfate and iron removal by lime precipitation before uranium recovery.

The eluate from RIP may contain appreciable slime, making clarification in filter presses difficult. In one instance, a 36 by 36-inch 45-frame press was inadequate for filtering 30 to 40 gal/min of a nitrate eluate. In another plant a similar eluate with the pH first adjusted to 3.1 with lime was filtered at a rate of 440 gal/min in a 54 by 54-inch 40-frame press. This is equivalent to less than 1 square foot of filter area per ton of solution per day.

Canadian mill practice is to use precoated drum filters or precoated leaves of the Moore type to clarify pregnant solution before ion exchange. The drum filters are designed to provide 0.2 to 0.4 ft^2/ton of solution per day, whereas clarifier leaves are installed on the basis of 2 to 3 ft^2/ton of solution per day. Eluate clarification and purification practice in the Blind River district is to precipitate with lime at a pH of 3.5 and to filter the precipitate continuously after thickening.

8–4.7 Filtering the uranium concentrate. Uranium is recovered from ion-exchange eluates and solvent extraction strip liquors by precipitation with NH_3, MgO, or NaOH. Both batch and continuous precipitation and filtration systems are in use. Plate-and-frame and Sweetland-type filters are used for batch filtration. The two 36 by 36-inch 45-frame precipitation presses at Monticello were dumped alternately on a 24-hour cycle. Each filter handled 150 to 200 tons of eluate per day, to yield 2500 pounds of product. This is equivalent to 4 to 5 square feet of filter area per ton of solution per day.

Uranium Reduction Company's plant at Moab, Utah, described in Section 11–6, employs a continuous system for precipitation, thickening, and filtration. Ammonia is progressively added to the eluate to adjust the pH to 3, 4.5, and 7 in three consecutive tanks. The yellow cake slurry is flocculated and then thickened in a 20 by 15-foot thickener. The flocculating solution is prepared continuously by feeding 0.6 lb/hr of a synthetic polymer into a mixing tank together with about 10 gal/min of water and 20 gal/min of stripped eluate. The barren eluate overflowing the thickener is clarified in three 36 by 36-inch 30-frame presses before being returned to the eluate makeup system. The thickener underflow, containing about 15 percent solids, is filtered and washed on two 3 by 4-foot drum filters in series. Designed for handling about 6 tons of product daily, the filters provide 4.5 ft^2/ton day per stage. Nylon filter cloths are used. The cake, at about 50 percent solids, is calcined at 450°C in a six-hearth roaster.

REFERENCES

1. J. B. ROSENBAUM and J. B. CLEMMER, Accelerated Thickening and Filtering of Uranium Leach Pulps, in *Proceedings of the International Conference on Peaceful Uses of Atomic Energy*, Vol. 8. New York: United Nations, 1955. (P/528, p. 38)

2. R. F. HOLLIS et al., *The Development of a Resin-in-pulp Process and Its Application to Ores of the White Canyon Area of Utah*, USAEC Report ACCO-42, American Cyanamid Co., 1954.

3. H. S. COE and G. H. CLEVENGER, Methods for Determining the Capacities of Slime-Settling Tanks, *Trans. Am. Inst. Mining Met. Engrs.* **55,** 356 (1916–1917).

4. M. E. WADSWORTH and I. B. CUTLER, *Flocculation of Mineral Suspensions with Coprecipitated Polyelectrolytes*, Technical Report No. IV, Institute for the Study of Rate Processes, University of Utah, June 1954.

5. E. J. ROBERTS, Thickening—Art or Science?, *Mining Eng.*, **1,** No. 3, 61 (1949).

6. G. J. KYNCH, A Theory of Sedimentation, *Trans. Faraday Soc.* **48,** 166 (1952).

7. W. P. TALMADGE and E. G. FITCH, Determining Thickener Unit Areas, *Ind. Eng. Chem.* **47,** No. 1, 38 (1955).

8. A. H. ROSS, *The Uranium Raw Material Industry in Canada*, paper delivered at the Sixtieth National Western Mining Conference, Denver, Colorado, Feb. 7, 1957.

9. W. KNOTT, The Processing of Uranium Ores of the Colorado Plateau by the Climax Uranium Co., *Mines Mag.* **45,** No. 1, 29 (1955).

10. R. C. TOERPER, Application of Solvent Extraction in Climax Uranium Co.'s Plant, *Mines Mag.* **47,** No. 3, 89 (1955).

CHAPTER 9

URANIUM RECOVERY BY ION EXCHANGE*

9–1. Introduction

Before the advent of atomic energy, the need for uranium was relatively minor, and the available ore was sufficiently high grade that it could be leached with either alkali carbonate or sulfuric acid to yield a filtrate from which a high-grade precipitate of uranium could be produced.

Since 1945, however, demand for uranium has increased so enormously that new sources of uranium have had to be developed. Most of these new sources have been of progressively lower concentrations and have required the development of new processing techniques. Since most present-day uranium ores contain only traces of uranium, their hydrometallurgy poses several difficult problems.

(1) Huge quantities of ore must be mined and hauled in order to obtain a small quantity of uranium.

(2) Large quantities of reagents are required to leach the uranium from these ores.

(3) The uranium must be recovered from a leach liquor containing a small amount of uranium in the presence of large quantities of impurities that interfere with the classical chemical methods of extraction and precipitation.

Since in most uranium ores, the uranium is thoroughly disseminated throughout all of the particles, the entire ore usually must be ground and chemically attacked before the uranium can be brought into solution. For economic reasons, most ores are leached with sulfuric acid to give leach liquors that contain large quantities of free sulfuric acid, iron, aluminum, vanadium, manganese, calcium, magnesium, titanium, and silica, as well as the small quantities of uranium. Minor quantities of cobalt, nickel, and thorium may also be present. The problem in the hydrometallurgy of such leach liquors is to recover the uranium as a high-grade concentrate as economically as possible. Direct precipitation techniques are both economically and technically infeasible for many leach liquors from low-grade ore.

Beginning in 1948 and early 1949, several groups within or under contract to the U. S. Atomic Energy Commission undertook a study of

---

* By Albert F. Preuss and Robert Kunin, Rohm & Haas Company.

uranium recovery from the leach liquors of low-grade ores. Because of the huge quantities of liquor that had to be processed to produce a high-grade uranium concentrate, an efficient and simple operation had to be devised. Several contractors associated with the AEC (Battelle Memorial Institute, Dow Chemical Co., Massachusetts Institute of Technology, and Rohm & Haas Co.), cooperated in developing an anion-exchange resin process to recover and concentrate uranium from the sulfuric acid leach liquors of low-grade uranium ores. The development of the process followed the discovery that hexavalent uranium in such solutions existed as an anionic complex $[UO_2(SO_4)_n]^{2-2n}$, and that the quaternary ammonium anion-exchange resins exhibited a high selectivity for such anionic species [1–4].

The process that was developed was first used commercially at West Rand Consolidated Mines, Ltd., near Krugersdorp in the Union of South Africa. This plant went on stream in October 1952, and since that time the ion-exchange process has been used to recover uranium in the United States, Belgian Congo, Canada, Australia, Rhodesia, Sweden, and France [5–9].

The ion-exchange process is based on the ability of anion-exchange resins to extract uranium selectively from sulfuric acid or carbonate leach solutions. After the uranium is concentrated in the resin, it is displaced by a suitable salt solution to obtain a more highly concentrated, relatively pure uranium liquor. This liquor is then treated with alkaline precipitants to yield a high-grade uranium cake.

The chief advantages of this process over direct precipitation are that it (a) reduces the volume of solution that must be chemically treated to recover uranium, (b) provides for quantitative recovery of uranium from solution, and (c) produces a uranium cake of higher purity.

9–2. Chemistry of the Ion-Exchange Process

The ion-exchange process involves the ability of hexavalent uranium as the uranyl ion, UO_2^{++}, to form anionic complexes with sulfate ions, $SO_4^=$, and carbonate ions, $CO_3^=$. In acid sulfate media, the uranyl ion exists in dynamic equilibrium with its sulfate complexes,

$$UO_2^{++} + n\,SO_4^= \rightleftarrows UO_2(SO_4)_n^{2-2n},$$

where $n = 1$, 2, or 3. In alkaline carbonate solutions, the uranyl ion is complexed strongly to form a well-defined species:

$$UO_2^{++} + 3CO_3^= \rightleftarrows UO_2(CO_3)_3^{-4}.$$

The ion-exchange process consists of adsorbing these anionic complexes selectively and quantitatively on an anion-exchange resin as illustrated in the following reactions, where R^+ represents the fixed ion-exchange sites of the resin.

$$4R^+X^- + UO_2(SO_4)_3{}^{-4} \rightarrow (R^+)_4 UO_2(SO_4)_3{}^{-4} + 4X^-$$

$$4R^+X^- + UO_2(CO_3)_3{}^{-4} \rightarrow (R^+)_4 UO_2(CO_3)_3{}^{-4} + 4X^-$$

where $X^- = NO_3{}^-$ or Cl^-. The above reactions are reversible, and the uranium may be desorbed or eluted from the resin by shifting the reactions to the left. This is usually accomplished with solutions containing either nitrate or chloride salts.

9–2.1 Resin characteristics. Typical resins used in uranium recovery are shown in Table 9–1. Cation-exchange resins contain structures such as carboxylic (—COO Na) and sulfonic (—SO$_3$Na) functional groups, where cations such as sodium ions are capable of exchange with other cations. Anion-exchange resins contain either weakly basic (—NH$_2$·HCl) or

strongly basic $\left(-N\begin{smallmatrix} \diagup CH_3 \\ -CH_3{}^+Cl^- \\ \diagdown CH_3 \end{smallmatrix} \right)$ functional groups, where the chloride

ions are capable of exchange with other anions. In uranium recovery only anion-exchange resins possessing strongly basic quaternary ammonium groups are currently of importance.

Chemical structure of anion-exchange resin. Typical of the resins used in uranium recovery is the product obtained by copolymerizing styrene

TABLE 9–1

ANION-EXCHANGE RESINS USED IN URANIUM RECOVERY

Operation	Resin	Manufacturer
Columnar	Amberlite IRA-400	Rohm & Haas Co., Phila., Pa.
Columnar	Amberlite IRA-400	Charles Lennig and Co. (G. B.) Ltd., London
Columnar	Deacidite FF	The Permutit Co., London
Columnar	Dowex-1	The Dow Company, Midland, Mich.
Columnar	Permutit (Ionac)SK	Permutit Co., New York, N. Y.
RIP	Amberlite XE-123	Rohm & Haas Co., Phila., Pa.
RIP	Dowex-11	The Dow Company, Midland, Mich.
RIP	Permutit SKB	Permutit Co., New York, N. Y.

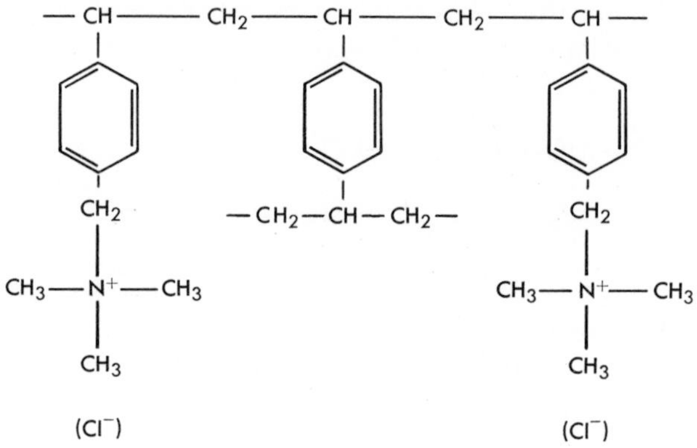

Fig. 9–1. Structure of a quaternary ammonium anion-exchange resin.

and divinyl benzene, chloromethylating the product, and reacting it with trimethylamine [10] to form an ion-exchange resin with the structure shown in Fig. 9–1.

Exchange capacity. The ultimate capacity of an ion-exchange resin is the number of fixed ion-exchange sites on the resin. This can be ascertained by measuring the number of mobile ions that may be adsorbed and desorbed from a given weight or volume of resin. Capacity measurements are normally reported both on a dry-weight and on a wet-volume basis. Since the capacity per unit volume determines to a certain extent the size of the ion-exchange equipment, this measurement is considered to be the more important of the two. Resins used in uranium recovery processes have total exchange capacities ranging from 3.5 to 5.0 milliequivalents per dry gram and from 1.2 to 1.8 meq/ml (milliequivalents per milliliter) of wet settled resin.

Hydration. All ion-exchange resins are hydrophilic because of the presence of the fixed ion groups. Although the fixed ion groups themselves may not be hydrated [11] because of steric effects, the mobile or counter ions are hydrated to approximately the same degree as are free ions in solution under comparable conditions. Therefore, the hydration of the resin is a function of its exchange capacity and its counter ion, as well as the nature of its functional group and the type of cross-linked polymer backbone. The equilibrium moisture content of resins used in uranium recovery is 40 to 60 percent.

Particle size. In columnar operations, the particle sizes of the resin must be such that exchange may take place in a reasonable length of time, solution flow may be maintained with minimum pressure loss, and the resin beds may be cleaned through a backwash step. In columnar operation, the majority of the resin beads are 0.3 to 0.9 millimeter in diameter (plus-48 to minus-16 mesh). This range is a compromise of exchange rates, capacities, and hydraulic characteristics of the resin. For the RIP operation, where the resin is held by a screen, the beads are larger, in order to effect a separation between ore slimes and resin beads. These tailor-made beads are 0.84 to 1.6 millimeters in diameter (plus-20 to minus-10 mesh).

Density. For ease of operation, an ion-exchange resin should have a true density greater than that of the medium in which it is used. Its apparent or bulk density is defined as the weight in pounds of backwashed and settled wet resin that will occupy one cubic foot of space. The apparent density is related to the true density by the relationship, apparent density = true density (1 — fraction of void space). The void space for ion-exchange resins that have been backwashed and allowed to settle is approximately 40 percent of the total volume. The apparent densities of ion-exchange resins used in uranium recovery vary from 38 to 45 lb/ft^3.

Attrition and solubility losses. Attrition losses in ion-exchange resins may be due to the swelling and contraction of the resin, abrasion caused by resin-resin contact, and abrasion caused by resin-equipment contact. Attrition losses in fixed-bed column operations are insignificant. However, in the RIP process, which requires larger beads and constant agitation, some resin losses due to attrition occur. The extent of resin losses does not appear to be of great economic significance, although the broken resin beads can cause operational difficulties by blinding the resin-retaining screens. Solubility losses are so small that solubility measurements cannot be made.

Hydraulic characteristics. The hydraulic characteristics of resins are analogous to those of any inert spherical particles. The two properties of concern to good column operation are pressure drop across the resin bed during downflow operations and bed expansion during upflow operations.

Pressure drop, the loss in head per foot of resin depth, depends on the particle size, uniformity, compressibility and shape of the resin beads and on the viscosity and linear flow rate of the leach liquor. Uranium recovery columns are normally operated in the range of streamline flow (1 to 6 gal/ft^2 per minute). At these rates the pressure drop across clean resin beds is 0.1 to 0.2 psi per foot of bed depth per gallon per square foot per minute of flow. When slime formation and precipitation occur in the resin bed, the pressure drop will increase. In addition, nonuniform flow or channeling occurs.

To prevent this buildup of slimes and precipitates, the resin beds are backwashed at convenient times, at the end of either the adsorption or the desorption cycle. Backwashing is the upflow operation that allows the resin bed to be expanded so that fine extraneous matter can be removed from the ion-exchange column. Ion-exchange columns are usually designed to allow room for 100 percent expansion of the resin bed during backwashing. The flow rate necessary to attain maximum expansion depends on the viscosity and density of the backwash fluid, the particle size and uniformity of the resin, and the true density of the resin.

The true density of the ion-exchange resin will not be the same throughout all ion-exchange operations, since it depends on the mobile ion associated with the fixed ion-exchange group [12]. For this reason the expanded bed volume of an ion-exchange column will vary both with flow rate and with ion form of the resin. Typical expansion curves are shown in Fig. 9–2.

Rates of exchange. The rate-determining step in the ion-exchange process is the diffusion of the ions into the resin matrix. In batch operation, the length of time required to reach 50 percent of the equilibrium values is about 10 to 15 minutes. In column operations, a retention time of from 3 to 10 minutes per column for the pregnant liquor is sufficient to saturate the resin with uranium and still produce a barren effluent.

Selectivity. For most efficient uranium recovery it is necessary that the resin be selective for the uranyl sulfate complexes over the ferric sulfate complex, bisulfate, and sulfate ions. If this were not so, uranium would

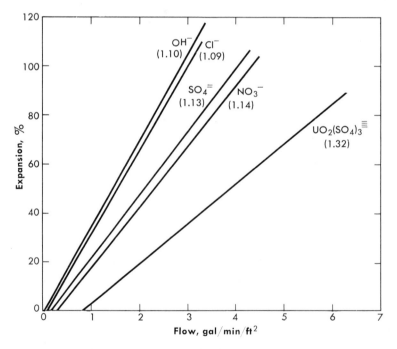

FIG. 9–2. Typical expansion curves for backwashing various ionic forms of Amberlite IRA-400 at 60°F. True resin densities (g/cm^3) are given in parentheses.

be displaced by these latter ions, all of which are present in much greater molar concentration than uranium. In some leach liquors, the molar ratio of total sulfate to uranium exceeds 3000 to 1, yet efficient uranium adsorption is realized.

Resin life. Ion-exchange resins must be replaced from time to time. Two conditions determine when they must be replaced: (1) when the ion-exchange unit can no longer treat all the leach liquor being produced, and (2) when the instantaneous operating costs begin to exceed the overall cost of resin replacement plus average operating cost to that point. These criteria determine the economic life of the resin. Although the resin may still possess sufficient capacity to be used for uranium recovery, use beyond this point is not the most economical.

The actual operating life of a resin depends primarily on the leach solution with which it is used. In the South African plants, where the presence of many extraneous substances in the leach liquors lead to a steady drop in uranium capacity, a two-year resin life is not uncommon. Resin used in mills processing other uranium ores should operate satisfactorily for significantly longer periods of time.

9–2.2 Solution characteristics of acid leach liquors. All acid leaching of uranium-bearing ores is made with sulfuric acid. Where the uranium exists in the ore in a reduced state, oxidants such as manganese dioxide, sodium chlorate, ferric sulfate, ferric hydroxide, and potassium permanganate may be used to oxidize uranium to the hexavalent state. The uranium thus dissolved is in solution primarily as anionic sulfate complexes. The mode of leaching, the nature and concentration of the chemicals used, the nature of the ore, etc., all have an important bearing on the efficiency with which the ion-exchange resins will adsorb uranium from the pregnant liquor.

The constituents appearing in the leach liquor include many different ions. Some of these, such as the ammonium ion, the alkalies, the alkaline earths, aluminum, and the transition elements which do not form strong sulfate complexes, do not affect uranium adsorption by the ion-exchange resin. The transition-element ions VO^{++}, Mn^{++}, Fe^{++}, Co^{++}, Ni^{++}, Cu^{++}, and Zn^{++} are all essentially harmless. The most important constituents (aside from "poisons," discussed later) in the leach liquor that affect the capacity of the resin for uranium are H^+, HSO_4^-, and $SO_4^=$. The following equilibria exist in the leach (ignoring, for the present, iron and other extraneous ions):

$$HSO_4^- \leftrightarrows H^+ + SO_4^=,$$
$$UO_2^{++} + 2SO_4^= \leftrightarrows UO_2(SO_4)_2^=,$$
$$UO_2(SO_4)_2^= + SO_4^= \rightleftarrows UO_2(SO_4)_3^{-4}.$$

The relative affinity of the resin for HSO_4^- is greater than that for $SO_4^=$. O'Connor [13] studied the adsorption of uranium on Amberlite IRA-400 and concluded that the main species present on the resin was $UO_2(SO_4)_3^{-4}$, with a small quantity of $UO_2(SO_4)_2^=$ also adsorbed. He found that the affinity of the resin for the trisulfato complex was greater than that for the disulfato species.

When a solution of two salts, M^+X^- and M^+Y^-, is passed through an anion-exchange resin until the effluent concentration and X^-/Y^- ratios are the same as the influent, the resin exchange sites will be occupied by both X^- and Y^- in solution.

In uranium adsorption from sulfuric acid solutions on an anion-exchange resin the situation is more complex. When a resin is fully saturated with uranium from a solution of uranyl sulfate, sulfuric acid, and a neutral sulfate salt, the ion-exchange sites will be occupied by HSO_4^-, $SO_4^=$, $UO_2(SO_4)_2^=$, and $UO_2(SO_4)_3^{-4}$ ions.

Adsorption reactions. The adsorption of uranium as the sulfate complex can be represented by the following equation, where R^+ represents the fixed ion in the resin matrix:

$$4R^+X^- + UO_2(SO_4)_3^{-4} \leftrightarrows (R^+)_4UO_2(SO_4)_3^{-4} + 4X^-$$

$$(X = NO_3^-, Cl^-, HSO_4^-, \text{ or } \tfrac{1}{2}SO_4^=).$$

Effect of pH and acidity. The effect of pH on uranium adsorption may be deduced by considering the solution equilibrium reactions. At a fixed uranium and total sulfate concentration, a reduction in acidity would

(1) decrease HSO_4^- concentration,
(2) increase $SO_4^=$ concentration, and
(3) increase $UO_2(SO_4)_2^=$ and $UO_2(SO_4)_3^{-4}$ concentration.

Conditions (1) and (3) would lead to an increase in uranium on the resin at saturation, outweighing the slight effect of an increase in sulfate concentration.

The effect of acid concentration on the capacity of the resin for uranium can readily be seen from the data in Table 9–2. Uranium capacity increases with decreased acidity (increase in pH). Further increases in pH will increase the uranium capacity still further [14]. However, there is an upper limit in pH values that may be used in actual practice. Ferric iron, which also forms a sulfate complex, is adsorbed quite strongly at pH values above 1.8.

Effect of uranium concentration. Referring to the equations above, it can be seen that an increase in uranium concentration should result in an increase in concentration of the sulfate complexes $UO_2(SO_4)_2^=$ and $UO_2(SO_4)_3^{-4}$. This effect is shown in Table 9–3.

TABLE 9–2

EFFECT OF FREE ACIDITY ON URANIUM CAPACITY
OF AMBERLITE IRA-400

Conditions: 1.18 g U_3O_8/liter, 30.0 g SO_4/liter total,
excess sulfate added as $MgSO_4$.

Run	Free acidity	pH	Uranium capacity of resin		
			g U_3O_8/liter	lb U_3O_8/ft^3	% of A
A	2.0 g H_2SO_4/liter	1.85	79.8	4.98	100
B	5.0 g H_2SO_4/liter	1.45	70.9	4.42	88.9
C	10.0 g H_2SO_4/liter	1.30	57.1	3.56	71.5

TABLE 9–3

EFFECT OF URANIUM CONCENTRATION ON URANIUM CAPACITY
OF AMBERLITE IRA-400

Conditions: 5.0 g H_2SO_4/liter, 30.0 g $SO_4^=$/liter total,
excess sulfate added as $MgSO_4$.

Run	g U_3O_8/liter	Uranium capacity of resin		
		g U_3O_8/liter	lb U_3O_8/ft^3	% of C
A	0.22	46.6	2.90	65.7
B	0.59	59.3	3.70	83.6
C	1.18	70.9	4.42	100.0
D	2.95	88.9	5.54	125.4

Effect of sulfate concentration. The uranium saturation capacity
is a function of sulfate concentration, as would be expected from the
equilibrium equations. Increase in total sulfate concentration leads to an
increase in $UO_2(SO_4)_2^=$ and $UO_2(SO_4)_3^{-4}$ in the leach liquor. However,
in the range of sulfate concentration of most leach liquors, the increase in
sulfate also leads to an increase in bisulfate ion which more than compen-
sates for the increase in uranium complexes. The net result is a gradual
decrease in resin capacity with an increase in total sulfate concentration,
as shown in Table 9–4.

TABLE 9–4

EFFECT OF TOTAL SULFATE CONCENTRATION ON URANIUM CAPACITY OF AMBERLITE IRA-400

Conditions: 1.18 g U_3O_8/liter, 5.0 g H_2SO_4/liter,
excess sulfate added as $MgSO_4$.

Run	g $SO_4^=$/liter	Uranium capacity of resin		
		g U_3O_8/liter	lb U_3O_8/ft^3	% of A
A	20	72.1	4.50	100.0
B	30	70.0	4.42	98.3
C	50	67.5	4.21	93.5

Effect of iron. In most leach liquors, iron is present in both the ferrous, Fe^{++}, and ferric, Fe^{+++}, states. Ferrous iron does not form a sulfate complex and, therefore, is not adsorbed by the anion-exchange resin. However, ferric iron forms sulfate complexes of the types $Fe(SO_4)_2^-$ and $FeOH(SO_4)_2^=$, depending upon the pH of the solution. These complexes are adsorbed on the resin, but less readily than the uranium complexes. At the start of the adsorption step, the resin becomes saturated with iron long before it is saturated with uranium. During most of the adsorption cycle, uranium is adsorbed on exchange sites occupied by ferric iron, bisulfate, and sulfate ions. As the uranium adsorption proceeds, the ferric complex is displaced, so that at uranium saturation only a small quantity of iron remains.

Some of the iron is removed during the flushing and backwashing stage. The remainder of the iron is eluted from the resin during the first few bed volumes of elution and appears in the pregnant eluate along with the uranium. The effect of iron on uranium capacity is small unless the ferric concentration is above 5 g/liter, at low pH values. At pH values above 1.8, the ferric ion is adsorbed to such an extent that it decreases the uranium capacity.

Effect of vanadium. Sulfuric acid leaching of carnotite ores solubilizes vanadium. Depending on the amount of oxidant used, vanadium will appear in the solution either as quadrivalent vanadium, possibly as VO^{++}, or in the pentavalent state as VO_3^- and $VO_4^=$. The latter species are capable of undergoing exchange on anion-exchange resin.

Small amounts of pentavalent vanadium offer little difficulty, since this vanadium is eluted along with the uranium and does not accumulate on the resin to any extent. However, it contaminates the uranium cake, which then requires additional treatment. In concentrations above 1 g/liter, vanadium will cause a decrease in uranium capacity. This behavior has been used for vanadium recovery from uranium-barren solutions where the vanadium, present in the quadrivalent state, is first oxidized with sodium chlorate to the pentavalent state and then adsorbed on the anion-exchange resin. It can then be eluted efficiently with a saturated SO_2 solution [15,16].

In practice, vanadium does not constitute a problem, since the leaching conditions can usually be adjusted so that only quadrivalent vanadium appears in solution. In most leach liquors, the oxidation state of the liquor is governed by the Fe^{+++}/Fe^{++} ratio. Since Fe^{+++} ion will oxidize U^{+4} to U^{+6}, its presence ensures that uranium will be in the hexavalent state. In turn, Fe^{++} will reduce V^{+5} to V^{+4}, and its presence similarly ensures that vanadium will be in the reduced state.

The standard half-cell potential for the Fe^{+++}/Fe^{++} couple is -484 millivolts measured against the saturated calomel electrode. It has been found that by lowering the emf to a potential between -350 and -400 millivolts, the bulk of the iron will be present as Fe^{++} [17]. The common method of lowering the emf is by treatment with scrap iron or ferrous sulfate. Zinc or aluminum will also serve as a reductant. Care must be used in this practice, since in some cases excess reductant will also reduce uranium.

The use of hydrogen sulfide, sulfur dioxide, or sulfites is undesirable because of the possibility of producing polythionates. The effect of polythionates will be discussed in a later section.

Effects of phosphate and arsenate ions. Phosphate and arsenate ions are both adsorbed on anion exchangers, as $H_2PO_4^-$ and $H_2AsO_4^-$. In pregnant leach liquors, phosphate and arsenate form anionic complexes with uranium, which are also adsorbed. The actual capacity of the resin does not seem to be greatly affected when the total phosphate and arsenate concentration is less than 0.1 g/liter. It has been found that in the presence of ferric ion the effect is less, since ferric ion will form both cationic and anionic phosphate complexes.

The problems which these two elements present are twofold. First, the uranium phosphate complex tends to precipitate in the resin during elution and causes slower removal of uranium from the resin. This can be remedied by use of a more acidic eluant. Second, phosphate (and arsenate) will contaminate the final uranium cake, requiring such additional treatment as repulping in caustic soda solution.

Effect of chloride and nitrate ions. Anion-exchange resins have a high affinity for chloride and nitrate ions. Their presence in leach liquors tends to decrease the saturation capacity of the resin by occupying exchange sites normally occupied by uranium. In cases where uranium is not eluted completely from the resin, chloride and nitrate will give rise to an early leakage of uranium during the adsorption cycle.

Chloride appears in the leach liquor from a variety of sources. Where a salt roast is used for vanadium recovery, the amount of chloride appearing in the leach liquor will be very high. Brackish mine waters contain sufficient chloride to decrease uranium capacity. Where chloride eluting solutions are used, the chloride appears in the first portion of uranium-barren effluent. Recycle of this barren to recover its acid and uranium values, if present, introduces chloride ion into the pregnant liquor.

The use of chlorate as an oxidant in the leaching process is an additional source of chloride. However, in the quantities used (2 to 3 lb $NaClO_3$ per ton of ore) the concentration in the final leach liquor is low enough not to constitute a problem. Excess chlorate is adsorbed very strongly by the anion-exchange resin [18], markedly reducing uranium capacity.

Nitrates are adsorbed by the resin less strongly than chlorate ion, but more strongly than chloride ion. Nitrate ions appear in the leach liquor only in those plants using nitrate elution. Nitrate can be introduced into the leach by recycling the early portions of the uranium barren effluent, from the effluent from backwashing after elution, and by seepage from the barren-liquor ponds.

The quantitative effects of these compounds are difficult to assess, since they will vary with each leach liquor. The results obtained on a synthetic leach liquor are given in Table 9–5.

Effect of temperature. Increasing the temperature of the leach liquor increases the rate of diffusion of the uranium molecule into the resin matrix.

TABLE 9–5

EFFECT OF CHLORIDE, NITRATE, AND CHLORATE IONS ON
URANIUM CAPACITY OF AMBERLITE IRA-400

Conditions: 1.18 g U_3O_8/liter, 30 g $SO_4^=$/liter total,
3.5 g H_2SO_4/liter, excess sulfate added as Na_2SO_4.

Concentration of anion added	% of original break-through capacity	% of original saturation capacity
0.02 M ClO_3^-	76	80.5
0.02 M Cl^-	96	98.3
0.05 M Cl^-	97	89.4
0.02 M NO_3^-	97	86.6
0.05 M NO_3^-	91	68.7

This results in an increase in capacity to break-through, but does not affect the saturation uranium loadings to any measurable degree.

At low temperatures, 35 to 40°F, the reaction rates slow somewhat and may lower the actual operating capacity, although saturation loadings are not affected. Temperature also affects the elution reactions. Eluate volume requirements decrease with an increase in temperature.

It will be shown later that, provided the resin is saturated each cycle, little or no chemical costs can be saved by operating at elevated temperatures. Because of the large volumes of liquor that must be heated, operation at an elevated temperature is not economically justifiable.

Elution reactions. Once the resin has been saturated with uranium, the next step is to effect the elution of the uranium with suitable agents, to recover the uranium quantitatively and economically from the eluate.

Two elution systems are currently practiced, differing primarily in the anion used. In one, 1 M nitrate is used to elute the uranium from the resin and in the other, 1 M chloride is used. Nitrates are more expensive than sodium chloride, but they are also more efficient eluting agents. The choice of eluate is a matter of economic availability and individual preference. The main elution reactions may be written as follows:

$$R_4UO_2(SO_4)_3 + 4X^- \rightleftarrows 4RX + UO_2^{++} + 3SO_4^=,$$

$$RHSO_4 + X^- \rightleftarrows RX + HSO_4^-,$$

$$R_2SO_4 + 2X^- \rightleftarrows 2RX + SO_4^=,$$

where $X = NO_3^-$ or Cl^-, and R is the fixed site on the resin.

Nitrate elution. Nitrate elutions are performed with 1 M nitrate solutions with an acidity of 0.1 to 0.4 M H^+. The remaining cations consist of either NH_4^+, Na^+, or Mg^{++}, depending on the uranium precipitant used.

When the uranium is displaced from the resin by nitrate ion, the resin becomes saturated with nitrate. The amount of nitrate absorbed on the resin is a function only of the ion-exchange capacity of the resin, not of the volume of eluate used. In practice, all eluting solutions are recycled, so that they contain significant concentrations of HSO_4^- and $SO_4^=$ ion. In nitrate elution, the nitrate ion will occupy about 90 percent of the total exchange sites, the remainder being occupied by HSO_4^- and $SO_4^=$.

The theoretical nitrate loss, then, for a resin having a volume capacity for nitrate of 1.30 meq/ml, would be 5.1 pounds of nitrate, as HNO_3, per cubic foot of resin. The uranium-rich eluate will then be deficient in nitrate by this same quantity. In plants using nitrate elutions, the lost nitrate is replenished by adding nitric acid or nitrates to the barren eluate after the uranium is recovered by neutralization and precipitation. The use of nitric acid not only makes up the nitrate losses but also provides acidity for the next elution cycle. Sulfuric acid may be used to provide necessary additional acidity.

The theoretical nitrate loss is always exceeded in practice because some nitrate values remain in the solution in the column. Significant quantities of nitrate are also lost to the "iron" and "uranium" cakes. In practice, the nitrate losses vary between 4.5 and 6.0 lb of HNO_3 per cubic foot of resin per cycle for column operations. For a resin originally loaded to 3 lb U_3O_8/ft^3, this amounts to 1.5 to 2.0 lb of HNO_3 per lb of U_3O_8.

The higher the nitrate concentration, the less the volume required for elution. Below 0.8 M NO_3^-, the elutions are very sluggish and prolonged. High nitrate concentrations, above 1.2 M, work very well. Use of these concentrations, however, increases the amount of nitrate lost by diffusion and soluble losses to the iron and uranium cakes. The optimum concentration appears to be 1.0 to 1.2 M NO_3^-.

The acidity used for nitrate elution depends upon the amount of nitrate replenished as HNO_3 and the total amount of solution used. The early portions of elution are less affected by acidity than the last half of the elution. The higher the acidity maintained in the elution circuit, the more efficient is the elution of uranium. If the acidity is less than 0.1 N H^+, the elutions become very sluggish. High acidities, 0.3 to 0.4 N H^+, are used whenever polythionates are present, since this appears to aid in their elution and destruction by oxidation. High acidities are also necessary whenever appreciable amounts of phosphate are adsorbed on the resin along with the uranium.

For every mole of uranium adsorbed on the resin as $UO_2(SO_4)_3^{-4}$, three moles of sulfate will appear in the uranium-rich eluate. Also, depending on the uranium capacity of the resin, several additional moles of sulfate, originally present as HSO_4^- and $SO_4^=$, will appear in the uranium eluate. When this eluate is neutralized and the uranium is precipitated, and either filtered or thickened, the barren eluate will contain nearly all the sulfate. On recycling, the sulfate concentration will build up to the point where sulfates will precipitate out of solution.

Increased sulfate decreases the efficiency of the eluting solution so that more eluate is required. To circumvent this buildup of sulfate, either a portion of barren eluate is bled from the circuit with the loss of its nitrate, or a lime precipitation is used. By carefully adding lime it is possible to decrease the sulfate concentrations to a value of 10 to 20 g $SO_4^=/1$ in the fresh eluate.

Chloride elution. Chloride elutions are made with 1 M sodium chloride solutions acidified with sulfuric acid. The effect of concentration is the same as for nitrate elution, with one exception. At high chloride concentrations, above 1.5 M Cl^-, and under acidic conditions, the efficiency of elution can actually decrease, since under these conditions the uranyl sulfate complex is converted to a chloride complex of the type $UO_2Cl_4^=$. The optimum chloride concentration used is about 1.0 M.

The theoretical consumption of chloride is about the same as for nitrate. Since the equivalent weight of sodium chloride is 58.5, compared with 63 for HNO_3, the theoretical loss for a 1.30 meq/ml would be 4.75 lb $NaCl/ft^3$ of resin. However, plants using chloride elutions generally operate with a high sulfate background in the eluting solution, so that the amount of HSO_4^- and $SO_4^=$ adsorbed on the resin at the end of the elution cycle will be higher. In addition, chloride is not held as tightly as nitrate, so that the over-all equivalent chloride loss is slightly less than the nitrate loss.

Acidity has about the same effect in chloride elution as in nitrate elution: the higher the acidity, the more efficient the elution. However, the optimum acidity is about 0.10 to 0.15 N H_2SO_4, since the acid will eventually be neutralized to precipitate uranium from the uranium-rich eluate. Sometimes, as when phosphates are present in the pregnant liquor, slightly higher acidity must be maintained.

Sulfate ion decreases the elution efficiency of the chloride solution in much the same manner as it does for nitrate eluates. One unusual effect has been noted [19]. When the excess sulfate is present as $MgSO_4$, the elution efficiency is decreased more markedly than when the excess sulfate is present as $(NH_4)_2SO_4$ or Na_2SO_4.

It has also been found that when $(NH_4)_2SO_4$ is present to the extent of 100 g $SO_4^=$/liter, the uranium elutions become more efficient than when intermediate concentrations (35 to 100 g $SO_4^=$/liter) are present. Many plants using chloride elution now operate at 100 to 120 g $SO_4^=$/liter in their eluate circuit.

Sulfuric acid elution. Sulfuric acid elution has the advantage of using a cheap and available acid for uranium removal. Unfortunately, uranium elutions with sulfuric acid are quite extended, and a very large amount of acid must be neutralized to remove the uranium. Several means of reducing the neutralization costs have been studied in the laboratory, such as electrodialysis through permselective anion-exchange membranes [20,21].

Eluex process. In the Eluex process, uranium is eluted with 10 percent sulfuric acid. The uranium in the sulfuric acid is then extracted with di-2-ethylhexyl phosphoric acid in a kerosene diluent [22]. Next, the organic phase is stripped with sodium carbonate, and the uranium is recovered either by caustic precipitation or, after acidification and boiling to remove CO_2, by precipitation with either $NaOH$, NH_3, or MgO.

This process shows promise in the RIP circuit, where the special resin, Amberlite XE-123, is eluted more readily with 10 percent H_2SO_4 than is Amberlite IRA-400. In addition, the current nitrate elution system requires a high rate of "bleed-off" of barren eluate to maintain a solution balance.

Neutral salt elutions. The use of a neutral sodium chloride solution has also been considered for elution, since no additional acid would be needed [23,24]. A typical elution would use only one volume of 5 M NaCl per volume of resin (called a bed volume or column volume). This salt solution converts the uranium sulfate complex to a chloride complex which can be removed readily with 4 bed volumes of water. Unfortunately, the chloride effluent is diluted to such an extent that considerably more than the theoretical amount of sodium chloride is needed to recycle the excess chloride.

9–2.3 Solution characteristics of carbonate leach liquors.

Carbonate leaching of uranium ores is usually performed only when the basic constituents ($CaCO_3$) of the ore preclude acid leaching because of high sulfuric acid consumption. To date, no commercial-size plant uses ion-exchange recovery of uranium from carbonate leach liquors, although it is chemically feasible [25,26]. The reason is that carbonate leaching ordinarily produces a leach liquor pure enough that ion exchange is not needed for additional purification.

However, ion exchange in carbonate liquors has been operated on a pilot-plant basis with both clear solutions and slurries. A resin-in-pulp pilot plant has been operated using unfiltered carbonate leach slurries at the AEC pilot plant at Grand Junction, Colorado [27,28]. In this process, although filtration is eliminated, the ability to recycle the uranium barren carbonate liquor remains virtually unchanged.

Adsorption reactions. Carbonate leach liquors contain as their main constituents Na^+, $UO_2(CO_3)_3^{-4}$, $CO_3^=$, HCO_3^-, and $SO_4^=$ ions. The uranium in solution is so strongly complexed that addition of acid converts the $CO_3^=$ to HCO_3^- before the uranium complex is destroyed [29]. Data on the effect of nature of the leach liquor are meager. The ion-exchange reactions involved can be written as follows:

$$4RX + UO_2(CO_3)_3^{-4} \rightleftarrows R_4UO_2(CO_3)_3 + 4X^-,$$

$$RX + HCO_3^- \rightleftarrows RHCO_3 + X^-,$$

$$2RX + CO_3^= \rightleftarrows R_2CO_3 + 2X^-,$$

where X = NO_3^- or Cl^-.

Effect of total carbonate concentration. Adsorption of uranium by ion-exchange resins from carbonate liquors containing 100 g $CO_3^=$/liter is very poor, principally because too much of the carbonate is adsorbed. However, when the total carbonate is in the 10 g $CO_3^=$/liter range, very efficient loadings may be obtained. At this level, the capacities of the resin approach theoretical, that is, one mole of uranium adsorbed per four moles of exchange sites.

Effect of carbonate/bicarbonate ratio. The quaternary anion-exchange resins have an appreciable affinity for bicarbonate ion over that for carbonate ion. Consequently, the ratio of these two ions in solution is important. Reduction in HCO_3^- content by adding caustic will increase the capacity of the resin for uranium.

Effect of other ions. Other anions tending to accumulate as the barren carbonate liquor is recycled will be sulfate, phosphate, and either chloride or nitrate, depending on the elution system used. At pH below 10.8, vanadium seriously competes with uranium for ion-exchange sites. Sulfate and phosphate in moderate concentrations can be tolerated, but chloride and nitrate reduce the capacity of the resin for uranium, as in sulfuric acid leach liquors.

Elution reactions. The main elution reactions are precisely the reverse of the adsorption reactions. The common eluting agents used are either 1 to 2 M NaCl or NH_4NO_3. The elutions are very efficient, with only about 3 to 4 bed volumes of eluate required for 99 percent elution. The remaining uranium can be readily removed if the eluting solution contains about 0.1 M Na_2CO_3. The rich eluate obtained can be treated by precipitation with excess caustic or by neutralization with an acid to precipitate uranium.

Acid elutions cannot be used effectively, since the acid will react with the carbonate to produce CO_2. This gassing not only causes difficulty in operation but also may shatter the resin beads.

9–3. Columnar Ion Exchange

9–3.1 Factors affecting extraction. Once the solution composition has been set, the saturation capacity of the resin for uranium has also been fixed. It then remains for the ion-exchange unit to be designed so that the resin will be saturated with uranium at the point it is to be removed from the adsorption stream and eluted. This is desirable from the standpoint of economy, because the elution costs per unit of resin are essentially the same regardless of the quantity of uranium adsorbed on the resin.

Description of equipment. The equipment used to house the ion-exchange resin employed for uranium recovery usually consists of a steel cylindrical shell lined with hard rubber to withstand the acidic leach solutions, acidic chloride or nitrate eluting agents, and caustic solutions for resin rejuvenation.

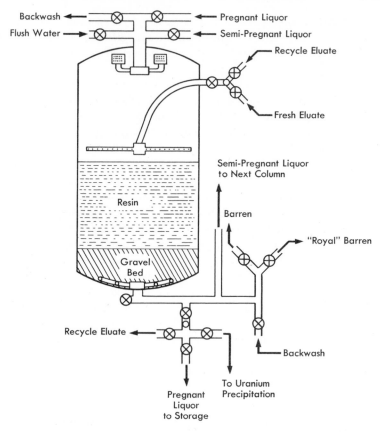

FIG. 9–3. Typical ion-exchange column used in recovery of uranium [9].

A typical column used in the uranium industry is 7 feet in diameter and 12 feet high (Fig. 9–3). At the bottom of the column is a graded gravel bed which supports 200 cubic feet of resin (5 feet depth). The eluate distributor for introducing the uranium eluting solutions is 6 inches above the resin bed. Above this is 5 feet of freeboard space, occupied by water in the water-dome units and by air in the air-dome unit. This void space is necessary for backwashing the resin. Enough space is usually provided for 100 percent expansion of the resin bed.

Near the top of the column is the distributor through which the pregnant liquor is introduced into the column. This distributor also serves as the solution outlet during backwashing.

Flow rates. The flow rates used in the uranium industry vary considerably. The optimum flow rate used is such that the first column in a multicolumn system will be fully saturated when uranium is detected in the effluent from the second column.

The flow rates used in uranium plants vary from 0.25 to 1.00 gal/ft^3 per minute. These rates correspond to a retention time (1 column) of 3 to 12 minutes. The flow rate depends upon the character of the leach solution and the condition of the resin. In the South African plants, because the leach solutions contain some resin poisons, use is made of the lower flow rates. Other plants are generally designed with units for a flow rate of 1.0 gal/ft^3 per minute (3-minute retention time) with a 20 to 50 percent safety factor.

9–3.2 Processing of pregnant liquor. The over-all uranium recovery operation is divided into 6 phases: (1) adsorption cycle, (2) flush, (3) back-wash and settling, (4) elution, (5) backwash and settling, (6) standby.

Adsorption cycle. When a pregnant uranium liquor is passed through a bed of ion-exchange resins, three main reactions take place. If we designate the fixed portion of the resin as R^+ and the mobile ions as X^-, these reactions may be written as follows:

$$R^+X^- + HSO_4^- \rightarrow R^+HSO_4^- + X^-,$$

$$2R^+X^- + SO_4^= \rightarrow (R^+)_2SO_4^= + 2X^-,$$

$$4R^+X^- + UO_2(SO_4)_3^{-4} \rightarrow (R^+)_4UO_2(SO_4)_3^{-4} + 4X^-.$$

The first two reactions remove $X^-(Cl^-$ or $NO_3^-)$ long before the capacity for uranium is realized. The uranium tends to saturate the upper portion of the bed and begins to form a concentration profile such as that depicted in Fig. 9–4.

For optimum efficiency, it is desirable to fully saturate a column of resin, bed depth $O\text{-}A$, before removing the uranium. To achieve this, a

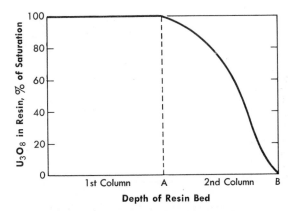

FIG. 9–4. Idealized concentration profile of uranium in resin vs. total bed depth at time of break-through of second column.

second column is placed in series with a bed depth *A-B*. When uranium appears in the effluent at point *B*, the first column is removed, and a third column is placed in series to adsorb the uranium leakage from the second column. When the third column begins to leak uranium, the first column, which has since been eluted, is then placed in series to adsorb the leakage from the third column. This cyclic process allows a continuous adsorption of uranium by a single set of 3 or 4 columns.

The length of the loading cycle will depend upon the flow rate, uranium concentration of the pregnant liquor, and on the capacity of the resin. Thus, for a 0.50 g U_3O_8/liter pregnant solution fed to a column of resin with a capacity of 48 g U_3O_8/liter (3 lb/ft^3) at 1 gal/ft^3 per minute, the length of time a column would be on stream as the first in series would be 12 hours.

During the course of the adsorption cycle, uranium analyses are made on the pregnant liquor feed, the effluent from the first column (semipregnant), and the barren effluent from the second column. At the point where uranium appears in the effluent from the second column, >0.001 g U_3O_8/liter, the semipregnant values are usually 80 to 100 percent of the pregnant uranium concentration. A typical semipregnant leakage curve is shown in Fig. 9–5.

Flush. When the second column begins to leak uranium, the pregnant-liquor feed is stopped, and fresh water is flushed through the first column into the second column at the same flow rate as that orginally used for adsorption. Generally, 1 to 3 bed volumes of water are used for this operation.

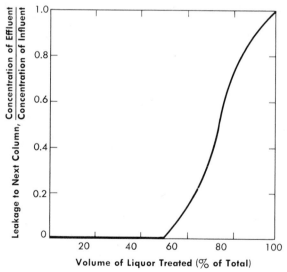

Fig. 9–5. Typical leakage curve for uranium.

The purpose of the flush is to displace the pregnant liquor which fills the resin voids and that which occupies the space above the resin in the column. The flush also reduces the acidity of the resin by hydrolysis:

$$2R^+HSO_4^- \xrightarrow{\text{H}_2\text{O}} (R^+)_2SO_4 + 2H^+ + SO_4^=.$$

A small quantity of iron and uranium is also removed during flushing.

Backwash and settling. The backwash operation is one of the most important mechanical operations involved in ion-exchange recovery of uranium. During the course of uranium adsorption, the liquor being fed to the ion-exchange units is mechanically filtered by the ion-exchange resin. The ion-exchange resin itself is a strong polyelectrolyte that can flocculate any colloidal materials which bypassed the leach-solution filters and clarification units. Thus, if 20 ppm of solids are flocculated by the resin, for a column on stream for 12 hr at a 1 gal/ft^3 per minute rate, a 200 ft^3 bed will collect 24 lb of solids. The solids generally collect as a small layer on the top of the resin bed. This causes nonuniform flow or channeling through the resin bed and high pressure drops across the bed.

To eliminate buildup of these solids, the resin is expanded hydraulically by passing water upflow through the bed. The solids particles usually have lower settling velocities than do the resin beads themselves, so that the former may be removed from the resin.

In backwashing, flow rates of the order of 3 to 4 gal/ft^2 per minute are necessary to keep the resin beds free of solids. The backwash operation should be continued until the overflow effluent is clear. This normally requires from 4 to 5 bed volumes of water. The backwash also removes a small amount of uranium (about 0.5 percent of that originally adsorbed). The effluent is recycled to the leaching circuit in order to recover its uranium values. After backwashing the resin is allowed to settle before elution is begun.

In many South African plants, the backwash at this point has been eliminated, and instead the resin is backwashed after elution. This will be discussed later.

Elution. The elution of uranium from the resin is achieved with acidified solutions of either 1 M nitrate or chloride salts. The nitrate ion is a more efficient eluting agent by a factor of 2 or 3. The total eluate required for nitrate elution is about 8 bed volumes, and up to 25 are required for the chloride system. In the chloride system, four column sets are required because of the relatively lengthy elution.

Multistage elution. The nature of the elution curve (Fig. 9–6) is such that the bulk of the uranium eluted appears in the first half of the cycle, and the second half of the cycle contains only a small amount. Only the first portion is precipitated; the second portion is recycled. In operation,

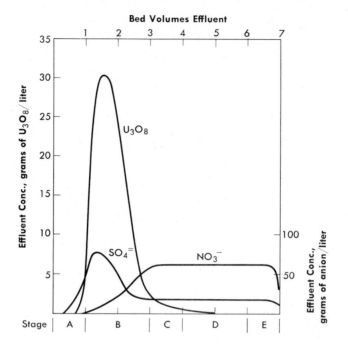

FIG. 9–6. Typical curves for 1 M nitrate elution of uranium.

TABLE 9–6

ELUTION OF URANIUM FROM THE ION-EXCHANGE RESIN

Stage	$NO_3{}^-$	Cl^-	From	To
A	0.5–1.0	1.0–1.3	Recycle eluate	Pregnant liquor
B	2.0–4.0	8–12	Recycle eluate	Precipitation
C	0.5–1.0	1–2	Fresh eluate	Precipitation
D	2.0–4.0	8–12	Fresh eluate	Recycle eluate
E	0.5–1.0	1.0–1.3	Water	Recycle eluate

the elution cycle is divided into five distinct stages, shown in Table 9–6. Flow rates on elution vary considerably from plant to plant. In the South African plants ($NO_3{}^-$ elution), flow rates as low as 0.05 gal/ft^3 per minute are utilized. Chloride elutions generally are conducted at a higher rate, 0.25 to 0.50 gal/ft^3 per minute.

Stage A. In this stage the eluting solution displaces the void water in the column. The nitrate or chloride ions also displace $SO_4^=$, HSO_4^-, and some iron from the ion-exchange sites. The uranium concentration is quite low (<1 g U_3O_8/liter), as is the eluting ion concentration, so that this solution is returned to pregnant liquor storage.

Stage B. In this stage, the bulk of the uranium is removed from the resin. The effluent is sent either to pregnant eluate storage or directly to uranium precipitation tanks.

Stage C. This stage employs fresh eluate to displace the return eluate in the resin voids and is continued until the effluent uranium concentration decreases to 1 to 2 g U_3O_8/liter. The effluent is sent either to pregnant eluate storage or directly to uranium precipitation tanks. The average uranium concentration of Stages B and C is numerically equal to the capacity of the resin, in g U_3O_8/liter of resin, divided by the total number of bed volumes of liquor sent to precipitation each cycle. Typical values would be 10 to 15 g U_3O_8/liter for nitrate elution and 5 to 8 g U_3O_8/liter for chloride elution.

Stage D. In this stage, fresh eluate is used to remove the remaining uranium from the resin. The effluent uranium concentration at the end of this stage is about 0.05 to 0.10 g U_3O_8/liter, with an average concentration of less than 1 g U_3O_8/liter. The effluent is sent to recycle eluate storage. For solution balance, the volume of solution used in this stage must be the same as that in Stage B.

Stage E. In this stage, fresh water is passed through the column to displace the nitrate or chloride values in the resin voids. It, too, is sent to recycle eluate storage. The amount of water used in this stage is limited by the volume of liquor used in Stage A.

Solution balance. Because of the value of the nitrate in the eluting solution, recycle of the eluate is of economic necessity. In a uranium plant, the elution system is essentially a closed circuit. The volume of new solution entering the circuit each cycle consists solely of the water introduced in Stage E. The volume of solution leaving the elution circuit is the bleed-off liquor in Stage A plus a smaller quantity removed with the iron precipitate (if two-stage precipitation is practiced) and with the uranium cake. The basic solution flow for a three-column installation is shown in Fig. 9–7.

Whenever precipitants such as lime, magnesia, or caustic soda are used, slurries or solutions of these compounds may be prepared in barren eluate, so as not to introduce additional solution into the circuit.

Electrolyte balance. Another important feature of the elution circuit is its electrolyte balance. If recycled eluting solution is to be utilized, it must not contain extraneous ions that would hamper its elution efficiency.

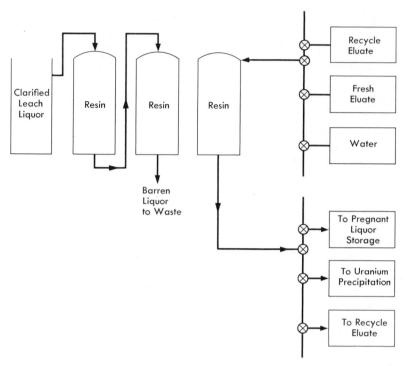

FIG. 9–7. Solution flow through a three-column ion-exchange circuit.

Since the electrolyte balance involves the precipitation of uranium it will be discussed here.

In the elution of uranium with fresh eluate solution, the uranium-rich effluent contains not only the original constituents less the nitrate adsorbed, but also the sulfate that was present on the loaded resin. The quantity of sulfate involved is a function of the pregnant liquor and the degree of loading. Three moles of sulfate will appear in the uranium-rich eluate for every mole of uranium present. Not all the ion-exchange sites are occupied by the uranyl sulfate complex; an additional one or more moles of sulfate are present as HSO_4^- and $SO_4^=$. Any HSO_4^- present will appear as sulfuric acid in the rich eluate.

When the uranium in the rich eluate is precipitated, the bulk of the sulfate remains in solution and is recycled. As this sulfate builds up in concentration, it causes the elutions to be less sharp, and also makes complete elution of the last traces of uranium from the resin more difficult.

To prevent sulfate buildup, some plants use a "two-stage" precipitation. In the first stage a dilute slurry of lime is added to the uranium-rich eluate to raise the pH to about 3.5. This operation serves several purposes: (1) it neutralizes the free acid with a cheap chemical, (2) it removes sulfate from the eluate as calcium sulfate, and (3) it precipitates the bulk of the iron present in the eluate, resulting in a purer uranium solution.

Unfortunately, a clean-cut iron-uranium separation is not realized. Even under good operating conditions, up to 5 percent of the total uranium is precipitated. This precipitate, called "iron cake," must be returned to the leaching circuit to recover its uranium values.

Three chemical agents are used to recover uranium from eluate. Either ammonia, caustic soda, or magnesia will precipitate uranium quantitatively from the eluate at a pH of 6.8 to 7.0. The choice of reagent is a matter of preference of the metallurgist, economic availability, and specifications imposed on the uranium concentrate by the refineries.

Backwash after elution. In many plants, there may be considerable time available after elution when the column is on standby, waiting to be used. It has been found in some of the South African plants that another backwash at this time serves to remove nitrate values still remaining in the resin voids and any that may have diffused into the upper portions of the ion-exchange column. When the column is placed on stream without this backwash, there is inevitably a small leakage of uranium called "royal barren." The uranium in the "royal barren" is that which was left on the resin at the end of the elution cycle. It can be removed by the nitrate that is displaced from the resin by the incoming semipregnant liquor. Any additional nitrate present in the water dome adds to this difficulty. The common practice had been to recycle "royal barren" to the pregnant liquor, thus adding nitrate to the pregnant liquor, which in turn competed for the ion-exchange sites during the subsequent loading cycle. This caused earlier break-throughs and lower capacities.

By backwashing after elution, the "royal barren" is decreased, resulting in a better over-all recovery of uranium. This backwash also removes solids that may have precipitated during the elution cycle. Since the resin after elution is in the nitrate or chloride form, the flow rates for backwashing after elution are lower than those for backwashing after adsorption (Fig. 9–2). This is a result of the higher density of the resin when in the uranium-saturated state.

Standby. After the column of resin is eluted of uranium, it is placed on standby to be used when the next changeover occurs. In some plants, rather than let the column stand idle, it is placed on stream as the third column on adsorption. In this way, the resin can be converted from the nitrate or chloride form to the bisulfate form before it needs to be used for uranium adsorption.

9–4. RESIN-IN-PULP ION EXCHANGE

Some uranium ores exhibit extremely poor filtering and settling characteristics after leaching. To avoid extremely large-size liquid-solids separation equipment, the ion-exchange process has been modified to extract uranium directly from the leach pulp. This is the modification called the "Resin-In-Pulp" or RIP process [30,31]. The chemistry of the process is precisely the same as that used in columnar ion exchange, but the equipment is radically different.

9–4.1 Factors affecting extraction. *Equipment.* In the RIP process, after the ore is leached, the largest particles of solids are first removed with classifiers. The final sand-slimes separation is effected with hydrocyclones. If this slurry were to be passed through a fixed-bed ion-exchange unit, the pulp would accumulate between the packed resin particles and impede solution flow. To prevent this accumulation of solids, the ion-exchange resin beads are contained in cube-shaped baskets, enclosed with Carpenter 20 stainless steel screens but open at the top. A typical screen is Tyler Ton Cap. 147, a nonblinding flexible screen with openings of 0.013 by 0.097 inch. The resins used are larger in size than for column operations, 95 percent being larger than 0.84 millimeter (20 mesh).

Present RIP plants consist of 14 rectangular tanks or banks each containing up to 10 such cube-shaped baskets. The baskets are connected to a

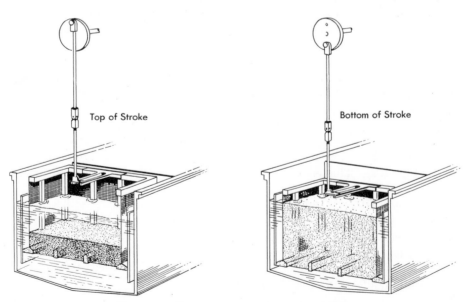

Fig. 9–8. Cross-section of RIP basket [27].

motor-driven crank so that they may be raised and lowered 5 to 10 times per minute. The expansion and contraction of the beads during the stroke are shown in Fig. 9–8. The pulp is pumped or flows by gravity from one stage to the next. The de-sanded pulp containing uranium in solution passes through the banks continuously. The movement of the baskets keeps the slimes in suspension and also keeps the resin bed expanded sufficiently for it to come into contact with the liquor for efficient uranium extraction.

Pulp-to-resin ratio. For maximum efficiency of uranium extraction the pulp-to-resin ratio is maintained at 6:1. Thus, for a bank containing 100 cubic feet of resin, the total amount of pulp in the bank at any one time would be 4500 gallons.

Retention time. Retention times in the RIP system are longer than those in column operations. The total retention time per bank is from 7 to 17 minutes.

9–4.2 Processing of pregnant pulp. *Loading cycle.* In the column operation, two or sometimes three columns are in series on adsorption at any one time. In the RIP process, as many as ten banks are on stream at one time, that is, if the banks are numbered from 1 to 14, banks 1 to 10 might be on adsorption at one particular time. The uranium-rich pulp is fed to bank No. 1 and circulated through the remaining nine banks, in order, up to bank No. 10. The pulp emerging from this bank should be barren of uranium. The uranium concentration profile for the 10 banks on stream is of the same type as that for the two-column system given in Fig. 9–4.

When uranium appears in the effluent from bank No. 10, the resin in bank No. 1 is saturated with uranium. This bank is then removed from the adsorption stream, and freshly eluted bank No. 11 is placed on the adsorption stream to adsorb the small amount of uranium leakage from bank No. 10. Changeover times are about 1.5 to 3.0 hours, depending on the uranium concentration of the pregnant pulp, the flow rate, and the uranium capacity of the resin.

Flush. When bank No. 1 is removed from the adsorption cycle, it is drained and hosed with a minimum amount of water to displace the holdup barren and to remove adhering slimes. The effluent from this wash is sent back to pregnant pulp storage to recover its uranium values.

Elution. Nitrate elutions are generally used in RIP plants because nitrates are more effective and less corrosive than chlorides. The eluate consists of 1 M ammonium nitrate acidified with nitric or sulfuric acid to 0.10 to 0.20 N H^+.

Multistage elution. Multistage elution is accomplished in a different manner than with columnar ion exchange. In the RIP circuit, 4 banks are eluted in series, with the fresh uranium-loaded resin in the last bank. Thus, at the changeover time when bank No. 1 is removed from the adsorption cycle, it becomes the fourth bank in the elution cycle, being preceded by banks 12, 13, and 14, in order. The fresh eluate is fed to the first bank (No. 12), where 45 gal/ft^3 of resin are added. The baskets move continuously but solution flow to the bank is stopped. At the changeover period (1.5 to 3.0 hours), the uranium-rich eluate in tank No. 1 is drained. The effluent is then sent to precipitation. The eluate in bank No. 14 is pumped into bank No. 1. The eluate in bank No. 13 is pumped into bank No. 14 while the eluate in bank No. 12 is pumped into bank No. 13. The resin in bank No. 12 is then rinsed with about 2.5 gallons of water per cubic foot of resin, and the effluent also is advanced to bank No. 13.

In this manner, an efficient elution of uranium is accomplished. The solution flow through a fourteen-bank circuit is shown in Fig. 9–9.

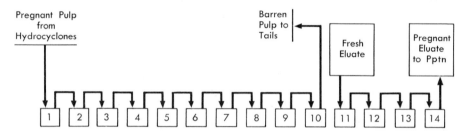

FIG. 9–9. Solution flow through a 14-bank RIP circuit.

Precipitation of uranium. The precipitation of uranium is conducted in the same manner as in columnar ion exchange. The only difference is that prior clarification may be required. Where two-stage precipitation is used, the slimes are coagulated effectively and are removed with the iron cake. Most uranium precipitations are carried out with a slurry of magnesium oxide.

Solution balance. A solution balance in the eluate circuit is harder to maintain economically in the RIP circuit than in the columnar ion-exchange system. In the latter, the first bed volume or so of effluent from elution of the ion-exchange columns can be bled back to the pregnant liquor, but in the RIP circuit this cannot be done. Consequently, about 10 percent of the barren eluate filtrate must be discarded each cycle, with an attendant loss of from 3.8 to 4.5 pounds of NH_4NO_3 per pound of U_3O_8.

Electrolyte balance. The electrolyte balance is maintained by the bleed-off used to effect solution balance. In two-stage precipitation, the sulfate buildup reaches equilibrium at about 40 g $SO_4^=$/liter, compared with 100 g $SO_4^=$/liter for single-stage precipitation.

9–5. SPECIAL PROBLEMS IN ION-EXCHANGE RECOVERY

9–5.1 Resin "poisons." In ion-exchange recovery, some materials adsorbed on the resin are not removed during the normal elution cycle, but gradually accumulate on the resin. This fouling has been called "resin poisoning," although sometimes the resin can be rejuvenated by special regeneration techniques.

For an ion-exchange recovery plant using a flow rate of 1 gal/ft^3 per minute, the resin will extract values from up to 300 times its weight in solution per day. At this large ratio, it is not surprising that trace impurities in the leach liquor become important. Two general types of "resin poisons" are encountered in uranium recovery.

The first is a "physical poison." This includes materials precipitating within the pores of the resin matrix. They do not occupy exchange sites, but do hinder the rate at which the uranium diffuses into the resin. The characteristic effect of this type of poison is to cause early leakage of uranium during adsorption. In some cases, saturation capacity is not reduced at all.

The second is a "chemical poison." Poisons of this type are ions adsorbed by the resin more strongly than the uranium complex. They also occupy exchange sites, decreasing the uranium capacity of the resin. Although all such poisons can be removed by specific elution techniques to rejuvenate the resin, the cost of regeneration agents sometimes exceeds the value of the resin.

Silica fouling. Silica is the most prevalent foreign matter which contaminates ion-exchange resins. In all sulfuric acid leach liquors, silica is present in concentrations ranging from trace quantities to several grams per liter. At concentrations which exceed the solubility of monomeric silicic acid more than tenfold, most of the silica must either be a colloidal solution of silica, or a supersaturated solution of silicic acid, or both. Silica in solution is extremely stable; aged leach liquors more than a year old still contain silica in the gram per liter range.

Two important factors affecting the stability of solubilized silica are pH and salt concentration. According to Iler [32], the maximum stability of silicic acid or colloidal silica is at a pH of about 2. Gelling is most rapid at pH 5 to 6. The theory is that at pH 2 to 5, the charge on silica is low enough for the individual molecules to collide and combine to form aggregates. Since OH$^-$ ions also catalyze the condensation reaction by placing a negative charge on the sol, the net effect is a minimum stability at pH 5 to 6. An increase in total salt concentration (ionic strength) minimizes the effect of charges on the silica so that this, too, will lead to gel formation.

In uranium recovery by ion exchange, the acidity of leach liquor that first comes into contact with the resin is reduced by the removal of HSO_4^- ions by the resin. This increase in pH reduces the stability of silica in the leach liquor. The stabilized silica in the leach liquor, since it is essentially undissociated, can penetrate the ion-exchange resin matrix. Here it comes into contact with a high ionic strength due to the ion-exchange capacity of the resin (about 5 molal). The solution inside the resin is also less acidic than the solution outside the resin. All these factors present conditions which lead to aggregation and precipitation of silica within the resin beads.

Later in the process, at the end of the adsorption cycle, the pregnant liquor in the resin voids is flushed out with water, resulting in a dilution of the liquor and an accompanying rise in pH. This, too, can lead to silica deposition. The deposited silica, although it does not occupy exchange sites, interferes with the rate-controlling diffusion process of ions into and out of the resin matrix. Silica buildup causes the resin to become sluggish in operation, resulting in low operating capacities. Lower flow rates must be used unless the silica is removed.

The rate of silica buildup can be reduced considerably by maintaining acidic conditions in the ion-exchange columns at all times. Acidification of all flush and backwash water helps maintain the acidity.

The most common means for removing silica from the resin is to dissolve it out with aqueous caustic soda. Since caustic soda regeneration is also used to remove other poisons, it will be discussed in detail in a later section. Another means of silica removal has been developed at the South Australian Department of Mines. This regeneration scheme utilizes a mixture of sulfuric acid and hydrofluoric acid, the latter added as ammonium acid fluoride. The hydrofluoric acid formed dissolves the precipitated silica to form fluosilicic acid:

$$6HF + SiO_2 \rightarrow H_2SiF_6 + 2H_2O.$$

Since $SiF_6^=$ would be adsorbed on the resin, the sulfuric acid serves to displace the $SiF_6^=$ completely from the resin. Studies at the Rohm & Haas laboratories indicate that 1 mole of SiO_2 is removed for each 6 moles of fluoride added, in accord with the stoichiometry of the above equation.

Polythionates. Polythionates belong to the class of sulfur compounds with the chemical formula $S_xO_6^=$, where $x = 3, 4, 5,$ and 6. Polythionates are completely adsorbed by the resin during the adsorption process. Since they occupy exchange sites, they reduce the capacity of the resin for uranium.

The source of polythionates in the leach liquor has been studied extensively by Robinson [33] in South Africa and by Napier and Miller [34] in England. Although at times the results of these researches conflict, in view of the many ways in which polythionate can be formed [35], it may be concluded that any reduced sulfur compounds in the leach slurry are potential sources of polythionates. Polythionate fouling is most prevalent in the South African plants which leach previously cyanided gold ores. It has also occurred in some Canadian plants, especially those treating ores containing pyrrhotite, an iron sulfide mineral.

The cyanided gold leach residues contain varying amounts of $SO_3^=$, $S_2O_3^=$, and CNS^-. Several ways that polythionates may be formed upon acidification during acid leaching include:

$$2S_2O_3^= + MnO_2 + 2H^+ \rightarrow S_4O_6^= + Mn^{++} + 2H_2O,$$

$$H_2S + 3H_2SO_3 \rightarrow H_2S_4O_6 + 3H_2O,$$

$$2Fe^{+++} + 2S_2O_3^= \rightarrow 2Fe^{++} + S_4O_6^=,$$

$$2Fe^{+++} + 2HSO_3^- \rightarrow 2Fe^{++} + S_2O_6^= + 2H^+,$$

$$2H^+ + S_2O_3^= + 4HSO_3^- \rightarrow 2S_3O_6^= + 3H_2O.$$

Of the polythionates formed, the most stable is the tetrathionate, $S_4O_6^=$. This is believed to be the main species that accumulates on the resin, although any of the various polythionates may be present in solution.

The most effective means for combating polythionates is to ensure a free-acid concentration of at least 5 g/liter in the leach liquor. Under these conditions the polythionates are less stable than at lower acidities. Concentrations of polythionate above 50 ppm of $S_4O_6^=$ in the leach liquor foul the resin rapidly.

The polythionate problem is combated further by maintaining a higher-than-normal acidity in the nitrate eluants. Acidities of 0.2 to 0.4 N H^+ in the eluate effectively control the amount of polythionate on the resin provided the pregnant liquor contains less than 50 ppm of $S_4O_6^=$. Some of the polythionate is removed from the resin by the exchange of $S_xO_6^=$ for NO_3^- on the exchange sites. The $S_xO_6^=$ subsequently is destroyed under the acid conditions in the eluate. The remaining polythionates are oxidized *in situ* on the resin to form $SO_4^=$. Unfortunately, some elemental sulfur is also produced, and apparently affects the resin in the same way as silica.

Anionic cobalt complex. Anionic cobalt fouling of the anion-exchange resin is the most difficult to remove. The cobalt-fouling problem is limited to those plants utilizing cyanided gold-plant residues. The South African gold ores all contain cobalt to some extent. Much of this cobalt is carried over with the slimes, which are subsequently leached with sulfuric acid. Along with the cobalt, the slimes also contain significant quantities of cyanide, both soluble and insoluble. Under the conditions in the leach, anionic complexes of cobalt and cyanide form. These complexes have been studied by Robinson [33], Nugent [36], and Pearson et al. [37]. Each investigator concluded that a different species was present, i.e.,

$$Co(CN)_6^=,$$

$$[Co(CN)_5 \cdot H_2O]^=,$$

$$[Co(CN)_4 \cdot 2H_2O]^=.$$

The loss in exchange capacity of the resin corresponds to 3 equivalents per mole of cobalt, indicating a charge of -3 for the complex. The total nitrogen increase of the resin, when fouled with cobalt, indicates a CN/Co ratio of 6/1. However, this value is complicated by the presence of other nitrogenous materials, including the nitrogen functional group of the resin, cyanides, ferrocyanide, and thiocyanate. Furthermore, the behavior of $Co(CN)_6^=$ on weak-base ion-exchange resins differs from the cobalt complex actually present in solution [37], which eliminates this species as a possibility.

The presence of anionic cobalt in concentrations of the order of 1 ppm of Co in the pregnant leach liquor can lead to a cobalt poisoning problem. Several means have been used to alleviate the seriousness of this problem, but it still exists to some extent. A thorough washing of the soluble cyanide out of the gold-slime residues in some cases reduced the amount of anionic cobalt appearing in the pregnant liquor. However, Nugent [38] has found that there are insoluble cyanides present which dissolve and liberate cyanide in the acid leach. Another innovation used to reduce cobalt fouling is to adjust the pH of the gold-slime residues prior to leaching, to form the anionic cyanide complexes purposely. The complexes so formed are then washed out of the ore on the nonacid filters before leaching.

Still another means is to leach the gold ore for uranium prior to gold extraction. This has shown promise as a means of reducing the quantity of resin poisons in the leach liquors [39]. This procedure is not always applicable because currently a considerable amount of the feed to the uranium plants is gold tailings that have been leached and stockpiled over the years.

Much effort has also been expended on means of removing the anionic cobalt from the resin. Unfortunately, most of the procedures developed are not economical, requiring either expensive reagents or long reaction times. Current practice is to replace the resin when 2.0 to 2.5 percent Co has accumulated on it. The anionic cobalt removal agents that have proved successful chemically have been those employing 5 to 10 percent ammonium thiocyanate, 20 percent sodium nitrite, or sodium carbonate solutions. All these treatments require relatively long boiling of the resin suspended in these solutions.

It would seem from the nature of the reagents which have proved successful that the mechanism involves replacing the cyanide ligand with either CNS^-, NO_3^-, or $CO_3^=$. Cyanide complexes such as $Co(CN)_6^=$ are extremely stable to acids, bases, oxidants, and temperature, but the above ions, which replace cyanide, are more easily decomposed.

Molybdenum. Molybdenum in the $+6$ state is quite similar to hexavalent uranium in its solution chemistry. Its ability to form complexes of the $MoO_2(SO_4)_n{}^{2-2n}$ type is not unexpected. Ion-exchange behavior of molybdenum in chloride solutions indicates that chloride forms a complex with molybdenum [40].

Molybdenum in pregnant uranium liquors is adsorbed more strongly on the resin than is the uranium complex. Under normal elution conditions in uranium plants, the molybdenum is not removed each cycle, but accumulates on the resin. When this happens the resin becomes sluggish in operation, with a definite reduction in uranium capacity, since the molybdenum occupies exchange sites.

One means of removing molybdenum preferentially from the pregnant liquor is by adsorption on carbon. Another method investigated is to precipitate it with hydrogen sulfide prior to uranium adsorption. Once on the resin, molybdenum may be removed by use of 20 to 50 percent sulfuric acid [41] or, preferably, 2 to 3 percent caustic soda plus $0.3 M$ $NaNO_3$ or NaCl. The caustic regeneration has the advantage of removing silica as well as molybdenum.

Titanium. Titanium, another metal with ability to form anionic sulfate complexes, will undergo ion exchange with the resin in leach liquors. Unlike the elements previously mentioned, titanium precipitates readily upon dilution or with a rise in pH. Thus, during the stages of operation where the pH rises at the beginning and end of each adsorption cycle, titanium will precipitate.

This problem first arose in Australia. It was found that by changing the leaching conditions, the quantity of titanium appearing in the leach liquor was drastically reduced. The hydrolytic precipitation was also reduced by maintaining low pH conditions in the ion-exchange columns during flushing and backwashing. These preventive measures are the same as those found to be successful for reducing silica buildup.

Titanium-fouled resin is reported to be very different from fresh resin. A means for removing titanium has been devised by Hartley and Laurie [42], who used a solution of sulfuric acid and ammonium bifluoride to dissolve the precipitated titanium and remove it from the resin. The cleaned-up resin was found to be similar to fresh resin in uranium adsorption properties.

Zirconium. Zirconium is similar to uranium, molybdenum, and titanium in that it also forms sulfate complexes. Zirconium is found in significant amounts in some of the Colorado Plateau ores. During conventional acid leaching, only minor amounts of zirconium are dissolved, but in the acid pugging process, the extent of dissolution can present a problem. Examination of a resin fouled with zirconium showed a Zr/P molar ratio of 1/1, indicating that the precipitated zirconium probably exists as $ZrOHPO_4$. Uranium capacities of the resin were not impaired, but leakage of uranium (>0.01 g U_3O_8/liter) occurred during most of the adsorption cycle.

Goren [43] found that 12 N sulfuric acid effectively removed precipitated zirconium from the resins. Tests at the Rohm & Haas Co. laboratories showed that 5 cycles of 12 N H_2SO_4-H_2O-NaOH-H_2O-NaCl did not adversely affect Amberlite IRA-400 either chemically or physically.

Thorium. Thorium forms an anionic sulfate complex which is weaker and less readily adsorbed on anion-exchange resin than uranium. At present, thorium is found in leach liquor only in the Blind River area of Canada. It fouls the resin as does zirconium. The thorium content of the Blind River ores averages approximately one-half that of the uranium content. It is leached along with uranium and appears in the pregnant liquor at about the same ratio. Thorium is adsorbed on the resin only to a small extent; the major portion passes through the ion-exchange column.

The behavior of the thorium sulfate complex is similar to that of the ferric sulfate complex. During the early part of the adsorption cycle, the resin becomes saturated with thorium. At this point, perhaps 5 g ThO_2 has been adsorbed per liter of resin. As the uranium adsorption progresses, the major portion of both the thorium and iron is displaced with uranium. This is another reason why it is advantageous to saturate the resin fully with uranium prior to elution.

During the elution cycle the remaining thorium is eluted along with uranium, with little or no fractionation. The thorium content of the final uranium cake is less than 2 percent. Although all the uranium is displaced from the resin, a small amount of thorium may remain. When this happens, the thorium can be precipitated during the initial, low-acidity stages of the next adsorption cycle. The thorium that accumulates by precipitation can be removed by elution with sulfuric acid.

Other contaminants. Ferrocyanide and thiocyanates also appear in South African leach liquors derived from cyanided gold residues. Both of these ions are formed as a consequence of the cyanide leach. Although both are held quite strongly by the resin and so lower the uranium capacity, they do not accumulate on the resin, since the presence of large concentrations in the leach is sporadic. Normal nitrate elution and subsequent uranium adsorption will displace these ions over a number of cycles.

The thiocyanate ion is capable of forming a complex with uranium which is eluted from the resin more slowly than is the sulfate complex.

Ferrocyanide ion on the resin not only occupies exchange sites but also is capable of precipitating cations such as iron and uranium. In effect, the ferrocyanide form of the resin acts as a cation exchange material. This is also true of most of the other resin poisons encountered.

9-5.2 Caustic-soda rejuvenation. A convenient method of removing many of the poisons is to treat the anion-exchange resins with caustic soda. This will remove silica, polythionates, sulfur, molybdenum, and other extraneous ions, but not the anionic cobalt cyanide complexes, titanium, or thorium to any extent. A small amount of zirconium will be removed under normal regeneration conditions because of the amphoteric character of this metal. To remove the zirconium and thorium more completely, a fairly concentrated sulfuric acid solution is used.

Caustic-soda treatment of the resin to remove silica is required at all operating uranium plants. Some plants need to rejuvenate the resin quite regularly, every month or so, while others may use this treatment only every year or two. Of necessity, most plants use the caustic-cleanup procedure when the operating capacity has dropped to the point where all the pregnant liquor can no longer be treated.

Pretreatment of the resin. The resin that is to be caustic-treated is fully eluted of uranium, so as not to lose any of this valuable metal. The resin is then backwashed thoroughly to remove any solid materials that may be likely to cement the underdrain of the resin column when the caustic solution is added.

In some plants, rather than shut down the set of columns for as long as 24 hours or more, the resin is transferred to an external regeneration unit. The actual transference of the resin has a beneficial effect in removing any solids which cling to the resin mechanically. By use of a spare charge of resin, it is possible to effect transfer in about one hour per column, so that no actual production time is lost.

Hydroxylation of the resin. At the end of the elution cycle, the resin contains the eluting ion (either nitrate or chloride) and various amounts of sulfate and bisulfate ion. The resin is neutralized by passing a 0.5 to 1.0 percent NaOH solution through the resin bed at a moderate rate (0.2 to 0.5 gal/ft^3 per minute) until the effluent pH rises to 7.0. This requires about $\frac{1}{2}$ pound of NaOH per cubic foot of resin.

Caustic-soda treatment. The next step in the rejuvenation procedure is to treat the resin with a more concentrated caustic-soda solution than that used above. This treatment, by forming soluble sodium silicate, dissolves the silica that has precipitated inside the resin.

Caustic-soda treatment for silica removal varies considerably, depending not only on the individual preference of the mill operators but also on the time available. Caustic-soda solutions in the range of 3 to 6 percent remove silica effectively with an expenditure of from 12 to 20 pounds of NaOH per cubic foot of resin. Flow rates as low as 0.05 gal/ft^3 per minute have been used when considerable time is available.

Most of the silica is removed with the first 3 bed volumes of 5 percent caustic passed through the resin. It is possible to use a split rejuvenation technique: the first 3 bed volumes of caustic soda are recycled solution, followed by 3 bed volumes of fresh caustic. The latter effluent is stored for the next regeneration. Similar recycling can be accomplished by passing the caustic soda through two or three resin columns in series, finishing off each column with fresh caustic solution. Where the primary effort of the caustic rejuvenation is to remove polythionates, molybdenum, or some other less readily removed poison, a higher concentration (10 percent) of caustic may be required.

Neutralization of the resin. The next step in the rejuvenation process is to reconvert the resin to a salt form. Direct loading of the resin with pregnant liquor at this point is equivalent to adding solid caustic soda to the pregnant liquor: all the hydroxides of iron, aluminum, etc., will precipitate within the resin bed, causing blockage, and the silica in the leach liquor will also precipitate, defeating the purpose of the original caustic-soda treatment.

A convenient means of reconverting the resin to a salt form is to pass a 3 to 5 percent sulfuric acid solution downflow through the resin until the effluent pH is below 7. In plants with polythionate problems it has been found that using a neutral salt solution, such as the uranium thickener overflow, followed by acid, is more satisfactory than using acid itself. It is believed that the neutral-salt treatment removes many of the sulfur-containing ions from the resin. Direct acidification increases the likelihood of sulfur deposition within the resin matrix.

Barren eluate for converting the resin to the salt form is applicable where uranium is precipitated from the pregnant eluate with ammonia or caustic. When magnesium oxide is used for uranium precipitation, the barren eluate contains a considerable quantity of Mg^{++}. Upon passage of this solution through the hydroxide form of the resin, $Mg(OH)_2$ precipitates out, causing blockage.

Backwashing the resin. The resin can be backwashed either before neutralization, while the resin is in the hydroxide form, or after neutralization and acidification. Since acidification of the resin may at times result in further precipitation of solids within the voids of the resin, it is preferable to backwash after acidification. Since the resin in its hydroxyl form has its lowest density, this also permits the use of lower backwash rates. The backwashing at this stage should be thorough to ensure complete removal of all extraneous materials. After the backwash, the resin is ready to be placed on adsorption.

9–5.3 Improvements in ion-exchange operations. The process of uranium recovery by ion exchange has been proved efficient and economical. In some plants, the cost of chemicals used in the quantitative recovery of uranium from clarified leach liquors amounts to less than 10 cents per pound of U_3O_8. There always remains, however, an area of small improvements which can be economically attractive on the basis of large volumes. In the ion-exchange process, a small but real saving in chemicals can be achieved by proper manipulation of the elution circuit, and production costs can be lowered by taking advantage of advances in mechanical operations.

Reduction in chemical costs. The improvements achieved in modifying the elution circuit consist mainly of recovering the elution reagent (chloride or nitrate) from the resin by displacement with the cheaper chemical, sulfuric acid.

Chloride elution. In the chloride elution circuit the chemicals consumed are:

(1) NH_3 or MgO   for precipitation of uranium,

(2) H_2SO_4 for acidification of eluate,

(3) NaCl   for elution of uranium.

The ammonia or magnesia consumption depends upon the acidity of the fresh eluate, the amount of acid on the resin, and the quantity of eluate used. The first two factors are more or less fixed. Any reduction in eluate volume that causes some uranium to remain on the resin and to be subsequently lost is false economy. A loss of only 1 percent of the uranium processed is equivalent in value to the total ion-exchange chemical costs.

The sulfuric acid concentration of the fresh eluate is fixed between 0.10 to 0.15 N H^+. A reduction in eluate volume will lower the sulfuric acid consumption slightly.

The sodium chloride consumption per unit of resin is fixed by the amount adsorbed on the resin at the end of the elution. This quantity is independent of the quantity of eluate used.

It has been found possible to reduce the chloride consumption by recovering the chloride from the resin by displacement with 5 to 10 percent sulfuric acid. The total quantity of sulfuric acid used is such that the amount of hydrochloric and sulfuric acids appearing in the effluent from this treatment is equal in total acidity to that of the sulfuric acid normally added to the barren eluate to produce fresh eluate. However, 1 to 2 bed volumes of additional solution are obtained. To achieve a solution balance, the first 1 to 2 bed volumes of uranium-rich eluate are precipitated separately, and the filtrate is discarded. This filtrate is low in chloride and high in sulfate. The net result in this modified elution system is to reduce the sulfate content of the recycled eluate, the volume of eluate required each cycle, and the sodium chloride consumption.

Nitrate elution.   In the nitrate-elution circuit, the nitrate losses are usually made up by adding nitric acid or nitrates, so that the chemicals consumed are

(1) lime, for partial neutralization of the pregnant eluate,

(2) NH_3, NaOH, or MgO for precipitation of uranium,

(3) HNO_3, or a nitrate and H_2SO_4, for elution of uranium.

The lime used for partial neutralization of the pregnant eluate to pH 3.5 essentially removes all the free acid. Since lime is relatively inexpensive, the quantity of acid neutralized, within limits, is of little consequence. The quantity of ammonia, caustic, or magnesia used depends solely on the quantity of uranium precipitated. Here, too, it is not possible to reduce costs. The nitrate consumption is fixed by the quantity adsorbed on the resin at the end of the elution and is independent of quantity of eluate used.

Part of the nitrate can be recovered by using sulfuric acid in the manner described for chloride recovery.   However, sulfuric acid removes nitrate from the resin much less efficiently than it removes chloride. To obtain more than 90 percent nitrate recovery, the nitrate concentration in the effluent from the resin is only about 0.3 N, which is too dilute for use in the elution circuit. To recover the nitrate values, several different methods have been proposed:

(1) The mixture of nitric acid and sulfuric acids is evaporated to increase its concentration, and the excess acid is neutralized with lime, removing the sulfate as gypsum [44].

(2) The nitric-sulfuric acid mixture is passed through a weak-base resin such as Amberlite IR-45.   The nitrate is selectively adsorbed, yielding a dilute sulfuric acid effluent which is reconstituted with additional acid to be used for the next nitrate elution. The nitrate is then removed from the weak-base resin with excess ammonium hydroxide. The excess ammonia is recovered by evaporators [45].

(3) The nitric acid may be selectively removed from the nitric-sulfuric acid mixture by use of a long-chain, oil-soluble amine dissolved in a kerosene diluent [46]. The nitrate may be recovered by stripping with any alkaline agent, using only the stoichiometric amount. Anhydrous ammonia will precipitate ammonium nitrate from the kerosene solution to yield solid ammonium nitrate, which then may be added as makeup nitrate to the barren eluate.

Advances in ion-exchange equipment. In the long-term analysis of the fixed-bed columnar ion-exchange process for recovery of uranium, the chemical costs of elution and precipitation of uranium exceed the cost of equipment and resin. The minimum chemical requirements are fixed, so that any real savings in the operation must stem from a reduction either in labor costs or in the costs of pretreatment of the liquor.

Ideally, the equipment should be truly continuous. To achieve a truly continuous, countercurrent operation it is necessary that both the inflowing pregnant liquor and the resin beads move. Since this can result in higher attrition losses and higher power requirements, the savings must offset increased resin or power costs.

In general, filtration and clarification costs exceed fixed-bed ion-exchange costs by severalfold. Hence another area for future savings is in equipment designed to treat ore slurries rather than clarified liquors.

During the past several years liquid-solid contactors have been developed for treating pulps. The RIP basket process described earlier has been successfully employed on a plant scale at several mills. Other equipment or devices that have been developed or are now in the development stage are listed below. The reader is referred to the references for further information concerning these devices.

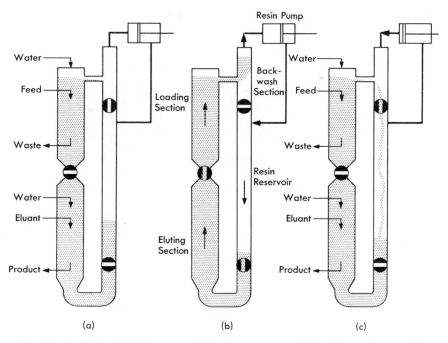

Fig. 9–10. Schematic diagram of Higgins contactor [45]. Operating positions are (a) pump stopped, solution pumping period (several minutes); (b) pump running, resin movement period (3–5 sec); (c) pump stopped, solution pumping period (several minutes).

Higgins contactor [47,48]. The Higgins contactor consists of a single resin loop with all the ion-exchange operations performed in individual fixed-bed sections (Fig. 9–10). The resin moves clockwise, countercurrent to both the feed slurry and the eluate. Following the movement of the resin around the loop, starting with the loading section, the resin first comes into contact with the pregnant pulp feed. When the resin at the top of the bed is saturated with uranium, all inlet and exit valves close for a few seconds. The resin pump produces a sudden hydraulic pressure which does three things: it moves resin from the resin reservoir into the eluting section; it forces a charge of the freshly eluted resin at the top of the eluting section into the bottom of the loading section; and it moves a charge of the loaded resin at the top of the loading section to a wash section. Then, solution flow is started again for several more minutes. The resin is backwashed in the backwash section by a portion of the water flow entering the top of the loading section, and then enters the resin reservoir by gravity.

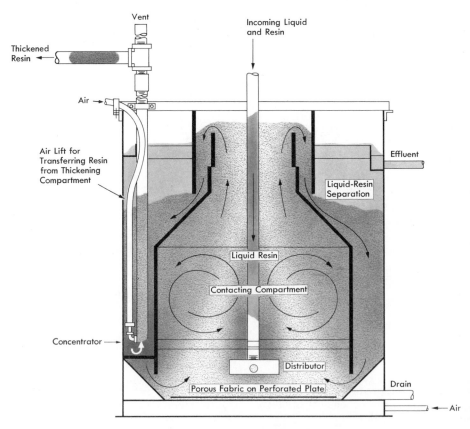

FIG. 9–11. Schematic diagram of the Infilco CST exchanger [47].

Infilco CST exchanger [49,50]. The Infilco CST exchanger (Fig. 9–11) was designed for carrying out ion-exchange reactions in turbid liquors and slurries. The equipment unit consists of a cylindrical shell with an inner draft tube. The operation consists of feeding pregnant liquor from a preceding unit and resin from the following unit into the center tube, where it is distributed into a contacting zone. The resin and liquor in the contacting zone are intimately mixed by air agitation. The air also lifts the mixture up through the inner draft tube, where it overflows into the annular spacing between the inner draft tube and the outside shell. The treated liquor is separated from the resin in a settling zone, with liquor overflowing to the next unit. The partially loaded resin is thickened and then air-

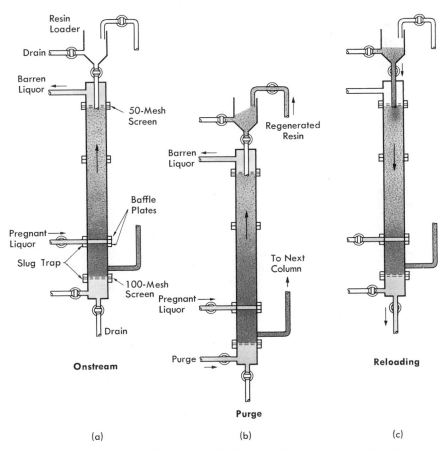

Fig. 9–12. Schematic diagram of the Porter column [48]. At left, the column is on stream, ready for removal of partially spent resin slug. At center, the partially spent slug is purged while the loader fills with regenerated material. At right, the fresh resin enters top of column from the loader and spent resin from bottom enters trap.

lifted back to the preceding unit. The liquor and resin traverse in opposite directions to give a countercurrent operation.

Porter column [51]. The Porter column consists of a column in which the resin is retained by a 100-mesh screen at the bottom and a 50-mesh screen at the top (Fig. 9–12). The influent liquor moves upflow through the column, entering at a point above the 100-mesh screen and exiting above the 50-mesh screen. When the resin in the space between the inlet valve and the 100-mesh screen (slug trap) is fully loaded, the slug trap is drained, and the resin is purged with pregnant liquor to the next column in series through a side exit valve. After the slug of resin is transferred, the influent liquor flow is temporarily stopped, and the column is partially drained. The resin immediately above the slug trap drops into this trap. At the same time, regenerated resin is added to the top of the resin bed. Influent liquor flow is then started, and the operation is continued until time for the next slug removal cycle. Elution of the fully loaded resin is performed in a separate slug column.

Weiss-Swinton pulsating column [52,53,54]. The Weiss-Swinton column was developed to extend the use of conventional ion-exchange procedures to the direct adsorption of soluble constituents from suspensions of finely divided solids, without the need for prior filtration. It has been piloted with suspensions containing up to 20 percent solids. The equipment (Fig. 9–13) may be arranged for either a pulsated downflow or pulsated upflow. In downflow operation "the resin is retained in the column by a 36-mesh screen, or a graded sand bed resting on a coarser screen. The offtake section below the screen has a rubber diaphragm attached to its base which is reciprocated by an eccentric. A bed of coarse packing between the diaphragm and the lower screen acts as a distributor for the pulsing flow. The suspension to be treated is fed through an open standpipe into the top of the column, and after passage through the bed leaves through an offtake just above the diaphragm. It is desirable to place a restriction or synchronized diaphragm valve in the outlet line to damp the pulsations" [53]. The equipment for the pulsated upflow operation differs from the downflow column mainly in that the inlet and outlet are reversed. The resin in the upflow column is in teeter, eliminating the necessity for backwashing.

Winchester fixed bed—RIP column [55]. When a desanded pulp is fed to even RIP-size resin in a standard column, solids accumulate at the resin-pulp interface and cause a serious pressure drop. Clevenger and Lynch found they could overcome this rapid accumulation of solids by use of an oscillating pulp distributor, shown at the center of the column in Fig. 9–13. At one oscillation per minute, it was possible to prevent accumulation of solids at the top of the resin bed. Packing of the resin bed itself was reduced considerably by fixing the discharge throughout the

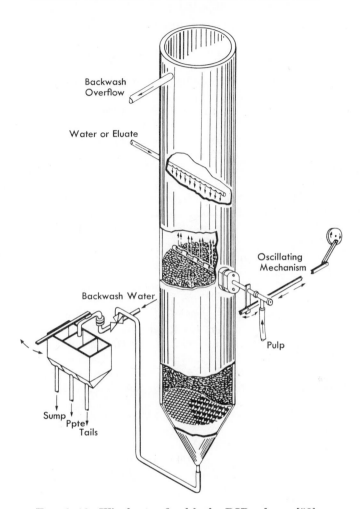

Backwash Overflow

Water or Eluate

Oscillating Mechanism

Backwash Water

Pulp

Sump
Ppte
Tails

FIG. 9–13. Winchester fixed bed—RIP column [52].

run at, or a little above, the top of the bed through a leg external to the column. When the bed did compact and the pressure drop became excessive, the bed was distended 4 inches (4-foot bed) by passing water countercurrent to the flow of pulp. This procedure interrupted flow of slurry for about one minute. Distention is required from 6 to 12 times during each adsorption cycle.

REFERENCES

1. S. AHRLAND, Complex Chemistry of the Uranyl Ion. IV. Complexity of Uranyl Acetates, *Acta Chem. Scand.* **5**, 1151 (1951).

2. G. A. LUTZ, *Recovery of Uranium from Aqueous Solutions*, U. S. Patent 2,743,159 (1956).

3. A. M. GAUDIN et al., Extraction Process for Gold-Uranium Ores, *J. Metals* **8**, 1065 (1956).

4. D. KAUFMAN and G. W. LOWER, *A Summary Report on the Ion Exchange Process for the Recovery of Uranium*, USAEC Report ACCO-68, American Cyanamid Co., 1955.

5. G. G. MARVIN and E. F. GREENLEAF, Uranium Recovery from Ores, in *Progress in Nuclear Energy, Series III, Process Chemistry*, Ed. by F. R. Bruce et al. New York: McGraw-Hill Book Co., Inc., 1956. (Chap. 1, Sec. 1–1)

6. R. KUNIN and A. F. PREUSS, Ion Exchange in the Atomic Energy Program, *Ind. Eng. Chem.* **48**, No. 8, 30A (1956).

7. T. V. ARDEN, The Concentration of Uranium from Low-Grade Ores, *Ind. Chemist* **32**, 202 (1956).

8. W. Q. HULL and E. T. PINKNEY, Uranium from Gold Wastes, *Ind. Eng. Chem.* **49**, 1 (1957).

9. D. E. R. AYRES and R. J. WESTWOOD, The Use of the Ion-Exchange Process in the Extraction of Uranium from the Rand Ores with Particular Reference to Practices at Randfontein Uranium Plant, *J. S. African Inst. Mining and Met.* **57**, 459 (1957).

10. C. ? . McBURNEY, *Resinous Insoluble Reaction Products of Tertiary Amines with Haloalkylate Vinyl Aromatic Hydrocarbon Co-Polymers*, U. S. Patent 2,591,573 (1952).

11. G. E. BOYD and B. A. SOLDANO, Osmotic Free Energies of Ion Exchangers, *Z. Electrochem.* **57**, 162 (1953).

12. S. FISHER and F. McGARVEY, *Recovery of Uranium by Ion-exchange Resins*, USAEC Report RMO-2518, Rohm and Haas Co., 1953.

13. T. O. O'CONNOR, *Ion-exchange Studies. Part I. Equilibrium Constants. Part II. Nature of Uranium Adsorption on IRA-400*, USAEC Report ACCO-61, American Cyanamid Co., 1954.

14. G. W. LOWER, *Systematic Ion-exchange Studies*, USAEC Report AECD-4113, Massachusetts Institute of Technology, 1951.

15. J. J. BRUNNER et al., *Preliminary Report on Recovery of Uranium from Low-grade Belgian Congo Ores*, USAEC Report ACCO-7, American Cyanamid Co., 1951.

16. C. S. ABRAMS and T. F. IZZO, *The Recovery of Vanadium by Ion Exchange*, USAEC Report ACCO-53, American Cyanamid Co., 1954.

17. J. G. TOOHEY and D. KAUFMAN, *The Relationship Between Oxidation-Reduction Potential and Valence State of Iron, Vanadium and Uranium in Sulfuric Acid Leach Liquors*, USAEC Report ACCO-60, American Cyanamid Co., 1954.

18. B. M. TAYLOR, *Can. Dept. Mines and Tech. Surveys, Mines Branch, Radioactivity Div.*, Report SR-287/54 (1954).

19. A. R. KAZANJIAN, *Systematic Elution Studies. Part I. The Effect of Sulfate*

Accumulation on the Elution of Uranium from Strong-base Ion-exchange Resins with Chloride, USAEC Report ACCO-59, American Cyanamid Co., 1954.

20. N. W. FRISCH, *Electrolytic Precipitation of Uranium from Flowing Ion-exchange Eluates,* USAEC Report RMO-2516, Rohm and Haas Co., 1953.

21. C. T. DICKERT, Rohm and Haas Co., unpublished.

22. H. G. PETROW et al., *Solvent Extraction of Uranium from Sulfuric Acid Eluates,* USAEC Report WIN-28, National Lead Co., Inc., 1956.

23. R. L. BARNARD, *A Preliminary Study of the Adsorption of Uranium(IV) and Other Metallic Ions by Anion-exchange Resins,* USAEC Report MITG-A97, Massachusetts Institute of Technology, 1950.

24. D. A. ELLIS, *Recovery of Uranium by Ion Exchange from an Acid Leach of Marysvale Ore,* USAEC Report Dow-59, Dow Chemical Co., 1951.

25. G. A. LUTZ, *Method of Recovering Uranium from Aqueous Solutions,* U. S. Patent 2,780,514 (1957).

26. E. T. HOLLIS, *Laboratory Studies in Carbonate Ion Exchange,* USAEC Report WIN-88, National Lead Company, Inc., 1958.

27. C. K. McARTHUR et al., *Preliminary Pilot Plant Testing of Resin-in-pulp Ion Exchange of Alkaline Leach Pulps,* USAEC Report WIN-11, National Lead Co., Inc., Apr. 25, 1955.

28. H. E. GARDNER et al., *Alkaline Leach Resin-in-pulp Pilot Plant Testing of Uranium Reduction Blend,* USAEC Report WIN-82, National Lead Co., Inc., Jan. 15, 1958.

29. J. HALPERN, Potentiometric Titration of Carbonate Solutions Containing Uranium, *Can. J. Chem.* **31,** 705 (1953).

30. R. F. HOLLIS et al., *The Development of a Resin-in-pulp Process and Its Application to Ores of the White Canyon Areas of Utah,* USAEC Report ACCO-42, American Cyanamid Co., 1954.

31. R. F. HOLLIS and C. K. McARTHUR, The Resin-in-pulp Method for Recovery of Uranium, *Mining Eng.* **9,** 442 (April 1957).

32. R. K. ILER, *The Colloid Chemistry of Silica and Silicates.* Ithaca, New York: Cornell University Press, 1955.

33. R. E. ROBINSON, Report Leaching No. 175, Government Metallurgical Laboratory (Union of South Africa), Johannesburg, October 1953.

34. E. NAPIER and R. P. MILLER, Scientific Report CRL/AE-126, Gt. Brit. Chemical Research Laboratory, Teddington, 1955.

35. M. GOEHRING, The Chemistry of the Polythionic Acids, *Fortsch. chem. Forsch.* **2,** 444 (1952).

36. E. A. NUGENT, *The Chemistry of the Poisons Associated with the Ion-exchange Process,* paper presented at the 10th Annual Convention of the South African Chemical Institute, September 1956.

37. D. PEARSON et al., Gt. Brit. Chemical Research Laboratory, Teddington, 1955. Unpublished.

38. E. A. NUGENT, *Progress Report, September/October* 1953, West Rand Consolidated Mines (Union of South Africa).

39. H. BRITTEN and S. K. DEKOK, Contribution to Discussion of "Basic Principles of Uranium Plant Design" by S. Craib and D. G. Maxwell, *J. S. African Inst. Mining and Met.* **57,** 695 (1957).

40. A. F. PREUSS, Ph. D. thesis, University of Wisconsin, 1952.

41. M. D. HASSIALIS et al., *Recovery of Uranium from Chattanooga Shales,* USAEC Report RMO-4002, Mineral Beneficiation Laboratory, Columbia University, 1954.

42. F. R. HARTLEY and D. W. LAWRIE, Report R. D. 17, Department of Mines, South Australia, Adelaide, 1955.

43. M. B. GOREN, *Restoration of Poisoned Ion-exchange Resins,* paper presented at the 132nd meeting of the American Chemical Society, New York, September 1957.

44. R. R. PORTER, Report Leaching No. 167, Government Metallurgical Laboratory (Union of South Africa), Johannesburg, January 1954.

45. E. A. NUGENT, *Progress Report, March 1954,* West Rand Consolidated Mines (Union of South Africa).

46. A. PREUSS, unpublished.

47. I. R. HIGGINS and J. T. ROBERTS, A Countercurrent Solid-Liquid Contactor for Continuous Ion Exchange, *Chem. Eng. Progress Symposium Ser.* **50,** No. 14, 87 (1954).

48. I. R. HIGGINS, *Mechanical Features of the Higgins Continuous Ion-exchange Column,* USAEC Report ORNL-1907, Oak Ridge National Laboratory, 1955.

49. *Chem. Week* **80,** 73 (March 30, 1957).

50. *Continuous Counter Current Resin-Slurry Ion Exchange Using CST Exchanger,* Bulletin 1930, Infilco, Incorporated, Tucson, Arizona, 1957.

51. *Chem. Week* **78,** 78 (June 9, 1956).

52. R. McNEIL et al., Continuous Ion Exchange, *J. Metals* **7,** 912 (1955).

53. E. A. SWINTON and D. E. WEISS, Extraction from Slurries by Ion-exchange Resins, *Australian J. Appl. Sci.* **7,** 98 (1956).

54. E. A. SWINTON and D. E. WEISS, *Method and Apparatus for Countercurrently Contacting Solids with Liquids,* U. S. Patent 2,735,795 (1956).

55. G. W. CLEVENGER and J. T. LYNCH, *The Recovery of Uranium from Ore Pulps Using Fixed Ion-exchange Resin Beds,* USAEC Report WIN-26, National Lead Co., Inc., 1955.

CHAPTER 10

URANIUM RECOVERY BY SOLVENT EXTRACTION*

10–1. Introduction

Solvent extraction with ethers and similar compounds has been used in the analytical separation of uranium for many years. In the early days of the Manhattan project, diethyl ether extraction of nitrate solutions was developed into a large-scale purification process. Later, tributyl phosphate (TBP) was developed as an alternative solvent. This process could not, however, be applied directly to the recovery of uranium from most ores; the high nitrate concentration required to form the extractable complex makes the process prohibitively expensive. Since then, solvent extraction processes have been developed for treatment of sulfate leach liquors. The solvents used extract uranium as ionic uranium complexes instead of molecular complexes as in the nitrate systems, and the chemical reactions involved are different.

A solvent extraction process in its simplest form involves two steps: extraction and stripping. In the extraction step, the organic solvent is contacted with the liquor to be treated, and the uranium is transferred to the solvent. In the stripping step, the loaded solvent is brought in contact with a suitable aqueous solution, and the uranium is transferred from the organic solvent back to an aqueous phase. By properly selecting conditions, it is possible in this operation both to purify and to concentrate the uranium. The solvent, after suitable conditioning if necessary, is recycled and can be reused indefinitely. Compared with the older direct precipitation methods for uranium recovery from acid-leach solutions, reagent requirements are lower, uranium recoveries and purities are higher, and costs are less. In these respects solvent extraction is comparable to ion exchange. Furthermore, solvent extraction has a theoretical advantage over ion exchange, in that its operation can more readily be made to approach a continuous countercurrent system. However, since more efficient extractants, ion-exchange resins, and equipment are still being developed, no general statements can be made as to the relative costs of the two processes. Total operating costs are now about equal for the two, but solvent extraction recovery requires less investment.

Solvent extraction processes are used in several uranium recovery plants on the Colorado Plateau [1]. As yet only clear, filtered liquors are being treated, but considerable work has been done on extraction from slurries,

---

* By David A. Ellis, Dow Chemical Company.

and it is possible that the ore filtration can eventually be eliminated [2]. Uranium is recovered from phosphoric acid by solvent extraction in several plants in Florida [3]. Processes have also been investigated for maximum recovery by solvent extraction from a number of other uranium sources, such as superphosphates [4], shales [5], and lignite [6].*

10–2. Chemistry of Solvent Extraction

10–2.1 Important properties of the solvent. A number of properties must be considered in choosing a compound suitable for use as an extractant for uranium. It must have the ability to extract uranium from the aqueous liquor, be sufficiently selective, be immiscible with the aqueous solution, and have low flammability and low toxicity so that it can be used with safety.

Extraction coefficient. The ability of an organic solvent to extract uranium is measured by its extraction coefficient and its saturation capacity [7–9]. The extraction coefficient is defined as the ratio of concentration of extracted species in the organic phase to that in the aqueous phase. It is usually indicated by the symbol K or Ko/a, although some authors use Eo/a. The extraction coefficient approaches a constant value at low concentrations in the organic. In all uranium-extraction systems the extraction coefficient decreases as the concentration of uranium in the extractant increases.

Saturation capacity. The saturation capacity of the extractant is the maximum concentration of the extracted species that the extractant can hold. Since in any system in which uranium is extracted the extraction is due to formation of definite complexes, the saturation capacity is restricted by the molar ratio of extractant to uranium in these complexes.

Distribution isotherm. A plot of the equilibrium concentration of the extracted species in the organic phase versus its concentration in the aqueous phase is a valuable aid in studying an extraction system. A convenient method for obtaining these data is to shake samples of the extractant with varying amounts of the aqueous solution and then, after equilibrium has been attained, to analyze each phase. The plot gives a smooth curve concave toward the aqueous axis (see Fig. 10–1). The curvature is due to the decrease in extraction coefficient as the concentration in the organic increases. The concentration in the organic approaches the saturation capacity at high aqueous concentrations. The slope of a line drawn from a point on the distribution isotherm to the origin is equal to the extraction coefficient for the equilibrium system represented by that point. The extraction coefficient is greatest at low concentration of extracted species in the organic phase.

---

* Detailed discussions of these sources are presented in Chapter 12.

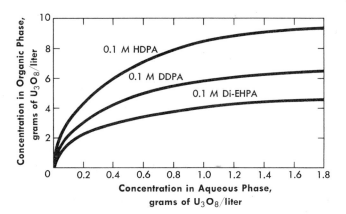

Fig. 10–1. Distribution isotherms for extraction of uranium from a Plateau leach liquor with alkyl phosphates.

Selectivity. Selectivity is a measure of the extraction of a given species in relation to the extraction of other species. This is an important solvent characteristic, not only because lack of selectivity for uranium leads to less purification in the extraction step but also because the active sites in the solvent which are occupied by other metals are not available for uranium extraction. Thus the saturation loading value and the extraction coefficient for uranium are decreased. The extraction of other metals causes the uranium distribution isotherm to begin to bend at lower concentration values and to approach a lower saturation value. In extreme cases, high extraction of other metals can cause the isotherm to bend over, forming an inverted U.

Selectivity is usually defined by the separation coefficient, which is the ratio of the extraction coefficient of the desired species, that is, uranium, to that of the other species. This definition gives a quantitative value that is not necessarily a constant; thus when comparing solvents for selectivity, it is necessary that the coefficients be measured under comparable conditions.

Stripping. For a solvent to be acceptable as a metallurgical extractant, there must be an inexpensive and simple method for recovering the extracted species. In most cases, recovery is accomplished by contact with an aqueous solution that alters the form of the extracted species in such a way that it is no longer preferentially held by the extractant. This process is known as *stripping*, and the aqueous solution is called the *stripping agent* or *stripping solution*. The stripping ability of a solution is measured by the stripping coefficient. This is the reciprocal of the extraction coefficient, that is, the ratio of concentration in stripping solution to concentration in extractant. It is indicated by the symbol Ka/o or Sa/o. The stripping coefficient is not a constant, and usually increases with increasing concentration in the organic phase.

The stripping behavior of a system can be represented by a distribution isotherm, which is usually plotted with the concentration in the organic as the abscissa so that the slopes of lines drawn from points on the curve to the origin will give the stripping coefficients directly. Distribution isotherms for stripping systems are sometimes called *stripping curves* or *stripping isotherms*.

Since the stripping solution and the reagents necessary to recover uranium products from it represent the major chemical costs in solvent extraction processes, the choice of the optimum solvent depends directly on estimating these factors reliably.

Solubility and entrainment. The value of the solvent in a typical extractant stream is of the same order of magnitude as the value of the uranium dissolved in it. Thus, for an economically feasible process, the amount of solvent lost in each cycle must be very small, and the solvent must be recycled many times. To be an acceptable solvent, a compound must have very low solubility in the aqueous solutions with which it is to be in contact. Low solubility in water is usually achieved by using compounds that contain large alkyl groups. The size of the organic group is limited, however, because the solvent must remain soluble in inexpensive diluents such as kerosene or toluene. The number of extracting groups per unit weight of solvent decreases with increasing size (or molecular weight) of the organic group. This size effect must also be considered, since the extraction coefficient for a given dilution of solvent will be decreased for the larger molecules. Since the permissible maximum solubility loss depends on the cost of the solvent, the optimum molecular weight of the solvent is a complex economic factor and must be evaluated separately for each type of solvent.

Loss of solvent by entrainment in the discarded leach liquor is ordinarily a more serious problem than the loss of dissolved material. It is also a more difficult problem to control in design and operation of a practical plant, since the amount entrained can vary widely for relatively small process changes. The magnitude of the loss is ordinarily a function of the type of mixing used, the degree of dispersion in mixing, and the holdup time for settling before final discharge of the aqueous phase. The actual separating or phase-disengagement properties of leach liquors vary quite widely with different samples and their individual treatment. Entrainment losses should, therefore, be studied with the exact liquor to be processed.

Ordinarily the final reduction of entrained organic can be best handled by a separate settler following the solvent extraction system. Holdup times of 10 to 60 minutes should be allowed.

Organic entrainments, after settling, of from 0.01 to 0.02 percent of the aqueous volume have ordinarily been found when treating clear liquors. In estimating solvent losses by entrainment and spillage, an allowance of 0.5 gallon of organic per 1000 gallons of leach liquor processed has been found to be more than adequate.

Diluent. The purpose of a diluent for the solvent is to decrease the viscosity and to extend the solvent so that contact with the aqueous solution is easier. Most solvents used in metal extraction are quite viscous in their pure form because of their high molecular weights. It is necessary that the diluent be cheap and that its solubility losses to the aqueous phases be small. In each of the uranium-extraction systems proposed so far, some type of kerosene is the preferred diluent. The magnitude of the extraction coefficients is affected by the choice of diluent. In general, coefficients are highest for solutions in aliphatic hydrocarbons, lower for solutions in aromatic diluents, and lowest for solutions in alcohols, but many amines are better extractants in aromatic than in aliphatic diluents.

The extraction coefficient with a given aqueous solution is a function only of the concentration of free (uncomplexed) extractant in the organic phase but, in general, it is not a linear function. In a system containing only one extractable component, the saturation loading values will be directly proportional to the initial extractant concentration in the organic phase, but the extraction coefficients measured at the same phase ratio will not generally be directly proportional to the initial extractant concentration. When more than one species is extracted, the saturation loading value is usually no longer directly proportional to the initial extractant concentration.

Stability. A solvent must be a relatively stable compound, so that it may be used for many cycles of extraction and stripping. However, if the extraction coefficient is very high, so that a very dilute solvent may be used, it is possible to operate economically with an unstable solvent. An example is the use of alkyl pyrophosphate solutions for extracting uranium from phosphoric acid.

Phase disengagement. It is important that the solvent and diluent be of such nature that phase disengagement is rapid and complete. Many promising extractants have a tendency to form stable emulsions when contacted with aqueous solutions. In some cases, this tendency can be overcome by changing the phase ratios in the mixers or the temperatures of the solutions, or by removing traces of impurities such as colloidal silica. It has been found that where some alkyl phosphates form emulsions if the aqueous phase is the continuous one, the phases will separate rapidly if the organic phase is continuous.

Inflammability and toxicity. For safety in the plant, the inflammability of the solvent and the diluent, and the toxicity of the vapors must be considered. Although extremely inflammable solvents are sometimes used, for example diethyl ether in uranium purification, the additional safety precautions that must be taken add considerably to plant costs. An inflammable solvent can be used without undue hazard, however, if the vapor pressure is low and the flash point is sufficiently high. Kerosene solutions of alkyl phosphates have flash points of about 160°F and have quite low vapor pressures. Other diluents are available with flash points above 200°F. Thus, using these solutions does not present an unreasonable safety problem. A low vapor pressure is necessary to decrease the danger of toxicity and to minimize solvent losses.

Cost. The cost of the solvent would be relatively unimportant if there were no losses and if all the solvent could be recycled indefinitely. However, in any plant there are appreciable losses due to solubility, entrainment, hydrolysis, and spillage. The relative costs of solvents and the costs of reagents necessary for stripping and product recovery must then be balanced against these losses.

10–2.2 Effects of leach liquor composition. *Nature of anions present.* Since uranium can exist in aqueous solution either as a neutral complex, a complex anion, or a cation, the organic solvents used in solvent extraction can be divided into three classes, according to the type of uranium complex extracted. The principal members of the first class are the ethers, the trialkyl phosphates, and the trialkyl phosphine oxides, all of which extract neutral complexes. The second class consists of alkyl amines, which extract anionic complexes. The third class consists of alkyl orthophosphoric acids (usually called alkyl phosphoric acids) and alkyl pyrophosphoric acids, which extract cations.

In choosing the extractant, then, the nature of the anions present in the aqueous phase is an important factor, since this determines the type of uranium complex available for extraction. In nitrate solutions uranium is largely present as neutral or cationic complexes. Thus it can be extracted with ethers, tributyl phosphate (TBP) or alkyl phosphoric acids. In solutions very high in hydrochloric acid, both anionic and neutral complexes seem to be present, since the uranium can be extracted by amines, ethers, and TBP, but not by alkyl phosphoric acids. In sulfate solutions, such as sulfuric acid leach liquors, both anionic and cationic uranium complexes are present. Complete extraction can be effected either with alkyl phosphates or with amines, since the equilibrium between anionic and cationic uranium complexes in the aqueous phase is shifted by the extraction.

The presence in the aqueous solution of more than one anionic constituent capable of complexing uranium makes the extraction more complicated. For example, small concentrations of chloride or nitrate in sulfate solutions have a marked deterrent effect on extraction of uranium anionic complexes with amines. Adding thiocyanate to sulfate solutions makes the uranium amenable to extraction with TBP. Uranium extraction from mixed phosphoric-nitric acid solutions, obtained by nitric acidulation of phosphate rock, is very poor with TBP, but reasonably good with alkyl pyrophosphates. However, if the phosphate ore used in the acidulation is high in aluminum, the extraction with TBP improves markedly because the aluminum complexes the phosphate, and extraction with alkyl pyrophosphate becomes poorer because of the competitive extraction of aluminum.

Oxidation state of uranium. The oxidation state of the uranium in the aqueous phase also affects the extraction considerably. Both uranyl and uranous complexes can be extracted from most solutions. TBP, primary amines, and some secondary amines show higher coefficients for the reduced species, but tertiary and a number of secondary amines extract the uranyl complexes more strongly than the uranous. Alkyl orthophosphoric acids extract both forms about equally from sulfate solutions.

Nature of cations present. Sulfate leach liquors from uranium ores usually have pH's of 1 to 2. Within this region an increase in the pH increases the extraction coefficients with both alkyl phosphoric acids and amines. When metals like iron and vanadium, which are more readily extracted at higher pH values, are present, the effect of increased pH on uranium extraction is less, and in extreme cases, uranium extraction at the higher pH may be less than at the lower. Iron is often present. Since ferric iron is extracted strongly by alkyl phosphoric acids, it is necessary in some cases to reduce it to the nonextractable ferrous form. Many acid liquors from the Colorado Plateau, however, are sufficiently low in iron so that reduction is not necessary. Amines are more selective for uranium over iron, and reduction of the iron is seldom necessary if they are used. Vanadium is extracted much less readily than uranium, and causes only a small decrease in uranium concentrations in the solvent.

Titanium also interferes with uranium extraction from sulfate solution by alkyl phosphoric acids. Its extraction may be prevented by complexing in the aqueous solution by phosphate or fluoride. The titanium content of most uranium leach liquors is low enough that uranium recovery is not greatly affected in a single extraction cycle. Titanium can be stripped from the extractant with carbonate to prevent buildup during recycling. However, when acid stripping is used, titanium is not removed from the organic phase, and a buildup occurs that leads to a progressive decrease in uranium extraction as the extractant is recycled. To use an alkyl phosphoric acid solvent for extracting a sulfate solution relatively high in titanium, with subsequent acid stripping, it therefore is necessary to insert a scrubbing operation with a dilute fluoride solution before recycle. Alkyl amine solutions do not extract titanium, and for this reason may be preferable for high-titanium leach liquors. Molybdenum is extracted both by alkyl phosphates and by amines. Since it is readily stripped from the phosphates with either strong acids or carbonate, it does not build up in these systems. However, it is not removed from amines by the dilute chloride or nitrate solutions used for stripping, and if amines are used to extract solutions high in molybdenum, either carbonate or MgO stripping must be used.

10–2.3 Extraction of neutral complexes. *Ethers and TBP.* The extraction of neutral uranium complexes has been used commercially for many years in the production of highly purified uranium compounds. The solvents now employed are diethyl ether and tributyl phosphate. The ether requires no diluent, but the TBP is diluted with kerosene. Uranium is extracted from nitric acid leach liquors of concentrates by the following reaction:

$$[UO_2{}^{++}]_{aq} + 2[NO_3{}^-]_{aq} + 2[TBP]_{org} \rightleftarrows [UO_2(NO_3)_2(TBP)_2]_{org}.$$

A high concentration of nitrate in the leach solution drives this reaction to the right. The loaded organic can be easily stripped with water, since a low nitrate concentration will drive the reaction to the left.

TBP solutions will extract nitrate, thiocyanate, or chloride complexes of uranium [10]. The extractable chloride complex is formed, however, only in concentrated HCl solutions. The chief advantages of extraction with TBP or with ethers are the ease of stripping and the high selectivity for uranium over the other constituents, resulting in a very pure product.

Phosphine oxides. Trialkyl phosphine oxides will extract neutral uranium complexes from sulfate solutions [11,12]. With leach liquors of the usual pH and sulfate content, extraction coefficients are lower than those with alkyl orthophosphoric acids. Stripping from the phosphine oxides requires carbonate solutions.

10–2.4 Extraction of cations. Alkyl phosphoric acids extract uranyl ions from sulfuric acid leach solutions [13,14]. Both mono- and dialkyl esters are effective, and the mechanisms appear to be similar. The reactions are

$$UO_2{}^{++} + 2R_2HPO_4 \rightarrow UO_2(R_2PO_4)_2 + 2H^+,$$

$$UO_2{}^{++} + 2RH_2PO_4 \rightarrow UO_2(RHPO_4)_2 + 2H^+.$$

Similar equations can be written for the extraction of the uranous form.

Preparation of alkyl phosphoric acids. Alkyl orthophosphoric acids can be made by reacting alcohols with phosphorus pentoxide or phosphorus oxytrichloride [15,16]. The reaction with $POCl_3$ produces both the tri- and the dialkyl esters:

$$3ROH + POCl_3 \rightarrow R_3PO_4 + 3HCl,$$

$$2ROH + POCl_3 + H_2O \rightarrow R_2HPO_4 + 3HCl.$$

Since trialkyl esters are made in this way in large volume for use as plasticizers, there is considerable by-product dialkyl ester available at a reasonable cost.

The reaction with alcohol and P_2O_5 produces pyrophosphoric acids, which are easily hydrolyzed to the orthoacids. If two moles of alcohol are used per mole of P_2O_5, the symmetrical dialkyl pyrophosphate is apparently formed:

$$2ROH + P_2O_5 \rightarrow RO-\overset{\overset{\displaystyle O}{\|}}{\underset{\underset{\displaystyle OH}{|}}{P}}-O-\overset{\overset{\displaystyle O}{\|}}{\underset{\underset{\displaystyle OH}{|}}{P}}-OR$$

On contact with acid solutions this compound is rapidly hydrolyzed to the monoalkyl ortho ester:

$$RO-\overset{\overset{\displaystyle O}{\|}}{\underset{\underset{\displaystyle OH}{|}}{P}}-O-\overset{\overset{\displaystyle O}{\|}}{\underset{\underset{\displaystyle OH}{|}}{O}}-OR + H_2O \rightarrow 2RO-\overset{\overset{\displaystyle O}{\|}}{\underset{\underset{\displaystyle OH}{|}}{P}}-OH$$

Monododecyl phosphoric acid (DDPA) and monoheptadecyl phosphoric acid (HDPA) are made by this reaction. The P_2O_5 is first slurried in kerosene or other diluent (about 1 liter per mole of P_2O_5), and the alcohol is then added rapidly. The diluent is used to control the temperature of the reaction. The reaction product is hydrolyzed at an elevated temperature with approximately one-fourth its volume of 1 M HCl. Volatile diluents are sometimes used instead of kerosene when the pure (undiluted) compound is desired.

Using a larger proportion of alcohol in the reaction with P_2O_5 produces a mixture of mono- and dialkyl esters. Such products are commercially available containing alkyl groups of various lengths up to octyl. The mono- and dialkyl esters can be separated by partition between immiscible solvents such as kerosene and ethylene glycol.

The strength of mono- and diester in these solutions can be determined by titration of an acetone solution with standard base. The monoalkyl acid gives a strong and a weak acid endpoint, and the dialkyl acid gives only a strong acid endpoint. Since symmetrical dialkyl pyrophosphates also give only the strong acid endpoint, they cannot be distinguished from dialkyl orthophosphoric acids by this means.

Aqueous solubility of alkyl phosphoric acids. The solubility of mono-alkyl orthophosphoric acids containing 8 to 17 carbon atoms has been measured by bringing them in contact with sulfate solutions similar in composition to typical leach liquors. The solubility losses found by analysis of the aqueous phases [15] are listed in Table 10–1. Diagrams of the carbon skeletons of these compounds are included in the table. These data indicate that increased branching of the chain increases the solubility in the aqueous phase, but that the decrease in solubility with increasing chain length is of much greater magnitude. The solubility of di(2-ethyl-hexyl) phosphoric acid (EHPA) in a similar sulfate solution was found to be less than 0.01 gram of ester per liter [17]. Thus, it is of the same order as the monoalkyl ester with the same total number of carbon atoms in the molecule.

Effect of nature of alkyl group. Although the ultimate saturation capacity per mole appears to be the same with all the alkyl phosphates tested, the uranium extraction coefficients for comparable points on the respective distribution isotherms vary with the composition of the alkyl groups. The coefficients for monoalkyl phosphates are higher than those for dialkyl phosphates containing the same alkyl group. The coefficients, compared on a molar basis, increase with length of alkyl group up to about 14 carbon atoms. The saturation capacity and hence the shape of the isotherm are also affected by the extraction of such other metals as vanadium, iron, titanium, and aluminum.

Commercially available alkyl phosphoric acids. At present, there are three phosphate esters commercially available for use as uranium extractants: monododecyl phosphoric acid (DDPA) made from 2, 6, 8-trimethyl-4-nonanol, monoheptadecyl phosphoric acid (HDPA) made from 3, 9-diethyl-6-tridecanol, and dioctyl phosphoric acid made from 2-ethylhexanol. The latter is variously abbreviated as EHPA, D2EHPA, HDEHP, or di-OPA. A comparison of the distribution isotherms of these solvents contacted with a typical Plateau leach liquor is shown in Fig. 10–1. It is clear from this figure that the extraction coefficients with DDPA and HDPA are considerably higher than those with EHPA. This does not mean that the same recovery cannot be achieved with EHPA as with the other extractants, but merely that either a faster organic flow rate, more stages, or a more concentrated EHPA solution must be used. In comparing isotherms it is important to keep in mind that the saturation capacity is a limiting value that is not actually reached. The maximum concentration attainable in the organic phase in any countercurrent extraction system is that which is in equilibrium with the aqueous head concentration.

TABLE 10–1

SOLUBILITY OF MONOALKYL PHOSPHORIC ACID ESTERS
IN SULFATE SOLUTION (pH 1.2)

Alkyl group	Carbon skeleton ($\times$ = PO_4H_2)	No. of carbons	Loss to aqueous, g ester/liter
n-Octyl		8	1.0
1-Methylheptyl		8	1.4
2-Ethylhexyl (mono-EHPA)		8	3.0
3, 3, 5-Trimethyl- -cyclohexyl		9	1.6
1-Isobutyl- -3-methylbutyl		9	1.1
1-Isobutyl- -3, 5-dimethyl- -hexyl (DDPA)		12	0.10
2-Butyloctyl		12	0.06
1-Isobutyl- -4-ethyloctyl		14	0.05
1-(3-Ethylpentyl)- -4-ethyloctyl (HDPA)		17	0.003

Removal of uranium from alkyl phosphoric acids. To strip uranium from DDPA it is necessary to use strong acid solutions. Hydrochloric and hydrofluoric acids give the highest stripping coefficients. The reaction is the reverse of the extraction reaction, the high acidity driving it to the left. The formation of uranyl chloride complexes with low extraction coefficients may also be involved. A typical stripping isotherm with 10 M HCl is shown in Fig. 10–2.

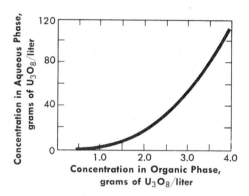

Fig. 10–2. Stripping isotherm for uranium removal from 0.1 M DDPA with 10 M HCl.

EHPA can be stripped either with strong acids or with carbonate solutions. To strip with carbonate solutions, the extractant must be modified by adding an equal amount of a higher alcohol or of TBP. Without this additive three liquid phases form in the settler: the upper phase is mostly kerosene, the middle is the sodium form of EHPA, and the lower is the carbonate solution. The addition of alcohol or TBP makes the sodium EHPA soluble in the kerosene and eliminates the third phase. The addition of alcohol has a deterrent effect on the extraction coefficient when the extractant is subsequently contacted with the leach liquor, but addition of TBP does not. TBP has a synergistic effect on the extraction coefficient which is pronounced at low uranium loadings.

Carbonate stripping probably involves the following reaction:

$$UO_2(R_2PO_4)_2 + 3Na_2CO_3 \rightarrow UO_2(CO_3)_3{}^{-4} + 4Na^+ + 2NaR_2PO_4.$$

Since the uranyl carbonate complex has almost no tendency to be re-extracted by the solvent, this reaction goes essentially to completion if sufficient carbonate is present. For the most economical operation the carbonate should be loaded nearly to capacity. Most of the other metals extracted from Colorado Plateau leach liquors form insoluble hydroxides at the pH of sodium carbonate solutions and precipitate.

This precipitation is advantageous, since it eliminates the buildup of impurities in the extractant that would interfere in the subsequent extraction step. However, the precipitate is difficult to filter. Subsequent precipitation of uranium from the filtrate results in a fairly pure product.

These extractants can also be stripped by direct precipitation of UF_4 from the organic. This can be accomplished by contacting the loaded solvent with aqueous HF solution to which a reducing agent such as $FeSO_4$ has been added. Although impure uranous fluoride is not an acceptable starting material for the present uranium purification plants, it may be acceptable for future plants using other purification procedures. The monoalkyl esters are probably preferable to dialkyl esters in systems where either strong HF or strong HCl would be used, since they are more resistant to hydrolysis.

Extraction with alkyl pyrophosphoric acids. Alkyl pyrophosphoric acids exhibit extremely high extraction coefficients for uranium in acid solutions but, since the extracted complexes involve one or two molecules of pyrophosphate per uranium atom, the saturation capacities are of the same order as those of the alkyl orthophosphates. These compounds are not very stable, hydrolyzing readily to the orthophosphates. With aqueous solutions relatively high in uranium, such as acid leach solutions of Plateau ores, alkyl pyrophosphates have no advantage over orthophosphates in extraction, since the equilibria represented by the upper part of the isotherm near saturation are used. However, with solutions containing very low concentrations of uranium, such as commercial wet-process phosphoric acids, the equilibria represented by the lower part of the isotherm are used [18], and the extremely high extraction coefficients in this region make it possible to employ very low concentrations of extractant (1 to 3 volume percent). Because of hydrolysis, the extractant lasts for only a few cycles.

The higher extraction coefficients with alkyl pyrophosphates compared with those with orthophosphates are probably due to the formation of chelate rings, as in the following reaction:

The chelate is probably formed more easily with uranous than with uranyl ion. Uranous ions are extracted more readily than uranyl from phosphoric acid both because of the greater ease of chelation with the alkyl pyrophosphate and because uranous ions are not complexed as strongly by aqueous phosphate ions. Uranium in phosphoric acid is reduced by treatment with iron before extraction.

10–2.5 Extraction of anionic complexes. *Extraction with alkyl amines.* Uranium can be extracted from sulfate leach liquors as a sulfate anion complex with oil-soluble amines [19–23]. High extraction coefficients have been obtained with various primary, secondary, and tertiary amines. The reactions are analogous to those with anion-exchange resins:

$$2R_2NH_2^+ + UO_2(SO_4)_2^= \rightarrow [R_2NH_2]_2UO_2(SO_4)_2.$$

These amines are comparable to weak-base resins. Typical distribution isotherms for extracting uranium from sulfuric acid leach liquors by alkyl amines are shown in Fig. 10–3 [23]. The data shown were obtained with a synthetic leach liquor similar to that obtained by leaching a Marysvale, Utah, ore.

Effect of structure of amine. A large number of commercially available amines have been screened in several laboratories and a number have been

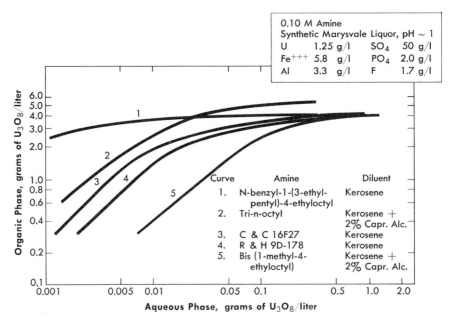

Fig. 10–3. Distribution isotherms for extraction of uranium from sulfate leach liquors by alkyl amines.

found which are good uranium extractants.   Straight-chain primary amines often form stable emulsions with the aqueous phase, but branched-chain primary amines containing 14 to 20 carbons separate readily from aqueous phases if no solids are present.   They are good extractants.   Secondary amines with either normal or branched aliphatic chains are good extractants, and unsaturation in the carbon chain does not appear to inhibit the extraction.   At least 10 carbons are required in the aliphatic groups to ensure low solubility in the aqueous phase.   High-molecular-weight tertiary amines with normal chains are also good extractants. Secondary and tertiary amines generally show less tendency to form emulsions than do primary amines.

Some secondary amines with one aromatic substituent (especially benzyl) have much higher coefficients than analogous aliphatic compounds, but tertiary amines with aromatic substituents are poorer extractants than the analogous aliphatic compounds.   Amines in which the aromatic group is attached directly to the nitrogen, such as the aniline derivatives, are poor extractants.   In many amines, especially tertiary, steric effects inhibit extraction.   For instance, if more than one of the chains is branched at the carbon next to the nitrogen, the extraction is poorer.

Diluent for amine extraction.   The nature of the diluent influences the extraction of uranium, but the effect is different with different amines. Generally, the use of more polar solvents, such as chloroform, decreases the extraction coefficient, perhaps because of association of the diluent with the amine; however, with some amines polar solvents give higher coefficients.   A more important requirement is the miscibility of amine chloride and nitrate salts with the diluent.   These salts are formed during stripping, and if the miscibility with the particular diluent is too low, a precipitate or a third liquid phase will form.   A high aromatic character in a solvent results in greater solvent power for these salts, but kerosene solutions are satisfactory in many cases.   Kerosene has the advantages of low cost and wide availability.

Kerosene is a suitable diluent for most long-branched-chain secondary amines and for straight-chain symmetrical tertiary amines with chains of 10 or more carbons.   In most other cases, it is necessary to add a small amount (2 to 5 volume percent) of a long-chain alcohol to the kerosene to make it a satisfactory diluent.   The addition of alcohol decreases the extraction efficiency slightly but increases the selectivity for uranium over other metals.

Selectivity of amines.   The selectivity for uranium over the other metals normally present in leach liquors is greater with amines than with phosphates.   Primary amines have the poorest selectivity and extract ferric iron strongly.   Secondary amines have good selectivity and tertiary amines,

TABLE 10–2

COMMERCIALLY AVAILABLE AMINES AND THEIR STRUCTURES

Trade name*	Chemical name	Structure
Amine 21F81 (Carbide)	1-(3-Ethylpentyl)-4-ethyloctylamine	CH_2CH_3 $H_2N-CH(CH_2)_2CH(CH_2)_3CH_3$ $(CH_2)_2CHCH_2CH_3$ CH_2CH_3
Primene JM-T (R&H)	Trialkylmethylamine	R $HN-C-R'$ R'' $(R + R' + R'' = 17\text{-}23$ carbon atoms)
Amine 9D-178 (R&H)	N-Dodecenyltri-alkylmethylamine, "dodecenyl" = 5, 5, 7, 7-tetramethyl-2-octenyl	CH_3 CH_3 $CH_2CH{:}CHCH_2CCH_2CCH_3$ CH_3 CH_3 HN $R-C-R''$ R' $(R + R' + R'' = 11\text{-}14$ carbon atoms)

Name	Description	Structure
(Carbide)	dimethylhexyl)amine	
Di(tridecyl P)amine (Carbide)	"Tridecyl P" = mixture of 13-carbon alkyls, probably principally 3, 5, 5, 7, 7-pentamethyl-octyl	$HN\left[-CHCH_2CHCH_2CHCH_3 \atop CH_2CH(CH_3)_2\right]_2$
N-Benzylheptadecylamine (Carbide)	"Heptadecyl" = 1-(3-ethylpentyl)-4-ethyloctyl	$HN\left[-CH_2CH_2CHCH_2CCH_2CCH_3 \atop CH_3\ \ CH_3\ \ CH_3\right]_2$ with $CH_3\ CH_3$
Triisooctylamine (Carbide) (Gulf)	"Isooctyl" = mixture of dimethylhexyls and methylheptyls, etc., principally 3, 5-, 4, 5-, and 3, 4-dimethylhexyl	$N\left[-CH_2CH_2CHCH_2CHCH_3 \atop CH_3\ \ \ CH_3\right]_3$
Butyldidodecenylamine (R&H)	"Dodecenyl" = 5, 5, 7, 7-tetramethyl-2-octenyl	$N\left[-CH_2CH{:}CHCH_2CCH_2CCH_3 \atop CH_3\ \ CH_3\right]_2$ and $(CH_2)_3CH_3$

N-Benzyl structure:
$$CH_2—HN—CH(CH_2)_2CH(CH_2)_3CH_3$$
$$CH_2CH_3 \qquad (CH_2)_2CHCH_2CH_3 \qquad CH_2CH_3$$

*Carbide: Carbide and Carbon Chemicals Co., New York. *Gulf:* Gulf Oil Corporation, Pittsburgh. *R&H:* Rohm and Haas Co., Philadelphia.

especially the symmetrical ones, are very selective for uranium. All classes of amines extract molybdenum strongly. Secondary and tertiary amines extract small amounts of ferric iron, but the extraction of the other metals found in ores of the western United States is quite low. Amines have a considerable advantage over phosphates as extractants for clear solutions with high ferric iron content, since reduction of the iron is not required.

Removal of uranium from amines. Uranium can be stripped from amines with carbonate, chloride, or nitrate solutions. Stripping with carbonate probably proceeds by hydrolysis of the alkylammonium cations to nonionic amine molecules. A reaction of the following type takes place with the carbonate. The exact formulations of the complexes involved are not definitely known.

$$(R_2NH_2)_2UO_2(SO_4)_2 + 5CO_3^= \rightarrow 2R_2NH + UO_2(CO_3)_3^{-4}$$
$$+ 2SO_4^= + 2HCO_3^-.$$

This reaction goes essentially to completion, and the uranium can be almost quantitatively removed in one stage if sufficient carbonate is present.

Stripping with chloride is comparable to elution from anion-exchange resins. The following type of exchange reaction is involved:

$$(R_2NH_2)_2UO_2(SO_4)_2 + 2Cl^- \rightarrow 2R_2NH_2Cl + UO_2(SO_4)_2^=.$$

The concentration of chloride that may be used for stripping is limited, since amines will extract uranium from solutions high in chloride. A concentration of 1 to 3 molar chloride has been used. Stripping is more efficient if a small amount of acid is added (0.05 M).

Nitrate solutions remove uranium from amines in the same manner as chloride solutions. Nitrate is a more efficient stripping agent. However, the amine cannot be directly recycled in the nitrate form because nitrate considerably inhibits the extraction of uranium. Nitrate is held very tightly by the amine, whereas chloride has only a small deleterious effect. Because of its higher cost, it is necessary to recover the nitrate salt. This can be done by treating the organic with ammonia or sodium carbonate solutions.

Commercially available amines. A number of commercially available amines suitable for uranium extraction are listed in Table 10–2 [24]. Much research is still being done in this field, and other compounds tailored expressly for this purpose will continue to be developed.

10–3. Equipment Used in Solvent Extraction

10–3.1 Rate of extraction. The rates of the chemical reactions involved in the solvent extraction of uranium have not been precisely measured, but they seem to be very fast. The measurable time necessary to attain equilibrium seems to be the time required for adequate physical contact of the phases. Some studies of contact time and intensity of agitation have been made which indicate that in most contacting equipment very short contact times are adequate [15,16]. The relationships among agitator geometry, paddle speed, size of dispersed particles, retention time, and extraction rate have not yet been clearly defined.

10–3.2 Multistage operation. Since solvent extraction processes usually do not involve reactions which go to completion, a single stage of extraction results in only partial recovery of uranium from the aqueous phase and also uses only part of the capacity of the extractant. If sufficient extraction stages are operated countercurrently, any desired recovery can be obtained, and the extractant capacity can be used effectively. The number of stages necessary for a given recovery can be determined from the distribution isotherm. If the isotherm is linear below the aqueous head concentration, the recovery attainable by a system with a given number of stages and a given flow rate can be determined directly from plots of the equations found in many textbooks on solvent extraction [7,8]. In the general case, however, where the isotherm is curved, the expected recovery for a system is most easily obtained by means of a McCabe-Thiele dia-

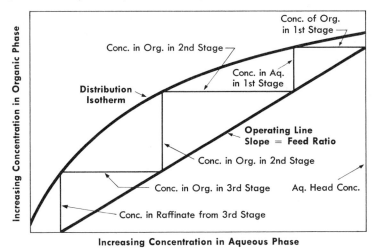

Fig. 10–4. Typical McCabe-Thiele diagram for three-stage countercurrent extraction.

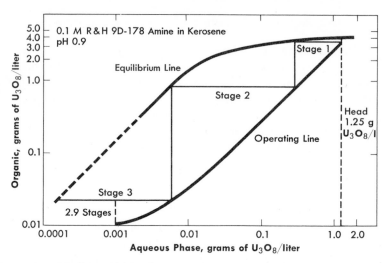

Fɪɢ. 10–5. McCabe-Thiele diagram for amine solvent extraction system.

gram. A typical diagram of this type is shown in Fig. 10–4. This diagram contains the distribution isotherm and an operating line of slope determined by the feed ratio, and location determined by the entering and exiting concentrations. The concentrations to be expected in each stage are given by lines connecting the distribution curve and the operating line. The number of ideal stages required for a given recovery are determined by these lines. Since the distribution curve is determined under conditions of equilibrium, these methods will predict the operation only of systems in which all mixing stages are at equilibrium and in which there is no bypassing. Although these conditions are not completely attained in actual operation, the predictions are a good approximation of the behavior of mixer-settler systems. These diagrams may be prepared in cartesian coordinates as in Fig. 10–4, or, to expand the area of low uranium concentrations, in log-log coordinates as in the diagram for an amine system in Fig. 10–5 [23].

10–3.3 Laboratory equipment. For bench-scale measurement of distribution isotherms, common laboratory apparatus such as separatory funnels, graduated cylinders, beakers, and flasks are sufficient. A mechanical shaker is desirable if many such experiments are to be done. Multistage operation can be simulated in the laboratory with separatory funnels, but this is rather awkward and time-consuming. A more elegant method for obtaining multistage data is by means of a bank of small-scale mixer-settlers. These are simple to construct and not difficult to operate. A drawing of a laboratory-scale mixer-settler apparatus is shown in Fig. 10–6.

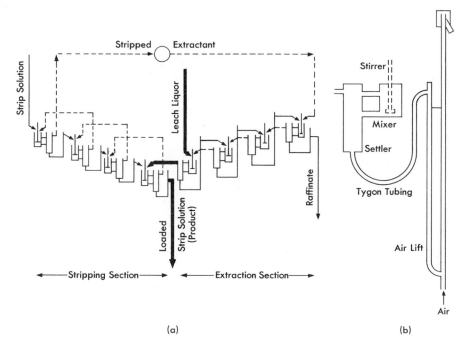

FIG. 10–6. Laboratory-scale countercurrent mixer-settler unit. (a) Flow diagram for 4 extraction stages and 4 stripping stages. (b) Detail of mixer-settler unit.

This type of unit is used in many laboratories. It consists of a series of cylindrical mixers and settlers, usually made of glass. Each mixer is connected to a settler by two openings. The purpose of the upper opening is to provide a means of feedback for the organic phase so that the relative volumes in the mixer will not be determined by the feed rates of the two phases. In these systems there is a tendency toward the formation of stable emulsions if the aqueous phase is the continuous one in the mixing operation. If the organic phase is continuous and the aqueous phase is dispersed, phase separation is sharp and rapid. The interface level in the settler can be set by properly positioning the overflow leg on the aqueous stream leaving the settler. The level is adjusted so that the mixer contains a greater volume of organic than of aqueous phase at all times. Thus, the suspension of aqueous in organic is pumped through the bottom connection from the mixer to the settler, and part of the separated organic returns to the mixer through the top connection.

In this manner, the internal mixing ratio in each stage can be controlled and is made independent of the external feed ratios to the system. Each mixer is agitated by a glass turbine-type stirrer rotated by a variable-speed electric motor. One phase flows through the system by gravity; the other is pumped from stage to stage by airlifts. The system can be operated equally well with either phase flowing by gravity or, if vertical space is too limited, both phases can be moved by airlifts. Each stream is fed into the system by a constant-flow-rate pump.

10–3.4 Commercial equipment mixer-settler design. Although many different types of equipment have been proposed for continuous countercurrent solvent extraction, they may all be classified either as mixer-settlers, column contactors, or centrifugal contactors. Several common types are illustrated in Fig. 10–7.

Mixer-settlers consist usually of separate mixing and settling tanks, but in some types the mixing takes place in a compartment within the settling tank or is accomplished in a centrifugal pump feeding the settler. Mixing and settling tanks may be of any shape, so long as adequate contact between the phases is attained in the mixer and sufficient area is provided in the settler to allow the phases to disengage completely. Design of mixers

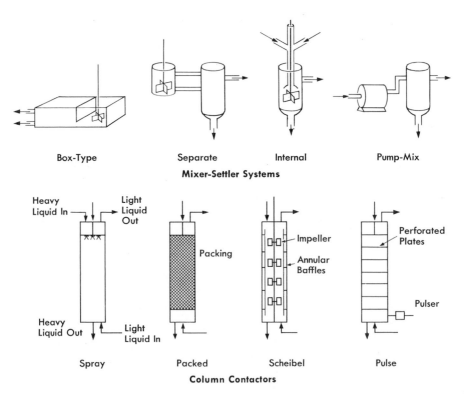

Fig. 10–7. Typical liquid-liquid contactors.

involves consideration of such factors as residence time and degree of dispersion [9,25,26]. Settler design involves the same considerations as thickener design. Scale-up factors for both mixers and settlers are reasonably well established. It is desirable in mixer-settler design to provide means for recycle of organic from the settler to the mixer so that emulsion formation can be minimized.

In uranium metallurgy, four types of mixer-settler designs are prominent: the separate mixer and settler, the internal mixer, the box type, and the pump-mix system. The separate mixer and settler is a scale-up of the laboratory unit described above. It is simple to design and relatively trouble-free. Vertical cylindrical tanks are usually used for both the mixers and the settlers. The mixing tank is equipped with baffles and is agitated by a turbine-type stirrer. In the internal mixer, both mixer and settler are combined in a single tank. Agitation is by a turbine-type stirrer enclosed either in a shroud or in a small tank with openings on the bottom placed inside and in the upper part of the settling tank. The box-type mixer-settler unit consists of a tank, usually rectangular, divided into two compartments by a baffle extending nearly to the bottom. The agitator is placed in one compartment and the suspension flows under the baffle into the other, where phase disengagement takes place. This type of equipment is easy to build but is usually rather inefficient because it is difficult to prevent part of the feed streams from bypassing the agitator. The pump-mix system [27,28] consists of a centrifugal pump and a settling tank. Both phases are fed into the pump, where they are mixed and then sent to the settler. Although the contact time in the pump is very short, the degree of dispersion achieved is so great that high extraction efficiency can be attained.

Column contactors. Column contactors make use of the difference in density of the two phases to achieve countercurrent flow. The heavier phase is fed to the top of the column and the lighter phase to the bottom. There are many types of columns [9,26]. The simplest is the spray column, consisting of a tube equipped with a spray nozzle. Extraction occurs as the droplets of the dispersed phase fall, or rise, through the continuous phase. The efficiency of the phase contact can be increased by introducing packing or various types of plates in the column. Spray, packed, and plate columns are widely used in both the chemical and petroleum industries. Long columns are necessary for adequate uranium extraction, and control of the mixing ratio is difficult. Columns can be made more efficient by introducing mechanical means for maintaining good dispersion. Several types use inline turbine blades driven by a central shaft through the center of the column. The Rushton and Oldshue columns [29,30] have annular baffles between the impellers to effect phase separation, and the Scheibel column has packing in the regions between the impellers. Another mechanical method for obtaining dispersion is that used in the pulse column [31,32]: a pulsing mechanism is placed either in the feed line of the lighter phase or in the bottom of the column and, by rapidly changing the liquid volume in the column, subjects the liquid to a rapid alternation of dispersing and settling cycles.

The criteria for designing and scaling-up column contactors are not so well known as those for mixer-settlers. The concept of the theoretical plate is useful. A theoretical plate is a section of column in which the same extraction is obtained as would be effected by a 100 percent efficient mixer-settler stage. The height of column equivalent to a theoretical plate can then be used both as a measure of the efficiency of a column and as an indication of the column height required for a desired recovery. The height equivalent to a theoretical plate is abbreviated HETP. The height of a transfer unit, HTU, is also a useful concept [7,8].

Since the HETP value for a given type of column is not a simple function of the diameter, it is difficult to predict the behavior of a large column from laboratory or pilot-plant data obtained with small columns. This hinders the adoption of column contactors in many cases, since the columns must be in-plant tested before the extraction efficiency can be known with certainty. Column contactors have a cost advantage over mixer-settlers if the number of theoretical stages desired is great. The cost of a single mixer-settler stage is usually less than that of an equivalent column. However, the cost of additional mixer-settler stages is relatively constant; the cost per column stage decreases rapidly with increasing number, since additional stages require only increased column length. It is estimated that capital costs for a column are lower than for a mixer-settler system if the number of stages exceeds 4 or 5.

For efficient operation of either columns or mixer-settlers, the phase separation must be rapid and complete. In uranium extraction, emulsion tendencies are usually less if the organic phase is continuous. The organic phase can be fixed as the continuous phase by locating the interface, or coalescence section, at the bottom of the column. The column then operates full of organic with aqueous droplets falling through it. If the degree of dispersion in a column is similar to that in a mixer-settler, the diameter required for the coalescence section would be the same as that required for a settler. In some cases this would necessitate an enlarged section at the bottom of the column.

Centrifugal extractors. Centrifugal extractors employ centrifugal force to increase the difference in driving force for phase separation. The Podbielniak extractor has been tested in several uranium extraction processes. This extractor consists of a long spiral chamber made by coiling a metal plate within a cylindrical drum. The chamber is rotated at from 2000 to 5000 rpm. In some models the spiral plate is perforated, and in some it is replaced by perforated rings. The liquids flow countercurrently through the spiral. These extractors require liquids entirely free of solids, since solids would cause considerable wear by abrasion. The liquids must be pumped in at high pressures because the extractors operate at centrifugal forces as high as 5000 times the normal force of gravity. A single Podbielniak unit has been found to be equivalent to about 3 to 4 mixer-settler stages when used in a uranium extraction system. The chief advantage of this type of apparatus is its smaller space requirement. Several other types of centrifugal extractors are also available.

10–4. CURRENT SOLVENT EXTRACTION PROCESSES FOR URANIUM

10–4.1 Recovery from sulfate leach liquors. Two types of extractants are being used to recover uranium from sulfate leach liquors: alkyl phosphoric acids and alkyl amines. Either monoalkyl or dialkyl phosphates can be used, and the phosphate process is called either the DDPA process (after dodecyl phosphoric acid) or the EHPA process (after di-2-ethylhexyl phosphoric acid), depending on which compound is used. The EHPA process is also referred to as the Dapex process (after dialkyl phosphate extraction). The amine process is called Amex (after amine extraction). Figure 10–8 shows an outline flow diagram for each of these processes.

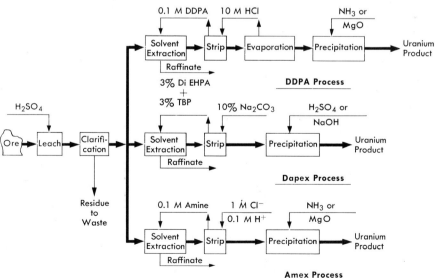

FIG. 10–8. Flow diagrams for solvent extraction processes to recover uranium from sulfate leach liquors.

DDPA process. In the DDPA process, a 0.1 M solution of DDPA is used as extractant and a 10 M HCl solution is used as the stripping agent [15,33]. The process was studied extensively in a 100 gal/hr pilot plant [34,35]. The extraction equipment consisted initially of eight 18-inch-diameter tanks, four of which were equipped with agitators. The tanks were connected so that the two liquid streams were alternately mixed and separated in four stages as they flowed countercurrently to each other. The four mixing tanks were later eliminated by placing hooded-turbine internal mixers inside the settling tanks. Both systems operated satisfactorily and extracted uranium from the leach liquor efficiently. The stripping section consisted of four similar mixer-settler stages but, instead of tanks, 4-liter beakers were used. The HCl solution leaving the stripping section contained about 40 g U_3O_8/liter. It was fed to a continuous evaporator, where most of the free HCl was distilled and recycled as 10 M HCl. The concentrate was continuously withdrawn from the evaporator at 500 to 1000 g U_3O_8/liter, and the uranium product was precipitated from this with ammonia. This process has been installed in one full-scale plant [36],* where the extraction equipment consists of four 20-foot-diameter tanks equipped with 20-inch-diameter hooded-turbine agitators.

EHPA or Dapex process. The EHPA or Dapex process employs as the extractant a kerosene solution containing 3 to 5 percent di(2-ethylhexyl) phosphoric acid (EHPA) and about the same concentration of TBP [16,17,37]. It differs from the DDPA process in that the stripping solution is 10 percent sodium carbonate. The TBP added to the extractant gives a synergistic increase in the extraction coefficient for uranium and increases the solubility of the sodium form of EHPA, formed during stripping, in kerosene. Without this addition, a third liquid phase would separate on contacting the extractant with the sodium carbonate stripping solution. This third phase formation can also be prevented by using long-chain, water-insoluble alcohols such as tridecyl alcohol, but at the cost of depressing uranium extraction somewhat.

The process was piloted by batchwise operation of a single 20-foot diameter tank which contained a mixer in an inner tank. Although these tests gave data for single-stage operation only, uranium recovery was so encouraging that a full-scale, four-stage, countercurrent extraction plant was built without further tests [38].† The extraction section of this plant consists of four 16-foot-diameter tanks each containing a 4-foot-diameter mixing tank. The stripping section consists of two 4-foot-diameter mixing units and two 8-foot-diameter cone-bottom settlers. After loaded sodium carbonate stripping solution is filtered, the carbonate is destroyed by

---

* For a description of the plant, see Article 11–4.6.
† For a description of the plant, see Article 11–5.5.

mixing the solution with sulfuric acid, and the uranium is precipitated with ammonia. Other plants employing this process are also in operation [39,40]. In some cases the final precipitation of the uranium product is effected by adding caustic soda to the stripping solution. When this procedure is followed, the filtrate can be recycled and the carbonate consumption is only about 2 pounds per 1 pound of U_3O_8.

Amex process. A large number of alkyl amines have the ability to extract uranium [19–23,41]. However, cost and availability factors have limited the amines proposed for commercial application to secondary amines with alkyl groups of about 12 carbons, trifatty amines, trilauryl amines, and triisooctyl amine. Although the extraction of uranium by amines is different chemically from extraction with alkyl phosphates, the physical operation of the process is almost identical. Stripping can be effected either with slightly acidic chloride or nitrate solutions, or with sodium carbonate solution, and the product can be recovered by precipitation with a base. An alternative recovery system is direct precipitation of the product from the organic phase by mixing with an aqueous slurry of magnesium oxide. The Amex process has been tested on a pilot-plant scale both in mixer-settler systems and in a Podbielniak extractor. It is being installed in several full-scale plants.

Extraction from slurries. Pilot-plant work has been done on the application of both the DDPA and the EHPA processes to slurries [42–44]. Extraction of uranium is as efficient as from clear liquor and, using the hooded-turbine internal mixers, the gross phase separation is satisfactory. However, the entrainment of the organic phase increases when solids are present, causing a serious economic problem that has not yet been solved.

Other processes. Several other solvent extraction processes for uranium recovery from sulfate solutions have been tested in the laboratory, but none has yet reached the pilot-plant stage. Trialkyl phosphine oxides will extract uranium and are easily stripped [11]. Their extraction coefficients are lower, however, and they are more costly than the alkyl phosphoric acids. TBP solutions extract uranium from sulfate leach liquors if thiocyanate is added [45]. The thiocyanate requirement is small, but it represents an additional cost not required in the other processes. Work has also been done on processes in which the extractant is dissolved in wax or adsorbed on charcoal. In the Waxco process [46,47], dioctyl pyrophosphoric acid (OPPA) is dissolved in melted wax, the wax is cooled and pelletized, and the solid particles are mixed with the leach liquor or slurry and then recovered by screening. The mechanical stability of the wax particles is apparently too poor, however, as the losses are rather high. In the char-in-pulp process [48,49], OPPA is adsorbed on charcoal and, after contacting the leach slurry, the charcoal is recovered by screening.

Recovery of vanadium as a by-product. In many of the Colorado Plateau ores, vanadium occurs in concentrations higher than those of uranium. Ores high in the mineral carnotite were formerly mined mainly for their vanadium content, and uranium was obtained as a by-product. Many other ores contain vanadium but not in concentrations high enough to afford treatment for its recovery alone. When these ores are mined and leached for their uranium content, however, the recovery of vanadium from the leach liquors becomes feasible. At present, vanadium is recovered from these liquors by chemical precipitation methods. Solvent extraction methods have also been studied. Vanadium in the $+4$ state can be recovered from acid leach liquors by extraction with alkyl phosphoric acids [16,17,24,50]. Either monoalkyl or dialkyl phosphoric acids can be used. Since the extraction coefficients for uranium are much greater than those for vanadium, a dilute extractant solution will extract only uranium, but both uranium and vanadium can be extracted by a concentrated solution; or vanadium alone can be extracted in a separate step, after uranium has been extracted with a dilute solution. Vanadium can be stripped from these extractants with dilute acids, which will not remove uranium.

Two methods of operation have been tested. In one, both uranium and vanadium are extracted with a 0.4 M solution of alkyl phosphoric acid in kerosene, the vanadium is stripped with 1 to 2 M sulfuric or hydrochloric acid, and the uranium is then stripped with 10 M hydrochloric acid or with sodium carbonate solution. In the other method, uranium is first extracted with a 0.1 M alkyl phosphoric acid solution and the aqueous raffinate is then contacted with a 0.4 M extractant solution for vanadium removal.

Alkyl amines can also be used to extract vanadium from acid liquors if it is first oxidized to the $+5$ state [24]. Recovery from the amine is accomplished by treatment with a mild reducing agent, such as an aqueous solution of SO_2.

10–4.2 Recovery from ion-exchange eluates. *Sulfuric acid eluates.* Pilot-plant studies have been made of a solvent extraction process to recover uranium from ion-exchange eluates [51,52]. This process, called the "Eluex" process, is essentially identical with the "Dapex" process. The ion-exchange resin is eluted with 1 M H_2SO_4 instead of the usual nitrate or chloride eluting solution. The eluate is contacted with EHPA and the uranium is stripped from the EHPA with 10 percent Na_2CO_3. A small amount of a long-chain alcohol or TBP is added to the EHPA solution to prevent the formation of a third phase when stripping. The uranium product is recovered from the carbonate as a diuranate. The sulfuric acid in the raffinate is not discarded, but is recycled to the leaching circuit. In the pilot plant, both pulse columns and mixer-settlers were tested in the extraction section. Stripping was in mixer-settlers. The process operates smoothly and might show some cost advantage over the usual processes for recovery from eluates in RIP plants. Other alkyl phosphates and alkyl amines can also be used to extract these eluates.

Nitrate and chloride eluates. Alkyl phosphate solutions have been tested as extractants for uranium from nitrate and chloride eluates [53] also and have been found effective. Alkyl amines cannot be used to extract either nitrate or chloride eluates, since these solutions are good stripping agents for uranium in amines.

10–4.3 Recovery from ores by direct solvent leaching. The aqueous leaching step in treatment of ores for uranium recovery is costly, not only because of the reagent consumption, but also because of the large equipment necessary for dissolution, settling, and filtration. It also introduces the problem of disposal of the aqueous waste after treatment for recovery of uranium. Thus, methods for treatment of the ore which would not include an aqueous leach are attractive.

TBP process. TBP solutions can be used to extract uranium directly from damp ore if sufficient nitrate is present [54–57]. The ore is first pugged with concentrated sulfuric acid and a small amount of water and then cured for several hours at about 100°C. The amount of acid used in this step is equivalent to that required for an acid leach. Before extraction, nitrate is added, either to the cured ore as concentrated ammonium nitrate solution, or to the extractant as concentrated nitric acid. The extractant is a 5 percent solution of TBP in kerosene or hexane. The ore can be contacted with the organic solvent either by agitating in a mixing tank, by percolating through a column, or by spraying the extractant solution on the ore as it travels on a moving belt. Uranium is removed from the organic by stripping with water and is then precipitated as the diuranate salt by addition of ammonia. The ore residue is washed with hexane to recover the entrained TBP, and the hexane is recovered by evaporation. The process has been tested in a pilot plant with a moving-belt extractor. It offers savings in the elimination of the settling and filtration steps, in the ease of stripping, and in the high purity of the product, but the reagent costs due to solvent loss are higher than those in the aqueous leach-solvent extraction processes using sulfuric acid.

Acetone-HCl process. The acetone-HCl process is based on the solubility of uranyl chloride in acetone [58,59]. The ore is first treated with concentrated hydrochloric acid or a mixture of hydrochloric and sulfuric acids and is then leached with acetone. Very rapid settling rates and high extraction of uranium are attained. The uranium is recovered from the acetone by precipitation with anhydrous ammonia. The cake is contaminated with other metals and with chlorides, but it can be upgraded to a 10 to 15 percent uranium product by repulping with water and filtering. The process has been tested in a small pilot plant and found to be workable. However, the cost is high because more acid is required than for an aqueous leach, and much of this acid is the more expensive hydrochloric acid.

OPA process. The OPA process makes use of the extraction of uranyl ion by an alkyl phosphoric acid [18]. This is the only process suggested so far that requires acid in quantities less than the stoichiometric equivalent of the lime content of the ore. High extraction of uranium has been obtained with as little as 10 percent of the acid required for an aqueous leach. The small amount of concentrated sulfuric acid is added either to the extractant solution before contact with the solid or to the slurry of ore and extractant. The extractant used in most of the tests has been a commercially available mixture of mono- and diisooctyl phosphoric acid (OPA), but other alkyl phosphoric acids can be used. OPA is usually used because of its low cost. Uranium is removed from the extractant by stripping with 10 M HCl. The process works well with ores containing secondary uranium minerals, such as carnotite, but recovers only part of the uranium from primary ores such as uraninite. It has not yet been tested in a pilot plant.

10–4.4 Recovery from phosphates. *Phosphoric acid.* In the manufacture of triple superphosphate, phosphate rock is acidulated with sulfuric acid to produce phosphoric acid. This acid is concentrated by evaporation and mixed with phosphate rock to make the final product. Several phosphate plants in Florida recover uranium as a by-product from this intermediary phosphoric acid [60–64].*

The uranium concentration in phosphoric acids is very low (less than 100 ppm). Since high extracting power is required to obtain uranium from this solution, dialkyl pyrophosphoric acids are used instead of the orthophosphoric acids. The uranium is reduced to the uranous state by addition of iron to the acid and is then extracted with a solution containing initially 1 to 3 percent octyl (OPPA) or nonyl pyrophosphoric acid in kerosene. Uranium is stripped from the organic by contacting with 48 percent HF. The organic is separated from the HF and the precipitated UF_4 by centrifuging. Although the time of contact with HF is very short, the extractant is partially hydrolyzed during each cycle to the ortho acids. A small amount of fresh OPPA must be added after each cycle to make up for this hydrolysis loss. Recovery of uranium by this process has the advantage that mining and leaching costs are borne by the phosphate products, but this advantage is offset by the high chemical costs. The process is applica-

---

* For further discussion of recovery from phosphates, see Section 12–2.

ble to the dilute acids (18 to 30 percent P_2O_5), but not to the concentrated (60 percent P_2O_5) acid, since the extraction efficiency of the solvent decreases with increased phosphate concentration.

Leached zone ores. Much of the phosphate rock in Florida is overlain by a phosphate layer of high alumina content called the *leached zone* because it was formed by leaching action on the initial calcium phosphate deposit. It contains about the same concentration of uranium as the phosphate rock under it (0.01 to 0.02 percent U_3O_8). At present this material is discarded in the phosphate mining operations, but several processes for the manufacture of salable fertilizer from it have been studied. In one such process the ore is leached with a mixture of sulfuric and nitric acids. A solvent extraction process to recover uranium from the leach liquor was developed and tested in a pilot plant [65–67]. The process consists of extraction in several countercurrent stages with a 20 percent solution of TBP, removal of nitrate and rare earths with a water scrub, and stripping of uranium either with water or by direct precipitation from the organic with anhydrous ammonia. The recovery of uranium by this process is efficient and economical but, since no manufacturer has yet undertaken to make this fertilizer, it has not been installed in a full-scale plant.

Superphosphates. Much of the phosphate ore mined in the United States is used to manufacture normal superphosphate. The procedure involves mixing the ore with sulfuric acid and allowing the mixture to "set-up." Since there is no intermediate liquid state, uranium recovery requires direct treatment of the final solid product. The concentration of uranium in the product is less than 0.01 percent, but since the amount of superphosphate made is so large that this represents a considerable potential source of uranium, a solvent leaching process has been developed to recover it [68]. The process has not been tested in a pilot plant; laboratory data indicate that it would recover uranium, but at a cost considerably higher than that of other sources. The fertilizer value of the residue would not be impaired.

In this process, a small amount of nitric acid (about 6 lb/ton of superphosphate) is added to the sulfuric acid used for the acidulation of the ore. After the superphosphate has cured, it is contacted with 0.5 percent OPPA in hexane. The loaded extractant is stripped with HF and the uranium is precipitated by reduction. The superphosphate is washed with hexane and the entrained diluent is recovered by drying.

REFERENCES

1. A. M. Ross, Solvent Extraction, Newcomer to the Colorado Plateau, *Mining Eng.* **9**(9), 997 (1957).

2. R. R. GINSTED et al., Solvent Extraction of Uranium from Acid Leach Slurries and Solutions, in *Proceedings of the International Conference on the Peaceful Uses of Atomic Energy*, Vol. 8. New York: United Nations, 1956. (P/523, p. 71)

3. R. S. LONG et al., Recovery of Uranium from Phosphates by Solvent Extraction, in *Proceedings of the International Conference on the Peaceful Uses of Atomic Energy*, Vol. 8. New York: United Nations, 1956. (P/524, p. 77)

4. R. S. LONG and J. F. VALLE-RIESTRA, *Recovery of Uranium from Normal and Triple Superphosphate with Organic Extractants*, USAEC Report DOW-98, Dow Chemical Co., 1953.

5. R. Q. WILSON et al., *The Recovery of Uranium from Chattanooga Shales*, USAEC Report BMI-274, Battelle Memorial Institute, 1954.

6. E. S. PORTER and H. G. PETROW, Recovery of Uranium from Lignites, *Mining Eng.* **9** (9), 1004 (1957).

7. T. K. SHERWOOD and R. L. PIGFORD, *Absorption and Extraction*. New York: McGraw-Hill Book Co., Inc., 1952.

8. R. E. TREYBAL, *Liquid Extraction*. New York: McGraw-Hill Book Co., Inc., 1952.

9. G. G. BROWN et al., *Unit Operations*. New York: John Wiley & Sons, Inc., 1950.

10. W. B. WRIGHT, Jr., *Critical Literature Survey of Tributyl Phosphate as a Uranium Extractant*, USAEC Report Y-838, Oak Ridge National Laboratory.

11. C. A. BLAKE et al., *Solvent Extraction of Uranium (and Vanadium) from Acid Liquors with Trialkylphosphine Oxides*, USAEC Report ORNL-1964, Oak Ridge National Laboratory, 1955.

12. C. E. HIGGINS et al., *Organo-Phosphorous Compounds for Solvent Extraction*, USAEC Report ORNL-1338, Oak Ridge National Laboratory, 1952.

13. D. C. STEWART, *Alkyl Phosphoric Acids as Extraction Agents for Uranium*, USAEC Report UCRL-585, University of California Radiation Laboratory, 1950.

14. D. C. STEWART and T. E. HICKS, *Alkyl Phosphoric Acid Extractions*, USAEC Report UCRL-861, University of California Radiation Laboratory, 1950.

15. D. A. ELLIS et al., *Recovery of Uranium from Colorado Plateau Ores by Solvent Extraction*, USAEC Report DOW-131, Dow Chemical Co., 1955.

16. C. A. BLAKE et al., *The Extraction and Recovery of Uranium (and Vanadium) from Acid Leach Liquors with Di(2-ethylhexyl) Phosphoric Acid and Some Other Organophosphorous Compounds*, USAEC Report ORNL-1903, Oak Ridge National Laboratory, 1955.

17. C. A. BLAKE et al., *Further Studies of the Dialkyl Phosphoric Acid Extraction (Dapex) Process for Uranium*, USAEC Report ORNL-2172, Oak Ridge National Laboratory, 1957.

18. R. H. BAILES, *Progress Report for January–February* 1956, USAEC Report DOW-141, Dow Chemical Co., 1956.

19. K. B. BROWN et al., *The Use of Amines as Extractants for Uranium from Acidic Sulfate Liquors*, USAEC Report AECD-4142, Oak Ridge National Laboratory, 1954.

20. J. G. MOORE et al., *Further Studies of Amines as Extractants for Uranium from Acid Sulfate Solutions*, USAEC Report AECD-4145, Oak Ridge National Laboratory, 1955.

21. D. J. CROUSE et al., *Progress Report on Uranium Extraction with Organo-nitrogen Compounds*, USAEC Report ORNL-2099, Oak Ridge National Laboratory, 1956.

22. A. PREUSS and J. SAUNDERS, *The Solvent-Solvent Extraction of Uranium from Sulfuric Acid Solutions with Oil Soluble Amines*, USAEC Report RMO-2533, Rohm and Haas Co., 1955.

23. D. J. CROUSE and K. B. BROWN, *Amine Extraction Processes for Uranium Recovery from Sulfate Liquors*, USAEC Report ORNL-1959, Oak Ridge National Laboratory, 1955.

24. K. B. BROWN et al., *Some New Solvent Extraction Processes for Use in the Hydrometallurgical Treatment of Uranium, Thorium and Vanadium Ores*, paper presented at annual meeting of American Institute of Mining, Metallurgical, and Petroleum Engineers, New Orleans, 1957.

25. J. L. FICK et al., *The Effects of Agitator Geometry in the Mixing of Liquid-Liquid Systems*, USAEC Report UCRL-2545, University of California Radiation Laboratory, 1954.

26. M. W. DAVIS, Jr. et al., *Liquid-Liquid Extraction*, USAEC Report UCRL-1013, University of California Radiation Laboratory, 1951.

27. J. K. DAVIDSON, *Theory of Pump-Mix Mixer Settler*, USAEC Report KAPL-130, Knolls Atomic Power Laboratory, 1949.

28. B. V. COPLAN and A. W. JOYCE, Knolls Atomic Power Laboratory, 1951. Unpublished.

29. J. H. RUSHTON, Applications of Fluid Mechanics and Similitude to Scale-Up Problems, *Chem. Eng. Progr.* **48**(1), 33 (1952); **48**(2), 95 (1952).

30. J. H. RUSHTON and J. Y. OLDSHUE, Mixing—Present Theory and Practice, *Chem. Eng. Progr.* **49**(4), 161 (1953).

31. W. A. BURNS et al., Hanford Atomic Products Operation, 1949. Unpublished.

32. R. L. STEVENSON and J. G. BRADLEY, Hanford Atomic Products Operation, 1951. Unpublished.

33. J. F. VALLE-RIESTRA, *Carnotite Solvent Extraction Process: Process Description*, USAEC Report DOW-123, Dow Chemical Co., 1954.

34. J. B. CLEMMER, U. S. Bureau of Mines, Salt Lake City, 1956. Unpublished.

35. J. F. VALLE-RIESTRA, *Proposed HCl Recovery System, Salt Lake City Pilot Plant*, USAEC Report DOW-119, Dow Chemical Co., 1954.

36. J. D. MOORE, *Uranium Recovery by the Solvent Extraction Process*, paper presented at annual meeting of American Institute of Mining, Metallurgical, and Petroleum Engineers, New Orleans, 1957.

37. D. A. ELLIS et al., *Recovery of Uranium from Plateau Ores by Solvent Extraction with Di-OPA*, USAEC Report DOW-140, Dow Chemical Co., 1956.

38. W. C. HAZEN and A. V. HENDRICKSON, Solvent Extraction of Uranium at Shiprock, New Mexico, *Mining Eng.* **9**(9), 994 (1957).

39. W. KNOTT, *Plant Application of Solvent Extraction in Uranium Milling*, paper presented at American Mining Congress, Los Angeles, 1956.

40. R. C. TOERPER, Solvent Extraction in Climax Uranium Company's Plant, *Mines Mag.* (*Denver*) **47**(3), 89 (1957).

41. B. B. KLIMA et al., *Design of an Amine Extraction Demonstration Plant*, USAEC Report ORNL-1963, Oak Ridge National Laboratory, 1955.

42. J. B. BYRNE, *Entrainment of Solvent in Extraction of Uranium from Heavy Slurries*, USAEC Report DOW-146, Dow Chemical Co., 1956.

43. J. R. ROSS et al., *Solvent Extraction Separation of Uranium from Acid Leach Liquors and Pulps*, USAEC Report AECU-3181, U. S. Bureau of Mines, 1956.

44. J. B. ROSENBAUM et al., *Innovations in Processing Uranium Ores*, USAEC Report AECU-3367, U. S. Bureau of Mines, 1956.

45. H. G. PETROW and H. N. MARENBERG, *The Recovery of Uranium from Sulfate Leach Liquors by the TBP-Thiocyanate Process*, USAEC Report WIN-24, National Lead Co., 1955.

46. A. E. RUEHLE et al., *Research and Development Progress Report*, USAEC Report NYO-1352, Mallinckrodt Chemical Works, 1953.

47. A. E. RUEHLE et al., Mallinckrodt Chemical Works, 1953. Unpublished.

48. P. NOBLE, Jr. et al., *Development of a Char-in-Pulp Process for the Recovery of Uranium*, USAEC Report RMO-2616, Arthur D. Little, Inc., 1955.

49. P. NOBLE et al., *Development of a Modified Char Adsorbent for the Recovery of Uranium from Ore Slurries*, USAEC Report RMO-2622, Arthur D. Little, Inc., 1956.

50. R. H. BAILES, *Progress Report for March–April 1955*, USAEC Report DOW-129, Dow Chemical Co., 1955.

51. W. D. CHARLES et al., *Pilot Plant Testing of Solvent Extraction of Acid RIP Pregnant Eluates*, USAEC Report WIN-75, National Lead Co., 1957.

52. H. G. PETROW et al., *Solvent Extraction of Uranium from Sulfuric Acid Eluates*, USAEC Report WIN-28, National Lead Co., 1956.

53. J. B. CLEMMER, U. S. Bureau of Mines, Salt Lake City, 1954. Unpublished.

54. P. GALVANEK and D. KAUFMAN, Massachusetts Institute of Technology, 1949. Unpublished.

55. P. GALVANEK and D. KAUFMAN, Massachusetts Institute of Technology, 1950. Unpublished.

56. KELLEX CORP., *Evaluation of Solvent Extraction Process for Pitchblendes*, USAEC Report KLX-1210, 1951.

57. P. GALVANEK and M. S. PELLAND, *A Solvent Leaching Process for the Production of High Purity Uranium Products Directly from Low-Grade Ores*, USAEC Report WIN–31, National Lead Co., 1955.

58. R. A. EWING et al., *Nonaqueous Extractive Methods for Western Uranium Ores*, USAEC Report BMI-279, Battelle Memorial Institute, 1955.

59. D. D. FOLEY et al., *Nonaqueous Extractive Methods for Western Uranium Ores*, USAEC Report BMI-280, Battelle Memorial Institute, 1955.

60. D. A. ELLIS, *The Recovery of Uranium from Industrial Phosphorus Acids by Solvent Extraction*, USAEC Report DOW-81, Dow Chemical Co., 1952.

61. J. F. VALLE-RIESTRA, Dow Chemical Co., 1952. Unpublished.

62. J. F. VALLE-RIESTRA, Dow Chemical Co., 1952. Unpublished.

63. G. E. WILKINSON, *The Recovery of Uranium from Commercial Phosphoric*

Acid by Solvent Extraction, USAEC Report RMO-4100, U. S. Phosphoric Products Div., Tennessee Corp., 1953.

64. P. J. QUINN, *Recovery of Uranium from Wet Process Phosphoric Acid,* USAEC Report AECD-3738, Armour Fertilizer Works, 1954.

65. C. F. COLEMAN, *Extraction of Uranium from LZ Nitric Acid Leach Liquor,* USAEC Report Y-B34-3, Oak Ridge National Laboratory, 1953.

66. TENNESSEE VALLEY AUTHORITY, *Utilization of Florida Leached Zone Material,* USAEC Report RMO-2715, June 1953.

67. BLAW-KNOX Co., *Nitrophosphate Fertilizer Plant for the U. S. AEC,* USAEC Report BKC-4175-2, 1954.

68. R. S. LONG and J. F. VALLE-RIESTRA, *Recovery of Uranium from Normal and Triple Superphosphate with Organic Extractants,* USAEC Report DOW-98, Dow Chemical Co., 1953.

CHAPTER 11

EXAMPLES OF URANIUM MILLING OPERATIONS

11–1. Introduction

In previous chapters, various aspects of uranium processing have been dealt with individually. It remains now to draw the parts together in a comprehensive picture, showing how the accumulated experience of those concerned with this comparatively new field has been put into practice. This chapter offers a representative sample of uranium milling technology.

To ensure that current practices in processing ores of all types are covered as completely as possible, descriptions have been obtained of a number of mills operating in the principal uranium ore-bearing regions of the United States, Canada, and South Africa. These descriptions were prepared by representatives of some of the major firms that have participated, along with various governments, in developing uranium-recovery processes and the uranium industry. Included are information on the location of mills and the ore-producing areas they serve; background on the development of the operation; descriptions, with flowsheets, of the process and the process equipment; and, in some cases, discussion of costs and operating experience.

To present the information in a uniform, readable manner, the editors have established a sequence of topics to be followed in describing each milling operation. The method admittedly leaves something to be desired, since the same types of information were not available in every case. However, each section follows as closely as possible the following general outline:

Introduction

Geology and Mineralogy

Ore Preparation
    Crushing
    Grinding

Uranium Extraction
    Acid leaching
    Carbonate leaching

Solid-Liquid Separation
    Countercurrent decantation
    Filtration

Uranium Recovery
    Direct precipitation
    Ion exchange
    Solvent extraction

Costs and Operating Experience

The outline was not strictly adhered to when it interfered with the continuity of the original author's presentation. Furthermore, it should be pointed out that some mills use only one of the methods of performing operations indicated in the outline. Other mills employ a combination of methods.

11-2. URANIUM MILLS IN THE BLIND RIVER AREA*

11–2.1 Introduction. The Blind River uranium area of Canada is located on the north shore of Lake Huron in the Province of Ontario. It is approximately midway between Sudbury and Sault Ste. Marie on the Trans-Canada highway and is also serviced by the Canadian Pacific Railway. The area was discovered in the spring of 1953 by Franc. R. Joubin, and since that time eight uranium production contracts, totaling nearly 1.1 billion dollars, have been awarded. The ore reserves have been conservatively estimated at more than one hundred million tons.

Uranium production under these contracts will come from eleven plants. These plants, in order of their starting dates, with their respective milling capacities in short tons of ore per day, are as follows:

Property	Plant capacity, tons/day	Starting date
Pronto Uranium Mines Limited	1500	October 1955
Algom Uranium Mines Limited, Quirke Property	3000	October 1955
Algom Uranium Mines Limited, Nordic Property	3000	January 1957
Consolidated Denison Mines Limited	5700	May 1957
Can-Met Explorations Limited	2500	July 1957
Northspan Uranium Mines Limited, Lake Nordic	4000	July 1957
Northspan Uranium Mines Limited, Spanish Amer.	2000	August 1957
Northspan Uranium Mines Limited, Panel	3000	October 1957
Stanleigh Uranium Mines Limited	3000	January 1958
Stanrock Uranium Mines Limited	3000	January 1958
Milliken Lake Uranium Mines Limited	3000	March 1958

Flowsheets for the steps in the milling process at the Milliken Lake mill have been included in each part of this section. The Milliken Lake mill typifies most of the mills in the area and the process it uses is much the

---

* By R. P. Ehrlich, Rio Tinto Management Services Limited.

same as those in nine of the eleven mills that are operating or will operate in the Blind River district.

The ore in the area can be considered low grade, slightly more than 2 pounds of U_3O_8 per ton. It is too early to state milling costs, but preliminary information seems to indicate that these should vary between $4.50 and $5.50 per ton of ore, depending on the capacity and design of the plants.

11–2.2 Geology and mineralogy. The ore in the Blind River area occurs as quartz pebble conglomerate reefs at or near the base of the Mississagi quartzite formation, which comprises the lowest strata of the Huronian sediments overlying the pre-Huronian basement complex.

Typical conglomerate ore consists of rounded, well-packed quartz pebbles, averaging $1\frac{1}{2}$ to 2 inches in size, most of glassy, milky-white, or smoky-grey variety, a few black cherts, and an occasional one of red jasper and of feldspar. The pebbles are set in a fine-grained matrix composed of sericite, chlorite, granular quartz, and pyrite. Pyrite, the chief sulfide, is present in amounts ranging from 3 to over 10 percent, averaging about 5 percent. The matrix contains the microscopic uranium mineralization in which uraninite, pitchblende, and brannerite have been identified. The hydrocarbon, thucholite, occurs rather commonly as a secondary mineral in mine workings on joints, and in fracture fillings. Sulfides other than pyrite are present only in minute quantities, and include chalcopyrite, pyrrhotite, galena, sphalerite, molybdenite, and cobaltite. Accessory minerals in the ore include monazite, feldspars, zircon, rutile, anatase, leucoxene, and titaniferous magnetite.

The average specific gravity of the ore is about 2.7, but in some mines where the pyrite content is high, the specific gravity may be as high as 3.0.

11–2.3 Ore preparation. *Crushing.* All mining in the Blind River area is underground, and the ore is hoisted through shafts varying in depth from 600 to 3600 feet, depending on the depth of the orebodies. At two plants a jaw crusher is placed underground, and the ore is crushed to about −5 inches before it is hoisted. At all other properties the jaw crushers are on the surface, a choice dictated primarily by the fact that time was lacking to install them underground. It should be mentioned that all plants were built as rapidly as possible, leaving insufficient time to develop fully the underground workings before the ore was required for the milling plants.

The −4 to −6 inch jaw-crusher discharge is passed over a grizzly, usually set at 2 inches. The grizzly oversize is crushed to $1\frac{1}{2}$ inches in a Symons standard cone crusher, with size depending on the capacity of the plant. The grizzly undersize and the cone-crusher discharge are combined and conveyed to a set of screens, set at $\frac{1}{2}$ to $\frac{3}{4}$ inch, and the undersize is the fine ore feed to the grinding circuit. Most screens are Symons rod decks, which accept fairly coarse feed material, thus allowing single-deck screens to be used. The screen oversize is conveyed to a Symons shorthead crusher, usually set at $\frac{5}{8}$ to $\frac{1}{2}$ inch, the discharge of which is conveyed back to the screens.

The Blind River ore is readily crushed; the quartz pebbles are fractured, and tend to shatter. However, the ore is very abrasive, and crusher wearing parts have a short life. In one case the bowl and mantle of a $5\frac{1}{2}$-foot shorthead crusher had to be changed after approximately 225,000 tons throughput.

Grinding. Test work has shown that if the proper leaching conditions are achieved, ore fineness has relatively little effect on the extraction obtained during leaching. For example, 40 percent minus-200 mesh ore will give the same extraction percentage as 80 percent minus-200 mesh ore if both are leached under identical conditions. Consequently, criteria for the mesh of grind are dictated entirely by handling characteristics of the ore in acid pulps. To date, one plant has been operating on a leach feed of about 55 percent minus-200 mesh, with few problems.

The crushed ore is delivered to the crushed-ore bins as minus $\frac{3}{4}$-inch material. Grinding tests have established a Bond grindability index varying between 14 and 15, and all plants have been designed with slightly more than 0.7 horsepower per ton per day installed capacity, which appears to be satisfactory. Ten of the eleven plants have two-stage, rod mill and ball mill, grinding circuits, as shown in Fig. 11–1. One plant, the smallest, has a single-stage ball-mill circuit. In the latter case, single-stage grinding was dictated by capital cost and flexibility considerations, although two-stage grinding is more efficient.

The crushed ore is fed to the rod mills in open circuit, where the grinding is in water. In many cases, the water is obtained from the neutral thickener overflow to conserve water pumped to the plants.

The rod mills vary in size from 6 feet in diameter by 10 feet long to $10\frac{1}{2}$ feet in diameter by 14 feet long, with installed horsepower ranging from 200 to 700. The mills have differently arranged grinding circuits. About half have two ball mills per rod mill for a grinding circuit, with a classifier in closed circuit with each ball mill. The others have only one ball mill in closed circuit with a classifier.

The rod-mill discharge flows by gravity or is pumped to one or two classifiers, depending on circuit arrangements. Dorr Type HX classifiers predominate, but some Akins and Wemco spiral classifiers are also used. The classifier overflow pumped to the neutral thickeners could be considered leaching plant feed. The classifier sands flow by gravity to the ball mills, which range from 9 feet in diameter by 10 feet long to $10\frac{1}{2}$ feet in diameter by 13 feet long. Some Tricone mills are also used. The installed horsepower on the ball mills varies from 400 to 800.

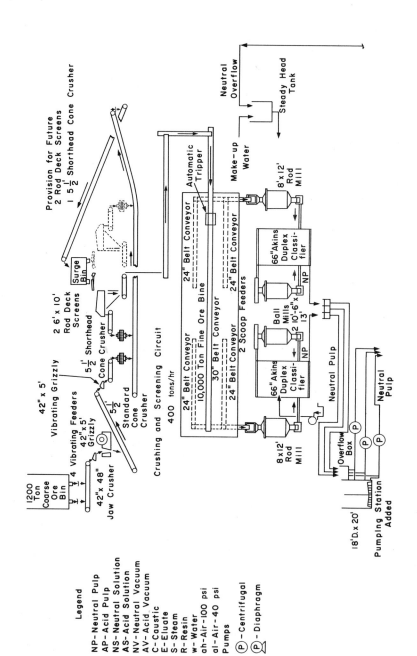

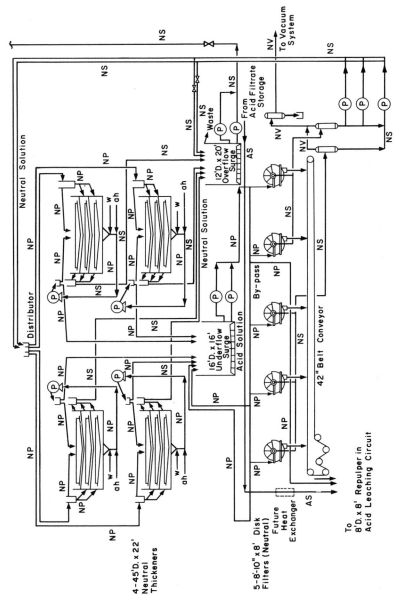

Fig. 11–1. Flowsheet of crushing and screening circuit, Milliken Lake mill.

TABLE 11–1

GRINDING CIRCUIT SCREEN ANALYSIS

Mesh	Rod mill feed %	Rod mill feed Cumulative %	Rod mill discharge %	Rod mill discharge Cumulative %	Classifier sands %	Classifier sands Cumulative %	Ball mill discharge %	Ball mill discharge Cumulative %	Classifier overflow %	Classifier overflow Cumulative %
+1	0.2									
+0.742 in.	4.4	4.6								
+0.525 in.	22.9	27.5								
+0.371 in.	16.4	43.9								
+0.262	11.4	55.3								
+4M	7.8	63.1								
+6M			4.3							
+10M			17.8	22.1						
+20M			20.3	42.4						
+35M			16.9	59.3						
+48M	36.9	100.0	7.1	66.4	46.2		23.8		0.1	
+65M			6.3	72.7	19.0	65.2	20.3	44.1	2.7	2.8
+100M			5.7	78.4	16.5	81.7	21.0	65.1	16.7	19.5
+150M			2.9	81.3	5.2	86.9	7.1	72.2	10.5	30.0
+200M			3.7	85.0	4.7	91.6	8.7	80.9	16.0	46.0
-200M			15.0	100.0	8.4	100.0	19.1	100.0	54.0	100.0
+325M			2.2		1.9		4.5		11.5	
-325M			12.8	15.0	6.5	8.4	14.6	19.1	42.5	54.0

Rods of 3-inch and $3\frac{1}{2}$-inch diameter have been employed, and 2-inch- and $2\frac{1}{2}$-inch-diameter balls are generally used. Rod consumption is about 1.0 lb/ton, and ball consumption about 2.5 lb/ton. Liner wear in the rod mills has proved high; several sets of manganese steel liners in an 8 by 12-foot rod mill were worn out after only about 200,000 tons throughput. Part of this wear was probably due to poor liner design, and experiments are under way with different designs. Manganese steel liners, or manganese steel wedge bars and chromium-molybdenum steel plates, are being used in the rod mills. Ni-Hard liners are utilized in the ball mills. Operating experience is short, however, and there is considerable variation in liner design.

A typical grinding-circuit screen analysis is shown in Table 11–1.

11–2.4 Uranium extraction. *Metallurgy.* The first ore samples from Pronto Uranium Mines Limited were submitted for testing in the fall of 1953. At first it was expected that the presence of brannerite minerals would cause difficulty in leaching the ore. Concentration studies on the ore by means of flotation and gravity methods looked interesting, but after the leaching process was developed, these methods became uneconomical.

Standard acid leaching procedures known at that time soon proved ineffective, but by increasing the free-acid concentration and leaching at elevated temperatures, extractions of 90 percent were quickly achieved. The leaching conditions developed in 1953 consist of treating ore for 48 hours at a temperature of 113°F, in contact with a solution having a free sulfuric acid concentration of about 40 g/liter. The ore itself contains few acid-soluble materials. Therefore, the quantity of acid required for this high concentration is relatively low, ranging from 60 to 110 pounds of sulfuric acid per ton of ore.

Many uranium recovery methods were tried, but the ion-exchange process soon proved best. Polythionate poisoning on the resin was anticipated, but this has not yet appeared in plant operation. During the initial laboratory and pilot-plant work, chloride elution and single-stage precipitation were used, only to be replaced with nitrate elution and two-stage precipitation because this method has shown better economics.

A uranium balance sheet for a month of operation at a typical Blind River mill is shown in Table 11–2.

Since ore at all eleven properties is similar, the process briefly described above is used in principle at all plants in the Blind River area. The detailed plant description that follows describes the general circuit, but points out differences where they exist.

Neutral thickening and filtration. The classifier overflow is pumped by means of SRL or Hydroseal rubber-lined sand pumps to the neutral thickeners. In all cases, they are Dorr-type ATB, balanced-tray thickeners with

TABLE 11–2

A TYPICAL URANIUM BALANCE SHEET

Tons of ore milled	2851 tons/day
Average head assay	2.44 lb U_3O_8/ton
Losses:	
Undissolved loss	0.13 lb U_3O_8/ton
Soluble loss	0.02 lb U_3O_8/ton
Barren solution loss	0.004 lb U_3O_8/ton
Total	0.16 lb U_3O_8/ton
Uranium recovery	93.5%

three compartments. The overflow is reused in the grinding circuit, not because water is a problem in the area, but because this reduces pumping costs from the supply lakes.

Separan is used as a settling agent, and it has been found that to obtain clear overflows, the pulp should be either slightly acid or slightly alkaline. If lime were added at this point to achieve a pH of about 8.0, additional acid would be required in the leaching circuit. Consequently, some barren solution from the ion-exchange circuit is added to obtain a pH of about 6.5, which provides a clear overflow.

The thickener underflow is pumped to a surge agitator of the center-airlift type, from which the pulp is pumped to the neutral filters. Eimco, Oliver, and Peterson disk filters are being used. The pulp is distributed by means of loop lines, with a takeoff at each filter, and with the end of the line returning to the surge agitator.

This neutral filtration step has a twofold purpose. First, it provides accurate control of the pulp density at a high level, so that a uniform feed is sent to the leach tanks. Second, it reduces the acid needed to obtain the high free-acid concentration necessary for efficient extraction by reducing the amount of pulp water that otherwise would dilute the acid. This is illustrated by the solution balance shown in Fig. 11–2.

For efficient leaching, a free-acid concentration of 40 g/liter is required, but for proper ion exchange, this must be decreased to 3 to 7 g/liter. The decrease could be achieved either by neutralization, which is expensive, or by excessive dilution, say tenfold, which is not practical. To achieve the desired results and at the same time reduce acid consumption, an acid filtration step is introduced at the end of leaching. The filtrate from this step, containing 40 grams of free acid per liter, is used to repulp the neutral, disk-filter discharge, thus reducing the quantity of fresh acid that has to be introduced. This procedure also reduces the

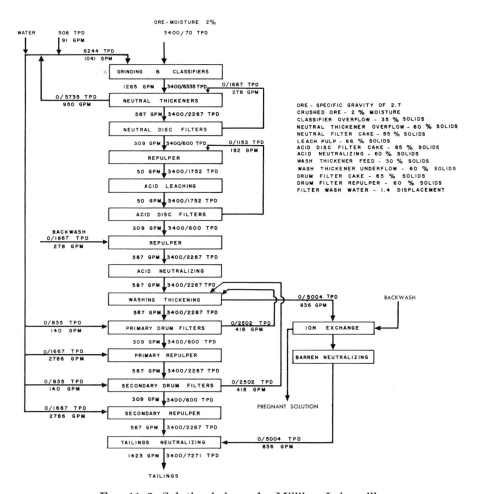

FIG. 11–2. Solution balance for Milliken Lake mill.

quantity of lime for proper ion-exchange conditions. The acid filter cake is diluted and washed, producing between 1.5 and 2.0 tons of pregnant solution per ton of ore treated. At this level of dilution, free-acid concentration for ion exchange is obtained without using lime for neutralization.

The pulp pumped to the neutral thickeners is about 35 percent solids. Thickener underflow fed to the neutral disk filters is 60 percent solids. Filter cake moisture varies between 15 and 20 percent, increasing to about 32 percent with acid filtrate. The pumps used to prevent pulp dilution in this circuit are Vacseal or Centriseal glandless, sand pumps. Wetted parts of the rubber-lined pumps handling the acid solution are made of Type 316 stainless steel.

Leaching. Blind River ore, to yield an extraction of 90 percent or better, must be treated for 48 hours with a solution having a free sulfuric acid concentration of 40 g/liter, at a temperature of 113°F. Initial laboratory work indicated that no oxidizing agent was necessary for this extraction. However, when the first operating plant started receiving fresh ore from underground, good extraction was found to be impossible without an oxidizing agent. Sodium chlorate is the most economical oxidizing agent for use in this area, and from 2 to 3 pounds per ton of ore are required.

Later plant work has shown that if the free sulfuric acid concentration is increased to between 50 to 60 g/liter, the greater quantity of uranium dissolved and recovered more than pays for the additional acid. Even though the ores are similar and come from the same geological formation, the acid-consuming constituents differ from property to property, so that acid requirements also differ. Currently acid requirements vary between 70 and 110 pounds of sulfuric acid per ton of ore. However, this is consumption without acid recirculation, and could possibly be reduced by 25 or 30 pounds per ton.

The acid filtrate used to dilute the neutral filter cake supplies some of this requirement, but more acid is added in the first agitator or Pachuca to produce the necessary strength. Additional acid goes into the leaching circuit as needed to maintain the acid concentration. All acid added is 93 percent sulfuric acid. To date, no satisfactory method of automatically controlling acid additions has been found, although conductivity measurements show promise. The acid concentration employed gives a pH of about 0.3. At this concentration, a pH meter cannot be employed, because relatively large differences show up only as very small scale readings on pH meters.

Sodium chlorate is added as a 25 percent solution to the first or second leaching tank. The quantity is controlled by either ferric iron titrations or emf measurements. To achieve leaching temperature, live steam is piped directly to the pulp in about half the leaching tanks. The steam enters through hoses fastened to the sides of the tanks about 10 inches below pulp level. It is automatically regulated by temperature recorder-controllers.

When the first plant went into operation, much difficulty came from pulp settling out and sanding up the agitators—an unanticipated problem. To increase what might be called the viscosity of the pulp, glue was added. Originally, it went in as a liquid form, but this brought on distribution problems. Glue is now added as a dry granular powder through vibrating feeders. In the plant, the operator controls glue additions manually by checking the pulp in a beaker from time to time. If sand settles rapidly to the bottom of the beaker, insufficient glue is present. If, after standing for about 2 minutes, the pulp can be poured out of the beaker without leaving a layer of sand behind, there is enough glue. Glue additions have varied from 1.0 to 2.2 pounds per ton of ore, depending on the grind, and also upon how much glue is employed in the filtration or CCD circuits.

In three plants, leaching is in Dorr, center-airlift agitators. The others use Pachucas, as shown in Fig. 11–3, and it is believed that these cause fewer operating difficulties. Agitator sizes have varied from 24 feet in diameter by 25 feet high to 32 feet in diameter by 30 feet high. Most of the Pachucas are $22\frac{1}{2}$ feet in diameter by 50 feet high, including a 60-degree cone. All agitator tanks are built of fir wood staves, with hoops protected against acid fumes by polyethylene tubes. The Pachucas are of welded mild steel lined with $\frac{3}{16}$-inch natural rubber, vulcanized at the site by means of exhaust steam. Agitator mechanisms are of Type 316 extra-low-carbon stainless steel. Since stainless steel is relatively soft and the leaching conditions are close to the critical point for stainless steel, Pachucas were chosen for later plants. If the leach solution is in a reduced state, the stainless steel will corrode rapidly, as was found in the early days of the first plant. Hence, care must be taken to ensure that the solution is always oxidized when stainless steel agitator mechanisms are employed. Corrosion is not a problem with Pachucas. They have slightly higher operating costs than airlift agitators, due to greater power requirements. However, they need less maintenance and possibly less glue, counteracting the higher operating costs.

Leaching circuits in each plant are so arranged that the pulp flows through by gravity. Some small agitators or Pachucas are provided at the end of the leaching circuits to act as surge tanks, and to facilitate lime addition if that is necessary. The final agitator or Pachuca is used as a surge tank ahead of the acid filters, to which the pulp is pumped by means of a loop line that returns to the surge tanks.

The purpose of these acid filters is to reclaim as much of the unused acid as possible. The filtrate is used to repulp the neutral filter cake ahead of the leaching circuit. These filters are of stainless steel and rubber-lined construction, with wooden sector parts. Dynel filter bags are used, but additional work is being done to find better types of acid-resistant materials.

To simplify the operation, the filter cake discharges onto a conveyor belt, which in turn discharges to a propeller-type agitator that serves as a repulper. This means that for pulp-density control only one point of dilution addition exists, leading to better control. Filtrate pumps are of stainless steel. Sand pumps are stainless-steel-fitted, glandless, and rubber lined. The vacuum pumps are protected by two or three moisture traps in the vacuum line, one of which is fitted with water sprays to scrub out any

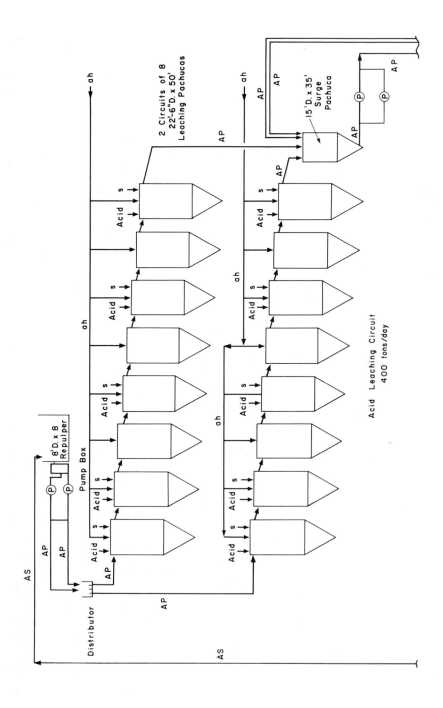

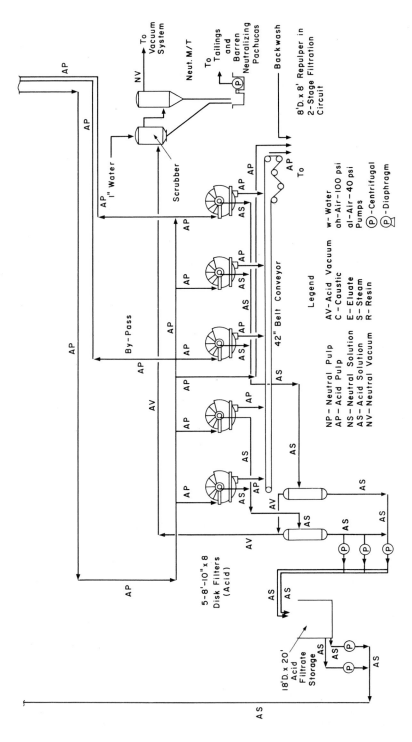

Fig. 11–3. Flowsheet of acid leaching circuit, Milliken Lake mill.

acid mist that may be carried through. The smaller piping, 10 inches or less in diameter, is rubber-lined steel, and the larger vacuum piping, where acid fumes are present, is stainless steel. The filtrate receivers and moisture traps are rubber-lined steel.

11–2.5 Liquid-solids separation. Two basic methods are used in the Blind River area to separate the pregnant solution from the leached ore. One plant employs countercurrent decantation. All other plants have two-stage filtration, preceded by a stage of washing thickeners, as shown in Fig. 11–4. More CCD plants probably would have been installed, but only at the one plant was the terrain suitable.

Countercurrent decantation. The Quirke plant of Algom Uranium Mines, Limited, is the installation using CCD liquid-solids separation. Ten 100-foot-diameter Dorr center-pier thickeners, divided into two circuits of five each, are employed. Initial calculations indicated that four stages were essential, a fifth stage would be profitable, but a sixth stage was not necessary. Hence five stages were installed, giving a soluble uranium recovery of 98.4 percent with an over-all ratio of 1.83 tons of pregnant solution per ton of ore milled.

The cake from the acid filters is repulped (usually with backwash solution from the ion exchange) to 60 percent solids, and pumped to the first stage of the CCD circuit. Overflow from the first stage, amounting to 1.83 tons of solution per ton of ore treated, flows to the unclarified pregnant solution tank and, after clarification, is fed to the ion-exchange circuit. At all stages, Separan is the flocculant, in the amount of 0.1 pound per ton of ore. During the initial operation, there was difficulty in keeping the overflow clear. A considerable amount of colloidal silica was found in the overflow, and it was not reduced by adding more Separan. After much experimentation, it was discovered that adding small quantities of glue to the surge tank ahead of the acid filters solved the problem.

The CCD circuit is operated according to common practice, with underflow moving counter to the overflow. Water is added as dilution in the last thickener, and sometimes sulfuric acid also is added to keep the pH of the solution low enough that uranium cannot precipitate as phosphates or arsenates. The critical pH point is considered to be 2.0, and the solution in the last thickener is kept below this point. Although the thickeners are in the open, no difficulty with freezing was encountered during the cold season, even though temperatures of $-42°F$ were experienced. The dilution water is heated and the feed to the circuit from the leaching agitators is very warm. Actually, some of the thickeners would operate with layers of ice floating on top. However, if thickeners became sanded and stuck, it was difficult to make them operative again in the very cold weather, since the water used to wash them out would freeze immediately. In such cases, the thickener was bypassed until there was a warm spell.

The thickener mechanisms are made of Type 316 stainless steel, as are the Dorr No. 8W underflow pumps. The underflow and the overflow are mixed in centrifugal sand pumps, which send the slurry to the next thickener. The underflow from, say, Thickener No. 1, would be mixed in a pump box with the overflow of Thickener No. 3 and pumped to Thickener No. 2. Separan goes into the feed launder of each thickener, because if it were added to the pump boxes, the flocs formed would break up in the pumps, and hence would not be effective.

Underflow from the last thickener is automatically sampled and pumped to the tailings-neutralization circuit, described later.

Two-stage filtration. Plants using two-stage filtration instead of CCD are different from regular filtration plants in that they have a set of thickeners ahead of the filters. These were installed principally to obtain the maximum soluble uranium recovery. Another reason for thus placing the thickeners, explained under "Leaching," is that the Blind River ore in an acid solution was very difficult to keep in suspension unless glue was present, and unless the maximum possible pulp density was employed. Therefore, without thickeners in the acid circuits of these plants, any spills (some are always bound to occur) would have to be pumped into an agitator or Pachuca tank, which would upset the pulp density.

In the filtration plants, the acid filter cake is again repulped with back-wash to 60 percent solids and pumped to the thickeners. Here the pulp is further diluted to obtain the same ratio as the CCD plant, that is 1.8:1 (35 percent solids), with first- and second-stage filtrate. All the first-stage filtrate is used, but if second-stage filtrate is left over after reaching the above ratio, it is employed as wash on the first-stage filters. If insufficient second-stage filtrate is available, either the wash is increased on the second-stage filters, or water is added to the thickeners. The thickener overflow goes to the unclarified pregnant solution tank, from which it is pumped to the ion-exchange circuit.

The thickener underflow is pumped at 55 to 60 percent solids to a surge tank ahead of the first-stage filters, where glue is added if required for better filtration. From the surge tank, which is either an agitator or a Pachuca, it is pumped by means of a loop line to the filters. The end of the loop returns to the surge tank. The first-stage filters are washed either with second-stage filtrate if available, or with water. Quantity is from 1.3 to 1.5 times the moisture left in the cake. The filter cake drops onto a conveyor belt that discharges into a repulper, where the cake is diluted with water and pumped to the second-stage filter surge tank. From here the pulp is pumped by means of a loop line to the second-stage filters, which

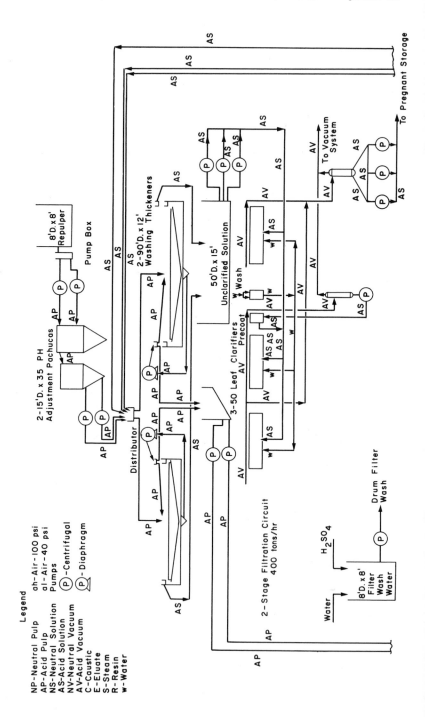

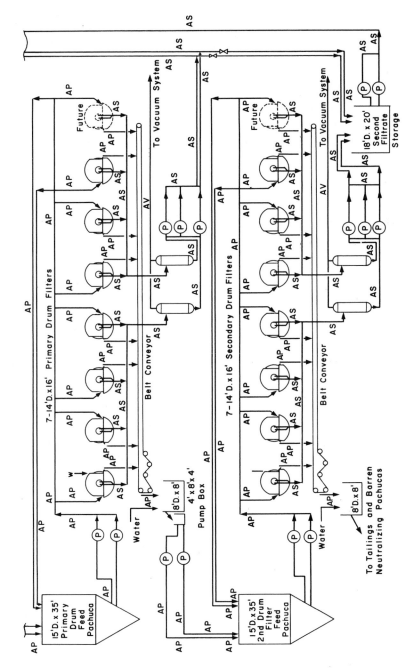

Fig. 11–4. Flowsheet of two-stage filtration circuit, Milliken Lake mill.

are washed with water, using the same ratio as the first-stage filters. The filter cake again drops onto a conveyor belt, is discharged into a repulper where it is repulped with either water or barren solution, and is pumped to the tailings neutralization section.

Thickeners, always used in pairs, are generally of the Dorr center-pier type, but some of the plants now under construction will have bridge or center-shaft types. Thickeners already installed, or planned, range from 75 to 110 feet in diameter, depending on plant capacities. Most of the filters being used are of the scraper-discharge type, incorporating a purge system, although some string-discharge filters will be used. The purge system utilizes double-row piping instead of single-row piping in the filter valve. One row of pipes comes from the leading edge of a section, and the other row from the trailing edge.

Blind River ore forms a dense cake on the filters. If the filtrate lines were not cleared before blowoff, solution would blow back at the scraper. With a purge system, the trailing-edge piping is opened to the atmosphere while the leading edge piping is still under vacuum, allowing the air to sweep or "purge" the filtrate lines of solution. When the filtrate lines are clear of solution, the vacuum is taken off the leading-edge piping, and the air blow is put on the trailing-edge piping, cleanly discharging the cake without blow-back.

Most of the filters are 14 feet in diameter with a 16-foot face, and are erected at the site. Some $11\frac{1}{2}$-foot-diameter by 16-foot-face filters in use are shipped assembled, but the larger filters are more economical. One set of $11\frac{1}{2}$-foot-diameter filters is fabricated completely of rubber-lined steel, but the rest feature fully open-end construction with wood decking. The filter boots or tanks are of rubber-lined steel, and the spiders are a combination of Type 316 stainless steel and rubber-lined mild steel. The filter agitators are of rubber-covered mild steel, some equipped with replaceable rubber wearing strips. The larger vacuum piping is stainless steel; the smaller sizes are of mild steel lined with hard rubber. Filtrate receivers and moisture traps are of mild steel, hard-rubber lined, with water sprays in one of the moisture traps to wash out any acid mist entrained in the vacuum lines.

Operating experience in the one larger filter plant has been short, but some data will be given. Dynel cloth, even though more expensive than cotton, is the most economical filter medium. The filters generally are fed a slurry containing between 55 and 60 percent solids. The filter discharge has a moisture content of about 20 percent. Filter duty has ranged between 0.75 to 1.0 ton per square foot per day, depending on the slurry conditions. The plants were designed on a basis of 0.65 ton per square foot per day or lower. Soluble uranium recovery in these modified filtration circuits has been as high as 98.7 percent and is expected to average better than 98.0 percent.

11–2.6 Uranium recovery. *Clarification.* The overflow from the thickeners in all plants is clarified in modified Moore leaf filters in which the solution is pulled, by vacuum, through precoated cotton sheeting stretched over stainless steel frames. Solution is pumped from the vacuum receiver to the clarified pregnant solution tank. These clarifiers give excellent performance and probably are the most economical type of equipment for this application, providing the solution is not too dirty. They are identical to the clarifiers employed in the Canadian gold-milling industry for many years, except that they are constructed of acid-resisting materials, mainly Type 316 stainless steel.

Ion exchange. All ion-exchange circuits in the Blind River area are of the fixed-bed type. One plant uses four-column units with chloride elution. Four use three-column units with nitrate elution. Six plants use what is called a "moving-bed" system with nitrate elution, shown in Fig. 11–5.

The principle of this special moving-bed system is that the resin is saturated, or loaded, by passing the pregnant solution through three columns in series. After a bed of resin has been loaded, it is moved with water to a backwash column to remove ore slimes. After backwashing, it is moved again with water to a set of three columns where the resin is eluted. In the meantime, a bed of eluted resin has been moved to the loading set, one column of which is now empty. This becomes the last column in the loading set.

A moving-bed unit consists of two sets of three loading columns, one backwash column, and one set of three eluting columns. The time cycle must be so arranged or the flow rate of pregnant solution so adjusted that a bed volume of resin can be eluted in less than one-half the time that it takes to load a bed volume of resin.

Loading and elution columns are 8 feet in diameter by 14 feet high on the straight side, and are filled to a height of 10 feet with resin. The backwash column is 8 feet in diameter by 16 feet high on the straight side, providing a 10-foot resin bed with 60 percent expansion, considered enough for cleaning saturated resin. A resin-outlet nozzle is on the side of the column about 2 feet above the gravel bed, and a resin-inlet nozzle about 1 foot above the maximum resin level, or 11 feet above the gravel bed. When a bed volume of resin is either loaded or eluted and is ready for moving, the resin-outlet valve is opened on the column from which the resin is to be moved, and the resin-inlet valve and bottom-drain valve are opened on the column which will receive the resin. The resin is moved by applying water through both the flush line at the top of the column and the backwash inlet line at the bottom of the column, and is forced through the internal pipe connected to the resin-outlet nozzle, which has a funnel-shaped end about 6 inches above the gravel bed. Water from both ends forces the resin out and into the receiving column. Excess water drains out. About 2 volumes of

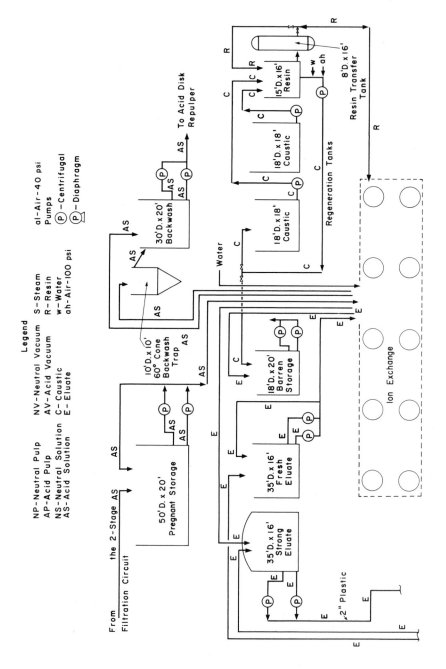

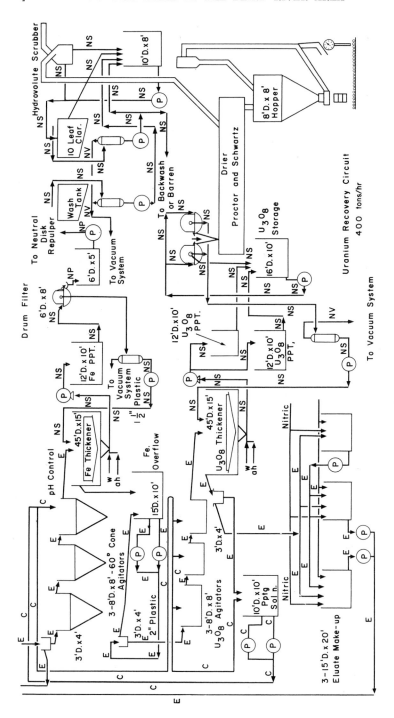

FIG. 11–5. Flowsheet of uranium recovery circuit, Milliken Lake mill.

water are required to move 1 volume of resin. Recent tests show that 400 cubic feet of resin can be moved in 18 minutes with a combined water flow rate of 250 U. S. gal/min.

This system has the following advantages over ordinary fixed-bed systems:

(1) For a given uranium capacity requirement, the capital costs of a plant are lower.

(2) The ion-exchange columns are more efficient in that they are almost completely filled with resin, since only the backwash column requires room for resin-bed expansion and is the only large column.

(3) Resin loadings during operation always should approach the saturation capacity; with three-column loading, no danger of breakthrough is present in the third column, before the first column is saturated.

(4) Instead of a two-stage elution, which is standard practice in column operation, a three-stage elution is possible without additional equipment, leaving a smaller volume of solution to be handled in precipitation.

Chloride elution. Pilot-plant work on Blind River ores employed chloride elution in the ion-exchange step. Later tests indicated that a nitrate elution system would be more economical and possibly more trouble-free. Therefore, only the first plant has a chloride elution system.

At Pronto Uranium Mines, Ltd., the first plant, a Dorr ion-exchange plant is installed, consisting of two sets of four columns each. The columns are 8 feet in diameter by 14 feet on the straight side, with an "air-dome" system. The air dome was first specified because it was believed that there would be serious elution diffusion into a hydraulic dome. In reality diffusion was found to be less a problem than anticipated, so all other ion-exchange plants are of the hydraulic-dome type. They are slightly less expensive, more flexible, and easier to operate than the air-dome type. At present, to handle slightly more than 3000 pounds of uranium per day, 300 cubic feet of Rohm and Haas IRA-400 strong-base anion resin is used in each column. The average pregnant solution assay is 0.75 g/liter, and the flow rate during loading is slightly more than 150 U. S. gal/min. These operating conditions give a resin loading, depending upon the condition of the resin, between 2.5 and 3.5 lb/ft^3, using three columns in series for loading. The resin is backwashed for one hour at a flow rate of 200 U. S. gal/min. At Pronto Mines, elution was originally accomplished with 24 bed volumes of eluate, 12 of which were a fresh solution of 0.15 N H_2SO_4 in 1 N NaCl. The flow rate was 75 U. S. gal/min through 250 cubic feet of resin per cell. The distribution of eluate, now greatly changed, was as follows:

> 1 bed volume recycle eluate to pregnant tank,
> 11 bed volumes recycle eluate to precipitation,
> 1 bed volume fresh eluate to precipitation,
> 11 bed volumes fresh eluate to recycle eluate,
> 1 bed volume water to recycle eluate.

Pilot-plant testing indicated that problems would be encountered with polythionate poisoning on the resin, so regeneration tankage was included in the initial installation. During plant operation, however, this poisoning did not occur. Instead, a different kind of poisoning was encountered which has not yet been fully explained. It is believed that zirconium and thorium might be the problem, but this theory has not been completely investigated. After seven months of operation, all resin in the plant had to be regenerated, first by washing with five bed volumes of a 42 percent sulfuric acid solution, followed by a water wash, and then by a wash of 5 bed volumes of a 10 percent sodium hydroxide solution. This restored the resin for a short period, but a rapid fall-off in the uranium capacity was soon noted. To overcome the loss of capacity, it was suggested that a sulfuric acid wash at the end of elution might possibly keep the resin clean. This was tried and worked out very well. It had the additional advantage that it recovered some chloride and also converted the resin to the sulfate form ahead of the loading cycle, thereby decreasing the initial uranium bleed. The acid wash contains 12.5 percent sulfuric acid.

This system, of course, raised some problems of what to do with the additional solution added to the elution circuit, since the acid-wash effluent, containing some uranium, could not be thrown out. It was decided that the acid-wash effluent should be the sulfuric acid makeup to the spent eluate. Thus acid costs remained the same, because the acid for making up the spent eluate was first passed through the eluted column, where it recovered 60 percent of the salt adsorbed on the resin, and was then sent to the eluate makeup tank.

To balance the elution circuit volumetrically, a volume equal to the volume of the acid wash used had to be discarded. A study of the elution curves showed that the first 2.5 bed volumes of concentrated eluate going to precipitation contained mostly uranium sulfate, and iron, and very little chloride. If the uranium were precipitated from this solution, the filtrate could be discarded. In the one tank used for this special precipitation, the precipitate is allowed to settle, the solution is decanted and discarded, and the precipitate is added to the remainder of the material from the regular precipitation.

The elution cycle used in this acid wash or chloride recovery technique at Pronto is as follows:

1	bed volume recycle eluate	to pregnant tank,
2.5	bed volumes recycle eluate	to special precipitation,
8.5	bed volumes recycle eluate	to regular precipitation,
1	bed volume fresh eluate	to regular precipitation,
11	bed volumes fresh eluate	to recycle eluate,
1	bed volume acid wash eluate	to recycle eluate,
1.5	bed volume acid wash	to eluate makeup tank,
1	bed volume water	to eluate makeup tank.

This technique has kept the uranium capacity of the Pronto resin up to 3.5 lb/ft^3. Reagent consumptions and costs for the chloride elution and recovery cycle, as used at Pronto, are given below, including the reagents employed on the single-stage precipitation:

Reagent	lb/lb U_3O_8	$/lb U_3O_8	lb/ton milled	$/ton milled
Sodium chloride	1.85	0.0231	3.76	0.0470
Sulfuric acid	1.65	0.0187	3.35	0.0378
Magnesium oxide	0.99	0.0446	2.01	0.0905
Total reagent cost		$0.0864		$0.1753

Before the chloride recovery step was adopted, the total reagent costs at Pronto were $0.1383 per pound of uranium produced and $0.2783 per ton of ore milled.

In the beginning, the ion-exchange plant was designed for automatic operation, but with the large number of changes in the circuit, it is now operated manually. One operator per shift has no trouble in running the plant manually, and also doing all the testing for break-through.

Nitrate elution. Plants employing nitrate elution have seven three-column sets installed. Each column contains 250 cubic feet of Rohm and Haas IRA-400 resin. The columns are 8 feet in diameter by 14 feet high on the straight side. The plants are on completely automatic operation, with one operator and one helper per shift. They have a capacity of 9000 pounds of uranium per day, and are being operated to handle over 7000 pounds per day.

All solution distribution to the seven sets is done by headers, with control valves at each set; hence, only one pump is required for each operation. The valves are operated by water instead of air, from a hydraulic control cabinet which is operated from the instrument panel.

Two columns are loaded in series at a flow rate of 130 U. S. gal/min with a solution containing 0.56 g U_3O_8/liter. Under these conditions, and with almost 100 percent saturation obtained in the lead column, the uranium loading varies between 2.75 and 2.90 lb/ft^3. These loadings are low, as the free-acid concentration in the pregnant solution is still high, about 6 g/liter. It is anticipated that when better control of the concentration is obtained, and it is reduced to 3 g/liter, these loadings should increase to 3.5 lb/ft^3. After using a nitrate elution for 7 months, no poisoning of the resin became evident. The ash content of the resin is about 1.5 percent. While two columns are on loading, the third is either on elution or standby. After loading, the resin is backwashed for 40 minutes to one hour at a flow rate of 192 U. S. gal/min.

After backwashing, the column is eluted at 30 U. S. gal/min. using the following volumes:

1 bed volume recycle eluate	to pregnant tank,
4 bed volumes recycle eluate	to precipitation,
1 bed volume fresh eluate	to precipitation,
4 bed volumes fresh eluate	to recycle eluate,
1 bed volume water eluate	to recycle eluate.

The fresh eluate is made up with nitric acid to be 0.2 N in HNO_3 and 0.8 N in $NaNO_3$. Recently, flow rates have been decreased to 18 U. S. gal/min, since plenty of time was available, and at the same time the quantity of eluate was reduced from 11 bed volumes total, as above, to 9 bed volumes total.

Costs for the nitrate elution, using two-stage precipitation with lime and sodium hydroxide, are as follows:

Reagent	lb/lb U_3O_8	$/lb U_3O_8	lb/ton milled	$/ton milled
Nitric acid	2.10	0.0788	3.64	0.1365
Sodium hydroxide	0.55	0.0248	0.96	0.0432
Lime	0.83	0.0083	1.44	0.0144
Total reagent cost		$0.1119		$0.1941

These costs are slightly higher than those for a chloride elution system using a chloride recovery step, but lower than a chloride elution system without a chloride recovery step. Work is now under way to investigate the feasibility of using a nitrate recovery step. The initial work looks promising and, if successful, should reduce the nitrate elution costs to about $0.06 per pound of U_3O_8 or about $0.11 per ton of ore milled, or even lower. Early results showed an 80 percent decrease in the nitric acid addition.

The nitrate elution system is preferred for the following reasons:

(1) Nitric acid solutions do not require the same expensive corrosion-resistant materials as acid chloride solutions, hence capital outlay is lower.

(2) Smaller volumes of solution are handled, hence equipment required is smaller and less expensive.

(3) Elution is faster and more efficient, hence the availability of the resin is greater and, for a given plant capacity, less resin inventory has to be carried.

(4) Using identical elution procedures, the cost of nitrate elution is less.

(5) Initial plant operation seems to indicate that on Blind River ore, most of the possible resin poisons are apparently eluted by the nitric acid eluate.

Precipitation. Three types of precipitation methods are practiced, or will be practiced, in the Blind River area.

(1) Single-stage batch precipitation with magnesium oxide.

(2) Two-stage continuous precipitation with lime and sodium hydroxide.

(3) Two-stage continuous precipitation with lime and magnesium oxide (not yet in operation).

The average uranium concentration in the eluate to the precipitation circuit is about 10 g/liter.

Single-stage, batch, MgO precipitation. Single-stage batch precipitation with magnesium oxide is employed at one plant, which is the one using chloride elution. Here, a number of tanks are utilized, each large enough to hold all the concentrated eluate from one elution. After the tank has been filled, a sample is precipitated in the laboratory to determine the quantity of magnesium oxide required. The magnesium oxide is prepared by mixing finely ground MgO in water and pumping it to the precipitation tank. Later investigation has shown that it is preferable to grind the magnesium oxide, so that finer, more reactive product can be obtained, lowering the consumption.

After magnesium oxide requirements are determined, this quantity is pumped to the precipitation agitators. Reaction proceeds for 6 hours. The pH endpoint is controlled between 6.5 and 7.0. Care is taken that 7.0 is not exceeded, because then the precipitate is difficult to filter and wash, probably because magnesium hydroxide forms. After the uranium has been precipitated, the resulting slurry is pumped to a thickener of the deep-well clarifier type. Overflow from this thickener is returned to the eluate makeup tank in the ion-exchange circuit. The split or special precipitation in this plant was discussed under "Ion Exchange." The precipitate from this method is also pumped to the thickener and combined there with the regular precipitate.

The underflow from the thickener is filtered on a series of 4-foot-diameter by 6-foot-face scraper-discharge drum filters. Four are employed in series to reduce the chloride content of the precipitate by dilution and washing and thus meet refinery specifications. The thickener underflow has a pulp density of from about 8 to 10 percent, and the filter discharges at about 30 percent solids. The filtrate from the first filter is returned to the thickener, since this solution contains valuable reagents. The filter cake from the first filter is repulped to about 10 percent solids with water, and fed to the second filter. Here a small amount of water is added to wash out the chlorides, and the cake again is repulped with water and sent to the third filter, where more washing is done. The third filter cake is repulped again with water and sent to the fourth-stage filter, from which the cake is repulped and sent to the drier. The filtrate from the last three filter stages is not returned to the eluate circuit, since it would upset the solution balance, but is discarded after all the uranium is removed in a small, leaf clarifier. The uranium so recovered is removed periodically and returned to the uranium thickener. Sodium sulfate, originally used in the wash and dilution water to the uranium filters to prevent peptization of the uranium, is no longer employed because it was found unnecessary.

At Pronto, which has the precipitation circuit just described, a Blaw-Knox Buflovac Twin-Drum drier dries the precipitate. The drier has two drums, 32 inches in diameter by 72 inches long, rotating in opposite directions. Steam at 70 psi is put into these drums, which rotate through a pan containing splashers. The splashers rotate rapidly in the pan, filled with precipitate, and splash the precipitate on the hot drums. As the drums rotate, the precipitate is dried and discharged into a screw conveyor by a scraper mounted just above the pan on the descending side of the drums.

The screw conveyors from each drum discharge to another screw conveyor, which in turn discharges to a precipitate storage bin capable of holding about 20,000 pounds. A Hydro-Volute scrubber discharges the moisture-laden air from the drier to the outdoors. The Hydro-Volute scrubber is an exhaust fan with water sprays directed into the eye of the fan. As the moisture- and dust-laden air passes through the fan, the dust particles are scrubbed out with the water, and the resultant slurry is returned to the uranium thickener. This scrubber is very efficient; in 18 months' operation, no precipitate has been noted in the exhaust air. It is inexpensive and compact.

The 30-gallon precipitate drums are filled from the storage bin by means of an electrically operated rotating bin valve. The drums, while being filled, are placed on a vibrator, which compacts the product as it fills the drums. After the drums are filled, they go along a roller conveyor to a scale incorporated in the conveyor. After weighing, the drums are covered and marked as directed by the buyer. With this arrangement, one man can

TABLE 11–3

TYPICAL PLANT METALLURGICAL BALANCE

Tons milled	2851 tons/day
Average head assay, U_3O_8	2.44 lb/ton
Undissolved loss U_3O_8	0.13 lb/ton
Soluble loss U_3O_8	0.02 lb/ton
Barren solution loss U_3O_8	0.004 lb/ton
Total tailings loss U_3O_8	0.16 lb/ton
Average quantity pregnant solution to ion-exchange plant	854 Imp. gal/min
Average pregnant solution analysis U_3O_8	0.64 g/liter
Average quantity of concentrated eluate to precipitation circuit	42 Imp. gal/min
Average concentrated eluate analysis U_3O_8	10.80 g/liter
Average uranium loading on IRA 400 resin	3.32 lb U_3O_8/ft^3
Average U_3O_8 content of precipitate	81.33%

handle as much as 7000 pounds of precipitate per shift. A typical metallurgical balance during early operation of the Pronto Mill is shown in Table 11–3.

Belt driers are installed in the other plants because the twin-drum drier is believed to have many disadvantages. In the author's opinion, the twin-drum type drier has one advantage, that of compactness, but this is more than outweighed by the following:

(1) The precipitate is splashed on the drums in a thin layer, which results in a very fine, dried precipitate. This means that a large amount of fine dust is carried out with the moisture-laden air. This dust is recirculated, thus making the net capacity of the drier relatively low. It has been estimated that as much as 25 percent of the precipitate might be recirculated. The dust load from a belt drier is nearly nil, since the precipitate is extruded into pellets before drying.

(2) Twin-drum capacity, on the basis of capital cost installed, is lower than a belt drier.

(3) Steam consumption is approximately 50 percent more than for a belt drier.

(4) To operate the twin-drum drier at full capacity, the pan must be kept full. With a uranium slurry, it is difficult to use a float control arrangement, because the pipelines plug rapidly; hence it is necessary to pump continuously from a surge tank, and let the overflow of the pan return to the surge tank. Since the precipitate slurry is heated while in

the pan, it tends to cake in the return pipelines and surge tank. This has caused considerable trouble, and requires shutting the drier down once a week to clean out the pipelines and surge tank.

(5) Because the precipitate is very fine, the bulk density is low, hence the amount of precipitate that can be put into the drums is low. This increases precipitate drum handling, inventory, consumption, and shipping costs.

Two-stage, continuous, lime-NaOH precipitation. The other method of precipitation now in use is a two-stage continuous system with slaked lime in the first stage and sodium hydroxide in the second stage. This differs from a similar method practiced in South Africa, in that caustic instead of ammonia is employed to precipitate the uranium. In contracts with Eldorado Mining and Refining Limited, the Canadian Government agency purchasing the uranium, specifies a very low (0.1 percent NH_3) maximum ammonia content. This means that if ammonia had been employed to precipitate the uranium, the resulting precipitate would have had to be calcined to drive off the ammonia. Since the precipitating costs of caustic and ammonia are very nearly the same, pilot-plant tests on caustic soda were made, indicating that it would cause no additional problems in the precipitation circuit. Operating plants have confirmed this, and a very high grade (83 to 86 percent U_3O_8 on a dry basis at 110°F) precipitate is produced. Magnesium oxide also was considered, primarily because it yields a more filterable precipitate. However, no filtering problems have been encountered with the caustic soda, and it was believed that the use of magnesium oxide would have the following disadvantages:

(1) Precipitation costs would be slightly higher with MgO than with NaOH.

(2) A slurry is difficult to handle, compared with a solution, when precise additions have to be made; an excess of MgO would always be necessary; control of caustic soda additions would be easier.

(3) The cheapest MgO available, on a MgO-content basis, has a very low reactivity; therefore, the contact time required for MgO is about 6 hours, compared with less than 90 minutes for caustic soda.

(4) Some excesses of MgO probably would be required, and since the available MgO contains up to 10 percent insoluble material, the grade of precipitate would be lower. Actually, this is not important, because Canadian contract requirements are for only 50 percent minimum U_3O_8 in the precipitate.

In a typical two-stage precipitation circuit, the high-grade, strong, or concentrated nitrate eluate from ion exchange is stored in a surge tank.

From this the strong eluate, containing between 12 and 18 g U_3O_8/liter, is pumped to a steady head tank that feeds the iron-gypsum precipitation circuit. Discharge from the steady head tank is controlled at a rate consistent with the quantity of eluate being produced. Overflow from the steady head tank is returned to the strong eluate storage tank. The iron-gypsum precipitation agitators are air-agitated, cone-bottomed tanks similar to Pachucas. The tanks vary in size, depending on plant capacity, but most are 8 feet in diameter by 8 feet high on the straight side, with a 60-degree cone. Three tanks are in series, with lime added to the first two. Lime additions are automatically controlled by measuring the pH in the agitators and regulating the lime feed accordingly. Regulation is by Kent lime or slurry feeders consisting of a movable trough traveling on an arc of about 45 degrees, which can discharge into two separated compartments. One compartment is piped to the precipitation agitator, and the other so that the lime returns to the lime-storage agitator. An air diaphragm controlled by the pH recorder moves the trough. Excess lime is pumped to the trough, and the position of the trough is controlled so that the proper amount of lime is added to the precipitation, and the remainder is returned to the lime-storage agitator. These feeders control the pH accurately.

Air agitation is employed in the first-stage circuit. South African experience has shown that less gypsum remains in supersaturated solution with air agitation than with mechanical agitation. The purpose of this iron-gypsum precipitation circuit is twofold. It controls the sulfate concentration in the eluate, and also precipitates the ferric iron. The endpoint pH is 3.5, since most of the ferric iron has been precipitated at that point. The desired final pH is obtained by adding a 10 percent caustic soda solution, again automatically controlled by a pH meter and an air-operated valve. The quantity of lime and caustic soda depends entirely upon the quantity of sulfate to be removed in order to maintain a sulfate concentration of 15 g/liter in the eluate. If the sulfate concentration is high, the lime neutralizing is carried close to the endpoint of 3.5, and only the final adjustment is made with caustic soda. If the sulfate is low, the lime may be added only to a pH of 2.8, and the remainder of the neutralization is with caustic soda. The complete operation is controlled automatically from a central instrument panel.

The discharge from the iron-gypsum precipitation circuit flows by gravity to the iron-gypsum thickener. The clear overflow from this thickener (a minute quantity of Separan is used here) goes to a surge tank, which supplies feed to the uranium-precipitation circuit. Underflow is pumped out of the thickener intermittently into a surge tank, where the iron-gypsum precipitate is further dewatered by decantation. Whenever the surge tank is full, approximately once per day, the iron-gypsum precipitate is filtered on a scraper-discharge drum filter to remove the uranium-bearing nitrate solution, repulped with water, and pumped to the leaching circuit. The purpose of this is to recover the small amount of uranium contained in the precipitate and in the moisture of the filter cake. The slurry (precipitate and solution combined) contains about 3 percent U_3O_8, representing about 6 percent of the uranium throughput of the plant.

The iron-gypsum thickener overflow is pumped to a steady head tank ahead of the uranium-precipitation circuit, the overflow of which returns to the surge tank. Uranium-precipitation agitators are equipped with slow-moving propeller agitators, and the tanks are flat-bottomed, about 8 feet in diameter by 8 feet high. Three in series are employed. A 10 percent caustic soda solution is added to the first and last agitator through a diaphragm-operated valve regulated by a pH recorder-controller. The pH is controlled at 6.8 in the last agitator, the overflow from which goes to the uranium thickeners. Plants using magnesium oxide as a precipitant will add the MgO through Kent feeders.

Very small amounts of Separan are added to the uranium thickener, the overflow of which goes to the eluate makeup tanks, where the nitric acid for makeup is introduced. To prevent dilution in the elution circuit, some of the uranium-thickener overflow is used to make up the 10 percent caustic soda solution for uranium precipitation. The caustic soda is stored as a 46 percent solution (lowest freezing point). When a new batch is needed, the proper quantity of the 46 percent solution is added to the storage tank and diluted with uranium-thickener overflow to 10 percent strength. The spent eluate is fortified with nitric acid so that the fresh eluate is 1.0 N in total nitrates, of which 0.2 N is nitric acid. With these concentrations, the circuit is in balance, so that only nitric acid need be added in an amount equivalent to the nitrates adsorbed on the resin. The eluate makeup operates on a batch principle. When a full tank has been made up, it is pumped to the fresh eluate storage tank ahead of the ion-exchange circuit.

The uranium-thickener underflow is pumped intermittently to two precipitate storage tanks in parallel. These are utilized mainly for further decantation of solution from the precipitate. The tanks contain steam coils to heat the precipitate, to promote settling of a thicker slurry. Two plants have a central drying plant, but others have their own self-contained driers, with precipitate filters mounted above the belt drier. At plants using the central drying plant, the thickened, settled, and decanted precipitate flows to two Eimco, roller-discharge drum filters in parallel. These filters, of panel construction with no wire winding, are 6 feet in diameter by an 8-foot face. They are equipped with a stainless steel roller about 5 inches in diameter, where the scraper is ordinarily located. The roller is driven from the drum of the filter at a peripheral speed approximately 5 percent faster than the filter drum peripheral speed, and in the same direction. At the discharge point or roller, blow-off air is applied to the cloth, forcing the precipitate on the cloth against the roller, where it sticks. The precipitate is scraped off the roller with a stainless steel blade, and drops into either a repulper or the drier. With the type of discharge mechanism on these filters, the caustic uranium precipitate (ordinarily difficult to handle on a drum filter) is as easy to handle as magnesium oxide precipitate.

The precipitate discharge from the filter is repulped with water and pumped to a storage agitator. From the storage agitator, it is pumped to a 2500-gallon tank truck trailer which hauls the precipitate to the central drying plant. Here the precipitate is discharged into a sampling agitator, where each lot is properly sampled. The slurry is then pumped to a surge agitator, from which it goes to two roller-discharge drum filters mounted on top of the rolling extruder of a Proctor & Schwartz belt drier. The overflow from the filter boots is returned to the surge agitator by gravity, making the filter operation very simple.

The precipitate from the filters drops onto the rolling extruder, and is pressed by two oscillating stainless steel rollers through a plate perforated with $\frac{1}{4}$-inch holes. The "pellets" of precipitate fall on a slowly moving stainless steel belt, which conveys the precipitate through a drying chamber 8 feet wide by 32 feet long. The precipitate is dried by hot air circulated through the pellets on the belt. At the end of the drying chamber, the precipitate is discharged into a storage bin, from which the precipitate drums are filled. The drier, in 6 months of operation, has given no trouble; it produces a dense, dry precipitate. The precipitate is compacted on the extruder before drying, so dusting is no problem; nevertheless, a Hydro-Volute scrubber is used to exhaust the drier air. This type of drier is excellent for uranium precipitate, being economical to operate, automatic, and efficient. Three of these units will be used in the Blind River area, serving six of the plants.

11–2.7 Tailings neutralization and disposal. No matter where the tailings are discharged in the Blind River area, some of the solution eventually flows into the numerous rivers and lakes. If the acid in these tailings were not neutralized, fish and vegetation would be destroyed; so all tailings, both solution and solids, are neutralized with slaked lime. Initially, it was planned to neutralize to a pH of 7.0 only, but upon recommendations by the Ontario Department of Lands and Forests, the pH is now taken to

8.0, as at that point all the metal salts are precipitated. Limestone was first considered for this job, but would readily raise the pH only to 3.5. From there to 8.0, lime would have to be used. After thorough investigation, it was decided to use lime only. Even though the actual reagent costs are slightly higher, need for a separate limestone grinding circuit is eliminated. The lime used here and in other places throughout the plants is purchased as quicklime, better than 90 percent available CaO, and slaked. This slurry is stored in agitators located adjacent to the major points of addition, from which the milk of lime is added to the process.

In most plants the barren solution and tailings pulp are neutralized in separate circuits, and then combined to be pumped to the tailings area together. Both agitators and Pachucas are used, and the whole operation is automatic, employing pH recorder-controllers and Kent lime feeders. An excess of air is added during this operation to precipitate as much gypsum as possible. This has worked out well; after 6 months of operation, no trouble has been encountered with gypsum precipitation in pumps and pipelines. Some gypsum precipitates in the agitators and Pachucas, but these are periodically shut down and cleaned.

A few of the plants will be putting the neutralized tailings through cyclone plants to produce backfill for underground filling. None of these cyclone plants is as yet in operation, so no operating data are available.

The tailings areas chosen are generally depressions that can be dammed off. Only a clear overflow runs into the lakes and streams. No plants anticipate having to build large tailings piles, since large areas are available for flooding. Since most of the tailings, discharged at one point or another, influence the water supply to the other plants, in the future the water for boiler and domestic purposes will probably have to be treated in demineralization plants. Work on this problem is now under way.

11–2.8 General information. In the future, as additional plants come on stream, numerous changes will no doubt be made in the flowsheets and equipment in an effort to improve the operation. The first sample of Blind River ore was received from Pronto for testing in September 1953, and the plant was in operation two years later; it has served as a large pilot plant for the area. The flowsheets of all the other plants still are generally based upon the original Pronto design, with modifications based on Pronto's experience.

Sulfuric acid, nitric acid, and quicklime were not available in sufficient quantities in Eastern Canada to supply area demands. To meet these requirements, five-year contracts were signed with suppliers of these reagents, so that new plant facilities could be built and amortized. The following quantities of reagents were required:

Reagent or supply	Approximate quantity, lb/ton	Price per lb, f.o.b. area	Daily tonnage
Grinding balls	2.5	$0.085	42
Grinding rods	1.0	0.075	17
Sulfuric acid (100%)	80	0.012	1450 (93%)
Nitric acid (100%)	3.5	0.0375	98 (60%)
Quicklime (92% CaO)	35	0.010	590
Sodium chlorate	2.5	0.090	42
Separan	0.1	1.05	2
Glue	1.5	0.19	25
Magnesium oxide	1.5	0.053	25
Sodium hydroxide (100%)	1.0	0.042	24 (73%)
Coal (for steam)	17	0.007	250
Total tonnage of reagents and major supplies			2565

11–3. Development of the Beaverlodge Mill*

11–3.1 Introduction. The Beaverlodge mill of Eldorado Mining and Refining Limited commenced operation in 1953. The plant treats ore from the company's mining operations near Beaverlodge Lake in the northwest corner of Saskatchewan Province immediately north of Lake Athabasca. When the plant was designed in 1951–52, the Ace orebody was expected to provide the major portion of the mill feed for some time to come, although it was anticipated that some custom ores would be treated. The plant originally was designed to treat 500 tons per day.

The choice of process had to be made at a time when Canadian experience in uranium leaching was limited to pilot-plant operations; the first Canadian leaching plant was then under construction at Port Radium, but did not commence operation until 1952. Although the Port Radium plant proved to be a very successful operation, the company engineers could not have guaranteed performance of an acid-leach plant at the time the Beaverlodge process was selected.

Bench-scale and pilot-plant operations were conducted on ore from the upper two levels of the Ace Mine during 1950–51. For these samples, a straight acid-leaching process looked fairly attractive. However, some concern was expressed by the company geologist that the carbonate content of the ore might increase at depth; furthermore, certain prospective custom ores contained a much higher percentage of acid-consuming min-

---

* By A. Thunaes, Eldorado Mining and Refining Limited.

erals. Accordingly, two methods were tested in the laboratory and on a pilot-plant scale:

(1) Cyclic leaching with sodium carbonate solution, precipitation of uranium with sodium hydroxide, and regeneration of sodium carbonate with flue gas.

(2) Flotation of calcite and other carbonate minerals, acid leaching of the flotation tailings (80 to 85 percent of the ore tonnage), and sodium carbonate leaching of the flotation concentrate.

It was finally decided to adopt carbonate leaching of all the ore.

11–3.2 Geology and mineralogy. All important ore deposits that have been explored in the Beaverlodge area are of hydrothermal origin. The pitchblende in Ace ore is invariably associated with calcite, chlorite, and hematite. Pyrite and chalcopyrite are present, and the average sulfur content was estimated to be 0.5 percent. The pitchblende occurs disseminated through the rock, intimately mixed with chlorite and calcite. Since very fine particles are dispersed through the calcite and in the siliceous gangue, fairly fine grinding is required for complete liberation.

The ore must be classified as hard to grind (Bond Work Index, 20), requiring 1 to 1.2 hp/ton to reduce from $\frac{1}{2}$ inch to 70 percent minus-200 mesh. The gangue is red-stained, glassy, or massive, and contains a high percentage of feldspar. A clay seam associated with the St. Louis fault contaminates the ore in varying degrees and at times affects crushing and settling operations.

11–3.3 Development of the process. Carbonate leaching of uranium ore had been carried out in the United States for a considerable time, usually in connection with roasting for the benefit of vanadium recovery. The ores treated by these older carbonate processes were carnotites and similar minerals, where the uranium was present in the hexavalent state and oxidizing agents were not required. Uranium and vanadium were precipitated from the carbonate solution by lowering the pH with acid.

The Radioactivity Division of the Mines Branch had developed a carbonate leaching process in 1949–50 for treating a pitchblende ore from one calcite-rich mine in the Beaverlodge field. This process was based on the use of sodium permanganate as an oxidizing agent, and the flowsheet included precipitation of uranium with excess sodium hydroxide, followed by regeneration of the barren solution with flue gas, in other words, a cyclic process. The process had been tried at atmospheric pressure at 140 to 158°F, as well as in laboratory autoclaves at 200 to 240°F and 100 psi. The importance of using sodium bicarbonate in leaching pitchblende was brought out during this development work. The principal drawback to the process was the fairly heavy cost for permanganate—up to $2.50 per ton.

Earlier attempts to leach pitchblende in carbonate solution with air as an oxidizing agent had not been successful. A few isolated attempts had been made to leach a calcite flotation concentrate from Port Radium ore, but only two hours leaching time was used, and the U_3O_8 recovery was only 50 percent. The experiments were discontinued, as it was decided to acid-leach all the Port Radium gravity tailings without preflotation of the carbonate minerals. The above information was available when a fuller investigation of the use of autoclaves in carbonate leaching was undertaken. Laboratory work at the University of British Columbia showed that Ace ore could be leached successfully in autoclaves at 100 lb/in^2 and 210 to 230°F, using air as an oxidizing agent. Considerable laboratory information was obtained on the effect of air rates and agitation.

Eldorado decided to pilot the process; this was done during 1951 in the Ottawa laboratories of Sherritt Gordon Mines Limited. In general, laboratory results were confirmed, and additional data were obtained on the effect of grind, agitation, air rates, and pulp densities, as well as some experience in operating pilot-plant autoclaves continuously. Eldorado prepared a flowsheet and capital and operating cost estimates for a 500-ton plant.

In the meantime, the Mines Branch laboratories had piloted a "combination process" which included flotation of sulfides, then flotation of carbonate minerals. The sulfides and carbonate flotation tailings were acid-leached by a system similar to the Port Radium process; the calcite flotation concentrate was leached in sodium carbonate solution.

Both processes had advantages, and the choice was difficult, but it finally was decided to use the all-carbonate leach process with autoclave equipment. Estimated costs for the "all-carbonate" leach were somewhat lower; and an alternative "all-carbonate" leach was under development at the Mines Branch laboratories. This latter process was operated at atmospheric pressure.

The flowsheet and equipment for the Beaverlodge plant has been changed considerably since the start of operation in May 1953. Three periods will be considered:

    (1) 1953–54 at 500 tons per day,
    (2) 1955–56 at 750 tons per day,
    (3) 1957 expansion to 2000 tons per day.

11–3.4 The original 500-ton per day mill. The new and unusual features, so far as plant-scale uranium leaching was concerned, were (1) the use of autoclaves on a continuous basis, (2) pulp-to-pulp heat exchangers, and (3) the use of a cyclic process. A schematic flow diagram of the original concept for a uranium extraction and recovery process is shown in Fig. 11–6.

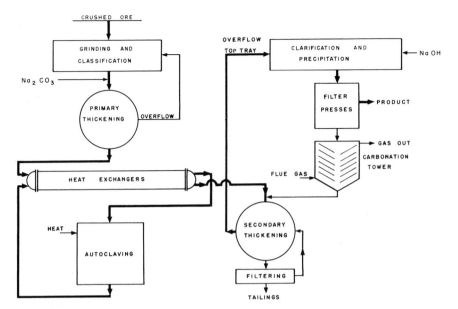

Fig. 11–6. Schematic flowsheet of 500-ton/day Beaverlodge mill.

Ore preparation. Crushing. The ore is crushed to 5-inch size while still underground, in a 30 by 42-inch Traylor jaw-crusher located on the 1000-foot level; it then is sent through a storage raise and loading pocket and hoisted by $3\frac{1}{2}$-ton skips to the surface, where it is dumped into an underground storage bin. The mill crushing plant is located close enough to the hoist that a 600-foot conveyor delivers to the 150-ton coarse ore surge bin in the crushing plant. The conveyor is 30 inches wide and at a 15-degree slope. The secondary crushing plant consists of a $4\frac{1}{4}$-foot Symons standard cone crusher in open circuit, followed by a $5\frac{1}{2}$-foot shorthead crusher in closed circuit with three Dillon screens, 4 by 10 feet. In the original flowsheet, the screens were double deck, and the product was about $\frac{5}{16}$ inch.

The crushed ore went to a cylindrical, round-bottom, steel fine-ore bin of 1000-ton capacity. Bin discharge was metered by a Merrick Weightometer.

Grinding. The grinding circuit consisted of one 9 by 9-foot Allis Chalmers high-discharge ball mill in closed circuit with a 78-inch Akins Simplex classifier; the ball mill was operated at 72 percent of critical speed and fed with 3-inch forged steel balls.

The primary overflow at approximately minus-20 mesh was pumped to the secondary classifier, a 54-inch Duplex Akins unit. This secondary classifier overflow was the final product from the grinding circuit, and the sands went to the secondary 9 by 9-foot Allis Chalmers ball mill, which discharged to the above secondary classifier.   The secondary ball mill also was operated at 72 percent of critical speed; the steel makeup was $1\frac{1}{2}$-inch and $1\frac{1}{4}$-inch balls.

An unusual feature in the grinding circuit was that the grinding solution contained 5 percent sodium carbonate plus about 10 percent sodium sulfate. The solution reached a density of 1.12 and the temperature was approximately 105 to 110°F.

The secondary classifier overflow at 27 to 29 percent of solids was thickened in a 55-foot diameter, 3-compartment thickener, with the overflow returning to grinding-solution storage.   The underflow was fed to the autoclave leaching circuit.   The aim was to obtain an underflow density in excess of 50 percent of solids.

Uranium extraction.   Heat exchangers.   Since leaching took place at elevated temperatures, the leach feed had to be heated from 110 to 230°F. Much of this was accomplished in flash-type heat exchangers, where heat contained in autoclave discharge pulp was transferred to the leach feed pulp.

The flash heat-exchange system consisted of eight tanks 24 inches in diameter by 81 inches high. One stage is shown schematically in Fig. 11–7. Four tanks carried cold pulp from the thickener and the other four carried hot autoclave discharge pulp. A system of impingement plates and baffles in each tank produced a film of pulp for easy release or condensation of

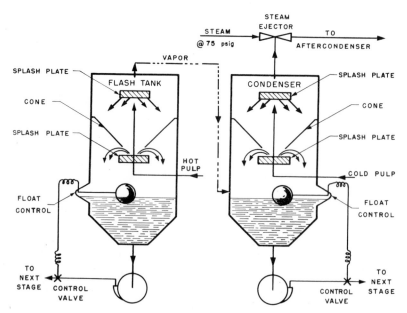

FIG. 11–7. Flash heat exchangers used in 500-ton/day Beaverlodge mill.

vapor. Each stage of the flash heaters was equipped with its own ejector. All ejectors discharged into a common header vented through the after-condenser to the atmosphere. Steam for the ejectors was supplied at 75 psig. As the vapor from the hot side condensed on the cold pulp a partial vacuum was created, causing the pulp in the flash tank to boil at a lower temperature.

The design estimates called for heating cold pulp from 85 to 185°F in the four stages, while the hot pulp would be cooled from 220 to 120°F. These estimates were more or less confirmed in actual practice. The disadvantage of the flash-type heat-exchanger system was the large number of auxiliary pumps and control valves, which demanded frequent maintenance and excessive down time. Contrary to expectation, wear was not a serious factor in the tanks.

Carbonate leaching in autoclaves. The heated pulp at about 180 to 185°F was pumped to the two lines of 9 autoclaves by two heavy 5 by 4-inch SRL pumps operating in tandem. The pumps performed well except for excessive gland water dilution.

The pumps discharged through separate flow controllers and control valves to the two lines of autoclaves. The flow controllers were Fischer & Porter Rato-Sleeve flowmeters connected to a Fischer & Porter Magna-bound pneumatic transmitter, operating a Fischer & Porter controller, which in turn controlled a Mason-Neilan No. 737 control valve on the pump discharge. The flow controllers were equalized; that is, if the rate of one was altered, the others were automatically adjusted.

A schematic diagram of one of the 18 autoclaves is shown in Fig. 11–8. Each autoclave was a cylindrical tank with dished ends, 8 feet in diameter by 25 feet long, with the axis horizontal. A glass-fiber mat 3 inches thick

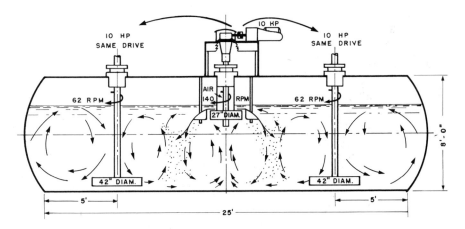

Fig. 11–8. Autoclaves used in 500-ton/day Beaverlodge mill.

was used for insulation. The tanks were agitated by two Turbo-Mixer agitators with 42-inch impellers to maintain suspension of pulp. A third Turbo-Mixer drive operated an aerator, consisting of a hood ring and a 27-inch impeller, at 140 rpm. A gas suction sleeve was around the shaft. The aerator dispersed air through the pulp to oxidize uranium. The autoclaves were operating with about 80 percent of the volume occupied by pulp, and air was continuously fed concurrently with the pulp. The aerator impeller was placed quite close to the surface of the pulp. Each impeller was operated by a 10-horsepower motor, making 540 horsepower for the 18 autoclaves.

Steam coils were provided in the first and third autoclave of each line; some heat also was obtained from oxidation of pyrite.

Compressed air was supplied from a 100-psi compressor in amounts varying from 1000 to 1200 ft^3/min. The autoclave-discharge pulp went to the washing thickeners via the heat exchange system described above. A "blow-down tank" with a float controller and a Mason-Neilan No. 737 control valve were used to discharge the pulp. Extremely severe wear made it necessary to use plugs and seats fitted with tungsten carbide inserts for these valves.

Liquid-solids separation. Liquid-solids separation and washing of tailings were accomplished in washing thickeners followed by one stage of filtration.

The washing thickeners consisted of two, 60-foot diameter by 41-foot-high, four-compartment tanks operated in parallel. Pregnant solution overflowed from these thickeners, while barren solution was fed to the bottom trays. The underflow went to four 11½ by 16-foot drum filters of the wire-wound type. These filters produced a final tailing for discard, and a filtrate which was returned to mill solution. Some barren solution and some water were used for washing.

The pregnant solution from the top compartment of the washing thickeners went through a bag-type clarifier consisting of 16 bags, 7 by 5 feet, and on to the precipitation circuit.

Uranium recovery. The equipment used for precipitation consisted of four tanks, 12 feet in diameter by 14 feet high, calculated to give 6 hours retention time; the tanks were mechanically agitated and precipitation was continuous.

The precipitant was a solution of caustic soda dissolved in barren solution to make a 15 to 18 percent NaOH solution. It was found advantageous to place a small, high-speed mixer ahead of the precipitation tanks, to give intimate mixture of caustic solution with barren solution. Sufficient caustic soda was added to convert the bicarbonate formed in leaching to normal sodium carbonate, plus an excess of 6 NaOH/liter.

The precipitated "sodium diuranate" was filtered off in four Perrin plate-and-frame presses, 36 by 36 inches. The press frames were originally 2 inches deep, but soon were changed to 4 inches.

Precipitate was dried in pans in over-type driers. The dried precipitate was dumped from the pans through a screen into a hopper and the precipitate was automatically elevated to a cyclone and bag-house. Drums were filled from the cyclone hopper.

The barren solution was sent to the carbonation circuit to produce carbonate from excess caustic soda by contact with boiler flue gas. The original equipment for the carbonation circuit was a stainless steel tower, $2\frac{1}{2}$ feet in diameter by 16 feet high, divided into two compartments. The first compartment was intended for removal of SO_2 by water scrubbing; the second (top) compartment was the actual carbonation unit where the reaction took place between CO_2 in boiler gas and $NaOH$ in barren solution.

11–3.5 The expanded 700-ton per day mill. The original installation at the Beaverlodge Mill was in many respects based on a "green" flowsheet, and the first two years of operation had many features of a large pilot plant. It was necessary to make a great many changes. This original flowsheet has been described in considerable detail to bring out the reason for the changes incorporated during the second stage of operation (1955–56). Note that, in spite of extensive alterations and maintenance, production was kept up to schedule and metallurgical results were creditable. The flowsheet at the end of this period is given in Fig. 11–9.

Ore preparation. Crushing. The tonnage was increased from 500 to 700 tons per day, mainly to provide treatment facilities for additional custom ores. This ore was crushed through a 15 by 30-inch Sawyer-Massey jaw-crusher to $2\frac{1}{2}$ inches, and was carried by a shuttle conveyor to one of three custom ore raises. The ore was transferred to the secondary crushing plant via the main 30-inch conveyor. A 10 percent cut was taken, as the $2\frac{1}{2}$-inch ore fell into the 150-ton surge bin, by a deflection gate. It was reduced to $\frac{3}{8}$ inch in a 2-foot Symons cone crusher discharge; the latter cuts were reduced to 6 to 8 mesh in a 16-inch Denver roll crusher, and a final 10 percent cut was taken for further processing in the sample room.

The openings in the crushing plant screens were changed to $\frac{1}{4}$ by 4-inch, to produce finer ball mill feed for the higher tonnage.

Grinding. The speed of the primary ball mill was increased from 72 to 85 percent of critical to prevent excessive slipping caused by grinding in high-density carbonate solution. Similar speedup was arranged for the secondary mill. A 5 percent increase in tonnage and some decrease in steel consumption resulted.

A 12-inch Dorrclone was installed to treat the secondary classifier overflow (density 1.13). The sands went to leaching, and only the overflow

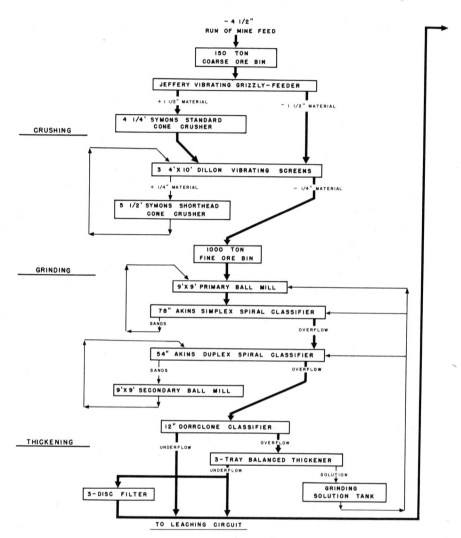

FIG. 11–9. Schematic flowsheet of 700-ton/day Beaverlodge mill.

was sent to the 55-foot grinding circuit thickener at a higher tonnage. At the same time the Dorrclone provided higher density for leaching of the combined Dorrclone sands plus thickener underflow.

An American disk filter was used intermittently for further dewatering of Dorrclone sands; the resulting density of leach feed was 58 percent of solids. Separan was added to the 55-foot thickener as an aid in settling the Dorrclone overflow. The consumption was up to 0.05 lb of Separan per ton of slimes.

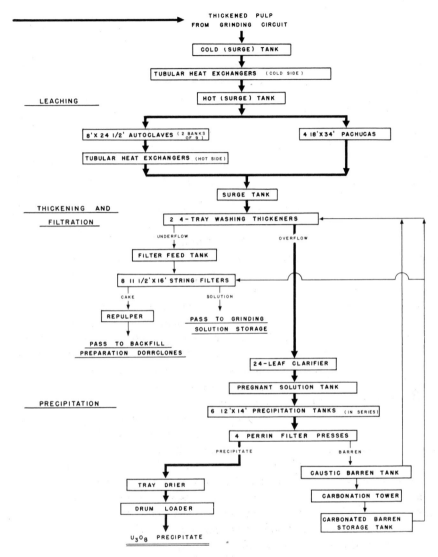

FIGURE 11–9 (*continued*)

These changes in grinding and thickening permitted handling 750 tons per day, with occasional rates up to 800 tons per day; the final grind, 65 to 68 percent minus-200 mesh, was somewhat coarser than desired.

Uranium extraction. The original pulp heat exchangers of the flash type were discarded in favor of concentric tube exchangers, fabricated at the property from 4-inch standard, and $2\frac{1}{2}$-inch heavy-duty, black iron pipe. The pipes were assembled in 70-foot lengths with 180-degree return bends.

The heat-transfer coefficient was of the order of 100 Btu/hr·ft²·°F; the leach feed pulp was heated from 110 to 150°F. The change eliminated excessive maintenance and down time experienced with the original heat-exchange system. Operating experience for the new exchangers has been good, and concern about plug-ups and excessive wear proved unwarranted.

The capacity of the leaching circuit was increased by installing four Pachuca tanks, in which leaching was carried out at atmospheric pressure. Air was introduced to these tanks by downcomer pipes at 30 to 35 psig and at a rate of 0.6 ft³/min per square foot of surface area. Flue gas was sparged to the first tank to increase the bicarbonate content of the solution. The tanks were of mild steel, 18 feet in diameter by 34 feet cylindrical height, plus a 60-degree cone bottom 15 feet high. The agitation was by an 18-inch central airlift discharging to 90-degree launders above the surface. The pulp was kept at 170°F by steam coils. Four tanks were used in series to provide a contact time of 90 to 100 hours. The reason for installing Pachucas instead of additional autoclaves was that operating costs plus tailing losses were expected to be lower; experience during the 1955–56 period confirmed this expectation.

Liquid-solids separation. The original system of washing thickeners plus single filtration was changed to double filtration in 1956. Considerable trouble was experienced with the two 60-foot-diameter, four-compartment washing thickeners in spite of the use of Separan; the sealing arrangement between the trays had a tendency to choke. It was not possible to maintain good washing and suitable underflow densities for filter feed, and the pregnant solution tonnage was excessive.

During the latter part of 1956 the filtration was conducted in two stages of four filters, $11\frac{1}{2}$ feet by 16 feet. A lower tonnage ratio of pregnant solution to ore resulted. Another significant change was the conversion to string-discharge filters (from wire-wound), with substantial increase in filtration rate per unit. Important improvements also were made in the filter wash system, further decreasing losses of soluble uranium. Toward the end of 1956, nylon filter cloths were found to be much superior to cotton cloth. The mill solutions, particularly when hot, caused rapid deterioration of cotton cloth. The leach pulp was cooled to 120°F before filtering. Addition of Separan, as a flocculant for filter feed, has been carried out since 1955; about 0.2 lb per ton is required to increase filter and washing rates.

Uranium recovery. The original system of precipitation was modified; instead of using NaOH dissolved in barren solution, the caustic-soda drums were stripped and the solid blocks were submerged in the flow of pregnant solution. The original caustic-soda dissolving tanks thus became part of the precipitation tank line, increasing the precipitation time. The precipitate grade was improved by 1 to 2 percent of U_3O_8 because the sodium sulfate content decreased. The sodium sulfate frequently was precipitated where caustic was dissolved in barren solution to give a 15 to 20 percent NaOH concentration.

11–3.6 The present 2000-ton per day mill. Following the expansion of the mill to 700 tons per day, underground development resulted in the discovery of the Verna orebody some distance from the Ace mine. It was decided to increase the milling rate to 2000 tons per day with about 60 percent of the feed being Verna ore. Since the latter contains 1.5 to 2.0 percent sulfur, the process was modified by floating off a pyrite concentrate, which then was acid-leached and filtered. The uranium in the filtrate was precipitated with magnesia, and this precipitate was combined with the flotation tailings as the feed to the carbonate leach circuit. The general scheme of plant operation is shown in Fig. 11–10.

Construction of the expanded Beaverlodge mill has been completed and tonnage has been gradually increased; the treatment rate of 1500 tons per day was reached by the last part of April 1957.

The flowsheet of the expanded mill is shown in Figs. 11–11, 11–12, 11–13, and 11–14. It is based partly on operating experience to date and partly on laboratory and pilot-plant work on the new type of ore that will be treated.

Ore preparation. Crushing. This section, shown in Fig. 11–11, remains unchanged except that coarser screen will be used to improve crushing capacity. The product from the crushing plant initially will be minus $\frac{1}{2}$ inch and may be somewhat coarser in the future.

Ore storage is increased by a catenary steel bin of 8000 tons capacity.

Grinding. Two 9 by 12-foot rod mills are followed by two 9 by 12-foot ball mills, plus the earlier 9 by 9-foot ball mills, all ball mills being in parallel and closed with classifiers. The new 9 by 12-foot ball mills are in

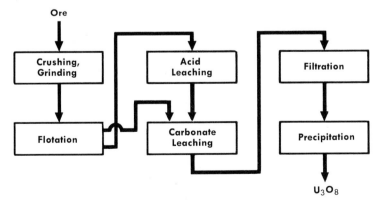

Fig. 11–10. Simplified flowsheet of 2000-ton/day Beaverlodge mill.

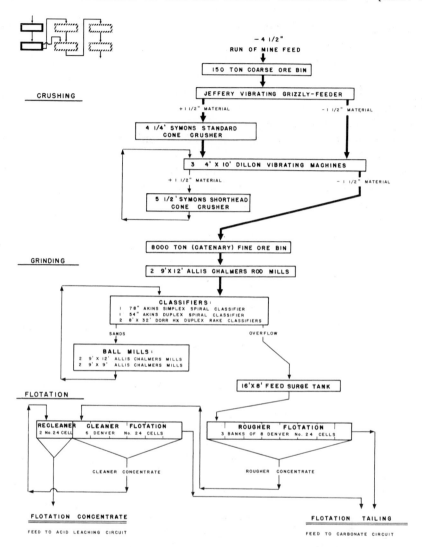

FIG. 11–11. Schematic flowsheet of crushing, grinding, and flotation sections of 2000-ton/day Beaverlodge mill.

closed circuit with 8 by 32-foot Dorr model HX classifiers. The grind will be to 72 to 75 percent minus-200 mesh. The original 60-foot washing thickeners are converted to settling thickeners. A Dorrclone station provides slime feed for these thickeners, while the Dorrclone sands go to the leaching circuit mixed with thickener underflow.

Flotation. The classifier overflow is pumped to the sulfide flotation cells, where pyrite (with graphite) is removed for separate treatment by acid

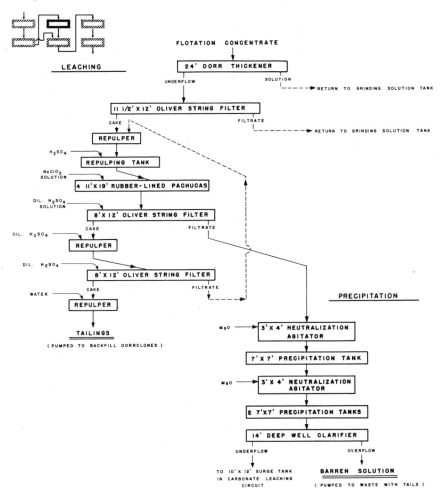

FIG. 11–12. Schematic flowsheet of acid leaching circuit of 2000-ton/day Beaverlodge mill.

leaching. About 60 tons of pyrite concentrate is removed per day. The equipment for flotation consists of 3 banks of 8 Denver No. 24 cells for roughing service, 6 cells for cleaning, and 2 for recleaning. Initial reagents are isopropyl xanthate and Dowfroth.

The flotation of pyrite reduces the reagent cost for carbonate leaching because each pound of sulfur consumes 3.3 pounds Na_2CO_3. The reagent consumption of the new mill feed would be prohibitive if the bulk of the sulfur were not removed.

Uranium extraction. The sulfide concentrate is thickened and filtered to remove alkaline solution. The repulped sulfides are pumped to the acid

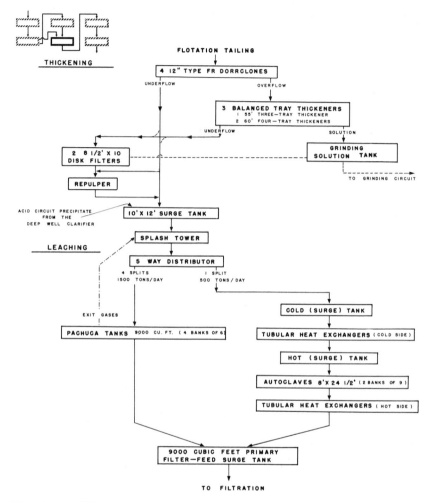

FIG. 11–13. Schematic flowsheet of carbonate leaching circuit of 2000-ton/day Beaverlodge mill.

leaching circuit shown in Fig. 11–12, where they are leached in 11 by 19-foot rubber-lined Pachuca tanks. The Pachuca discharge is filtered in two stages and the pregnant solution precipitated with $Mg(OH)_2$ to give a crude precipitate, which is settled and sent to the main carbonate leach circuit (Fig. 11–13).

The reason for including acid leaching is that pitchblende is attached to some of the pyrite in a very intimate mixture, and recoverable uranium values in the pyrite are greater than the cost for acid leaching.

The carbonate leaching circuit (Fig. 11–13) is similar to the 1955–56

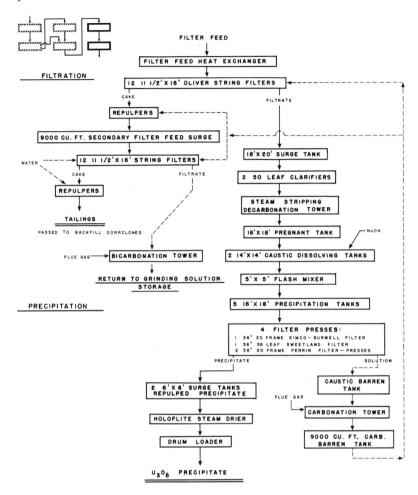

FIG. 11–14. Filtration and uranium precipitation in 2000-ton/day Beaverlodge mill.

system except that the autoclave circuit is retained to treat about 1/4 of the tonnage. The additional leaching capacity is provided by Pachuca tanks similar to those used during the 1955–56 period. The Pachuca exit air exhausts countercurrent to incoming leach feed in a splash tower; the reason for this arrangement is to conserve heat. A total of 24 Pachucas and 18 autoclaves are in operation. The autoclaves are the original installation of 2 parallel banks of 9 each, and the Pachuca section consists of 4 banks of 6 tanks each.

Liquid-solids separation. The leaching circuit discharge goes directly to filtration (Fig. 11–14) but the pulp is cooled to 130°F by heat exchangers to prevent steaming in the filter bay and to increase filter cloth life. The filters are arranged as 12 primary and 12 secondary units. Pregnant solution is produced by the primary filters, with the secondary filtrate returning to mill solution. The new flowsheet includes steam stripping of the pregnant solution to reduce its bicarbonate content before precipitation. The pregnant solution is clarified in drag-type classifiers before entering the precipitation section. The average composition of the pregnant solution is as follows:

U_3O_8:   2.0–2.5 g/liter,

V_2O_5:   0.02–0.03 g/liter,

Sodium bicarbonate: 8–12 g/liter,

Sodium carbonate: 50–70 g/liter.

Uranium recovery. The method of precipitation is similar to that used in 1956, in which solid caustic soda in block form was used. Equipment consists of five 16 by 18-foot tanks in series, which provide a contact time of 6 to 7 hours. Precipitate filtration is done in one Eimco-Burwell 36-inch, 20-frame filter press and one 36-inch, 36-leaf Sweetland filter press. The precipitate is dried in a steam-heated twin-screen Holoflite drier, then repulped and fed to the drier by a Moyno pump. Two Perrin presses are available for standby or for scavenging solids in filtrate. The average composition of the precipitate is as follows:

U_3O_8: 72 to 77 percent,

H_2O: 2 to 4 percent,

V_2O_5: 0.5 to 0.7 percent,

$SO_4^=$: 0.4 to 0.5 percent,

Cl^-:   0.02 to 0.05 percent.

The barren solution from precipitation, containing 6 to 7 grams of excess caustic soda per liter, goes to carbonation towers.

11–3.7 Remarks on operating experience. The percentage of uranium extracted and ore tonnage treated have been maintained at a satisfactory level since the start of the plant. However, cost of maintenance and alterations to equipment has been higher than estimated. Corrosion has been a principal cause for the high maintenance cost, but recent research has given encouraging leads that may reduce or eliminate serious corrosion in the future. Power consumption is high compared with that for acid-leach plants; about 75 kwh per ton. Reagent consumption has been close to estimates.

Leaching conditions have not varied appreciably from those established by pilot-plant work. The principal factors that promote good leaching are:

Bicarbonate content: 20 g/liter,

Density, maximum: 55 percent solids,

Temperature: 230°F in autoclaves,
170 to 175°F in Pachucas,

Aeration: About 1200 ft³/min for autoclaves,
and 0.5 to 0.6 ft³/min per sq ft of
pulp surface in Pachucas,

Agitation: Mechanical or airlift agitation must
be maintained at high level for
optimum leaching rate.

The high buildup of sodium sulfate in the circulating leach solutions (110 to 120 g/liter) has not affected leaching rates. Settling of ore in the sodium carbonate mill solutions required the use of flocculating agents. Separan has been used successfully. String-discharge filters gave better capacity than the wire-wound type.

The precipitation of uranium by caustic soda works well providing the excess caustic soda is 6 to 7 g/liter and the contact time is 6 hours.

The carbonate leaching flowsheet is fairly complex; training of operators has been a particularly important phase of the operation. As is usual in the far northern plants, labor turnover is high, making it necessary to train a great number of men each year.

11–4. URANIUM RECOVERY BY VITRO URANIUM COMPANY*

11–4.1 Introduction. Vitro Uranium Company, a Division of Vitro Corporation of America, operates a uranium mill at Salt Lake City, Utah, to produce a high-grade concentrate for sale to the United States Atomic Energy Commission.

Located southwest of metropolitan Salt Lake City, Vitro's plant covers more than 80 acres and includes 18 buildings with a net area of more than 75,000 square feet. Throughput, initially 550 tons per day, was increased to 660 tons per day in late 1957, when a $1,200,000 expansion program was completed. Included in this program was a plant employing the solvent extraction process to replace the original phosphate precipitation process.

* By the staff of Vitro Corporation of America.

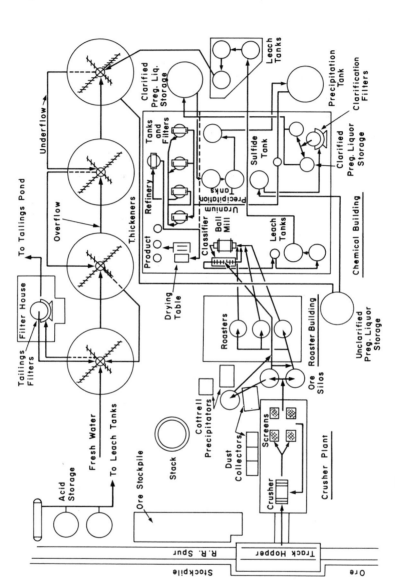

Fig. 11-15. Arrangement of equipment for Salt Lake City mill.

11–4.2 Ore. Various types of ores are handled by the mill. They range from refractory sandstone and limestone to easily slimed, clay-bearing materials. Current ores processed by Vitro come from mines in the Big Indian Wash, Green River, and Marysvale areas of Utah; Front Range and Canon City districts of Colorado; and the Gas Hills area of Wyoming.

Major ore suppliers include the Four Corners Uranium Company, Hidden Splendor Mining Company, Vanadium Corporation of America, Vitro Minerals Company, Denver Golden Mining Company, and Juniper Oil and Mining Company. Ores treated contain primarily uraninite, autunite, and carnotite minerals in sandstone sediments and various alterations.

11–4.3 Ore preparation. *Crushing.* Ore is shipped to Salt Lake City in bottom-dump gondola railroad cars and routed to the Utah Ore Sampling Company plant at Murray, Utah, for weighing, crushing, sampling, and moisture determination. At the sampler, the ore is crushed to pass a 1-inch screen. Three sample cuts are made, giving approximately 10 pounds of sample per ton of ore handled. From this sample a quantity (usually 5 pounds per lot of ore) is removed for testing by Vitro at its mill site. Final pulp samples, of minus-200 mesh, are distributed to both buyer and seller with weight and moisture certificates on the shipment. Two pulps are retained by the sampler for distribution to umpire analysts, should the need arise. Exchange assays by Vitro and the shipper are made and settlement is effected if the two assays agree within 0.01 percent U_3O_8. An umpire analysis is generally called for if the difference exceeds this range; however, either buyer or shipper may call for an umpire analysis at any time.

The general arrangement of equipment at the Salt Lake mill, before the solvent extraction system was installed, is shown in Fig. 11–15. A complete flowsheet, including the solvent extraction, is shown in Fig. 11–16. The diagrams will be useful in following the process description presented below.

The sampled and crushed ore is reloaded in rail cars, weighed, and transferred to the Vitro mill site some 5 miles away. Ore arriving at the mill may be dumped into a 100-ton track hopper or stockpiled along either side of various railroad spurs. First concern is to blend the various ores to provide a uniform plant feed, approximately 0.30 percent U_3O_8, which is amenable to the process conditions employed.

All ore is conveyed by a 30-inch belt conveyor to the crushing plant, where it enters the mill circuit through the track hopper. Here the minus 1-inch ore is reduced to minus $\frac{1}{2}$-inch in a 30 by 30-inch Cedar Rapids impact breaker operating in closed circuit with four 4 by 8-foot electrically heated Tyler vibrating screens with $\frac{1}{2}$-inch openings.

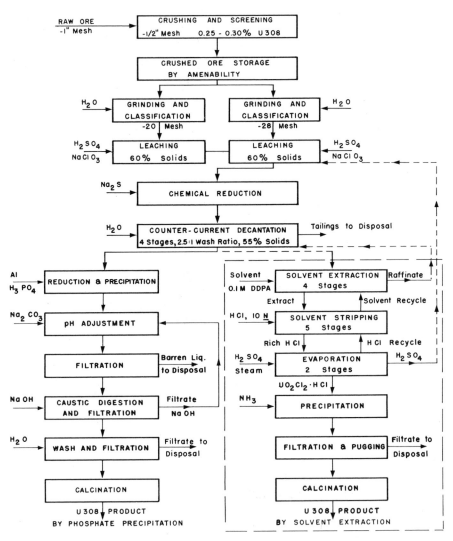

FIG. 11–16. Schematic flowsheet for Salt Lake City mill.

Screened ore is stored in three vertical precast-concrete silos to provide additional blending of mill feed. The ores first are separated according to acid requirements for leaching, and one group, classed as "more amenable," is divided further according to lime (CaCO₃) content. From the silos, the ores may be fed by belt conveyors to the roasters, or can bypass roasting and be fed directly to the two grinding circuits. Feed streams are measured and controlled by Fairbanks-Morse Weightometers.

Grinding and roasting. Inasmuch as Vitro no longer receives asphaltic-base ores, roasting has been eliminated; however, when necessary, ore is fed into 3 gas-fired, multiple-hearth Skinner roasters, where temperatures range up to 1470°F and retention time is about 3 hours. Roasting of carbonaceous ores, in general, frees the uranium, since carbon compounds are very resistant to attack by the usual acid-leaching procedure. Roasting also very often improves leaching efficiency and aids settling characteristics of leached pulp produced from carbonaceous ores. Roaster gases, carrying dust, are treated in cyclones and electrostatic precipitators for dust recovery before being vented to the atmosphere. Calcined ore and recovered dust are transferred by spiral conveyors and pumps to the grinding circuit prior to leaching.

Ore less amenable to leaching is conveyed from storage to the first of the grinding circuits by belt conveyor across the Weightometer. It is discharged to a Marcy 6 by 4½-foot ball mill operating in closed circuit with an Aikins spiral classifier. Grinding is carried out at 60 percent of solids, with size reduction to minus-28 mesh. From the other two silos, more amenable ores are belt-conveyed to another grinding circuit for reduction to minus-20 mesh. Here grinding also is carried on at 60 percent of solids, but with an Eimco 6 by 5-foot ball mill operating in closed circuit with a Dorr-type duplex rake classifier.

Great care is exercised to determine accurately the quantity of ore fed to each circuit, and to obtain samples of these feed streams. Automatic two-stage sample cutters remove approximately 1 pound per ton of mill feed from each stream. A daily assay pulp sample is prepared for chemical analysis.

11–4.4 Uranium extraction. Leaching is carried out in five 13,000-gallon acid-resistant tanks placed in series. Agitation is supplied by rubber-covered, cast-steel, turbine-blade paddles operated at the minimum speed required to maintain the ore particles in suspension. The flow pattern, which is established by entry of the pulp at the tank bottom and discharge to the next tank by gravity overflow, reduces short circuiting to a minimum.

The less amenable ores are fed to the first leach vessel and meet the more amenable ores at a point farther along in the process. Sulfuric acid and sodium chlorate are fed at both the first leach tank and the point of entry of the second ore stream. Acid addition in the amount of 150 to 500 lb per ton, depending on the ore composition, is controlled by free-acid concentrations at both points and at the end of the leach process, to maintain an average pH of 0.1 to 0.8. The oxidant (sodium chlorate) addition in the amount of 1 to 5 pounds per ton is controlled by the ratio of ferric-ferrous iron concentration at the last leach vessel.

Uranium minerals from the various ores are oxidized to the hexavalent state. If the ores contain vanadium, about 25 percent of it is solubilized.

Reduction of the ferric iron and precipitation of some heavy metals in the leach slurry is carried out in the final stage. Reduction is effected by adding flake sodium sulfide, with control established by ferric iron concentration.

11–4.5 Liquid-solids separation. Leached residues and heavy metal sulfides are separated from the uranium-bearing pregnant liquor by countercurrent decantation in four 70-foot-diameter washing thickeners. These are equipped with Type 316 stainless steel rakes. Underflow solids are pumped by Dorrco diaphragm pumps, with the final stage underflow going to tailings ponds.

To aid settling, Separan is added in each stage. The overflow from stage one, containing 1 to 1.5 g/liter U_3O_8, is pumped to storage to provide an even flow of feed either for the phosphate precipitation recovery procedure or for the newer solvent extraction process.

11–4.6 Uranium recovery. *Precipitation of uranous phosphate.* Uranium precipitation begins by reducing the uranyl sulfate to the uranous state with powdered aluminum. It is then precipitated as a phosphate by adding phosphoric acid. Reactions for this process are as follows:

$$3UO_2SO_4 + 2Al + 6H_2SO_4 \rightarrow 3U(SO_4)_2 + Al_2(SO_4)_3 + 6H_2O$$

and

$$3U(SO_4)_2 + 4H_3PO_4 \rightarrow U_3(PO_4)_4 \downarrow + 6H_2SO_4.$$

Reduction and precipitation are carried out in a series of acid-resistant tanks with mild agitation to ensure adequate mixing. In the final stage of this circuit, primary wash water from caustic upgrading, together with fresh sodium carbonate solution, is added for pH adjustment, to complete the precipitation.

Refining. The precipitated slurry is pumped through plate-and-frame filter presses; the barren liquor is disposed to ponds, carrying with it the solubilized vanadium. The recovered filter cake is treated by two hot caustic soda washes, and a final water wash. The upgraded product is finished by calcination in a multiple-hearth Skinner roaster. The following are suggested as possible reactions that occur during refining:

$$U_3(PO_4)_4 + 16NaOH + 20_2$$
$$\text{(air)}$$
$$\rightarrow 2Na_2UO_4 \downarrow + U(OH)_4 \downarrow + 4Na_3PO_4 + 8H_2O$$
$$\llcorner\rightarrow Na_2U_2O_7 + Na_2O$$

and upon calcination:

$$U(OH)_4 \cdot Na_2U_2O_7 \xrightarrow{1100\text{-}1500°F} U_3O_8 + Na_2O + 2H_2O.$$

The dried product from the calciner, with specifications of 75 percent U_3O_8, is packaged in barrels and then handled on a roll conveyor. Barrels are weighed, sampled, sealed, and stored in preparation for shipment. Each barrel is sampled by an electrically operated 1-inch auger bit, drilled at various points for the total depth of the drum. The drums are loaded onto a common carrier at the plant site for periodic shipment to the Atomic Energy Commission in Grand Junction, Colorado.

Solvent extraction. Vitro Uranium Company has recently (1957) installed a solvent extraction recovery circuit to replace the phosphate precipitation. The ferric ion concentration is reduced by treatment with sodium sulfide before solvent extraction to minimize the amount of iron taken into the organic phase. The solvent, dodecyl phosphoric acid (DDPA) in kerosene diluent, is stripped of uranium with hydrochloric acid; the hydrochloric acid is later recovered by evaporation. Precipitation of the evaporator bottoms by anhydrous ammonia yield a high-grade uranium concentrate.

The solvent (DDPA) is readily formulated from the raw materials, phosphorus pentoxide and dodecyl alcohol (2,6,8-trimethylnonanol-4). Reactions involved in preparing the solvent are

$$2\,ROH + P_2O_5 \rightarrow R\!-\!O\!-\!\overset{\displaystyle O}{\underset{\displaystyle OH}{\overset{\|}{P}}}\!-\!O\!-\!\overset{\displaystyle O}{\underset{\displaystyle OH}{\overset{\|}{P}}}\!-\!O\!-\!R$$

$$R\!-\!O\!-\!\overset{\displaystyle O}{\underset{\displaystyle OH}{\overset{\|}{P}}}\!-\!O\!-\!\overset{\displaystyle O}{\underset{\displaystyle OH}{\overset{\|}{P}}}\!-\!O\!-\!R + H_2O \xrightarrow[\Delta]{HCl} 2R\!-\!O\!-\!\overset{\displaystyle O}{\underset{\displaystyle OH}{\overset{\|}{P}}}\!-\!OH,$$

where "R" represents the dodecyl radical (2,6,8-trimethylnonanol-4). The solvent is prepared as a nominal 1 M solution and is diluted with kerosene to the operating concentration of 0.1 M.

Housed in a fireproof concrete and steel building, the plant is constructed of neoprene-covered steel tanks, neoprene-covered agitators, corrosion- and abrasion-resistant pumps, and appropriate process piping materials. Insofar as possible, instrumentation provides for automatic control.

As shown in the block flow diagram of Fig. 11–16, the solvent extraction plant is divided into 6 sections.

Extraction. Leach liquor from the countercurrent decantation step is fed to the solvent plant, where the solubilized uranium is extracted in four-stage countercurrent fashion. Intimate contact between the aqueous and organic phases is provided by Turbo-Mixers designed and located to provide a continuous organic phase. The feed ratio is 6:1, aqueous to organic. Phase separation is effected within each of the extractor vessels by maintaining constant inventories of each phase. Interface sensing elements actuate control valves on extractor underflows to maintain the desired inventories of each phase. Feed streams are automatically measured and controlled. The chemistry of the extraction procedure is believed to proceed as shown by the following equation:

$$UO_2SO_4 + 2R{-}O{-}\overset{\displaystyle O}{\underset{\displaystyle OH}{\overset{\|}{P}}}{-}OH \rightarrow$$

$$R{-}O{-}\overset{\displaystyle O}{\underset{\displaystyle OH}{\overset{\|}{P}}}{-}O{-}UO_2{-}O{-}\overset{\displaystyle O}{\underset{\displaystyle OH}{\overset{\|}{P}}}{-}O{-}R + H_2SO_4.$$

Solvent at concentrations of 0.1 M is highly selective for the uranyl ion. However, ferric iron is also strongly extracted, and there is some pickup of thorium and titanium.

Solvent stripping. Uranium is removed from the solvent in countercurrent fashion in five stages with strong hydrochloric acid. Stage contact between phases is provided by the mixer of each mixer-settler unit. The paddles also pump the mixed phase to the settler for phase separation. As in extraction, feed-stream control is maintained by automatic flow-indicator controllers that actuate control valves. Hydrochloric acid (10 N) is employed to provide the necessary hydrogen ion for organic regeneration. The following reaction is thought to take place during stripping:

$$R{-}O{-}\overset{\displaystyle O}{\underset{\displaystyle OH}{\overset{\|}{P}}}{-}O{-}UO_2{-}O{-}\overset{\displaystyle O}{\underset{\displaystyle OH}{\overset{\|}{P}}}{-}R + 2HCl \rightarrow 2R{-}O{-}\overset{\displaystyle O}{\underset{\displaystyle OH}{\overset{\|}{P}}}{-}OH + UO_2Cl_2.$$

Hydrochloric acid recovery. Evaporation and condensation effects additional concentration of the uranium and recovery of hydrochloric acid for recycle. Two-stage evaporation with a sulfuric acid scrubber is employed to recover 10 N HCl for recycle. Hydrochloric acid vapors from the first stage are passed directly to the condenser, with the bottoms providing the feed to the second stage. Vapors from the second stage are scrubbed with sulfuric acid to remove water, and then fed to the condenser. This circuit is controlled automatically to provide adequate quality of products.

Precipitation. Uranium-rich evaporator bottoms are cooled, diluted, and precipitated by neutralization with anhydrous ammonia in three stages. The precipitation circuit is automatically controlled to maintain proper pH in each tank. Although the chemistry of the process is not definitely established, the following equations are offered:

$$3UO_2Cl_2 + 8NH_3 + 7H_2O \rightarrow (NH_4)_2U_2O_7 \downarrow + U(OH)_6 \downarrow + 6NH_4Cl$$

and upon calcination:

$$(NH_4)_2U_2O_7 \cdot U(OH)_6 \xrightarrow{1112°F} U_3O_8 \downarrow + 2NH_3 \uparrow + 4H_2O \uparrow.$$

The precipitated slurry is dewatered with an Eimco 6 by 8-foot drum filter equipped with string discharge. The wet concentrate is discharged to a multiple-hearth Skinner roaster for calcination.

Completely dried concentrate is handled in the manner described previously. No provision is made for recovering vanadium.

11–5. Shiprock Uranium Mill*

11–5.1 Introduction. By 1953, uranium-vanadium orebodies developed in the Lukachukai Mountains of northern New Mexico necessitated the installation of a new uranium mill. Contract negotiations between Kerr-McGee Oil Industries and the Atomic Energy Commission for a 200-ton mill were completed in August of that year, and construction began in December. During construction, more ore was found in the area; therefore the contract was renegotiated to increase the capacity of the mill to 400 tons per day. This larger mill was in operation in November 1954. The process flowsheet for the crushing, grinding, and leaching operations is shown in Fig. 11–17. The flowsheet for ion exchange or solvent extraction operations for uranium recovery and the uranium precipitation operation is shown in Fig. 11–18.

---

* By J. E. Quinn, Denver Equipment Co., and W. C. Hazen and A. V. Hendrickson, Kerr-McGee Oil Industries, Inc.

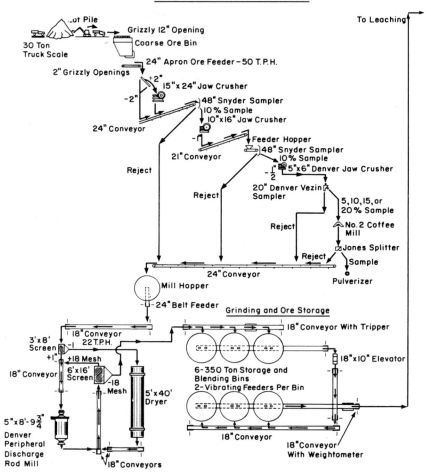

Fig. 11–17. Flowsheet of crushing, grinding, and leaching circuits in Shiprock mill.

The plant originally was designed to treat low-lime, high-vanadium ores from the Lukachukai Mountains. The process utilized, known as the "acid cure," had been developed for the most part by the Atomic Energy Commission to increase recovery of vanadium values. Briefly, it involved pugging the ore with 10 percent water and 400 to 500 pounds of concentrated sulfuric acid per ton of ore. The product was allowed to cure for 6 or more hours to convert the uranium and vanadium values into water-soluble salts. However, this process proved expensive because of high acid consumption and labor costs. With increased mill capacity, the char-

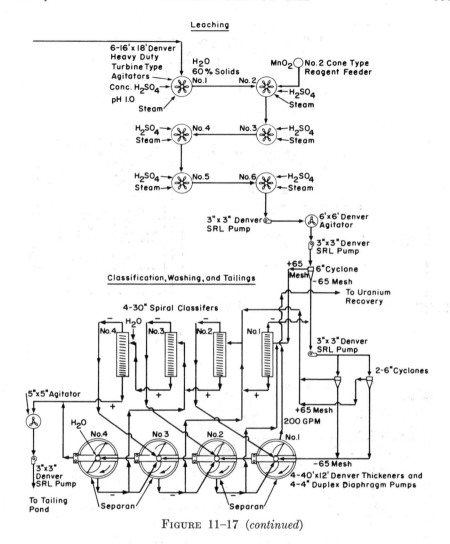

FIGURE 11–17 (*continued*)

acter of the ore feed from the new sources of supply changed to high-lime and low-vanadium content. Vanadium recovery was discontinued; the processing method was changed from "acid cure" to "raw leach," reducing processing costs to a minimum.

Other major changes have also been made in the method of extracting uranium and vanadium values from the pregnant solution. Kerr-McGee carried out the development work to apply solvent extraction to the Shiprock mill. Approximately 50,000 gallons of pregnant solution per day were treated in a batch pilot unit. In September 1956, a continuous solvent ex-

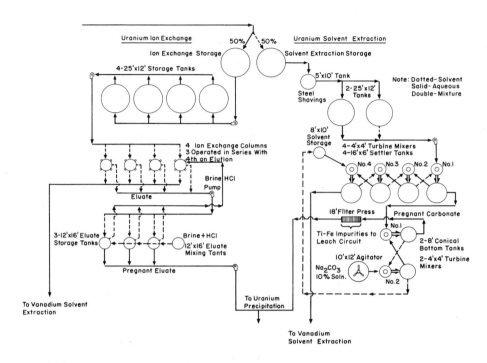

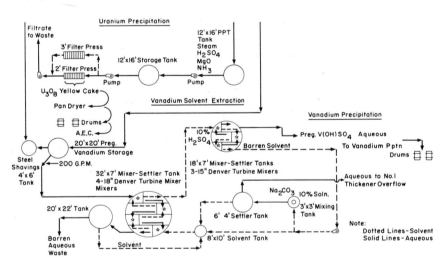

FIG. 11–18. Flowsheet of ion exchange, solvent extraction, and uranium recovery circuits in Shiprock mill.

traction unit, to treat 50 percent of the pregnant solution produced, was installed. The unit performed well, and has operated satisfactorily since that time.

The mill is located on the Navajo Indian Reservation just south of the town of Shiprock, New Mexico, on the banks of the San Juan River, approximately 30 miles from Farmington. Virtually all of the mill laborers, helpers, and some operators are Navajo Indians, well trained for their particular duties.

11–5.2 Mining. Ore assaying approximately 0.25 percent U_3O_8, slightly under 1 percent V_2O_5, and 6.5 percent $CaCO_3$ is received at the mill from company-owned and -operated mines and from custom ore suppliers. Virtually all the production from the company mines is carnotite-roscoelite ore from the Salt Wash of the Morrison formation. Deposits of ore occur in pockets; mining is by a modified room-and-pillar method. As new raises are driven, old rooms are worked out and the pillars are pulled on retreat. Spotty occurrence of the ore pockets makes it almost impossible to predict their size and location accurately, even with core drilling on close centers.

Ore is hauled to the mill by contract carrier. Fourteen-ton tandem trucks are used for the rugged trips from the mines to the mill.

11–5.3 Ore preparation. *Crushing and sampling.* Ore is trucked to the mill site, weighed, and grab sampled for moisture. Truckloads from each respective ore supplier then are dumped on a stock lot. After 150 to 200 tons of ore is accumulated, it is delivered to a 50-ton receiving hopper and passes through the crushing and sampling plant (Fig. 11–17). Ore is fed from the receiving hopper by a 24-inch apron feeder across a 2-inch grizzly, with the oversize being crushed in a 15 by 24-inch jaw-crusher. The minus 2-inch product is conveyed to a primary 48-inch Snyder sampler, where a 10 percent sample is taken and dropped by gravity through a 10 by 16-inch jaw-crusher for reduction to minus 1 inch. The crushed product is conveyed to a 48-inch Snyder sampler, where a 5 or 10 percent cut is made. The sample drops to a 5 by 6-inch Denver jaw-crusher for reduction to minus $\frac{1}{2}$ inch. The crushed product is passed through a 20-inch Vezin sampler capable of taking 5, 10, 15, or 20 percent samples, depending on the grade and quantity of ore. The sample is further reduced in particle size and quantity by means of a pulverizer, blender, and Jones-type splitter.

The crushing and sampling plant is operated five days a week on a two-shift basis. It is very compact, equipped with dust-collecting equipment, and designed so that all sample rejects join a common 24-inch conveyor and are delivered either to a mill storage bin or to a receiving hopper for haulage to the crushed-ore stockpile for blending or storage. The capacity of the plant is 50 tons per hour. Approximately 60 percent of the ore as received from the mines is minus 2 inches. This, together with the friability and softness of the ore, accounts for the fact that only primary jaw-crushing is required to prepare the material for rod mill feed.

Grinding. Crushed ore is fed from the mill storage hopper by a 24-inch belt feeder with a variable speed, rheostat-controlled drive. Controls are located at the rod mill so that the operator can regulate the feed rate as desired. The ore is conveyed to a 3 by 8-foot vibrating screen with 1-inch cloth. The plus 1-inch material, containing 3 to 4 percent moisture, is conveyed to the 5 by 8-ft-$9\frac{3}{4}$-inch Denver peripheral-discharge rod mill. The minus 1-inch material containing 8 to 10 percent moisture is fed to a 5 by 40-foot, direct-fired Standard Steel dryer for removal of moisture down to 3 percent. The dried product drops to an 18-inch conveyor and thence to the 18-inch rod mill discharge conveyor, which feeds the 6 by 16-foot vibrating screen. The screen, equipped with 18-mesh electrically heated cloth, operates in closed circuit with the rod mill. The minus-18 mesh product is conveyed to one of six 350-ton blending and storage bins, each of which is equipped with two vibrating feeders.

The minus 2-inch size feed to the rod mill is not detrimental. The rods are reversed periodically to minimize the tapering effect on the feed end. Rod consumption is 0.25 pound per ton and, at the time of this writing, the original liners were still in service after 3 years of operation. Feed to the grinding circuit is 25 tons per hour. The unit is operated on a three-shift basis. The rod mill consumes approximately 90 horsepower. Efficient wet dust collecting systems are installed throughout this section. Wet sludge is pumped to the leaching section.

Completed studies of wet grinding versus dry grinding show that both offer advantages, with wet grinding preferred. The mill now employs wet grinding.

11–5.4 Uranium extraction. Ore ground to minus-18 mesh and properly blended for uranium and lime content is fed to an 18-inch conveyor across a Weightometer at a rate of 22 tons per hour. A Denver automatic sampler provides a mill head sample. Water and concentrated sulfuric acid are added to obtain a pulp density of 60 percent of solids and a pH of 1.0. The agitation section consists of six 16 by 18-foot Denver heavy-duty agitators designed for 16-hour contact of the pump and equipped with 60-inch-diameter turbine-type propellers. Live steam is added to each unit to maintain 125°F pulp temperature. Flow through the units is in series, with one unit maintained as a standby. The No. 1 and No. 2 agitators operate at 73 rpm and draw approximately 13 horsepower. The remaining four units operate at 63 rpm and consume approximately 10 horsepower. The first two agitators are operated at higher speed to ensure that the coarse material stays suspended until the acid has had time to react and provide buoyancy to the slurry. Additional horsepower was provided in the design in case it was found that more power was required for extraction. At present, uranium extraction is 97 percent, and analysis indicates that 2 percent of the loss is in the plus-35 mesh fraction, indicating that finer grinding could increase extraction to 99 percent.

All units are mounted on the same level, with a common service walkway. Each tank overflows through a baffle box to eliminate short circuiting; each has an airlift to ensure removal of any coarse material that might accumulate in the bottom of the tank. Both the overflow and airlift discharge at 60 percent of solids. Pulp levels and launders are arranged so that in case of trouble any unit may be bypassed without shutting down the entire section. Superstructures are mounted directly on 4-inch-stave wood tanks. Wood-bottom wearing plates are provided. Bands are protected from corrosion by polyethylene and grooved staves. Tanks Nos. 1, 2, and 3 are covered and vented to carry off the acid and CO_2 fumes.

Units are designed so that a complete propeller assembly can be removed and replaced to minimize down time in the event of difficulty. To date, the units have been in operation 9 months and show only slight wear, even with the coarse ore. Propellers and shafts are rubber-covered, each with an Acme thread connection and seal for simplicity in propeller removal and replacement.

Additional sulfuric acid is added to the Nos. 2, 3, 4, and 5 agitators to maintain a pH of 1.0. Average total acid used is 200 pounds per ton of feed. Five pounds of MnO_2 per ton of ore is added to the No. 2 agitator as an oxidant to increase the uranium dissolution.

The agitator discharges to a 3 by 3-inch SRL pump which pumps to a 6 by 6-foot, Denver turbine-type agitator, where 1 pound of iron powder per ton of solids is added to reduce ferric to ferrous iron.

Liquid-solids separation. A sand-slime separation is made on the leached ore pulp by cyclone, with the plus-65 mesh sands being washed countercurrently in four 30-inch spiral classifiers, and the minus-65 mesh slimes washed in four 40 by 12-foot Denver thickeners. Sixty percent of the solids appear in the sand circuit, 40 percent in the slime. The slurry from the iron reduction agitator is delivered by a 3 by 3-inch SRL pump to a 6-inch cyclone. The minus-65 mesh slime and the No. 1 classifier overflow join and are pumped by a 3 by 3-inch SRL pump to two 6-inch cyclones in parallel. Sands from these cyclones drop to the No. 2 classifier, and the slime overflow, together with the No. 2 classifier overflow and part of the solution overflow from thickener No. 2, make up the feed to the No. 1 thickener. Thus, a portion of the thickener overflows are advanced from stage to stage via the sand classifiers. In this way the sands are washed with a minimum of dilution. Fresh water is added to No. 4 classifier and also to No. 4 thickener. The washed classifier sands go to final tailings.

A feed to the thickeners of 10 percent solids is desired. Separan is added to the thickeners at a rate of 0.10 pound per ton of solids. A portion of the thickener overflows is recycled to accomplish this. Centrifugal pumps elevate the thickener overflows and discharge them into baffled launders, where they mix with the thickener underflows, which are metered by 4-inch duplex diaphragm pumps. This aids in breaking up flocs and reduces soluble loss in the thickener circuit. It also disperses the settling agent better.

Clear uranium-vanadium pregnant solution overflows the No. 1 thickener at a rate of 200 gal/min. Uranium concentration is 1.0 g/liter.

The underflow from No. 4 thickener and the sands from the No. 4 classifier are blended in a 5 by 5-foot Denver heavy-duty agitator. A 3 by 3-inch SRL pump delivers the slurry at 40 percent solids through a 4-inch line a distance of 1500 feet to the tailings disposal area.

11–5.5 Uranium recovery. *Ion exchange.* As mentioned previously, 50 percent of the pregnant solution, which is the clear overflow from the No. 1 thickener containing both uranium and vanadium values, is pumped to a single set of four ion-exchange columns, each seven feet in diameter. The columns are operated with three in series receiving new feed, while a fourth is being eluted with brine and hydrochloric acid. Resin loading is normally slightly over 3 lb U_3O_8/ft^3.

Three-stage elution, employing about 5600 gallons per stage, is used to build up the uranium content of the eluate to 12 g/liter. Brine and hydrochloric acid are mixed in a propeller-agitated 12 by 16-foot tank producing a 0.9 M NaCl and a 0.2 M HCl solution. After the No. 1 feed column becomes loaded, eluate from the No. 1 storage tank is used to strip the freshly loaded column, becoming pregnant eluate, for precipitation. The resin is stripped further with eluate from No. 2 and No. 3 storage tanks, which then are advanced to the No. 1 and No. 2 tanks, respectively. Fresh brine and HCl are added to the No. 3 tank. After three-stage elution, the resin in the column is again ready to receive pregnant sulfate solution.

Solvent extraction. Process development. The process in the new solvent extraction plant utilizes di-2-ethylhexyl phosphoric acid in equimolar amounts with tributyl phosphate, both dissolved in a high-flash-point kerosene to a total nominal concentration of 3 percent. The uranium-laden solvent is stripped with a 10 percent sodium carbonate solution. The uranium-bearing carbonate liquor from the stripper is acidified, and the uranium is precipitated with ammonia or magnesia.

In determining the particular solvent to use, consideration was given to amines and to alkyl phosphates. The Oak Ridge "Dapex" process, using

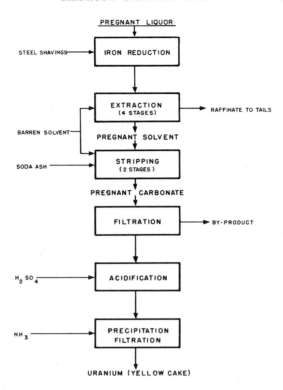

FIG. 11–19. Schematic flowsheet of solvent extraction process used at Shiprock mill.

di-2-ethylhexyl phosphoric acid, was chosen because it was suitable for the Shiprock feed liquors and the solvent was readily available commercially.

A schematic flowsheet of the process is shown in Fig. 11–19.

Reduction circuit. In the Dapex process the acid liquor must be relatively free of ferric iron, since this element is readily extracted under the conditions used for uranium recovery.

Ferric iron is reduced to ferrous by passing the acid liquor from the thickener overflow through a bed of scrap-steel shavings. These steel shavings are loosely packed to a depth of 6 feet in a 5-foot-diameter wooden tank having a false bottom. The solution flows into the bottom of the tank, rises upward through the steel shavings, and is reduced in this upward passage.

Provided that there are always enough shavings and that fine material does not clog the tank and cause channeling, the ferric iron is reduced easily and cheaply. It has been found by experience that if the liquors are reduced to an emf between −275 and −300 millivolts, substantially no iron is picked up in the solvent extraction circuit.

Extraction circuit. The extraction section is composed of 4 mixer-settlers arranged in a cluster, differing in elevation from one unit to the next by 12 inches, so that the aqueous phase flows by gravity. Solvent is transferred uphill from one stage to the next by airlifts. The design capacity of the extraction unit is for an aqueous flow of 120 gal/min, the quantity of pregnant liquor produced from 350 tons of ore per day. At this liquor capacity, the extraction system is designed for a maximum solvent flow of 40 gal/min.

Each mixer-settler stage comprises one 16-foot-diameter by 6-foot-deep wood-stave tank and a 4 by 4-foot stainless steel mixing tank placed on legs inside the settler, against the wall. The mixers were placed inside the settlers to facilitate piping, since connections between mixer and settler pass through holes cut in the wall of the mixer tank.

The mixers are agitated by 18-inch-diameter Turbo-Mixers with V-belt drives. Two of the four mixers operate at 150 rpm, and two at 200 rpm. Both speeds seem to give about the same performance.

The airlifts for advancing the organic phase are constructed of polyvinyl chloride plastic pipe and are set in each settler inside a plastic pipe "boot" into which the solvent overflows. The total height of organic in any settler can be raised or lowered easily by changing the position of this plastic boot. The aqueous phase flows from one settler into the succeeding mixer through a 6-inch-diameter flexible Carlon hose. Both aqueous and solvent flow are measured by recording rotameters. A schematic diagram of two stages of this four-stage unit is shown in Fig. 11–20.

Stripping circuit. The stripping circuit is composed of a two-stage mixer-settler, with the mixers outside the settlers and connected to them by piping. In this circuit the solvent flows by gravity, while the sodium carbonate stripping solution is advanced in countercurrent fashion by airlifts. All equipment in this part of the plant is built of mild steel, since the solutions are not corrosive.

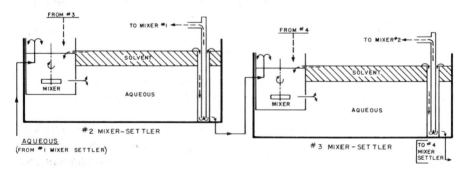

Fig. 11–20. Arrangement of mixer-settlers for extraction circuit in Shiprock mill.

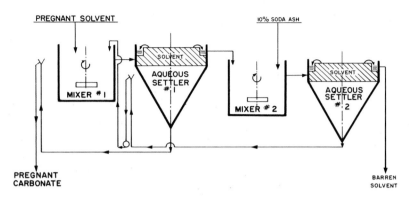

FIG. 11–21. Arrangement of mixer-settlers for stripping circuit in Shiprock mill.

Mixers are the same size as those used in the extraction circuit: 4 by 4 feet, equipped with 18-inch-diameter Turbo-Mixers. Steam coils made of three turns of 2-inch pipe are in each mixer.

The settlers are 8-foot-diameter cone-bottom tanks with internal launders for solvent overflow. Cone-bottom settlers are used because of the presence of small amounts of precipitates of titanium and iron hydroxides, or their basic carbonates, formed during stripping.

In operation of the stripping unit, the pregnant organic solvent from the first extraction-unit settler is pumped by a centrifugal pump to mixer No. 1, where it is agitated with the advancing carbonate liquor. Solution from the mixer flows by gravity to settler No. 1 where the phases separate, the organic overflowing by gravity to mixer No. 2, and the carbonate liquor (which contains some suspended solids) flows, via an underflow leg, to a pump and storage tank.

This pregnant carbonate liquor is pumped through a plate-and-frame press to remove suspended solids, and the clear filtrate is sent to the uranium precipitation circuit.

The 10 percent sodium carbonate solution is made up in a 5000-gallon agitated batch-tank from which it flows by gravity through a recording rotameter to the stripping circuit. A schematic flow diagram of the stripping circuit is shown in Fig. 11–21.

Operating results. The solvent extraction plant is simple to run—only one operator per shift is needed for extraction and stripping. A set of typical operating conditions are given in the following table:

Aqueous flow	100 gal/min
Solvent flow	20 gal/min
Aqueous feed analysis, emf	−300 millivolts

pH	1.3
Temperature	90°F
U_3O_8	1.4 g/liter
V_2O_5	0.6 g/liter
Sodium carbonate to strippers	2.5 gal/min
Stripping temperature	110°F

For long periods of time it has been possible to operate the solvent extraction unit with a tailing solution assay averaging less than 0.005 g U_3O_8/liter, corresponding to better than 99.7 percent recovery. During a period of stable operation, samples have been taken through the entire system and analyzed for uranium content. A typical set of such analyses is shown below:

	Organic phase U_3O_8, g/liter	Aqueous phase U_3O_8, g/liter
Extractor No. 1	8.95	1.27
No. 2	7.92	0.43
No. 3	2.29	0.023
No. 4	0.47	0.002
Stripper No. 1	0.37	55.6
No. 2	0.010	2.6

The consumption of reagents in this plant has been close to that predicted from laboratory work. It is as follows:

Iron for reduction	0.75 lb/lb U_3O_8
Sodium carbonate	2.0 lb/lb U_3O_8
Solvent loss	0.5 gal/1000 gal aqueous treated
Sulfuric acid to destroy carbonate	1.6 lb/lb U_3O_8
Ammonia for precipitation	0.15 lb/lb U_3O_8

The amount of iron required for reduction is a function of the properties of the leach solution, primarily, of the ferric iron content. Soda ash consumption can be reduced to close to theoretical amounts, but will depend, to some extent, on the titanium content of the feed liquor and on the care used in operating control.

Solvent losses given above were determined for the first 10,000,000 gallons of feed liquor treated in the plant. This loss occurs in two ways. The first is by the actual solubility of the solvent in the aqueous phase, and the second is the loss of organic carried out by the raffinate as small droplets. The solubility factor is rather small. Measurements of entrainment loss show that it accounts for at least half the total solvent loss, some of which would undoubtedly be prevented by a trap tank. Another possibility would be to operate the mixers with a continuous organic phase, by recycling solvent from the settlers back to the mixers. This has been found experimentally to decrease entrainment of solvent. Both alternatives are now under consideration for the Shiprock installation.

The cost given for sulfuric acid required to destroy the carbonate, and the ammonia required for precipitation of yellow cake, are for the amounts that would be required if the acid eluate from ion exchange were not mixed with the carbonate strip liquor.

The use of a high-flash-point kerosene as a diluent has been of great aid in processing because of the decreased fire hazard. The diluent used at Shiprock is a high-flash-point kerosene sold under the trade name "Napoleum 470."* It has a flash point of 160°F, compared with about 105°F for ordinary kerosenes available in the Shiprock area. The price is $18\frac{1}{2}$ cents per gallon delivered at Shiprock, but the relief from fire danger is well worth the extra cost.

One question always raised in discussing solvent extraction is that of emulsion formation. At Shiprock, the only problem of this sort has resulted from the graphite introduced into the system by the dissolution of a small amount of scrap iron present in the steel shavings. There is no clarification filter on the feed-liquor system, and graphite freed from the iron is carried into the first-stage extractor, where it enters the organic layer in the No. 1 mixer. In the plant design, provision was made to remove such solid material by filtering the solvent at periodic intervals. However, it has never been necessary to use this solvent cleaning equipment because of an unforeseen but fortunate circumstance. The graphite-stabilized clods of emulsion, which have been called "seaweed," float to the surface of the solvent in the settler instead of remaining at the interface as had been anticipated. These clods pass over the organic overflow and into the sodium carbonate stripping circuit. In the first stripping mixer this emulsion is broken. The solvent is released, and the solids drop out with the solid hydroxides and are removed in the by-product filter. In time this gummy material can cause trouble by plugging pipelines and pumps, but it is intended that a clarification filter will be installed on the feed liquor to eliminate the trouble at the source. In the meantime, no problems have been encountered by the presence of these "seaweed" clods.

Flow rates have been easy to maintain and control at any desired ratio. The control of interface levels has turned out to be no problem at all. The level of the aqueous phase in each settler is, of course, set by the height of the weir on the discharge pipe from that settler. The elevations of these

---

* A product of Kerr-McGee Oil Industries, Inc.

weirs were set by calculation when the plant was designed, and have not been altered.

The design of the settlers includes enough freeboard so that if the organic should stop flowing for any reason, such as airlift failure, there is room for the entire solvent excess to accumulate in any one settling tank. Thus it is impossible to spill solvent over the top of a settler.

Precipitation. The pregnant eluate and sodium carbonate solutions coming respectively from the ion-exchange and solvent extraction systems are combined in a 12 by 16-foot propeller-agitated tank. The pH is adjusted to 3.0 with sulfuric acid. Steam is added to bring the solution to the boiling point and drive off CO_2. MgO and NH_3 are added to precipitate uranium. Ammonia is cheaper, but MgO precipitates large crystals, making subsequent filtration easier.

The precipitated slurry is pumped to a 12 by 16-foot propeller-agitated holding tank and from there is sent to two 20-frame filter presses (one 24-inch, one 36-inch). Filtrate goes to waste, and the uranium concentrate drops to pan driers. After it is dried to 4 percent moisture, the "yellow cake," assaying 79 percent U_3O_8, is packed in drums and shipped to market.

11–5.6 Vanadium recovery by solvent extraction. The barren solution from the uranium ion exchange is passed through a 4 by 6-foot false-bottom tank containing steel shavings to reduce the ferric iron to ferrous, to an emf of -275 to -300 millivolts, for vanadium solvent extraction. It is combined with the barren solution from the uranium solvent extraction recovery system and stored in a 20 by 20-foot tank. The extraction system includes 4 vertical turbine mixers with 18-inch propellers and $7\frac{1}{2}$-hp motors. The stripping section includes 3 mixers with 15-inch vertical turbine propellers and 5-horsepower motors.

The extraction mixers are installed in a 32-foot-diameter by 7-foot-deep tank with three parallel partitions. Within each section is a mixer and settler chamber. The same design is employed in the stripping section, with a tank 18 by 7 feet. This arrangement reduced installation cost considerably, since little piping is required. The tanks have covers, so no building is needed.

The aqueous sulfate solution containing vanadium values is introduced to the No. 1 feed mixer and solvent (mixture of di-2 ethylhexyl phosphoric acid, tributyl phosphate, and kerosene) is introduced into the No. 4 mixer. The aqueous phase and the solvent travel countercurrently, with the pregnant solvent being removed from the No. 1 mixer-settler unit and the barren aqueous liquor being removed from the No. 4 settler unit and collected in a 20 by 22-foot tank.

The pregnant solvent then is introduced to the No. 1 mixer-settler unit of the stripping section, with 10 percent H_2SO_4 solution being introduced to the No. 3 mixer-settler unit for countercurrent operation. The vanadium values enter the sulfate solution, which is sent to the vanadium precipitation section.

The stripped solvent is pumped to an 8 by 10-foot solvent-storage tank and reused in the extraction section. Since a small amount of uranium is contained in the barren solvent, a 5 percent side stream of it is passed through a 3 by 3-foot mixer and 6 by 4-foot settler. A 10 percent solution of Na_2CO_3 is added to the mixer, and the carbonate aqueous liquor containing the small amount of uranium joins the No. 1 thickener overflow.

11–5.7 General information. Three 350-kilowatt generators, driven by natural-gas-fired water-cooled engines, furnish 3-phase 60-cycle power at 480 volts. Normal consumption is 700 kilowatts. Natural gas rated at 1000 Btu/ft^3 is available. A standby 85-kilowatt generator is available for emergencies.

A 150-horsepower water-tube boiler, fired with natural gas, supplies steam to the mill. A second 150-horsepower boiler is available for standby or peak loads. Boiler feed water is softened.

Water, which is pumped from the San Juan River, must be treated before use in the plant because of its high solids content—as much as 15 percent during runoff season.

The river pump delivers against a 110-foot head to a 30-foot Denver thickener. The pump is supended by cable and raised or lowered as the river level changes. Approximately 0.06 pound of Separan per ton of water is added to the thickener feed. The Separan is mixed in a 4 by 5-foot agitator, pumped to a 3 by 12-foot storage tank, and metered to the thickener by a $\frac{3}{4}$-inch diaphragm pump. Underflow from the thickener is metered back to the river by a 3-inch diaphragm pump. Overflow is pumped by a centrifugal pump to two 30 by 30-foot water-storage tanks at the mill site.

Water from the storage tanks is pumped at 85 psi through a 6-inch mill distribution line by a 4-inch centrifugal pump driven by a 25-horsepower motor. Opening a fire hose valve starts a standby gasoline-powered pump, available for emergencies.

11–6. Moab Mill of Uranium Reduction Company*

11–6.1 Introduction. The Moab mill of Uranium Reduction Company is on the Colorado River adjacent to the Government ore-buying station at Moab, Utah. The site was chosen principally because of the adequate water supply.

---

* Theodore Izzo and Lew Painter, Uranium Reduction Co., and Roman Chelminski, Knowles Associates.

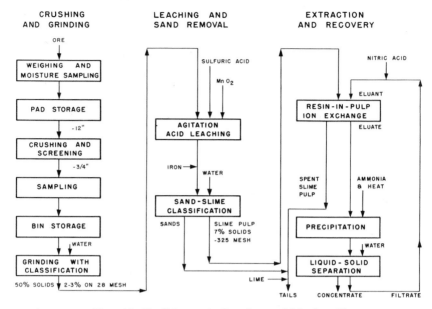

FIG. 11–22. Schematic flowsheet of Moab mill.

The hydrometallurgical process closely follows that used in the RIP (Resin-in-Pulp) pilot plant operated by the Atomic Energy Commission at Grand Junction. It comprises a sulfuric acid leach for dissolution, RIP ion exchange for extraction, nitrate elution of the resin, and ammonia with heat for precipitation of ammonium diuranate from the eluate. Resin-in-pulp was chosen over resin-in-column because of the poor filtration and thickening characteristics of the ores in the area.

The design capacity of the mill per 24-hour day is 1500 tons of ore containing 0.3 percent U_3O_8. Recovery of uranium from raw ore averages about 90 percent, and the concentrate contains about 75 percent U_3O_8. This gives a concentration ratio of 250 to 1. A schematic flowsheet of the process used is shown in Fig. 11–22. This mill serves the area in and around the Big Indian Wash area as shown on the map, Fig. 11-23.

11–6.2 Geology and mineralogy [1]. Most of the ore tributary to the Moab Mill comes from the Moss Back member of the Chinle formation in the Big Indian Wash area (Fig. 11–23). The largest of these deposits are found in the northern end of a mineral belt $\frac{1}{2}$ mile wide and 15 miles long. Nearly all deposits within this belt fall between 6200 and 6700 feet above sea level. They are elongated approximately parallel to the strike of the beds. The ore averages 8 feet in thickness.

The Moss Back host includes medium- and fine-grained sandstone, silt-

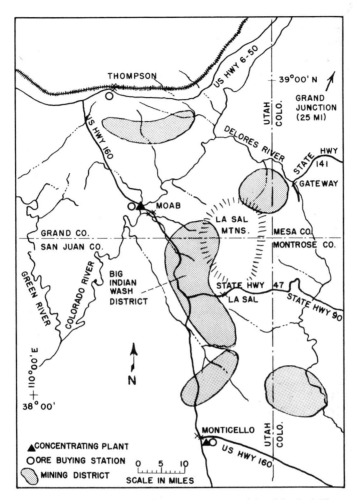

FIG. 11-23. Ore-producing area served by Moab mill.

stones and conglomerates. The conglomerates contain pebbles of mud-stone and limestone. The best ore is found in the sandstone, especially where it has a calcareous cement.

The dominant ore mineral is uraninite. The uraninite contains minute intergrowths of coffinite. Vanadium hydromica and montroseite are the main vanadium minerals. Some oxidized minerals have developed along, and adjacent to, joint surfaces. These include tyuyamunite, corvusite, and pascoite.

11-6.3 Ore preparation. *Receiving and storage.* At Uranium Reduction Company, the usual problems of custom mills are aggravated. For the most part, uranium producers ship in small lots, and weighing the ore alone becomes a big job. A 50-ton Fairbanks Morse scale with a 10 by 60-foot platform is located near the entrance gate. At the time of weighing, a sample of each load is taken for moisture content. Moisture analysis is carried out in a combination scale and wet sample house.

The costs of mine-run storage and handling are high. The variable nature of the ores requires blending to give a fairly constant feed. Therefore, lots of ore from each producer must be accumulated in separate stockpiles to make more economically manageable quantities. The production rates of some of the larger mines permit dealing with 1000-ton units, but the output of other mines must be handled in smaller batches.

Incoming trucks dump at a designated section on a 200-foot-diameter, 3000-ton capacity, concrete slab. Radial walls partition the sections. Later, a loader or bulldozer blend-feeds the ore to a 12-inch grizzly at the center of the pad. Below the grizzly is an 80-ton capacity steel bin from which a 48-inch belt feeder loads an inclined belt going to the crusher.

A schematic drawing of the crushing and grinding area, including the storage pad and the sampling tower, is shown in Fig. 11–24.

Crushing and sampling. A 36-inch-wide belt conveyor, equipped with a Stearns magnetic head pulley, carries the ore to a 24 by 36-inch Traylor Type H jaw-crusher, which is fed by a Tyler vibrating screen having a 5 by 12-foot rod deck with 2-inch openings. The minus 2-inch ore is conveyed by a 30-inch-wide belt from the jaw-crusher to a Norberg Symons $5\frac{1}{2}$-foot shorthead cone crusher, where it is further reduced in size to minus $\frac{3}{4}$ inch. The cone crusher operates in closed circuit with two 5 by 12-foot Tyler vibrating screens with $\frac{3}{4}$-inch openings which return the oversize to the cone crusher. The minus $\frac{3}{4}$-inch material is conveyed on a 24-inch belt over an automatic scale to the sampling tower.

In the sampling tower, the belt discharges into a Geary-Jennings sampler which splits out 10 percent of the ore stream. The remaining 90 percent is chuted onto another belt going to ten 300-ton storage bins. The 10 percent sample flows by gravity to a Syntron vibrating feeder and thence to a 20 by 24-inch Rogers Joplin roll crusher, where it is reduced to minus $\frac{1}{4}$ inch. Another 10 percent sample of the ore is taken by a second Geary Jennings sampler as it emerges from the roll crusher. The second sample cut passes through a 10 by 16-inch Denver roll crusher, the product of which is split by a third G-J sampler taking a 5 percent cut. The main streams from the second and third samplers are returned to the belt going to the storage bins.

The final sample (1 pound per ton of ore) is further processed by hand. It is first mixed in a 10-cubic-foot blender and then split in half on a Jones riffle. One-half is rejected; the other half is dried in a rotary drier and then ground in a coffee mill grinder. The fine material is mixed again in a 2-

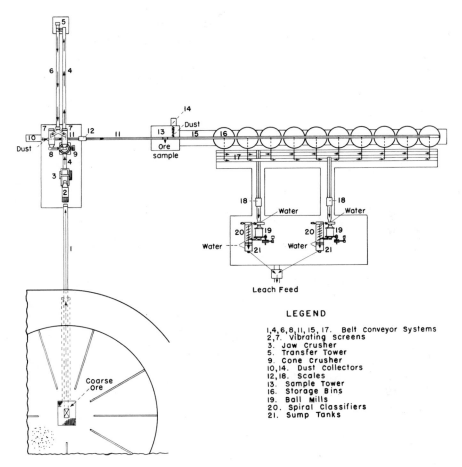

FIG. 11–24. Flowsheet of crushing, grinding, and sampling, Moab mill.

cubic-foot blender and riffled down to 10 pounds. The ground ore is pulverized to 100 mesh in two stages, with mixing and riffling after each stage to reduce the quantity to $2\frac{1}{2}$ pounds. This final sample is rolled out and split into five samples for distribution to the parties concerned.

Grinding. The chute and belt conveyor system between the fine-ore bins and the ball mills in the grinding circuit is designed to permit feeding from any bin into any ball mill. A 24-inch belt feeder at the base of each bin empties into a chute with two outlets permitting discharge onto either of two 24-inch cross-feed belts, each of which is made up of two sections of different lengths. The sections are arranged so that both cross-feed belts can discharge to either of two more 24-inch belts leading to the ball mills. The ore is weighed on these belts as they pass over automatic scales.

The ore is ground in two 7 by $7\frac{1}{2}$-foot Denver ball mills powered by 250-horsepower motors. The ball mills operate in closed circuit with two 78-inch Aikins spiral classifiers having $6\frac{1}{2}$ by $26\frac{3}{4}$-foot pools. The sands from the classifiers are returned to the ball mills for further grinding, and the slimes are pumped directly to the leach system by two Wilfley centrifugal sand pumps.

Dust control is an important economic and safety feature of the process from crusher to ball mill. The fines in some uranium ores present a dust problem, particularly in the crushing section of the mill. All equipment in the crushing plant is hooded, and dust vents are provided at the sampler- and chute-discharge points in the sampling tower, and at other necessary points in the bin structure. Dust from the crushing operation is drawn into a three-unit Western Precipitation Dualaire dust collector bearing the size designation 4-20-26, equipped with a 21,000 ft^3/min Sturtevant fan and a dust-return screw conveyor. A similar unit is provided in the sampling tower.

11–6.4 Uranium extraction. The uranium ore is leached in two circuits each containing five mechanically agitated tanks, as shown in the first part of the flowsheet in Fig. 11–25. Leach feed pulp, sized at 2 to 3 percent on 28 mesh, is pumped from the grinding section at 50 percent solids. The tanks are 24 feet in diameter by 14 feet high, and are neoprene-lined, with brick bottoms. Each tank is equipped with three high-speed agitators; 54-inch Desco impellers with alternately pitched curved blades are used in the first two tanks, and Turbo Simplex units are used in the other eight. The piping is arranged so that any tank in either circuit can be by-passed for repairs.

Sulfuric acid is pumped from two 40-foot-diameter by 22-feet-high, 1100-ton storage tanks to the first leach tank in each circuit. If necessary, acid can be added to the second tank to maintain a pH of about 1 in the pulp discharge. Acid consumption varies widely, depending on the $CaCO_3$ content of the ore, but averages very close to 27 pounds per ton of ore for each 1 percent of $CaCO_3$ present.

Depending on the type of ore being processed, enough manganese dioxide is added to the first or second tank to maintain an emf of -400 to -500 millivolts. This usually requires from 5 to 10 pounds of commercial grade MnO_2 (80 to 85 percent MnO_2) per ton of ore.

11–6.5 Sands separation. The leach discharge flows to two drag-classifier sections, as shown in the flowsheet of Fig. 11–25. There are eight $7\frac{1}{2}$ by 17-ft Knowles-designed rubber-lined drag classifiers in each section, arranged in two parallel lines of four classifiers in series. The ore is moved through these units by two sets of 38-inch-long stainless steel blades mounted on two parallel rubber belts. The overflow from the first

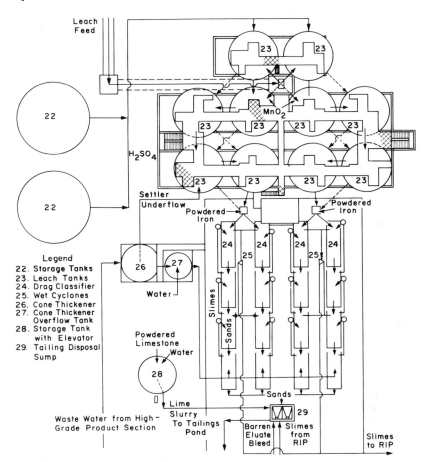

Fig. 11–25. Flowsheet of uranium leaching section, Moab mill.

classifiers in each leach section is pumped to a bank of three 14-inch Knowles-designed rubber-lined wet cyclones in parallel. The overflow from the cyclones is pumped to a second, identical bank of cyclones. The underflow from both cyclone banks is returned to the third classifiers in each section. The overflow from the second cyclone bank, containing about 0.67 g U_3O_8/liter, goes to the RIP feed tanks, after passing through 35-mesh screens to remove any trash.

The sands leave the fourth classifier and go to the tailings sump, where powdered limestone slurry is added to neutralize the acid. Spent slimes from the RIP circuit are also returned to this sump for neutralization, and the combined tailings are pumped to a pond. The limestone required to neutralize tailings varies from 40 to 100 pounds per ton of ore processed.

Part of the wash water for the classifiers is supplied by the waste water from the high-grade product section, described later. This water is settled in an 18-foot-diameter cone thickener from which the underflow is returned to one of the leach tanks to prevent loss of uranium values. The thickener overflow goes to an 11-foot-diameter tank, where water is added to make up the required volume of wash. The wash water is pumped to the fourth classifier in each series.

11–6.6 Uranium recovery. *Resin-in-pulp ion exchange.* The anion exchange is done in open rectangular tanks in which wire-screen baskets holding resin are moved up and down through a pregnant slime pulp. For proper mechanical and metallurgical performance, the feed pulp may not contain over 7 percent solids which must be essentially all minus-325 mesh. The pulp is maintained at a pH of 1.6 ± 0.1. As a result of this high dilution requirement, the water used in the classifier circuit is 4 to 5 tons per ton of ore. The actual dilution requirement is determined by the slime content of the ore. The resin used is Rohm & Haas Co.'s Amberlite XE-123, a strong-base (quaternary amine) anion-exchange type of a large bead size (about plus-20 and minus-10 mesh) especially manufactured for the RIP process. The flowsheet for the RIP section is shown in Fig. 11–26.

When the resin has been loaded to capacity, pulp flow is cut off, the pulp is drained, and the resin is washed with water to cleanse it of pulp. Elution is accomplished with a nitrate solution.

During each step of the cycle the resin remains in its stainless steel basket. The dilute pulp, wash water, and eluate are pumped successively into the tank which holds the basket of resin, and after an appropriate contact time are drained out again.

Flow through the 14 "banks" in each of the two circuits is in series, with airlifts being used to transfer pulp and solution from one bank to the next. At any given time, some of the banks (11) are loading in series; the others are being eluted. An advance or "changeover" occurs every $1\frac{1}{4}$ to 2 hours, depending on the rate of production and grade of ore. Countercurrent flow is practiced, with the pulp flow arranged so that the most freshly regenerated bank is the last loading bank. Likewise, the last bank in the eluting circuit is the most fully loaded bank, having just come off loading.

Loading is continuous. The contact or "retention" time is about 100 minutes—the time elapsed from the moment a given element of pulp enters the first bank until it leaves the last. The time interval between changeovers is preset to produce a calculated loading on the resin. The loading obtained is generally in the range of 2.5 to 3.5 pounds U_3O_8 per cubic foot of resin, depending on a variety of factors, all of which may have an important influence on the ion-exchange resin performance. Some of these

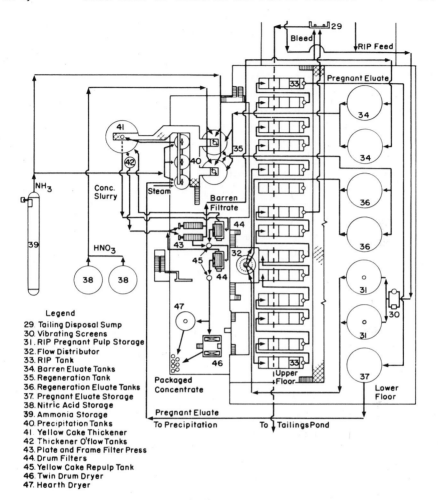

Fig. 11–26. Flowsheet of resin-in-pulp uranium recovery, Moab mill.

factors are number of banks on loading cycle, grade and pH of pregnant pulp, viscosity of pulp, rate of plant feed, condition of resin (poison content, etc.), and condition of basket screens.

To obtain maximum recovery of values with maximum loading of the resin, careful and frequent sampling of the ion-exchange circuit are required.

"Poisons" (strongly held ions) gradually build up on the resin and cut its capacity to absorb unranium. The principal poison is molybdenum, which is readily removed from the resin by a wash with a solution containing 2 percent NaOH and 2.5 percent $NaNO_3$.

Each resin basket is a cube 6 feet on a side and holds 45 cubic feet of resin. There are four in each bank. The screens are made of Type 316 stainless steel, and have approximately 50 mesh openings per inch. Agitation of baskets is done carefully to prevent blinding of screen and packing of beads. Experience at Moab has established a frequency of 11 strokes per minute with an amplitude of 12 inches as best. It is difficult to estimate resin wear, particularly as this factor is overshadowed by occasional screen breakage which results in resin escape from the circuit. To eliminate resin losses from this source, vibrating screens are employed on all effluent lines from the ion-exchange circuit. They have proved very effective in trapping resin. Also, resin appearing on one of these screens gives warning of a break or hole in a basket.

Elution is a cyclic, rather than a continuous, operation. The water wash given the bank just coming off loading takes about 30 minutes, involving dumping of feed, filling with water, agitation-washing for 5 minutes, dumping, water-spray rinse for 10 minutes, and a final dumping. All runoffs are returned to the feed pulp tank. Elution is done with agitation at the same rate as in loading. A measured volume of eluant solution is used per bank. The quantity is determined so that 99 percent of the uranium is eluted from the resin; the resultant pregnant eluate contains about 8 g U_3O_8/liter. The eluant is a 1 M mixture of ammonium nitrate and nitric acid.

Precipitation. Precipitation of uranium salts is done continuously. The eluate is heated with steam to about 140°F and then neutralized with ammonia in three steps, at pH 3.8, 4.6, and 7.0. The resultant slurry goes to a thickener, the overflow of which is filtered in plate-and-frame filters. The filter cake rejoins the final product stream at the first repulp (mentioned below), and the filtrate is cooled in a flash cooler and regenerated to eluant by the addition of nitric acid.

The thickener underflow is pumped to two drum filters in series, with mechanical repulp between them to wash out unwanted salts. The first filtrate is returned to the thickener; the second filtrate discarded to tailings.

Cake from the second drum filter is pugged with enough water to permit pumping to a Skinner roaster for drying before packaging for shipment. The roaster permits upgrading of the yellow cake to 76 percent U_3O_8 by calcination at 450°F, which drives off ammonia and water of crystallization.

11–7. SOUTH AFRICAN URANIUM MILLS

11–7.1 Historical development [2]. The existence of uranium in the gold ores from the Witwatersrand was first made known in a paper by R. A. Cooper which was read before a meeting of the Chemical, Metallurgical, and Mining Society of South Africa in October 1923. However, the fact aroused little interest until the discovery of the fission chain reaction and the development of the atomic bomb. In response to the sudden demand for fissionable materials required in the manufacture of the bomb, a world-wide search for the raw materials was started in 1944. The Combined Development Agency was set up by the governments of the United States and Great Britain to find uranium for the nuclear programs of both countries.

American geologists reported to the United States Government that radioactive minerals were present in the Witwatersrand ores and gold slimes. Accordingly, both American and British authorities approached the South African Government in 1945 about the possibility of extracting uranium from the ores.

The South African Government became keenly interested, and set about determining the magnitude of the Witwatersrand uranium deposits and how these deposits could best be developed. In the course of this work, over 400,000 samples sent by the various mining companies to the Geological Survey were tested for uranium by Geiger counter to assess the potentialities of the mines.

A Government committee started an investigation into methods of treating South African ores for uranium recovery. Similar research programs were initiated in England at the Chemical Research Laboratory at Teddington, and in the United States at the Massachusetts Institute of Technology and elsewhere.

In considering the recovery of uranium from gold ores, the first thought was to reduce the quantity of material that would have to be leached with sulfuric acid. Accordingly, initial research efforts were devoted to the study of gravity and flotation methods of concentration. When it became apparent that maximum recovery of uranium was the most important goal, regardless of increased costs, flotation work was discontinued and research on leaching of the total ore was started. A variety of ores from many different mines were processed in the laboratory, and high recoveries were obtained from a sufficient number of these to justify the erection of two acid-leach pilot plants—one at Blyvooruitzicht, the other at Western Reefs. These plants were operated satisfactorily for about three years until, in 1953, commercial plants at these same sites came into production.

After preliminary discussions in 1949, the South African Atomic Energy Board reached an agreement in 1950 for the production of uranium oxide in South Africa for sale to the United States and Great Britain. It was agreed that the capital required to install uranium plants and pyrite recovery and sulfuric acid plants required would be lent by the purchasers of the uranium output, subject to repayment during the 10-year period of the purchasing contract. Production was to be commenced with the least possible delay.

11–7.2 Geology and mineralogy. In the Witwatersrand district, uranium occurs primarily in the form of uraninite grains in a quartzitic matrix, in which are embedded round, quartz pebbles in closely packed array. The matrix also contains other recoverable values: gold, silver, osmiridium, and pyrite. The matrix and the pebbles make up a conglomerate, which exists in thin layers or "reefs" separated by layers of quartzites or shales. The shales, like the pebbles in the conglomerate, contain no recoverable values.

The Witwatersrand geological system comprises a number of reefs situated at various depths below the surface. Listed in descending order, they are as follows:

Elsburg Reefs	Johnstone Reef
Kimberley Reefs	Main Reef Series
Bird Reef Series	Carbon Leader
Monarch Reef	Government Reef Zone
White Reef	Dominion Reef Series
Livingstone Reef	

Western Reefs is the only mine operating on the Elsburg Reef, while both Daggafontein and Vogelstruisbult are extracting uranium from ore from the Kimberly Reefs. The ore from the Bird Reef series, though low in gold content, is being mined for its relatively high uranium content by East Champ d'Or, West Rand Consolidated, Luipaards Vlei, and Randfontein Estates. A large number of companies are mining the Monarch Reef, which is also known as the Vaal Reef in the Klerksdorp district, and as the Basal Reef in the Orange Free State. Among the companies that are, or will be, mining these reefs are New Klerksdorp, Freddies Consolidated, Western Reefs, Western Holdings, Stilfontein, Vaal Reefs, President Brand, President Steyn, Harmony and Virginia, Welkom, Free State Geduld, and Ellaton. The Livingstone and Johnstone reefs are of little importance in the uranium industry. The next important stratum is the Carbon Leader at the bottom of the Main Reef series, from which both gold and uranium are being taken by Doornfontein, West Driefontein, and Blyvooruitzicht. The Government Reef Zone, below the Main Reef Series, has two active uranium mines, one at Babrosco and one in the Afrikander Lease areas. At the lowest level is the Dominion Reefs mine, which obtains uranium from the Dominion Reef series.

All the reefs in the Witwatersrand contain uranium to some extent, but in some the uranium content is not high enough to make its recovery economical. In the area between Roodepoort and Springs there are large quantities of residues from gold-mining operations that have little or no uranium value. There appears to be no relationship between the gold and uranium content of the various reefs, but there is some indication of an association of uranium with a carbonaceous material known as thucholite, a name derived from the initials of the five predominant elements in the material—thorium, uranium, carbon, hydrogen, and oxygen. In addition to these elements, thucholite also contains rare earth oxides and silica.

11–7.3 Metallurgical practice. The technology of the South African uranium mills is strongly influenced by the gold-mining industry, which is still the primary industry in that area. Ores are selected for milling on the basis of their gold value and, in most cases, are processed for gold recovery before being sent to the uranium mill. Thus, the uranium mill feed may be one of three types: newly mined ore, fresh slimes from the gold mills, or reclaimed slimes from old slime dams. The uranium content of the various feeds is highly variable, which makes it difficult to control the level of the uranium values entering the uranium plants.

The residues from the gold mills contain about 50 percent by weight of cyanide-lime solution having some dissolved gold values. It had been standard practice to recover part of this solution by decantation from the slime dams. To preserve this practice, the first step in the uranium recovery process is to filter the gold residues on nonacid rotary filters. This step serves a fourfold purpose:

(1) It recovers part of the lime, cyanide, and gold for reuse in the gold plant.

(2) It reduces sulfuric acid consumption in the uranium, and removes the danger of generation of HCN.

(3) It removes salts such as cobalticyanide, which would poison the ion-exchange resins in the uranium plant.

(4) It dewaters slimes reclaimed by hydraulicking of old slime dams.

The filtered residue is then passed through a three-stage process in which the uranium is dissolved, the uranium-bearing solution is separated from the solids, and the uranium is recovered from the solution. The uranium is dissolved in rubber-lined Pachuca tanks. The filtered residue is repulped with the weak acid filtrate, from a secondary acid filtration stage (to be described later), and is pumped to the Pachucas, where it is mixed with the required amount of strong sulfuric acid and manganese dioxide. Most of the uranium is dissolved after about 16 hours of air agitation in the presence of ferric sulfate, which is obtained mainly by the action of the sulfuric acid on the particles of steel balls and linings worn from the grinding mills of the gold plant. Heat is usually applied to aid in dissolving the uranium.

The leach pulp is next subjected to a two-stage filtration on acid-resistant, rotary filters, with the primary filtrate going to the uranium recovery section. The cake from the primary filters is repulped with weak acid and is agitated for about 5 hours more before being filtered again. The secondary filtrate is returned to the Pachucas, as mentioned previously, to repulp the cake from the nonacid filters. The secondary filter cake is repulped with water and is either processed for the recovery of pyrite before being discharged to a slime dam, or pumped directly to the slime dam. Filter aids, usually liquid glue, are added to the Pachucas just before the primary filtration step.

Uranium is recovered from the pregnant solution by passing the solution through columns containing ion-exchange resins, after it has first been clarified on sand filter beds. The uranium, plus a small amount of iron, is absorbed and retained by the ion-exchange resins; the barren effluent is passed on to the manganese recovery section. Here the pH of the liquor is raised in two steps, first to 4.5 and then to 9.0, by adding ground limestone. At pH 4.5 ,the iron is precipitated, removed by thickening and filtration, and discharged to the slime dam. At pH 9.0, the manganese is precipitated in the hydroxide form, the slurry is thickened, and the underflow is pumped to a storage dam, where the oxidation to manganese dioxide is completed. The manganese dioxide returned to the uranium mill from the storage dam amounts to about half that required in the initial leach stage.

The uranium and iron are eluted from the loaded resin with a nitric acid-nitrate salt solution, and the iron is precipitated by adding ground limestone to a pH of 7. The iron hydroxide slurry is thickened, filtered, and returned to the primary Pachucas to avoid losing the soluble uranium values in the wet cake. The uranium is precipitated as ammonium diuranate from the iron-free liquor by the use of ammonia. After thickening and filtration, the uranate wet cake is sent to a central calcining works, where it is converted to uranium oxide, sampled, and packaged. The liquor from the uranium thickener and filter is fortified with additional nitric acid and nitrate salt, and is returned to the ion-exchange columns for reuse in the elution step.

11–7.4 Sulfuric acid production. Among the solvents considered for use in the South African uranium mills were sodium carbonate, nitric acid, and hydrochloric acid, in addition to sulfuric acid. Sodium carbonate was rejected because there were technological difficulties to be faced in the oxidation of uranous salts in carbonate solutions, and because carbonate was in short supply in that area. Costs were prohibitive for nitric acid, or for a hydrochloric acid-oxidant system. Sulfuric acid was selected because there was an adequate supply of pyrite in the gold ores, from which the acid could be made, and because with a suitable oxidizing agent, it was capable of handling the lower oxides of uranium. Manganese dioxide, occurring naturally in abundant supply in Africa, and ferric sulfate, available from pyrite by the autooxidation process, were both considered for use as the oxidant. Early preference was given to a double-leach process utilizing ferric sulfate and sulfuric acid; however, it was soon found that certain design considerations favored the use of manganese dioxide. Finally, the recommendation was made that contact plants be erected to produce sulfuric acid to be used in combination with manganese dioxide.

11–7.5 The Daggafontein Mill [3].* *Introduction.* Daggafontein was the first company in the Anglo-American group to produce uranium from residual gold slime; it is one of the largest producers in South Africa. Its uranium extraction and sulfuric acid units, costing $11,000,000, began operation in early 1953. In 1954, estimated profits from the sale of uranium and sulfuric acid totaled $4,000,000 and these increased to $4,700,000 the following year.

Feed for the uranium plant comes from three sources: the final concentrates from pyrite flotation in the South gold plant, which is a product of both recovered and current slime from the South reduction plant; current slime from the North gold reduction plant; and recovered slime from the dams of the North reduction plant. They are approximately in the following amounts:

	Dry tons/ month	*Percent solids*
Reclaimed slime from North plant	15,000	45
Current slime from North plant	90,000	50
Concentrates from South flotation plant	15,000	40

The flowsheet for the uranium mill is shown in Fig. 11–27. The general flow of materials at Daggafontein Mines is illustrated in Fig. 11–28.

The three feeds are blended in an elevated mild steel tank, 50 feet in diameter by 12 feet high. Mixed feed has a solids content of approximately 50 percent. The feed includes, in addition to the pulp (which contains the small percentage of uranium), large amounts of water used in hydraulicking old slime dams, and cyanide and lime solution. Pulp is separated from these by nonacid rotary filters. In removing the lime and cyanide before

---

* Abridged from Vol. 49, p. 1, January, 1957, of *Industrial and Engineering Chemistry.* Copyright 1957 by the American Chemical Society, and reprinted by permission of the copyright owners.

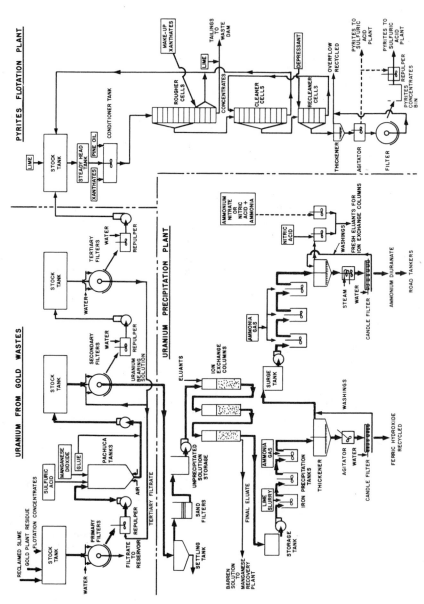

FIG. 11-27. Flowsheet of uranium mill at Daggafontein Mines.

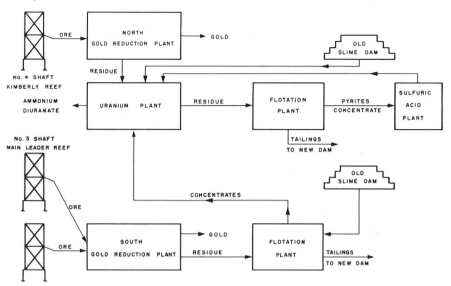

Fig. 11–28. General flow of materials at Daggafontein Mines gold and uranium plants.

the pulp is dissolved, acid consumption is decreased. In addition, certain salts, chiefly cobalticyanides, and sulfur compounds are removed that would otherwise seriously poison ion-exchange resins used in recovering the uranium.

Blended slime from the main stock tank (specific gravity, 1.4) flows by gravity to one of 8 nonacidproof rotary drum filters, 14 by 16 feet, constructed of mild steel. These primary filters are arranged in two rows of four each with a 42-inch belt conveyor traveling between the two rows. Filters are equipped with fitted floats for the automatic control of the pulp level in filter pans. Suction is supplied by a battery of four 31 by 13-inch vacuum pumps with capacity of 2800 ft^3/min, driven by 100-horsepower motors. Air for blow-off is supplied by low-pressure compressors delivering air at pressure of 10 psi. Filter cloths are scrubbed every third day with a weak hydrochloric acid solution by rotary brushes turning at 130 rpm. Cloth life is about 80 days.

A fresh-water wash is applied to filter cake to remove the compounds previously mentioned. Filters reduce the water content of cake to approximately 24 percent, filtrate being pumped to a reservoir for reuse. The cake must be repulped before adding acid to dissolve the uranium. It is carried by conveyor to a rubber-lined, twin-impeller, mechanically agitated repulper. Dilute sulfuric acid solution (filtrate from tertiary rotary filters later in the process) is added to the repulpers in sufficient amount to lower the solids content to 60 to 65 percent.

Extraction. The repulped material, containing a minimum of harmful impurities, is now ready for dissolution of its uranium content. It is pumped to a series of 10 rubber-lined Pachuca leaching tanks, 45 feet in over-all height and 22½ feet in diameter, the lower section being an inverted cone. Tanks are air-agitated with 35 to 40-psi air supplied by 3 high-pressure compressors. Approximately 0.70 ft^3/min of air is used for each ton of dry solids.

To the Pachucas are added acid, manganese dioxide (which serves as an oxidant), and animal glue. Sulfuric acid (99 percent) from 1000-ton storage tanks, supplied by Daggafontein's own acid plant, is fed through a rotameter from a steady head tank to the first Pachuca in series. Approximately 50 pounds of acid (100 percent basis) is used per ton of pulp. Manganese dioxide is metered as a water slurry (specific gravity, 1.4), at the rate of 12 pounds of manganese dioxide per ton of solids, through a splitter-box to the second Pachuca in series. Slurry is prepared from pyrolusite ore containing 35 to 45 percent MnO_2, which is first ground in a ball mill (6½-foot diameter by 8 feet) to 72.5 percent minus-200 mesh. About 90 percent of the uranium in the original ore is leached from the pulp in the Pachucas.

It is necessary to have an oxidant present in addition to free sulfuric acid to dissolve uranium in the uranous form. Free iron, present from wear of grinding balls in ball and tube mill, reacts with sulfuric acid in the presence of manganese dioxide to form ferric sulfate, thus assisting excess MnO_2 in its role as oxidant of uranium.

The order of adding acid and manganese is important. The ore contains reducing compounds, such as iron sulfide and metallic iron, which, when acid is added, generate hydrogen sulfide and hydrogen gas. If the oxidant were added at same time as acid, the reducing gases would consume a major part of the oxidant. Manganese dioxide is thus added several hours after the acid, so that all reducing gases formed by adding acid to pulp are evolved and removed.

The delay in adding the oxidant reduces the consumption of acid by 3.5 pounds and of manganese dioxide by 3.1 pounds per ton of solids. The removal of the reducing gases facilitates the development of optimum oxidizing conditions which, on the average, is promoted by adding about 10 pounds per ton of solids.

The pulp is agitated in the Pachucas for 16 to 18 hours, by which time all uranium that can be economically recovered is in solution. Approximately 0.5 to 1 hour before filtration of the leached pulp, animal glue (10 percent solution) is metered by gravity into the pulp at a rate of 0.45 pound per ton of ore. The glue serves as a filtering aid; the timing for its addition is important, since the maximum rate of filtration occurs within 0.5 to 1.5 hours after it has been added.

Reactions in the Pachucas can be shown by the following equations:

$$2FeSO_4 + MnO_2 + 2H_2SO_4 \rightarrow Fe_2(SO_4)_3 + MnSO_4 + 2H_2O,$$

$$U_3O_8 + 2H_2SO_4 + 2Fe^{+++} \rightarrow 3UO_2^{++} + 2SO_4^{--} + 2Fe^{++} + 2H_2O,$$

$$UO_2^{++} + 3SO_4^{--} \rightleftarrows UO_2(SO_4)_3^{-4}.$$

Effective operation of the entire uranium plant depends on proper control of the leaching process. Unusual care must be directed to leaching in this plant because of the three varying feeds, which require varying quantities of acid. Strength of the residual acid in the leach tanks must range from 4 to 6 g/liter—a compromise between two opposing factors. The free acid must not drop lower because, at lower concentrations, polythionates increase and poison the ion-exchange resins. At higher concentrations the absorption of uranium on the resins is affected adversely.

Control of leaching is maintained by the following tests:

(1) Free-acid content every hour in 1st, 3rd, and final Pachucas.

(2) Titrations for ferric and ferrous iron content at the same points.

(3) Daily check on leach liquor for polythionates (concentration is kept below 40 mg of sulfur, as S_4O_6, per liter, since column efficiency in the ion-exchange plant is seriously affected if a content of 60 mg per liter is reached).

Pressure leaching—in which an aqueous pulp is treated with air or oxygen at elevated temperatures and pressures—has been tested by the Central Metallurgical Laboratory of the Anglo-American Corporation of South Africa, Ltd., with complete success. Pilot-plant operations are now projected to investigate corrosion problems, to determine the most satisfactory method of transferring abrasive and corrosive pulps at high temperatures and pressure, and to solve the difficulties of heat transfer.

Liquid-solids separation. The next step is to separate the uranium solution from the leached pulp. From the Pachucas, pumps delivering 640 gal/min convey the mixture (specific gravity, 1.66) through 8-inch rubber-lined pipe to a rubber-lined elevated stock tank, 50 by 12 feet. There is a 1.5 to 2-hour delay in this tank, again emphasizing the importance of correctly timing the glue addition. The pulp flows by gravity from the tank to a group of eight 14 by 16-foot rotary vacuum filters, arranged in two rows of four filters each. A 48-inch belt between the two rows receives the filter cake.

Vacuum is supplied by a battery of 5 pumps. The wash applied is generally from the tertiary filters. The filtrate, or pregnant solution, containing the dissolved uranium is pumped to a settling tank in the precipitation plant, where the uranium is recovered. Blow-off pressure on these filters is 4 to 5 psi and the average life of filter cloth is 60 days.

Filtering efficiency of the secondary filters is 75 percent, leaving a significant quantity of uranium in the cake. This is recovered by tertiary filters.

Cake is diluted in a rubber-lined repulper to 55 to 65 percent solids by adding water. Repulped material is pumped to a rubber-lined elevated stock tank, with a retention time of 1.5 to 2 hours, and flows by gravity to a group of eight 14 by 16-foot rotary vacuum filters. These are of stainless steel and rubber construction, similar to the secondary filters, and are similarly arranged.

A 48-inch belt conveyor carries the cake from these filters to a repulper, where it is again diluted to approximately 63 percent water content. This cake, containing the pyrite, is pumped to a 50 by 12-foot elevated stock tank in the flotation section, where its pyrite content is concentrated for use in the sulfuric acid plant.

The filtrate from the tertiary filters is pumped to a rubber-lined storage tank and is used for dilution in primary repulper and for acid wash on secondary acid filters. If there is a surplus of tertiary filtrate, it is added to pregnant solution and is sent to the precipitation plant; if there is a deficiency, it is made up with water. All of the uranium previously dissolved in the Pachuca tanks passes to the precipitation plant in the filtrate from the secondary filters. Too, all water added during repulping (except for the final stage) leaves the plant in this pregnant solution stream. A balance between the two must be maintained at all times.

The tertiary filters operate at a blow-off pressure of 10 psi and the average life of filter cloth is 70 days. Secondary and tertiary filters are scrubbed with rotary brushes and water at 160°F at the rate of two per day in each section.

Uranium recovery. Ion exchange. The pregnant solution from the acid leach, or tertiary filtrate, is complex, containing the sulfates of acid-consuming constituents of the ore, cyanide compounds, silica, and the paramount (at this point) constituent, uranium.

Analysis of a typical solution shows the following:

Solution*	Grams/liter
UO_2^{++}	0.2 to 1.0 [4]
Fe^{+++}	3.5
Fe^{++}	0.5
Al_2O_3	2.6
Mn	4.5
CaO	0.6
MgO	3.0
PO_4^{---}	0.2
As_2O_3	0.2
SO_4^{--}	33.0
SiO_2	1.0

* Cu, Co, Ni, Cr, V, Mo, and Ti are also present in small, significant quantities.

The uranium is present in the ionic form, UO_2^{++}. It is also probably present in complex forms such as UO_2SO_4, $UO_2(SO_4)_2^{--}$, and $UO_2(SO_4)_3^{-4}$. Actual distribution of uranium is important in the ion-exchange process.

In the precipitation plant, the uranium-bearing solution is passed through ion-exchange columns, where the uranium is absorbed as an anionic complex $UO_2(SO_4)_3^{-4}$. It is then eluted from the columns, filtered, and precipitated as ammonium diuranate, $(NH_4)_2U_2O_7 \cdot 3H_2O$, as which it leaves the plant in a thick slurry form.

At Daggafontein, the pregnant solution from the 8 secondary filters first passes through a settling tank and is then clarified through sand filters. The filtrate is free of all solid particles, and is sparklingly water-clear at this stage. It is pumped to a storage tank that feeds the ion-exchange plant.

There are 4 sets of ion-exchange columns operating in parallel, each of which consists of 3 columns, 12 feet high and 7 feet in diameter. The columns are made of mild steel and rubber lined. Each holds a 5-foot bed of strong-base polystyrene quaternary amine ion-exchange resin, Amberlite IRA-400.

In the operating cycle, two columns in series are used for absorption while the third is eluted in stages. The uranium and small amount of iron retained on the resin, and the effluent sulfuric acid or barren solution containing no uranium but considerable amounts of iron and manganese sulfate, are passed to the manganese recovery section. The eluting solution used to remove the uranium complex from the resin contains a mixture of 0.4 N nitric acid and 0.6 N ammonium nitrate.

Figure 11–29 is a flow diagram of the Daggafontein ion-exchange plant in 6 stages. In each case, the solid curves show the state of absorption in columns B and C, where absorption is carried out in series, and the stage of elution in column A, which has just been saturated at the beginning of the cycle shown.

Stage 1. At the break-through point of uranium from column B, after absorption in columns A and B in series, column A has reached its maximum saturation. The flow of pregnant solution to column A is stopped. Pregnant solution which remains in A is displaced with a water wash through columns B and C. (Washing stage not shown.) No elution is conducted at this stage.

Stage 2. The pregnant stream flow is transferred to columns B and C in series in that order. The first partially used eluting solution is added to column A, displacing the wash water, and the stream is sent to the pregnant solution circuit. Absorption is increasing in column B and beginning in C.

Stage 3. The flow of eluant continues in column A and emerges as a rich uranium eluate, which is sent to precipitation plant. Absorption continues in columns B and C.

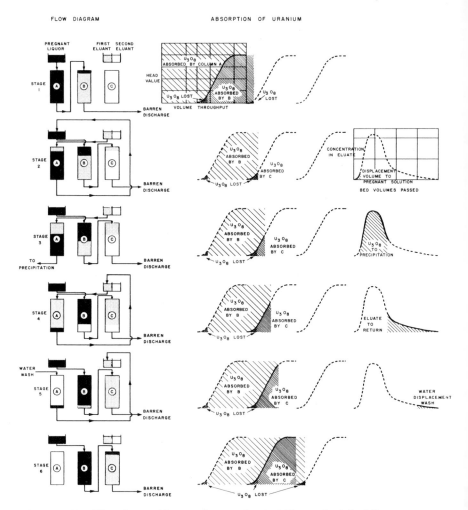

FIG. 11–29. Flowsheet of ion-exchange plant at Daggafontein Mines.

Stage 4. After required quantity of first eluant has passed through column A, elution is continued with second eluant, which consists of pure ammonium nitrate-nitric acid solution containing no uranium. A portion of this eluate is sent to precipitation plant to maintain the volumes of first and second eluants in balance. The eluate from column A is then transferred to the first eluant tank for reuse.

Stage 5. The last of the eluate in column A is displaced from the column with water, and the eluant goes to the first eluant tank for reuse. Absorption in column B is approaching saturation and uranium breakthrough from column C is near.

Stage 6. Column A is now ready for reuse and is left standing. Breakthrough has occurred from column C in the B-C absorption circuit, and column B is completely saturated and ready for elution. The cycle continues with absorption through C-A.

Precipitation. The final eluate from the ion-exchange columns contains uranium together with a small amount of iron. The iron must be removed before precipitating the uranium. The pregnant solution is stored in the strong eluate tank, 30 feet in diameter and 18 feet high. From this tank, it is pumped to the first of three 5 by 5-foot cyclindrical rubber-lined agitating tanks. In the first, lime slurry is added to neutralize essentially all the free acid present, and the pH is adjusted in the last agitator to 3.5 with ammonia gas. Iron present precipitates as ferric hydroxide, which is settled in a thickener, 25 feet in diameter and 12 feet high.

From the thickener, the thick ferric hydroxide underflow passes to a stainless steel agitating tank, 8 feet in diameter and 8 feet high. It is filtered in a vacuum candle filter consisting of 15 cloth bags, 4 inches in diameter and 41 inches in length. After a water wash, recovered cake, containing some uranium, is fed back to the main Pachuca leaching tanks for redissolution. Washings join the filtrate from the candle filter, and the combined solution is added to the thickener overflow in the surge tank.

Uranium is now precipitated from this solution. From the surge tank, the solution passes through a series of three 5 by 5-foot cylindrical agitating tanks. Ammonia gas is supplied from storage tanks through a vaporizer until pH 7.0 is reached. At this point, uranium precipitates as a rich yellow ammonium diuranate, $(NH_4)_2U_2O_7 \cdot 3H_2O$.

The uranium precipitate is collected in a thickener (25 feet in diameter by 12 feet high) from which it passes to an 8 by 8-foot cyclindrical stainless steel agitating tank equipped with steam coils. The thick precipitate is removed by a candle filter composed of 25 cloth bags of the same size as those used in filtering the iron. These operate under vacuum of 20 to 21 inches of mercury. After washing, the final product of ammonium diuranate contains about 65 percent moisture. To minimize health hazards, it is sent in this form by road tanker to Calcined Products, Ltd., a central calcining plant, where it is dried, extruded in pellet form, and calcined to U_3O_8.

For conversion to uranium oxide, U_3O_8, the dried ammonium diuranate is heated to 650 to 900°F. The over-all reaction is represented by:

$$9(NH_4)_2U_2O_7 \rightarrow 14NH_3 + 6U_3O_8 + 15H_2O + 2N_2.$$

The temperature range is important, since below 650°F UO_3 is present, and above 900°F oxygen is driven off.

After sampling, the extruded pellets, black in color, are packed in steel drums for overseas shipment and subsequent conversion to uranium metal.

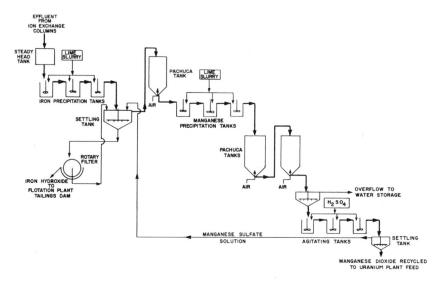

FIG. 11–30. Flowsheet of manganese recovery plant at Daggafontein Mines.

The washings and filtrate from the candle filter and the overflow from the thickener are brought up to nitrate strength by the addition of nitric acid. Occasionally, ammonium nitrate or nitric acid and ammonia may be added to adjust nitrate strength. The adjusted solution is recycled to ion-exchange columns for reuse.

Manganese recovery. Approximately 18,000 tons of manganese ore (40 percent MnO_2) are required monthly by the South African uranium industry for the oxidant in leaching processes. At present, pyrolusite ore is obtained cheaply from local deposits. As a protection against depletion of pyrolusite reserves, however, most of the uranium plants include manganese recovery facilities, which may be used if necessary.

Recovery involves removing the iron, aluminum, and silica, present as hydrated oxides, and precipitating the manganese from the separated solution, as shown in Fig. 11–30. Daggafontein's plant is equipped for manganese recovery with 75 percent recovery efficiency. Effluent from ion-exchange columns has the following average composition:

	Grams/liter
Fe^{+++}	3.0
Fe^{++}	4.0
Mn^{++}	6.0
Al	6.0
Free acid	3–4
Total sulfate	35

At the present time, this plant is used to neutralize the barren solution. Effluent passes from a steady head tank to a bank of three 10 by 10-foot cylindrical agitators in series; here, the pH is adjusted to 9 by adding lime slurry. Precipitated iron and manganese hydroxide are pumped to a slime dam.

When manganese is being recovered, the ion-exchange column effluent passes to the same agitating tanks, where the pH is adjusted first to 4.5 by adding lime slurry. Precipitated iron is concentrated in a 50 by 12-foot thickener, filtered by one of two 14 by 16-foot rotary vacuum filters, and the cake is conveyed to a waste dam. The clear thickener overflow, together with the filtrate from iron separation, are agitated in a 15 by 45-foot Pachuca and then pumped to a second and similar series of agitating vessels. The pH is raised to 9 with lime slurry. Precipitated $Mn(OH)_2$ is air-agitated in two $22\frac{1}{2}$ by 45-foot Pachucas in series. In the Pachucas, the $Mn(OH)_2$ is converted to manganous manganite, $MnO\text{-}MnO_2$ (i.e., Mn_2O_3).

The slurry from the agitators is settled in a 50 by 12-foot thickener, the overflow from which is pumped to the return water reservoir. Thickened underflow is pumped to a third series of three acidproof agitating tanks, where concentrated sulfuric acid (8 to 20 pounds per 100 pounds of solid Mn_2O_3) is added. The manganous manganite is converted into insoluble manganese dioxide and soluble manganese sulfate. After being settled, recovered MnO_2 is recycled to uranium plant feed. The manganese sulfate solution is returned to the iron separation thickener.

Pyrite recovery by flotation. Most sulfuric acid used in the uranium industry is made from pyrite present in the residual pulp of uranium plants. Additional acid is made from pyrite recovered from gold tailings from nonuranium producers. The pyrite content in the original ore is about 5 percent, and it is necessary to concentrate this prior to use in the sulfuric acid plant.

Daggafontein's production of pyrite is 225 tons per day, of which 200 tons go directly to the acid plant and 25 tons go to the stockpile. The pyrite is present in the final tertiary filter cake from the uranium plant (Fig. 11–28) which contains approximately 5.0 percent FeS_2. This is pumped to a 50 by 12-foot acid-resisting stock tank, where lime is added to adjust pH to 5.7 (5 tons per day). Then it is circulated through a steady head tank and flows by gravity to 3 conditioning tanks in parallel, which, by means of launders, feed 3 banks of 12 rougher cells each (one tank of 10 cleaner cells, and a final bank of 5 recleaner cells). All cells are square units of the Fagergren type, equipped with rubber-covered stators and rotors. Rougher cells are 66 inches in size, and cleaner and recleaner units are 56 inches.

In the flotation plant, the following agents are added at the points indicated and in amounts shown:

Reagent added	Point of addition	Amount added, lb/ton of solids
Xanthate 301*	Conditioning tank	0.10
Pine oil	Conditioning tank	0.022
Xanthate 301*	Rougher cell, 9th	0.01–0.03
Depressant 620*	Recleaner cell, 1st	0.09

Flow through the flotation plant is shown in Fig. 11–28. Final clean concentrates from the recleaner cells, containing 40 percent sulfur representing 5 percent by weight of the original feed, are pumped to one of two thickeners, 50 and 60 feet in diameter, where the specific gravity is built up to 1.8 or 1.9.

Thickened pyrite is pumped to 20 by 10-foot agitator tanks, from which it is transferred to the primary slurry tank in the acid plant, or is filtered on a 14 by 16-foot rotary vacuum filter, the cake being sent to a stockpile.

Tailing residue from the flotation plant is adjusted to pH 7.5 by addition of lime; it is then pumped through a 2200-foot line to a waste dam.

Sulfuric acid production. The sulfuric acid plant at Daggafontein employs the conventional contact process, using sulfur as raw material, except that the pyrite concentrate is roasted in slurry form in a fluid-bed reactor rather than as a dry solid. This is the first application of the slurry roasting process to sulfuric acid production. The plant has a rated production of 220 tons of 100 percent acid per day.

The final slurry feed has a solids content of about 67 percent (specific gravity, 2.0). It is fed into 3 fluid-bed roasters by single air injectors. Feed rate to each roaster is about 100 tons of slurry every 24 hours. Low-pressure turbo-blowers (5 psi) driven by 200-horsepower motors supply 3200 ft^3/min of air to each roaster. Water sprays maintain the roaster bed temperature at 1400 to 1500°F.

Sulfur dioxide gas, excess air, water vapor, nitrogen, and particles from calcined concentrates compose the roaster discharge. This is passed through a stainless steel cyclone which removes approximately 65 percent of solids, which, together with calcined grate discharge from the roaster, are treated for gold recovery.

The gas is then passed through two mild-steel cooling and scrubbing towers in series. These are lined with lead and chemical brick and packed (approximately 50 percent of volume) with 6-inch ceramic spiral rings. Flow is upward in each tower. In the second tower, fresh-water sprays are countercurrent to gas flow at three levels. In the first tower, effluent from the second tower feeds sprays at three corresponding levels. Dis-

* Products manufactured by the American Cyanamid Co.

solved sulfur dioxide in the wash water (effluent from the first tower) is removed in a stripping tower and effluent, containing calcines, flows by gravity to the effluent disposal pumps.

Gas from the second quench tower contains some acid mist, minute quantities of dust, and is saturated with water vapor. The mist and dust are removed by two parallel electrostatic mist precipitators operating at 62,000 to 65,000 volts.

At Daggafontein's acid plant there is only one drying tower, rather than the usual three. It is constructed of mild steel, is 16 feet in diameter and 42 feet high, and is lined with chemical brick. Both $1\frac{1}{2}$- and 3-inch spiral ceramic rings are used as packing. Sulfuric acid (93 percent) is circulated through the gas entering the tower from the mist precipitators and removes the final trace of moisture.

The dry, cool gas from the drying tower is too concentrated for efficient conversion to sulfur trioxide. Air is drawn into the mixture at the drying tower by the main blower, which is located between the drying tower and heat exchangers. The blower has an inlet capacity of 26,000 ft^3/min and is driven by a 600-hp, 1480-rpm motor. The air-gas mixture is forced through three heat exchangers, leaving the last one at a temperature of 820°F.

From the heat exchangers, the sulfur dioxide-air mixture passes through primary and secondary converters in series. In the converters, vanadium pentoxide catalyst, supported on cast-iron grids, converts sulfur dioxide to sulfur trioxide, which is then passed to a single absorption tower where it is absorbed in 98 percent sulfuric acid circulating through the tower.

The temperature of the 98 percent acid from the absorption tower is reduced to 200°F in water-sprayed acid coolers and returned to the circulating acid tank. Product acid is bled off from the circulating acid to the absorption tower and pumped to 1000-ton storage tanks.

References

1. J. W. ISACHSEN and C. S. EVENSEN. Geology of Uranium Deposits of the Shinarump and Chinle Formations of the Colorado Plateau, in *U. S. Geological Survey Professional Paper* No. 300. Washington, D. C.: U. S. Government Printing Office, 1956. (pp. 273-275)

2. C. S. MCLEAN and T. K. PRENTICE, The South African Uranium Industry, in *Proceedings of the International Conference on the Peaceful Uses of Atomic Energy*, Vol. 8. New York: United Nations, 1955. (P/997, p. 100)

3. W. Q. HULL and E. T. PINKNEY, Uranium from Gold Wastes, *Ind. Eng. Chem.* **49,** 1 (1957).

4. D. E. R. AYRES and R. J. WESTWOOD, The Use of the Ion Exchange Process in the Extraction of Uranium from the Rand Ores with Particular Reference to Practice at the Randfontein Uranium Plant, *J. S. African Inst. Mining Met.* **58,** 459 (1957).

CHAPTER 12

URANIUM RECOVERY FROM PHOSPHATE ROCK, MONAZITE, LIGNITE, AND SHALE

12–1. INTRODUCTION*

Preceding chapters have dealt with various aspects of developing, mining, and processing what is considered to be commercial ore. There still remain tremendous reserves of uranium-bearing materials which for one reason or another are at best marginal in the sense that they may not be mined and milled at a profit in today's uranium market. These sources have been known for some time. They include the marine phosphate deposits in Florida and in the western states, the monazite sands of Florida and Idaho, the uraniferous lignites of the Dakotas, and the Chattanooga shales.

Prior to the discovery of the Colorado Plateau and Canadian deposits and the subsequent tremendous increase in reserves in those areas, the Atomic Energy Commission expected that it would be necessary to recover uranium from some, if not all, of these sources. As a result, beginning in the late forties, a major development effort was undertaken on shales and phosphates. After the discovery of high-grade uraniferous lignites in 1953, these were also included in the development study.

12–1.1 Uraniferous phosphates. The marine phosphate deposits in Florida and the western states provide a large reserve of low-grade uranium-bearing material. Unlike other low-grade sources, this material contains other values: the phosphates. The rock that is commercially processed today for fertilizer and phosphate chemicals contains approximately 0.01 percent U_3O_8. When the Commission initiated development on the recovery of uranium from this source, it was apparent that any technology that would be useful must include phosphoric values as a primary product. To consider commercial phosphate rock solely as a source of uranium was technically impractical and economically impossible.

The development studies sponsored by the Commission successfully developed processes to recover uranium as a by-product in the production of phosphoric acid. Since there were already in existence a number of

---

* Introduction by T. B. Upchurch, U. S. Atomic Energy Commission.

large phosphoric acid plants, it was decided that this development program would not only be carried out through the pilot-plant stage, but would be put into production to obtain full-scale engineering and economic data. The Commission entered into several production contracts for recovering uranium from wet-process phosphoric acid. Even as a by-product, the uranium is more expensive than uranium produced from Colorado ores, except in the case of one phosphate plant that is in a unique process situation. However, the extensive beds of phosphate rock may some day become an important source of uranium.

In addition to the commercial rock deposits, there is in Florida an overlying phosphatic material known as the leached zone, consisting essentially of aluminum phosphate. The uranium content of the leached zone is slightly higher than that of phosphate rock, averaging 0.015 percent U_3O_8. Beginning in 1950, development studies for uranium extraction from the leached zone were sponsored by the Commission. Since it was apparent that uranium from this source would be prohibitively expensive if it bore the total processing cost, these studies were also directed to recovery of phosphorous and aluminum values. A process to produce a phosphatic fertilizer, metallurgical-grade alumina, and uranium was developed through the pilot-plant stage. The cost of recovering uranium from the leached zone is higher than for western ores, even when credits for other products are taken. However, several companies have investigated the possibilities of processing leached zone material commercially, and at some future time they may go into full-scale production.

12–1.2 Monazite. Although monazite concentrates usually receive consideration only as sources of thorium and the rare earths, frequently they also contain substantial amounts of uranium. It would be economically impractical to process monazite for its uranium content alone, but if a satisfactory market exists for thorium and rare earths, it is entirely feasible to recover uranium as a valuable by-product. In the older methods still used for processing monazite by digesting with sulfuric acid and processing the materials to obtain thorium and rare earth compounds, the uranium is not readily recoverable because it is dispersed through the various fractions. Recently, however, methods have been developed to recover the uranium in the acid process, or even more readily by the newer sodium hydroxide digestion process.

The best known deposits of monazite are certain beach sands in Brazil and India, but some monazite is also found in Florida and Idaho and in other parts of the United States.

12–1.3 Lignite. The lignites of the Dakotas have several characteristics that prevent their being treated by techniques used to extract uranium from conventional ores. In grade, some lignites are comparable to the conventional ores being processed throughout the Colorado Plateau. Their high organic content, however, prevents the usual leaching and ion exchange or solvent extraction. Roasting prior to leaching eliminates this difficulty, but the acid requirement for leaching is high. Although lignite, at the time of this writing, is not being processed for uranium recovery, it may be utilized in the future.

The uraniferous lignite beds vary in thickness from 12 to more than 24 inches. Overburden ranges from almost nothing to 100 or more feet, but the average is 30 to 40 feet. Mining would undoubtedly have to be by stripping. The narrowness of the beds, their softness, and the overburden ratio pose special mining problems.

12–1.4 Chattanooga shale.

The Chattanooga shales form a uranium reserve that can be measured in millions of tons of U_3O_8. Orebodies are generally continuous and uniform, but the grade is extremely low, averaging about 0.006 percent U_3O_8. The uneconomic character of such a material is obvious. It would take 10 to 12 tons of shale to produce 1 pound of uranium, compared with 5 pounds recovered from 1 ton of normal uranium ore in the United States. The complex nature of the shales is another obstacle in devising recovery techniques. For all practical purposes, there is no discrete particle of uranium in shale; it is uniformly distributed throughout the highly organic, finely divided matrix.

Serious development activity on shales as a source of uranium began in the early 1950's when the AEC launched expanded programs and required increased uranium tonnages. It was recognized that uranium from shale sources might cost as much as $60 per pound of U_3O_8. Even so, the Commission was prepared to sponsor a major shale project. Bench-scale studies at Columbia University demonstrated that uranium can be recovered from shale at a price considerably less than originally contemplated, although still much higher than prices paid for uranium from commercial ores. At present, good cost estimates cannot be made because the technical developments in the laboratory have had no pilot-plant test. The magnitude of any program to recover uranium from shales would necessitate pilot-plant investigations before full-scale operations could be considered.

Nevertheless, shales are still the largest known source of uranium. Unless uranium requirements change drastically, it should not be necessary to turn to shale sources for many years. Moreover, discovery of new deposits of high-grade ore may continue rapidly enough to keep pace with the needs for low-cost uranium.

12–2. Recovery From Phosphate Rock*

12–2.1 Recovery from phosphoric acid. Three producers are recovering uranium as a by-product from the manufacture of wet-process phosphoric acid. Approximately 150 tons per year of U_3O_8 are extracted from phosphatic solutions by two different processes [1].

One method involves solvent extraction of uranium from crude phosphoric acid during the manufacture of triple superphosphate and dicalcium phosphate. With minor modifications, this process is used by the U. S. Phosphoric Products Division of the Tennessee Corporation and by the International Minerals and Chemicals Corporation. Uranium costs are somewhat higher than those on the Colorado Plateau.

A second method, practised by the Blockson Chemical Company (a division of the Olin-Mathieson Chemical Company), is reduction of an aqueous solution of monosodium phosphate to precipitate a uranous phosphate [2].

Both processes use much the same technology employing sulfuric acid to solubilize the phosphatic and uranium values in the phosphate. In the Blockson process, the phosphate rock is calcined prior to digestion with sulfuric acid. At International Minerals and U. S. Phosphoric, uncalcined rock is treated with sulfuric acid and recycled dilute phosphoric acid to solubilize the values directly. From this point on, the two processes differ to a marked extent.

International Minerals and Chemical Corporation process. At the Bonnie Chemical Plant, near Bartow, Florida, International Minerals recovers uranium from 26 percent P_2O_5 phosphoric acid in a small auxiliary plant adjacent to the main operation. A process flowsheet is shown in Fig. 12–1. The dilute acid is pumped to a settling tank equipped with a specially constructed rake mechanism. Calcium sulfate and sodium silicofluoride settle out, and the clarified phosphoric acid is cooled from about 140°F in vertical cascade towers with air. After additional settling in a 90,000-gallon storage tank, the acid is pumped to a continuous reduction reactor where iron punchings come in contact with the acid in a rotary reducer similar to a tube mill in appearance.

At this stage the dilute, clarified, cooled, and reduced acid contains from 90 to 200 mg U_3O_8/liter. The acid now goes to solvent extraction, where it is brought into contact with an alkyl pyrophosphoric acid (bis-trimethylhexyl pyrophosphoric acid or, more simply, nonyl pyrophosphoric acid) in a 1 to 2 percent solution in kerosene. The organic phase makes up about 10 percent of the mixture. The solvent extraction is a

---

* By P. D. V. Manning, I. M. LeBaron, and Foster Crampton, International Minerals and Chemical Corporation.

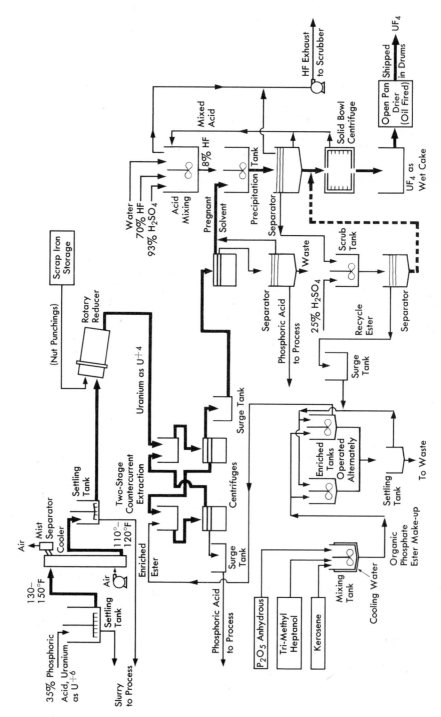

Fig. 12–1. Process flowsheet of International Minerals and Chemical Corporation process for the recovery of uranium from phosphoric acid.

two-stage countercurrent centrifuge operation. Pumping between tanks and phase-separating centrifuges intimately contacts the two phases. The centrifuges separate the phases, and the raffinate (extracted, aqueous-phosphoric phase) is returned to the main phosphoric acid plant for evaporation and subsequent processing. The organic phase is sent to a small centrifuge to separate emulsion, which is discarded.

The pregnant solvent containing the uranium goes to precipitation, where it meets an aqueous solution containing 8 percent HF and 16 percent H_2SO_4.

The slurry from precipitation then goes to a settling tank. Overflow from the settling tank is scrubbed with 25 percent sulfuric acid and recycled as extractant for a fresh quantity of phosphoric acid. The underflow from the settling tank is pumped to a basket centrifuge which separates the uranium tetrafluoride from the aqueous liquor. The aqueous liquor is returned to the precipitation step, and the centrifuge cake goes to a tray drier prior to shipment. The dried cake contains approximately 40 percent U_3O_8.

Blockson Chemical Company process [2]*. The Blockson Chemical Company manufactures wet-process phosphoric acid which it then converts into monosodium phosphate and other phosphorus derivatives. A uranium by-product is precipitated from the monosodium phosphate stream. The 35 percent wet-process acid (before being partially neutralized to form monosodium phosphate) is oxidized in towers with chlorine to assure that all the uranium is in the $+ 6$ valence. Otherwise, part of the uranium would be precipitated when the pH is raised to produce monosodium phosphate. About 2.4 pounds of chlorine is required per thousand gallons of acid, to oxidize to an emf of -300 millivolts. After oxidation, the acid goes through Blockson's standard step of partial neutralization to form monosodium phosphate, and from this, the liquor goes to the uranium recovery system. A schematic diagram of the process is shown in Fig. 12–2.

First the monosodium liquor is heated to approximately 60°C and clarified by filtering. Then it goes to a reduction-precipitation step where 1.7 pounds of sodium hydrosulfite ($Na_2S_2O_4$) and 2.1 pounds of filter aid are added per 1000 gallons. Retention in this step is 1 hour, with reduction to an emf of $+50$ millivolts. This liquor, containing dissolved monosodium phosphate, filter aid, and precipitated uranium, is filtered and the filtrate is returned to the phosphate-processing plant. The precipitate, containing about 5 percent U_3O_8, goes to an upgrading step; it is slurried in

---

* This description is based on the pilot plant that preceded the current full-scale plant.

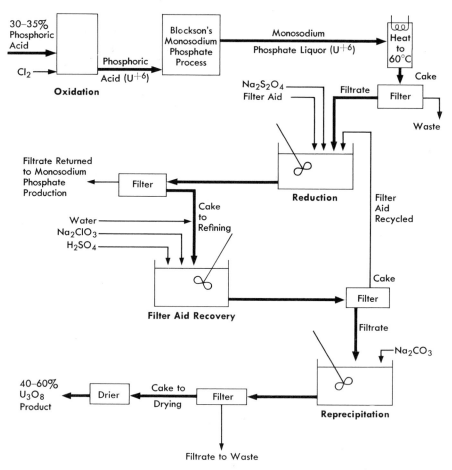

Fig. 12–2. Schematic flowsheet of the Blockson process for the recovery of uranium from phosphoric acid.

water at the rate of about 1 pound per gallon, and 4 to 6 pounds of H_2SO_4 and 0.2 to 0.3 pounds of $NaClO_3$ per pound of U_3O_8 are added to redissolve the precipitate. Sodium chlorate (or some other oxidizing agent) must be present to oxidize the uranium to the $+6$ valence to make it soluble in the dilute sulfuric acid. After redissolution, the slurry (since the filter aid does not dissolve) is filtered. The filter cake, essentially filter aid, is recycled to the precipitation step, and the filtrate proceeds to the reprecipitation step. Here, a soda ash solution (3 pounds per gallon) is added to the filtrate over a 3-hour period, to ensure a precipitate in proper physical form, until a pH of 3.5 is reached. This slurry is filtered. The filtrate goes to waste, and the precipitate of uranous phosphate, containing 40 to 60 percent U_3O_8, is dried for shipping.

12–2.2 Recovery from Florida phosphate leached zone. The "leached zone" deposits of Florida phosphatic clay are associated with the pebble phosphate deposits, found principally in Polk, Hillsborough, Manatee, and Hardee Counties, in west central Florida. The deposits lie above the Hawthorne strata of the Miocene Age. The phosphatic matrix seems to be Pliocene. Above the matrix is an overburden of the leached zone material. This material gets its name because much of the calcium phosphate it once contained has been removed by the aqueous leaching of geological weathering. Above this part of the overburden is often found topsoil or Pleistocene sand.

In general, the uranium concentration in the leached zone material averages somewhat higher than in the phosphatic pebble matrix lying below. In places the thickness of the leached zone is as much as 30 feet, but it averages about 5 feet in areas now being mined. The pebble matrix is the part used to produce the phosphate concentrates, and the leached zone overburden is discarded.

Physically, the leached zone is a finely divided material of which about 30 percent is minus-200 mesh. Approximately 70 percent of the total uranium content, most of the Al_2O_3, and a large percentage of the P_2O_5 is contained in the minus-200 mesh fraction. Mineralogically, the leached zone consists of a mixture of aluminum phosphate, calcium aluminum phosphate, aluminum silicate, and smaller quantities of fine sand and finely divided calcium phosphate pebbles. The major crystal phases are quartz, wavellite, and pseudowavellite. Feldspar, fluorapatite, and kaolinite are present, as are certain heavy minerals.

The uranium content is quite small (0.015 percent), and therefore the cost of recovery is so high that the possibility of competing economically with uranium from the Colorado Plateau is precluded. During the early 1950's, however, before the discovery of the Colorado Plateau deposits, the urgent need for uranium justified research to develop a process to extract it from leached zone material.

In early 1951, therefore, the AEC contracted with the Tennessee Valley Authority and the International Minerals and Chemical Corporation to develop a process for uranium recovery. Research and development continued until mid-1955. As the final step, pilot-plant testing of some of the processes was carried out on a scale of 12 to 15 tons of feed per day, and this work was followed by process evaluation studies and preliminary engineering. Readers interested in details beyond those presented here are referred to the Bibliography at the end of this chapter.

Averaged chemical analyses for mineable leached zone and mineable transition zone are given in Table 12–1 [3].

The average thickness of leached zone in the area is 5.4 feet and the average thickness of the transition zone is 1.9 feet. Leached zone and transition zone weigh approximately 100 pounds per cubic foot and con-

TABLE 12–1

AVERAGED CHEMICAL ANALYSES FOR MINEABLE LEACHED ZONE
AND TRANSITION ZONE

Screen size	Weight	Weight percent, dry basis					
		Al_2O_3	CaO	Fe_2O_3	Insol.	P_2O_5	U_3O_8
		Mineable leached zone					
+14 mesh	5.19	12.03	13.64	2.38	49.82	19.35	0.018
−14 +200 mesh	61.68	2.30	3.39	1.86	90.31	4.38	0.004
−200 mesh	33.12	26.98	7.91	2.79	40.39	16.11	0.029
Head	100	10.98	5.42	2.20	71.67	9.04	0.013
		Transition zone					
+14 mesh	7.4	8.4	21.92	2.59	37.11	20.56	0.018
−14 +200 mesh	62.4	1.47	7.28	2.59	83.28	6.74	0.0045
−200 mesh	29.2	20.22	11.17	2.98	37.39	16.91	0.027
Head	100	7.10	10.05	1.28	70.25	11.29	0.013

tain approximately 20 percent moisture. In areas mined for the production of phosphate concentrates, about 75 percent of the uranium in the leached zone resides in the 30 percent of the weight represented by the minus-200 mesh fraction. The top part of the phosphate matrix is similar in chemical analysis and physical characteristics to the minus-200 mesh portion of the leached zone.

If it is assumed that in the uranium *from the leached zone*, the phosphate content would be a by-product, then both the minus-200 mesh fraction of the leached zone and the minus-200 mesh fraction of the upper matrix could be processed for uranium, phosphate, and alumina. For example, from present operations in the area, the 1000 tons of saleable phosphate concentrates *from the matrix zone* would make available the following:

From the upper matrix: 200 tons −200 mesh at 0.03 percent U_3O_8

From leached zone: 300 tons −200 mesh at 0.03 percent U_3O_8

Total   500 tons −200 mesh at 0.03 percent U_3O_8

This corresponds to a uranium content of about 0.15 ton of U_3O_8 per 1000 tons of phosphate rock product. Since the area produces about 12

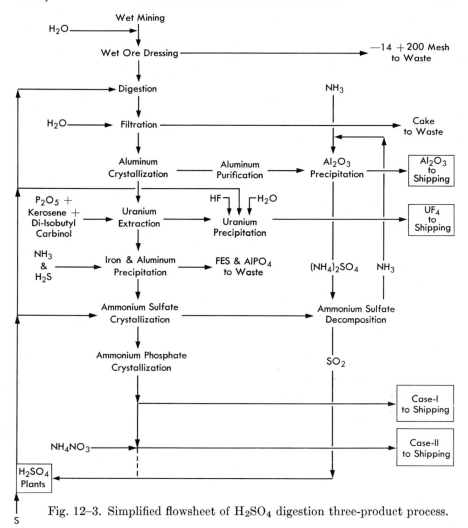

Fig. 12–3. Simplified flowsheet of H_2SO_4 digestion three-product process.

million tons of phosphate concentrates per year, the uranium available
in the leached zone is estimated at approximately 1800 tons per annum.

Research and pilot-plant work developed the following processes for
treating the leached zone material.

First alternative process [3]   In the first process, three products were
made: (1) uranium tetrafluoride, (2) metallurgical-grade alumina, (3) ammonium phosphate fertilizer.   A simplified flowsheet of this process is
given in Fig. 12–3.

After mining, the material was beneficiated by wet ore-dressing methods.
The mined material was hydraulically piped to the beneficiation plant,

where it first passed through a trommel screen. The oversize went through a hammer mill and returned to the trommel. Discharge from the trommel passed to two hydroclassifiers. The overflow from the first hydroclassifier passed to the second, from which the overflow passed to a settling basin. Minus-200 mesh product from the basin went to a blending pit and then, after being mixed with the plus-14 mesh product, passed to the processing stage. The underflows from the two hydroclassifiers were combined and passed to a bowl desilter. The overflow from this returned to the main hydroclassifier feed, and the underflow was sent through a blade mill. The oversize returned to the main hydroclassifier feed. The discharge from the blade mill was screened. The plus-14 mesh material was carried by a conveyor to a drier, then through a grinder to the blending pit which fed the leaching section. The minus-14 mesh from the screen passed to another bowl desilter, and the minus-14 mesh plus-200 mesh discharge was run to waste. The overflow from this bowl desilter returned to the main classifier feed.

Sulfuric acid, produced both by burning sulfur and recovering sulfur dioxide from the decomposition of ammonium sulfate, was pumped from the acid section to the digestion pits. In the pits, the acid reacted with the plus-14 mesh and minus-200 mesh material from the ore-dressing section. The gases, principally fluorides, carbon dioxide, and steam, were cooled and discarded. The acid slurry from the digestion pit was cooled and pumped to the filtration section. In the filtration section, the solubilized values were removed from the waste cake in a four-stage countercurrent filtration operation. The cake, mainly calcium sulfate, was pumped to waste.

The filtrate passed next to the alumina recovery station. Alumina was removed from the filtrate by the addition of ammonia to form an alum, with subsequent recovery of the ammonia as ammonium sulfate, which was decomposed to ammonia and sulfur dioxide. The later passed to the sulfuric acid plant for recovery. The alumina was washed, dried, and stored for shipment.

From the alum crystallizer the mother liquor passed to the uranium solvent extraction plant. Here the uranium was separated by nonyl pyrophosphoric acid, as described in Article 12–2.1. From the solvent the uranium was precipitated, as the tetrafluoride, by hydrofluoric acid. The barren solvent was recycled.

The aqueous barren liquid discharged from uranium extraction passed to a precipitator, where residual iron and alumina were precipitated by means of ammonia and hydrogen sulfide. The precipitate, a mixture of iron sulfate and aluminum phosphate, was run to waste. After filtration, the mother liquor passed to a crystallizer, where ammonium sulfate was crystallized out. The crystals entered the ammonium sulfate decomposition stage previously mentioned. The filtered mother liquor then passed to the ammonium phosphate section. Ammonium phosphate was crystallized, dried, and stored for shipment.

The catalytic process for recovering ammonia and sulfur dioxide from ammonium sulfate has been described in detail in reference 4.

Second alternative process. The second alternative process yielded two products: uranium tetrafluoride and aluminum phosphatic fertilizer. In this alternative the leached zone was beneficiated by dry classification. A simplified flowsheet of the process is shown in Fig. 12–4.

In beneficiation the dry-mined leached zone material passed to hammer mills, and then was dried in rotary driers. Since the plus-14 mesh and minus-200 mesh portions of the leached zone were found richest in uranium,

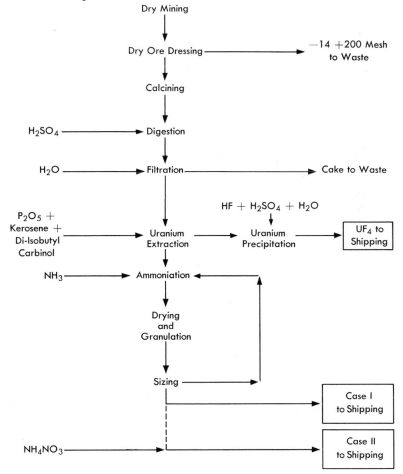

Fig. 12–4. Simplified flowsheet of H_2SO_4 digestion two-product process.

the discharge from the drier was screened and air-classified to recover the minus-200 mesh fraction. Afterward, the plus-200 mesh material was screened at 14 mesh, and oversize of this screening was combined with the minus-200 mesh product from the air classification. The combination was then calcined. The minus-14 plus-200 mesh passed to waste. Calcination was required to decrease the amount of alumina that went into solution in sulfuric acid during the later digestion step. Calcining was carried out at 1600°F, with a 2-hour retention.

Following calcination, the product was digested with sulfuric acid and then leached with water in a four-stage countercurrent system. Apparently, the calcining step also prevented some of the uranium from going into solution, since the dissolution of uranium values was found to be lower than that obtained in the first process.

Filtrate from the leaching step was treated with metallic iron to reduce the valence of the uranium present. The reduced uranium solution was

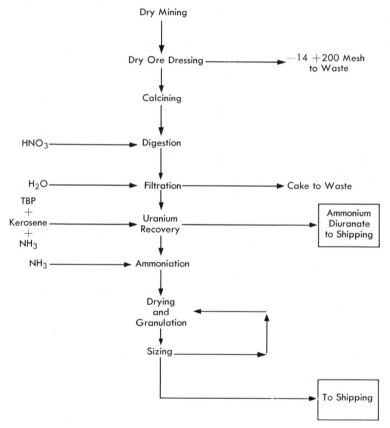

FIG. 12–5. Simplified flowsheet of HNO_3 digestion two-product process.

extracted by nonyl pyrophosphoric acid, as described in Article 12–2.1. Uranium was precipitated from the extractant, as the tetrafluoride, by a mixture of HF and sulfuric acid.

The aqueous barren liquor from solvent extraction was ammoniated to produce ammonium phosphate, which was dried and granulated.

Third alternative process. A simplified flowsheet of this modification is given in Fig. 12–5. There are two products from the process: ammonium diuranate and aluminum phosphatic fertilizer. The ore was beneficiated and calcined as in the second alternative process. Most of the uranium and phosphatic compounds were dissolved by digestion with nitric acid. Filtration and washing followed, and the cake was discarded. The filtrate passed to the solvent extraction station, where the uranium was extracted with tributyl phosphate in kerosene, and precipitated from the solvent with ammonia. Further ammoniation of the aqueous barren liquor was carried out to produce an impure ammonium phosphatic fertilizer.

Tennessee Valley Authority process. A different approach to the problem of producing uranium economically from leached-zone material was taken by the Tennessee Valley Authority. A method using the TVA nitrophosphate process No. 5 was piloted at Muscle Shoals, Alabama.

This process differed from the work by International Minerals in that all leached zone material was used as feed to the plant. The leached zone ore, crushed to minus one inch, was fed to a rotary drier where the moisture was reduced from approximately 15 percent to 5 percent. After drying, the ore was crushed to minus $\frac{1}{2}$ inch and calcined.

Calcining at 2000 to 2100°F was essential for economical filtration after acidulation. Following the calcining step, the ore was cooled to approximately 180°F. It was conveyed to screens and a double-roll crusher to reduce the size to a minus-10 mesh, and then stored in bins.

The calcine from the storage bins was leached with strong nitric acid and sulfuric acid. Three tanks provided with twin turbine agitators and air foam breakers were used in series for the acidulation step. From the last acidulation tank, the slurry was pumped to filters. The cake received 3 washes before being discharged. After washing, it was discarded to waste.

The filtrate from the filtration section was pumped to the uranium solvent extraction unit. Here the uranium from the nitrophosphate solution was transferred to an organic solvent. The solvent, 20 percent tributyl phosphate in kerosene, was brought into contact with the aqueous solution in a countercurrent box-type mixer settler. Six steps of extraction were provided. The barren aqueous phase, containing the nitrophosphate solution, was sent to the ammoniation section in the main plant.

Solvent, containing the uranium, overflowed from the extraction unit and was pumped to the product recovery section. The uranium product was recovered by treating the solvent with ammonia. A rotary vacuum filter removed the precipitate from the solvent. The solvent from the filter was cooled, washed with water, and recycled. The filter cake, containing the uranium and ammonium nitrate, was then washed with water in an agitating vessel to dissolve the ammonium nitrate. The slurry from this operation went to a centrifuge, where the uranium was removed as cake. When dried, the uranium product was weighed, sampled, and prepared for shipment.

As noted above, the nitrophosphate solution from which the uranium had been recovered was returned to the main plant. Here, ammonia and muriate of potash were added in a series of operations to produce a 20–20–0 fertilizer product.

12–3. URANIUM RECOVERY FROM MONAZITE*

12–3.1 Type of ore. Monazite sand is one of the most important sources of thorium and the rare earths. Chemically, it contains principally phosphates of these elements. By physical methods, the beach sands are upgraded to produce the concentrates that are processed chemically. The mineral monazite is honey-yellow to brown in color. The grains have a resinous luster, and range from translucent to opaque. Primarily composed of rare earth phosphates, it contains, along with numerous other minor constituents, varying amounts of thorium and uranium. The uranium oxide (U_3O_8) content may be as high as 0.5 percent, substantially higher than many commercial uranium ores. Compositions of some typical monazite concentrates are shown in Table 12–2 [5].

12–3.2 Chemistry of extraction. Rather drastic conditions are required to decompose the metal phosphates found in monazite, in order to make available the thorium, uranium, and rare earths. Digestion with concentrated sulfuric acid is the conventional method used in the United States [6] but for uranium recovery it presents difficulties. Decomposing the metal phosphates with aqueous sodium hydroxide at high temperatures shows much promise as a method of opening up the monazite mineral for further processing [5,7]. Early in this process, the phosphate is removed as trisodium phosphate, and thus does not interfere with later separation steps. After the sodium phosphate is removed, the residual oxides of thorium, uranium, and the rare earths can be dissolved in acid, then processed to yield a thorium-uranium precipitate and a rare earth precipitate. Afterward, the thorium and uranium can be separated and purified, for example by solvent extraction techniques, based on the fact that uranium nitrate ordinarily has a much higher distribution coefficient toward organic solvents than does thorium nitrate.

---

* By A. E. Bearse, Battelle Memorial Institute.

TABLE 12–2

COMPOSITION OF MONAZITE SAND CONCENTRATES

Constituent	Composition, percent		
	Brazilian	Indian	Domestic*
ThO$_2$	6.5	9.8	3.1
U$_3$O$_8$	0.17	0.29	0.47
(RE)$_2$O$_3$	59.2†	58.6†	40.7†
Ce$_2$O$_3$	26.8	27.2	——
P$_2$O$_5$	26.0	30.1	19.3
Fe$_2$O$_3$	0.51	0.80	4.47
TiO$_2$	1.75	0.40	——
SiO$_2$	2.2	1.7	8.3

* Florida sand containing about 70 percent monazite.
† Includes Ce$_2$O$_3$.

12–3.3 Processes. It has long been known that monazite can be decomposed by alkali fusion. However, the resulting melt is difficult to process. More recently, an improved process employing digestion of the monazite with concentrated solutions of sodium hydroxide has been developed in France [7] and independently in the United States [5]. The sodium hydroxide method has been used on a large scale since 1949 at São Paulo, Brazil, to process about 2000 tons of monazite per year, and at Alwaye, India, in a plant processing about 1500 tons per year. Only recently has this process been used industrially in the United States, by the Heavy Minerals Company at Chattanooga, Tennessee. Since details of the industrial processes are not available, the following description is based on a small pilot-plant operation which has been operated successfully [5].

In this investigation the monazite sand concentrate was first ground by wet ball-milling to 96.5 percent minus-325 mesh (100 percent minus-200 mesh). A 10-pound charge of the ground sand was fed to a heated, agitated, stainless steel reaction vessel containing caustic soda and water. The ratio of NaOH to sand was 1.5 and the ratio of water to sand was 1.7. The mixture was then heated to 280°F and maintained there for 3 hours, with moderate agitation, after which it was diluted and the slurry digested for 1 hour at 220°F to facilitate later filtration.

The digested slurry was filtered at 180°F to remove the hydrous oxides from the solution of trisodium phosphate and excess caustic soda. The hydrous oxide cake, containing the uranium, thorium, and rare earths, was washed in the filter with water until practically all soluble elements were removed. The filtrate and washings were further processed to recover trisodium phosphate and caustic soda for recycle.

The hydrous oxide cake was next placed in a 5-gallon, steam-jacketed, glass-lined kettle fitted with an agitator. To it was added 37 percent hydrochloric acid, 1.5 pounds of acid per pound of sand. The mixture was heated at 175°F for 1 hour to dissolve the essential materials in the cake. A portion of the cake, largely unreacted rutile and zircon, remained insoluble in the acid and was carried along as suspended solid matter. This procedure avoided filtration of the hydrochloric acid solution.

The acid solution was then transferred to a neutralization vessel and diluted with water. Sodium hydroxide solution was added slowly, with high-speed agitation of the mixture, until an equilibrium pH of about 5.8 was reached. At this point all thorium and uranium were precipitated and about 3 percent of the total rare earths. After neutralization, the slurry was allowed to settle prior to decantation and filtration to separate the solids from the solution. The latter was further neutralized to extract the rare earths.

Thorough washing of the thorium-uranium cake by repulping several times was required to obtain a good separation from dissolved solids. A thoroughly washed cake was found to contain over 99 percent of the uranium and thorium introduced in the original monazite sand concentrates and only about 2 percent of the rare earths. This thorium uranium cake contained some acid-insoluble material (silica, rutile, and unreacted monazite).

To separate uranium and thorium from impurities and from each other, the cake can be dissolved in nitric acid. The solution is filtered to remove acid-insoluble material, and subjected to solvent extraction to remove the thorium and uranium from the impurities [8,9]. The nitrate solution is contacted countercurrently with the solvent, tributyl phosphate in hydrocarbon diluent. The resulting extract is scrubbed with water or dilute nitric acid to remove rare earths and other impurities. The thorium nitrate is re-extracted into water under conditions that retain the uranyl nitrate in the organic phase. This is possible because of the much higher distribution coefficient of uranyl nitrate than thorium nitrate toward the organic phase. The uranyl nitrate can be re-extracted into an aqueous phase by lowering the acidity or by using some other stripping agent such as dilute sodium carbonate solution. By adding sodium hydroxide, the uranium is recovered as sodium diuranate.

An alternative process of separating thorium from uranium, starting with the crude thorium hydroxide cake produced by the caustic soda treatment, has been described by Krumholz and Gottdenker [10]. Using a crude cake (from a large-scale industrial operation) containing 50 to

65 percent ThO_2 and 1.5 to 2.5 percent UO_3, it was found that the thorium and uranium could be dissolved easily in dilute sulfuric acid to form a highly supersaturated solution. The crude hydroxide was suspended in water and 50 percent sulfuric acid at 45 to 50°C was added until the solution contained about 20 grams of free sulfuric acid per liter. Solids were removed by decantation and leached twice more. Thorium and uranium recovery in the solution was almost quantitative. Thorium sulfate was crystallized from the supersaturated solution, on cooling after addition of 5 to 15 percent ethanol. Crystallization occurred slowly over 3 days at 0°C. The practical yield of crystallized thorium sulfate was 85 to 88 percent. Precipitating the mother liquor with oxalic acid removed nearly all remaining thorium and other impurities. Uranium was recovered from the oxalate mother liquors by precipitating uranyl phosphate at a pH of 5 to 5.5. The crude uranyl phosphate was extracted with hot sodium carbonate solution to dissolve the uranium. The uranium was then reprecipitated with sodium hydroxide as sodium uranate of about 97 percent purity.

Average recovery by this process was 98 to 99 percent for thorium and 95 to 97 percent for uranium, based on the amount in the crude hydroxide cake. This process has operated successfully to produce several hundred tons of thorium sulfate and several tons of sodium uranate. It is not capable of yielding as pure thorium or uranium as can be obtained by the tributyl phosphate extraction of the nitrate solution already described.

A separation procedure based on sulfuric acid digestion of monazite was developed at the Ames Laboratory, Iowa State College [11]. After the diluted digestion mixture had settled, it was decanted from unreacted material. This monazite sulfate solution was diluted further and partially neutralized with ammonium hydroxide to a pH of about 1.0. Under suitable conditions, nearly complete precipitation of the thorium was obtained with about 5 percent of the rare earths. The precipitate, because of the high initial content of rare earths, was about half thorium phosphate and half rare earth sulfates.

On further neutralization to about pH 2.3, most of the rare earths were precipitated. The filtrate and decantate from this step were then neutralized with ammonium hydroxide to a pH of about 6.0. At this point the remaining rare earths and the uranium were precipitated. The uranium precipitate, containing about 1 percent uranium, was purified in a subsequent step.

This process was operated on a pilot-plant scale. It does not appear to give the clean-cut separations obtained by starting with the caustic-soda digestion process and proceeding from the crude thorium hydroxide cake either by the solvent extraction method or by the method of Krumholz et al.

12–4. URANIUM RECOVERY FROM LIGNITE*

Occurrences of uranium in lignites have long been known in Idaho, Wyoming, Montana, and North and South Dakota. By far the largest domestic uraniferous deposits are found in a wide area where Montana and North and South Dakota join [12]. Early investigations sponsored by the AEC were made at Battelle Memorial Institute [13] and at Oak Ridge National Laboratory [14] to study the possibility of recovering uranium from less than 0.01 to as much as 0.05 percent U_3O_8. These studies demonstrated that although the uranium is soluble in acid and alkaline systems, reagent consumptions per ton are high, with the result that costs are excessive per pound of uranium extracted.

In 1954 when in the western Dakotas lignite deposits were discovered to contain uranium in concentrations equivalent to ores processed on the Colorado Plateau, further process development studies were initiated by the AEC. Studies have been made at the Raw Materials Development Laboratory, Winchester, Massachusetts [15] and the AEC Pilot Plant, Grand Junction, Colorado [16,17]. A large number of lignite samples were received at Winchester and tested by standard metallurgical techniques for amenability to various recovery procedures. These samples, containing as much as 2 percent U_3O_8, but generally representing deposits averaging 0.1 to 0.2 percent U_3O_8, originated from orebodies in Harding County, South Dakota, and Billings and Slope Counties, North Dakota. Based on procedures developed at Winchester, a testing program was carried out on several 500-ton lots of lignite at the Grand Junction Pilot Plant. A description of the pilot-plant test program and a discussion of the observations and conclusions arising from the Winchester and Grand Junction investigations are given below.

12–4.1 Laboratory studies. The uraniferous lignite samples studies at the Winchester Laboratory typified a low-grade fuel with a heating value of 2500 to 4000 Btu per pound of dry solids and an ash content of from 30 to 60 percent. Most of the uranium appears to be associated with carbon in the lignite as a urano-organic complex. Molybdenum is similarly associated with the carbon, and its concentration generally parallels that of the uranium. The noncarbonaceous material is principally gypsum, jarosite, bentonite, sandstone, and miscellaneous carbonates and silicates.

Many procedures for recovering uranium from raw lignite were investigated at Winchester. It was concluded that organic fouling of resin or solvent, high reagent consumption, and difficult liquid-solids separations made calcination necessary. Proper roasting removes the organic

---

* By E. S. Porter and H. G. Petrow, AEC Raw Materials Development Laboratory, National Lead Co., Inc.

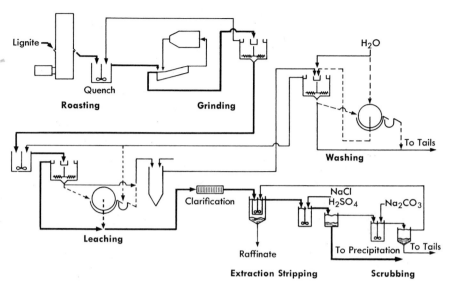

Fig. 12–6. Roasted lignite acid leach-solvent extraction process.

fouling problem, reduces the size of leaching plant required for a comparable uranium throughput, and usually provides equal or better acid-leaching efficiency with a lower acid requirement per pound of uranium recovered.

Although the uranium could be dissolved by a carbonate solution, serious liquid-solids separation difficulties were encountered when raw lignite was treated. Roasting, charring, or retorting rendered the lignite refractory to carbonate leaching which, therefore, was deemed inferior to acid leaching of lignite calcine.

The recovery procedure evolved from the Winchester investigations and tested at the Grand Junction Pilot Plant is depicted in Fig. 12–6. Although other types of roasting equipment may be used to process lignites, this method employs a fluid-bed reactor to produce a calcine. After grinding and classification, the calcine is subjected to a 2-stage countercurrent acid leach, and the uranium-bearing acid solution is separated from the leached residue by thickening and filtration. The pregnant liquor is clarified, and the uranium is recovered by solvent extraction using an amine as the active agent.

12–4.2 Roasting of lignites. Restrictions are necessary when the lignite is roasted, since combustion temperatures much in excess of 600°C inhibit the solubility of uranium in acid solution. Roasting to a dead-burned ash in a laboratory furnace at a nominal 450°C provided a calcine amenable to acid-leaching procedures. When pilot-plant scale equipment was used (3-foot-diameter multiple-hearth roaster), a heat dissipation problem was encountered in controlling the combustion temperature. Restricting air to control the temperature caused chemical reduction of the uranium, detrimental to acid-leaching efficiency. Moreover, as complete carbon removal is required for optimum leaching extraction, enough oxygen must be present for complete carbon combustion. Laboratory investigations indicated that the carbon content of incompletely roasted lignite calcines can be controlled by flotation. Residual carbon can be floated out of the ash and recycled to the roaster.

At the Grand Junction Pilot Plant, fluid-bed roasting of lignite was approached with the objective of producing a dead-burned calcine at the maximum feed rate, because partially roasted products gave inferior leach results. Extensive roasting tests of three lots of lignite totaling more than 1200 wet tons were carried out at the Grand Junction Pilot Plant in a 3-foot-diameter fluid-bed reactor. Average burning rates were 1.0 to 1.4 ton of raw wet (39 to 46 percent moisture) lignite per square foot of roaster cross-sectional area per day, resulting in 2.1 to 2.7 tons per day of dead-burned calcine. Roaster temperatures ranged from 1130 to 1600°F in the fluidized bed, and from 1270 to 1800°F in the freeboard. To hold down combustion temperature, water was injected into the bed and freeboard while an excess of air was maintained. However, since a windbox temperature of 1200 to 1300°F was required to maintain combustion, and localized water addition often caused clinkering, these cooling procedures were only partially successful. Reduction of feed rate was ordinarily the most effective procedure for lowering combustion temperature and producing the most satisfactory ash.

12–4.3 Acid leaching. Efficient recovery of uranium from lignite ash by acid leaching called for large quantities of sulfuric acid. The ash was ground in water, thickened, and treated with enough sulfuric acid to maintain a leaching pH of about 0.5. Adequate mixing required a pulp density no higher than 40 percent solids, because the mixture thickened excessively when the acid met the ash. High leaching temperatures (70 to 90°C) benefited uranium dissolution, but much of the heat was supplied by the reaction of the acid and the ash. Sulfuric acid required in a conventional leaching circuit would be from about 500 to 1000 pounds per ton of ash (150 to 600 pounds per ton of raw, dry lignite). However, because optimum leaching extraction demanded considerable free acid at the end of leaching, two-stage countercurrent leaching procedures were effectively utilized. Up to about half the concurrent leaching acid requirement was saved by this procedure, which utilizes the excess acid to neutralize the acid-consuming minerals in the ash.

Conventional leaching of lignite ash, with its high acid requirement, also resulted in a solution containing relatively heavy concentrations of undesirable metal ions and salts. The high molybdenum, ferric iron, and sulfate concentrations precluded direct ion-exchange treatment of acid liquors, although this technique could be applied after pretreatment. Solvent extraction methods, however, apply directly, and are generally preferred for uranium recovery from lignite leach liquor.

Ash from the Grand Junction fluid-bed reactor was leached with hot, dilute sulfuric acid in two countercurrent stages. Uranium extraction averaged 88 percent, requiring 360 pounds of sulfuric acid per ton of raw, dry lignite.

12–4.4 Filtration and thickening. The high salt concentrations obtained by acid leaching lignite ash caused a difficult thickening and filtration problem. Thickening and filtration were, in fact, impractical unless flocculation aids were used. Flocculants were most effective in producing satisfactory thickening rates when added as a dilute solution to the leach pulp. The amount of flocculant required was several times that for the average uranium ore treated on the Colorado Plateau, and practical filtration rates were usually obtained only after a prior stage of thickening, owing to the viscous nature of lignite ash acid pulps. However, when the ash was properly handled, the thickener and filter area requirements were low.

Thickener underflows and filter cakes produced from liquid-solids separations of acid pulps tended to retain a realtively large amount of solution. The lignite ash, after acid leaching, could only rarely be thickened to 50 percent solids. In some cases, terminal thickening densities of 30 to 35 percent solids were encountered. Filter cakes generally retained about 50 percent moisture. This tendency of the ash to retain solution resulted in a high soluble loss of uranium from conventional washing circuits. A combination of thickening and filtration appears desirable to avoid excessive loss of dissolved uranium in acid-leached residues. Testing at Grand Junction indicated thickener area requirements of from 3 to 7 square feet per ton of solids per day, and filter rates of about 1000 pounds per square foot per day, when using 0.4 to 0.7 pound of flocculant per ton of solids. The flocculant used was a mixture of 67 percent bone glue and 33 percent Separan. The total soluble uranium loss, using two stages of countercurrent decantation and one stage of filtration on the leach tails, was less than 1 percent of the U_3O_8 dissolved in the circuit. Uranium in the acid solution was recovered by solvent extraction, with test results for the most part corroborating those found at Winchester.

12–4.5 Solvent extraction. Recovery of uranium by solvent extraction from sulfuric acid leach liquor by amines has been intensively studied

[18–23].   There are commercially available, or potentially available, 5 long-chain amines that are excellent uranium extractants.   These are triisooctylamine (TIOA)[1], trilaurylamine[2], Amine S-24[3], Amine 9D-178[4], and Alamine[5].

The principal advantage of the amines is their selectivity for uranium. Of the ions commonly found in the lignite leach liquors, only molybdenum seriously interferes with uranium extraction.   Nevertheless, a very clean separation of uranium and molybdenum is easily achieved in the re-extraction or stripping operation.   Chloride ion, which will quantitatively strip uranium from a pregnant uranium-bearing solvent, re-extracts only minor quantities of molybdenum.   The molybdenum, however, is stripped from the solvent by an alkaline wash, and under nearly stoichiometric conditions.   Either aqueous ammonia or sodium carbonate can be used for stripping molybdenum from the uranium-free solvent.

Ferric iron does not seriously interfere with amine extractants.   For this reason, an amine is preferable to the organic phosphates for treating lignite leach liquors.   Especially is this true of the tertiary amines such as TIOA.   Other ions, e.g., ferrous iron, magnesium, calcium, aluminum, vanadium +4, copper, and manganese, are not extracted.

Table 12–3 shows the composition of a typical leach liquor prepared by single-stage acid leaching of lignite calcine.   Concentrations of ferric iron, sulfate, molybdenum, and aluminum are unusually high.   This leach

TABLE 12–3

COMPOSITION OF LEACH LIQUOR
PREPARED FROM LIGNITE ASH

Constituent	Grams/liter
U_3O_8	0.85
Mo	0.30
Fe	8.8
Fe^{+++}	6.0
SO_4	130.
Al_2O_3	20.
pH 0.9	

---

1. Manufactured by Carbide and Carbon Chemicals Co.
2. Manufactured by Archer-Daniels-Midland Corporation.
3. A secondary amine manufactured by Carbide and Carbon Chemical Co.
4. A second amine manufactured by Rohm & Haas Co.
5. A trifatty amine manufactured by General Mills, Inc.

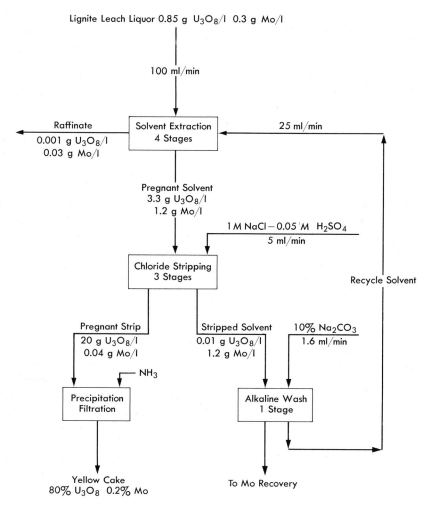

FIG. 12–7. Solvent extraction flowsheet for lignite ash.

liquor and others containing even higher concentrations of foreign ions have been successfully treated by the process shown in Fig. 12–7. In this case, a 5 volume percent solution of Amine S-24 in kerosene containg 2.5 volume percent of primary decyl alcohol was the solvent. Added alcohol increases the rate of phase disengagement in both the extraction and stripping circuits.

The solvent extraction is in four mixer-settler stages. Four stages in the extraction circuit have been found adequate for efficient uranium recovery. With a leach liquor of the composition described in Fig. 12–7, an organic-to-aqueous flow ratio of 1 to 4 gives nearly quantitative uranium recovery and 90 to 95 percent molybdenum extraction. This results in a pregnant solvent containing 3.4 g U_3O_8/liter and 1.2 g of Mo/liter.

Uranium can be re-extracted from the pregnant organic with 1 M NaCl $-$ 0.05 M H_2SO_4. At an organic-to-stripping solution ratio of 6 to 1, three stages of conventional mixer-settlers are enough for 99.9 percent uranium stripping.

The uranium is easily recovered from the pregnant stripping solution (containing about 22 g U_3O_8/liter) by precipitation with either ammonia or magnesium oxide. In either case, a final product containing about 80 percent U_3O_8 and 0.2 percent Mo is obtained after drying at 100°C.

The uranium-free solvent may not be recycled to the extraction circuit without first removing the molybdenum. This is accomplished in a single stage by washing the solvent with a 1 M sodium carbonate solution at an organic-to-aqueous ratio of 15 to 1. The solvent, nearly free of molybdenum, is recycled. Molybdenum in the alkaline wash may be easily recovered by acidifying with sulfuric acid and precipitating molybdenum sulfide with hydrogen sulfide.

12–5. RECOVERY FROM CHATTANOOGA SHALE*

12–5.1 Nature of Chattanooga shale. Structurally, the Chattanooga shale is made up of five horizontal beds. Various designations have been assigned these beds [24,25]. The two lowest beds which make up the Dowelltown member are not of process interest, since they are exceedingly low in uranium content. The next three overlying beds, making up the Gassaway member, are the subject of the present discussion. The composite uranium content of these three beds varies from 0.0058 to 0.0065 percent. In over-all thickness, the Gassaway member ranges from 15 to 18 feet. The three Gassaway beds are referred to, in descending order, as: Top Black or "E"; Upper Silt, Upper Grey, or "D"; and Middle Black or "C." The Top Black is richest in uranium (approximately 0.0080 percent), but mining considerations indicate that it would be more economical to mine and mill the entire Gassaway member [26].

Most of the process development work employed samples taken from, or adjacent to, the Sligo adit, near Sparta, Tennessee. The material is composed of approximately one-third quartz and feldspar, one-third illite and kaolinite clay, and one-third organic matter and pyrite (marcasite).

The organic matter serves as a matrix in which the inorganic constituents are dispersed. Fine horizontal bedding is evident, and leads to a

---

* By M. D. Hassialis, Columbia University.

very high ratio of horizontal to vertical permeability; however, even the horizontal permeability is low.

The mode of occurrence of the uranium is not known. It is so finely disseminated in the shale that extensive mineralogical studies failed to indicate the presence of a specific uranium mineral [27].

12–5.2 Chemistry of uranium extraction from shale. *Raw shale.* The chemistry of severance of uranium in shale is, at best, vague. Up to about 80 percent can be extracted from raw shale by a hot (80° to 90°C) acid leach, as shown in Table 12–4. Acid concentration for extraction must be 7 to 10 percent, which means an acid-to-shale ratio of 425 pounds per ton if the leach is carried out at 33 percent pulp density. Only about half the acid is consumed. If the shale is leached in countercurrent stages, permitting higher solid-to-liquid flow ratios, the acid ratio can be cut to approximately 140 pounds per ton. In any case, acid consumption beyond 9 percent of the weight of the shale (180 pounds per ton) offers little return in further uranium extraction.

Uranium can also be extracted from shale by carbonate leaching, but the recovery is always much lower than by acid extraction under comparable conditions.

Extraction increases with fineness of grind, down to 65 mesh, but grinding below 65 mesh offers little improvement.

Roasting and retorting. The presence of recoverable oil in the shale (about 8 gallons per ton may be recovered from the approximately 10 gallons per ton contained) and of pyrite (approximately 10 percent by

TABLE 12–4

COCURRENT LEACHING OF SHALE

Acid/shale ratio fed, w/o	U extracted, %	Product solution		Acid consumed	
		Uranium, mg/liter	Acidity, pH	g acid / g shale	g acid / g acid fed
0.071	47	18	1.05	0.044	0.63
0.142	61	23	0.60	0.076	0.54
0.213	73	26	0.25	0.093	0.44

Condition: Shale: Top black, 0.0079 % U, −65 mesh
          Leach: 3 hr at reflux
          Flow ratio: 2 ml of product solution per g of shale fed
          Acid: H_2SO_4 as indicated

weight) indicate that a uranium recovery system employing a means for oil by-product recovery, coupled with acid production from the pyrite, might prove attractive. The oil and about half the sulfur could be removed by retorting. The leachability of the uranium is severely reduced by such an operation [5,6] so that retorting must be followed by oxidation roasting. Although roasting the retorted shale produces the necessary oxidation, the roasting temperature must be closely controlled at about 525°C to permit effective subsequent leaching [28]. Again because of the large tonnages that must be handled, the cost of such a controlled roast by any method is very high per pound of uranium.

Pressure leaching. Sulfide minerals can be decomposed by aqueous oxidation to form a metal sulfate and sulfuric acid. Forward and Halpern [29] showed that the reaction could be applied to extract uranium from pyritic pitchblende ores. Two major reactions involved are postulated as

$$FeS_2 + 3\tfrac{1}{2}O_2 + H_2O \rightarrow FeSO_4 + H_2SO_4,$$

$$U_3O_8 + \tfrac{1}{2}O_2 + 3H_2SO_4 \rightarrow 3UO_2SO_4 + 3H_2O.$$

Since the shale contains about 10 percent pyrite, application of the above reactions appeared promising, and was investigated. Results of the investigation of factors affecting batch pressure-leaching with oxygen overpressures were:

(1) Grind: Extraction improved with fineness of grind down to 65 mesh.

(2) Temperature: Extraction steadily increased with increasing temperature, but beyond 175°C serious corrosion of Type 316 stainless steel was encountered. Hence, the temperature was limited to this value.

(3) Pressure: Reaction rate increases with oxygen overpressures up to about 75 psi, beyond which increasing the pressure is of little benefit. At 75 psi overpressure, all the pyrite in the shale was consumed in about 50 minutes.

12–5.3 Extraction processes. As a result of extensive studies carried out at Columbia University for the AEC Raw Materials Division, two alternative processes were proposed as technically feasible for extracting uranium from shale. They are (1) a relatively straightforward countercurrent decantation acid leach, and (2) a pressure leach using oxygen overpressure to produce acid by oxidation of the pyrite in the shale. These two processes were arrived at by a comparative cost evaluation of many alternatives. The estimated cost difference between them was not large enough to justify selection of one over the other.

Countercurrent decantation acid leach. The schematic flowsheet in Fig. 12–8 is based on conditions cited in Table 12–5 for a mill treating 20,000

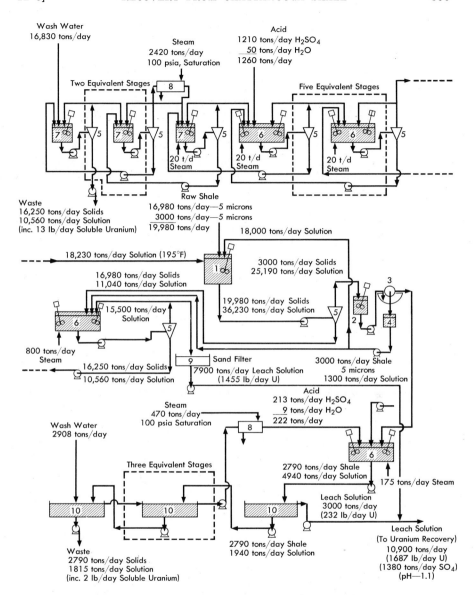

Fig. 12–8. Flowsheet for CCD acid leach process. (1) Prepulper, (2) filter feed tank, (3) filter, (4) filtrate receiver, (5) cyclones, (6) leaching vessel, (7) washing vessel, (8) heat exchanger, (9) sand filter, (10) thickener.

tons of shale per day. The crushing and grinding circuits are not indicated. They are quite straightforward, save that dry grinding is employed to achieve as high a uranium concentration as possible by minimizing the amount of water fed to the system. The necesssary operating temperature

TABLE 12–5

CONDITIONS FOR CCD FLOWSHEET

A. 16,980 *tons/day of coarse material* (+5 *microns*)

Basic layout	7 leach stages and 4 wash stages
Temperature	90°C (all leach stages and first wash stage)
Time	30 minutes per leach stage
Acid	0.071 ton per ton of shale (96% acid)
Flow ratio	0.5 ton of product liquor per ton of shale
Pulp dilution in leach stages	2 tons of liquor per ton of solids
Uranium leached	72%
Shale weight loss	4.3%

B. 3000 *tons/day of slimes* (−5 *microns*)

Basic layout	1 leach stage and 5 wash stages
Temperature	90°C (leach stage only)
Time	2 hr in leach stage
Acid	0.071 ton per ton of shale (96% acid)
Flow ratio	1 ton of product solution per ton of shale
Pulp dilution in leach stage	2 tons of liquor per ton of shale
Uranium leached	65%
Shale weight loss	7.1%

---

ruled out conventional thickeners for liquid-solids separation between stages, since substantial cooling by evaporation and convection would take place in a thickener.

Separation in liquid cyclones was selected, since these devices have a low holdup, and therefore a low heat loss. However, with cyclones, the slimes cannot be moved countercurrently, necessitating the separate, one-stage treatment of slimes shown in the flowsheet.

In the process as outlined, the minus-35 mesh raw shale is prepulped with leach solution from stage two. This pulp, at about 33 percent solids, is passed through a cyclone that makes a separation at 5 microns. The cyclone underflow becomes the feed to the coarse-solids CCD system. The overflow, containing the slimes, passes through a pressure filter that removes the fines for feeding to a one-stage leach. The filtrate is returned to the first stage of the countercurrent system.

The countercurrent leaching is carried out in a series of covered vessels. Provision must be made for internal recycle of cyclone overflow in each stage to permit control of pulp dilution in the leach vessels. Heat losses are balanced by sparging steam into each leach vessel and into the hot-wash stage. The initial heating of the shale is also by sparged steam at the solids feed stage. The wash water is heated prior to the hot-wash stage by condensing steam in a pipe exchanger, since this is the point of greatest heat input, and sparging would lead to undesirable dilution. The one-stage leach for the slimes is conventional with a leach vessel and four stages of CCD washing. This slimes-handling circuit is much the same as the coarse-handling circuit except that only one leaching stage (rather than seven) is employed.

The product solution is concentrated and purified by solvent extraction. The details are the same as those for pressure-leaching given below.

Pressure-leaching with oxygen overpressure. The following conditions have been selected as typical of the more favorable results [30].

Temperature	175°C
Oxygen partial pressure	90 psia
Total system pressure	370 psia
Residence time	60 minutes
Over-all liquid-to-solid feed ratio	1
Liquid-to-solid ratio in autoclave	2
Oxygen feed purity	95 mole percent
Uranium extraction	72%

The temperature and oxygen overpressure have been chosen to yield 72 percent extraction in 1 hour for the slurry density used. Increasing the oxygen overpressure has only minor effects. Increasing the temperature leads to corrosion difficulties in the vessel and increases the total system pressure because of the rapid increase in water vapor pressure.

A schematic flowsheet for a 20,000 ton per day mill is given in Fig. 12–9. The shale is dry-ground (for the same reasons as in the CCD leach) to minus-65 mesh, and prepulped with recycle leach solution from the wash circuit. The slurry is heated in the prepulp tank from 50 to 140°F by adding the vent steam from the blow-down tank. The slurry is then pumped to the leaching vessel and subjected to oxygen overpressure. The heat of the reaction is sufficient to maintain the temperature at the desired 175°C. The partial pressure of oxygen is maintained at 90 psia by continuous addition of 95 percent oxygen into the slurry and by venting the composite gas from the freeboard.

Slurry is discharged from the leach vessel into the blow-down tank. The cooled slurry from the blow-down tank is then washed by countercurrent decantation.

Pressure vessels for the operation must have a volume totaling about 545,000 gallons (including 15 percent freeboard). They must withstand a sulfuric acid-sulfate solution with pH in the range of 0.4 to 0.5 at a temperature of 175°C and a pressure of 370 psia. The solution is high in ferric iron. The slurry must be well agitated.

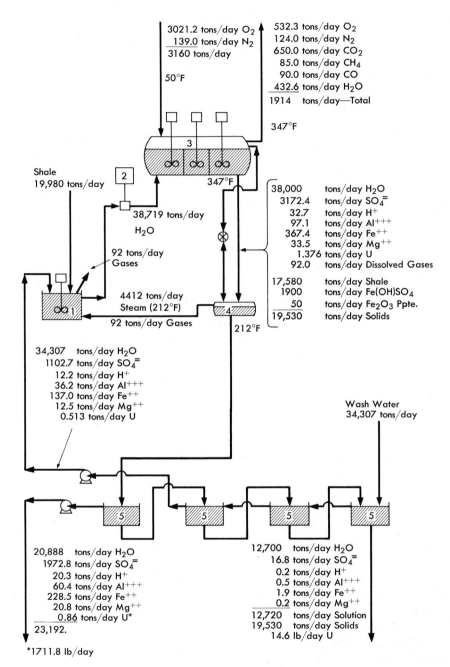

FIG. 12–9. Flowsheet for pressure leaching process. (1) Prepulper, (2) pump, (3) autoclave, (4) blowdown tank, (5) thickener.

These are obviously stringent conditions, and the pressure vessels must be a matter of some concern. Experimental work was conducted in a vertical cylindrical autoclave made of Type 316 stainless steel. For large-scale operation, horizontal cylindrical vessels with dished ends are presumed. Each vessel is to be partitioned into three compartments (to minimize short circuiting), with four propeller-type agitators in each compartment. The basic vessels are to be constructed from Type 5A-212-B carbon steel with a $\frac{1}{8}$-inch liner of Type 316 stainless steel. An additional lining of fiberglass mat, covered with one course of acid-proof brick set in acid-proof cement, keeps the temperature of the Type 316 stainless steel low enough for satisfactory corrosion resistance.

Each of the three discharge vessels has a 10,000-gallon capacity. One 6 by 48-foot vessel for each stream could provide the necessary discharge volume, but a number of smaller vessels with staggered discharge cycles would permit smoother operation and reduce the size of the valves required.

Thickening. Thickening is not a serious problem with shale. The use of 0.02 pound of Separan per ton of solids per stage requires an area of 4.5 square feet per ton of dry solids per day for minus-325 mesh shale, a reduction in area by a factor of about 2.5 from that required without Separan.

Uranium recovery. Ion-exchange recovery can attain a concentration factor of, at best, 20, whereas liquid-liquid solvent extraction permits concentration factors of 300 or more [31,32]. Of all the extractants studied, 6-benzylamino-3, 9-diethyltridecane has demonstrated the most outstanding characteristics. In addition to high extraction coefficients and excellent selectivity for uranium, this amine exhibits rapid phase break, good solubility of its sulfate salts in the organic phase, and low loss to the aqueous phase. All other extractants studied are inferior in extraction coefficients and lack one or more of the other required properties mentioned above.

Carbonate stripping is preferred, since the highly stable tricarbonate complex of uranium is formed, and because the carbonate converts the amine sulfates, produced during extraction, directly to the free amine for recycle.

Extraction is carried out countercurrently in three stages of mixer-settlers. Provision must be made for internal recycle in each mixer-settler so that a phase ratio of about one organic to three aqueous is maintained in the vessels, even though the over-all flow ratio through the system is 36 aqueous to 1 organic. From laboratory studies of dispersions, it appears that the most desirable phase break characteristics will be obtained when the extraction is run with the organic as the continuous phase at a volumetric ratio of 3 aqueous to 1 organic. Only one stage of sodium carbonate stripping is required.

REFERENCES

1. R. H. KENNEDY, personal communication.

2. E. M. STOLTZ, JR., *Uranium Recovery from Wet-process Phosphoric Acid*, USAEC Report RMO-2850, Blackson Chemical Co., 1953.

3. R. F. McCULLOUGH and E. E. WREGE, *Uranium Production Process Designs for Leached Zone Plants. Volume XIV. Summary of Economics for Three Process Alternates*, USAEC Report RMO-2020, International Minerals and Chemical Corp., November 1953.

4. J. W. DELAPLAINE and R. F. McCULLOUGH, Pilot Plant for Decomposing Ammonium Sulfate Uses Moving Bed, *Chem. Eng. Progr.* **51,** 499 (1955).

5. A. E. BEARSE et al., Thorium and Rare Earths from Monazite, *Chem. Eng. Progr.* **50,** 235 (1954).

6. H. E. KREMERS, The Rare Earth Industry, *Trans. Electrochem. Soc.* **96,** 152 (1949).

7. C. DE ROHDEN and M. PELTIER, *Treatment of Monazite*, U. S. Patent 2,783,125 (Feb. 26, 1957); French Patent 995,112 (Nov. 28, 1951); British Patent 674,400 (June 25, 1952).

8. G. D. CALKINS et al., *Recovery of Thorium and Uranium from Monazite Sand*, Volumes I and II, USAEC Reports BMI-243 and BMI-243A, Battelle Memorial Institute, Sept. 15, 1950.

9. C. A. BURKART et al., *Purification of Thorium Nitrate by Solvent Extraction with Tributyl Phosphate. II. Mixer-Settler Pilot Plant Investigations*, USAEC Report BMI-263, Battelle Memorial Institute, July 31, 1952.

10. P. KRUMHOLZ and F. GOTTDENKER, The Extraction of Thorium and Uranium from Monazite, in *Proceedings of the International Conference on the Peaceful Uses of Atomic Energy*, Vol. 8. New York: United Nations, 1956. (P/133, p. 126)

11. M. SMUTZ et al., The Ames Process for Separation of Monazite, *Chem. Eng. Progr. Symposium Ser. No. 50(13)*, **167** (1954).

12. J. E. CRAWFORD, Uranium, Radium, and Thorium, in *Minerals Yearbook*, U. S. Bureau of Mines. Washington, D. C.: U. S. Government Printing Office, 1953.

13. R. A. EWING et al., *Recovery of Uranium from North Dakota Lignites*, USAEC Report BMI-237, Battelle Memorial Institute, July 31, 1950.

14. K. B. BROWN et al., *Recovery of Uranium from Lignites*, USAEC Report ORNL-1569, Oak Ridge National Laboratory, June 1, 1955.

15. R. J. WOODY et al., *Laboratory Investigation of Dakota Lignites*, USAEC Report WIN-54, National Lead Company, Inc., Apr. 1, 1957.

16. G. R. PITMON et al., *Pilot Plant Testing of Dakota Lignites*, USAEC Report WIN-81, National Lead Company, Inc., Oct. 18, 1957.

17. W. D. CHARLES, Recent Developments in the Study of Uraniferous Lignite Treatment, in *Recent Developments in Uranium Milling Technology*, Uranium Institute of America, Grand Junction, Colorado, May 18, 1957.

18. K. B. BROWN et al., *The Use of Amines as Extractants for Uranium from Acidic Sulfate Liquors: A Preliminary Report*, USAEC Report AECD-4142, Oak Ridge National Laboratory, May 27, 1954.

19. J. G. MOORE et al., *Further Studies of Amines as Extractants for Uranium from Acid Sulfate Solutions*, USAEC Report AECD-4145, Oak Ridge National Laboratory, June 24, 1955.

20. D. J. CROUSE and K. B. BROWN, *Amine Extraction Processes for Uranium Recovery from Sulfate Liquors*. Volume I, USAEC Report ORNL-1959, Oak Ridge National Laboratory, Sept. 30, 1955.

21. D. J. CROUSE et al., *Uranium Extraction with Organo-nitrogen Compounds*, USAEC Report ORNL-2099, Oak Ridge National Laboratory, May 14, 1956.

22. A. PREUSS and J. SAUNDERS, *The Solvent-Solvent Extraction of Uranium from Sulfuric Acid Solutions with Oil Soluble Amines*, USAEC Report RMO-2533, Rohm and Haas Co., Apr. 14, 1955.

23. H. G. PETROW et al., *Techniques for the Evaluation of Amines as Uranium Extractants and Properties of Some Satisfactory Amines*, USAEC Report WIN-61, National Lead Company, Inc., Aug. 26, 1957.

24. P. B. STOCKDALE, *An Investigation of Chattanooga Black Shale of Tennessee as a Source of Uranium*. *Progress Report, January 1, 1953, to June 30, 1953*, USAEC Report ORO-106, University of Tennessee, March 1954. H. J. KLESPER, *An Investigation of the Chattanooga Black Shale of Tennessee as a Source of Uranium*. *Progress Report, July 1, 1956, to June 30, 1957*, USAEC Report ORO-167, University of Tennessee, Aug. 1, 1957.

25. L. C. CONANT, *Origin of the Chattanooga Shale*, Trace Elements Investigation Report 237, U. S. Geological Survey. Washington, D. C.: U. S. Government Printing Office, 1952.

26. E. D. GARDNER et al., *Preliminary Report, Chattanooga Shale Project*, U. S. Bureau of Mines. Washington, D. C.: U. S. Government Printing Office, Mar. 1, 1954.

27. T. F. BATES and E. O. STRAHL, Mineralogy, Petrography, and Radioactivity of Representative Samples of Chattanooga Shale, *Bull. Geol. Soc. Am.* **68,** 1305 (1957).

28. MINERAL BENEFICIATION LABORATORY, COLUMBIA UNIVERSITY, NEW YORK, *Recovery of Uranium from Chattanooga Shale*. *Part A. Chlorination Studies*. *Part B. Leaching Studies*, USAEC Report RMO-4005, September 1955.

29. F. A. FORWARD and J. HALPERN, Acid Pressure Leaching of Uranium Ores, *J. Metals* **7**(3), 463 (1955).

30. MINERAL BENEFICIATION LABORATORY, COLUMBIA UNIVERSITY, NEW YORK, *Recovery of Uranium from Chattanooga Shale*, USAEC Report RMO-4014, September 1957.

31. R. A. EWING et al., *Recovery of Uranium from Shales*. Volumes I and II, USAEC Report-BMI-JDS-210, Battelle Memorial Institute, Sept. 30, 1949.

32. MINERAL BENEFICIATION LABORATORY, COLUMBIA UNIVERSITY, NEW YORK, *Recovery of Uranium from Chattanooga Shale*. *Part B. Leaching Studies*, USAEC Status Report RMO-4009, September 1956.

CHAPTER 13

HEALTH AND SAFETY PROBLEMS ASSOCIATED WITH URANIUM MINING AND MILLING*

13–1. Introduction

Mining and milling uranium ores involve exposing workers to several health hazards, some common to all mines and ore processing plants and others peculiar to this industry. In addition to crushing and grinding, uranium milling is commonly understood to include the necessary chemical processes to produce a uranium concentrate containing from 65 to over 85 percent U_3O_8. A study of the health and safety aspects of the uranium-producing industry on the Colorado Plateau is being conducted by the U. S. Public Health Service and other Federal Groups, and by State Health Departments, Bureaus of Mines, and Industrial Commissions. To date, this study has defined the extent of the primary health hazards and has developed methods of controlling exposures. Both the medical and environmental phases are continuing.

13–2. General Health and Safety Considerations

In uranium ore mining and milling, all the usual hazards of such operations are present, in addition to those produced by radioactive elements. In all these industries, one of the primary health hazards is exposure to silica dust. Nearly all uranium ores in the United States contain 35 to 70 percent free silica. Therefore the common methods of controlling silica dust, such as wet drilling, wetting the muck pile, and providing sufficient ventilation, are required. Where diesel engines are used underground, the controlling factor on ventilation will usually be the air necessary to remove diesel exhaust gases. The U. S. Bureau of Mines now recommends that from 100 to 200 cubic feet of fresh air per minute per brake horsepower be provided underground. In most dieselized uranium mines, this ventilation rate will exceed that needed to reduce the radon concentrations to the recommended working levels.

In the ore sampling and crushing areas of the mills, control measures must be used to maintain the atmospheric concentrations of silica dust below the threshold limit of 5 million particles per cubic foot. These controls should include enclosing and exhaust-ventilating crushers and

---

* By Duncan A. Holaday, U. S. Department of Health, Education, and Welfare.

406

screens, hooding and exhaust-ventilating ore transfer points, exhaust-ventilating ore storage bins, and, where possible, means for wetting the ore at the crushers. If these controls can maintain the atmospheric concentrations of silica dust at or below the threshold limit, the atmospheric concentrations of radioactive elements will also, in most instances, be below the recommended levels.

Uranium ores may contain arsenic, selenium, vanadium, or other toxic elements, and the possible presence of such materials must be considered in designing plant equipment and devising milling processes. The occurrence of a death from arsine poisoning in a uranium refinery has demonstrated the need for control measures. In general, all chemical reaction vessels must be enclosed and vented to the outside air, and operations which produce dust or fumes should be hooded and exhaust-ventilated. The need for other specific control measures must be determined by a study of the particular situation in each refinery.

All uranium-producing states have regulations for the safe operation of mines, and uranium mines are subject to these general requirements. In some states a bureau of mines has responsibility and in others an industrial commission has jurisdiction; in either case, state inspectors survey the mines regularly. On public lands, the U. S. Bureau of Mines and the state agency both have jurisdiction. It would not be feasible to list here the items covered by the various State and Federal mining codes, since they are extensive and varied. Because many small uranium mines are operated by men with little mining experience who are not familiar with safety requirements, mining companies should obtain copies of state codes and discuss the regulations with the mine inspectors.

13–3. URANIUM MINING

13–3.1 Radon inhalation. Preliminary surveys of uranium mines indicated that the primary radiation hazard to miners probably was from high atmospheric concentrations of radon and its immediate daughters in the working areas. This problem was thoroughly studied, and the results are detailed in Public Health Service Publication No. 494, "Control of Radon and Daughters in Uranium Mines and Calculations on Biologic Effects" [1].

The summary from this report is given below. The publication gives details of methods of air sampling and specific recommendations for controlling radon and its daughters.

"Surveys of Colorado Plateau uranium mines have shown that 65 percent of the miners were exposed to concentrations of radon and its daughters comparable to those reported to exist earlier in European mines. Extensive control measures will be necessary to reduce these concentrations to the suggested working level.

"Radiation dosage from breathing a radon-containing atmosphere arises principally from radon daughter products accompanying radon in the air. Substantial portions of these daughter products, RaA(Po^{218}) through RaC'(Po^{214}), are retained in the lungs. The two alpha-emitting isotopes of these daughters, RaA and RaC', are the principal direct sources of radiation dosage. RaB(Pb^{214}) and RaC(Bi^{214}) retained in the lungs decay to RaC' and therefore may be assumed to be indirect sources of alpha radiation. The beta and gamma rays from RaB and RaC are relatively of negligible importance.

"Sufficient time has not elapsed to permit stating that no American miners have been injured by exposure to radon and its daughters. In certain central European mining regions, it is possible that exposure to these elements may have been responsible for an increased incidence of bronchial carcinoma. The concentration of radon that was present in these European mines is only an estimate at best.

"No reliable toxicity data exist from animal experiments that allow a calculation of permissible radon daughter concentrations for atmospheres breathed by man such as are encountered in mining operations. However, experimental data are available on the magnitude of the retention of radon daughter products in the respiratory system of experimental human subjects and animals. Moreover, measurements have been made in animals of the distribution of these retained daughter products in the respiratory system. With these data, and with a knowledge of the physical nature of radon, it is possible to estimate radiation doses to the respiratory system of human beings exposed to radon and its daughters.

"There is much uncertainty in interpreting these calculations in terms of maximum permissible concentrations of radon daughter products in mines and industrial plants. Until biologic information is available which will assist in determining these concentrations, a working level is suggested for use in the uranium mining industry.

"Radon in mines may be determined by measuring the alpha activity of air samples collected in these mines. Radon daughter product concentrations can be measured by determining the alpha or gamma activity of membrane filters through which known volumes of mine air have been drawn.

"The polonium content of urine may provide a measure of the total exposure of an individual to radon and radon daughters.

"Investigations were performed into the effect of ventilation on concentrations of radon daughters under a variety of mine conditions. Moreover, limited studies were made of the concentrations in uranium mines as affected by mechanical ventilation, and varying outside air temperatures.

"It would seem that the material presented in this report leads to the following conclusions:

"1. A working level of 1.3×10^5 Mev of potential alpha energy per liter is suggested for radon daughter products. The recommended field method described in section V measures the total alpha energy which will be delivered by the decay of any mixture of RaA, RaB, and RaC through RaC'. A total concentration of these elements of 300 micromicrocuries per liter of air as determined by the field method will release 1.3×10^5 Mev of alpha energy.

"2. To meet the working standard virtually all uranium mines will require mechanical ventilation during all seasons of the year.

"3. In the uranium mines where ventilation is present, it is in most instances inadequate, often used only occasionally or after blasting, and is seldom delivered at a point close enough to the working face to be effective.

"4. The amount of air necessary in a working place to reduce the radon daughter concentration to a given value can be estimated from determinations of the air-change rate and the atmospheric concentrations of radon daughters, or radon.

"5. Reasonable amounts of ventilation will reduce the radon daughters to acceptable levels in uranium mines.

"6. Maximum use should be made of natural ventilation, but this cannot be relied upon to reduce concentrations to acceptable levels under all temperature conditions.

"It is emphasized that the above recommendations apply only to present uranium mines with relatively nonextensive underground workings. If uranium mining operations approach other metal mines in size and activity, further study will be necessary to determine what practices beyond standard metal-mine ventilation are required to control the hazards from radioactive materials."

The uranium-producing states have issued regulations establishing threshold limits for atmospheric concentrations of radon daughters which are similar to the working level proposed in the bulletin. No threshold limit has been established for radon, because this element is usually of relatively minor importance as a source of radiation dosage to the lungs.

13–3.2 Other radiation hazards. In addition to radon and its daughters, miners may be exposed to all other radioactive members of the uranium family in the form of airborne dust. Atmospheric concentrations of these dusts bear no relationship to the amount of radon present, since they are produced only by active mining operations, while the radon continuously emanates from the ore whether work is proceeding or not. Of these elements radium appears the most significant as a health hazard, while uranium would be of relatively minor interest. The threshold limit for radium is 24 micromicrograms per cubic meter of air, and that for insoluble uranium compounds, as given by the American Conference of Governmental Industrial Hygienists, is 250 micrograms per cubic meter of air, or a ratio of 1:10,000,000. In ores at equilibrium the ratio of radium to uranium is 1:3,000,000. Analysis of several hundred air samples taken in mines showed that the threshold limit for radium was exceeded in only approximately 10 percent of the cases. This would indicate that the percentage of samples exceeding the threshold limit for uranium is even lower. Urinary uranium levels in miners have been consistently low, with nearly all samples containing only a few micrograms of uranium per liter. Thus, it appears that in uranium mines, as now operated, standard mine practices required to control silica dust are effective in maintaining low atmospheric concentrations of radium and presumably of other radioactive dusts.

After removal from the mines, the ores are stored essentially in open air, and therefore there is no appreciable hazard from radon or its daughters around ore bins or dumps. Exposure to airborne radium and uranium will occur when the material is loaded into trucks, since these operations can produce considerable quantities of dust if the ore is dry. However, such exposures are intermittent. Usually the operators can avoid this dust by remaining on the upwind side, but where this is impractical the use of respirators approved for protection against silica dust is a feasible control.

13–3.3 Gamma radiation. Miners may be exposed to external gamma radiation from the orebodies and from the radioactive dust in the atmosphere. Some immediate daughters of radon are beta-gamma emitters, and will contaminate clothing or skin surfaces. It has been exceedingly difficult to evaluate the amount of gamma radiation to which miners are exposed. In areas of high radon concentration instruments become contaminated very rapidly and give high readings that are impossible to interpret in terms of radiation dosage. Measurements made near ore stockpiles above ground show that the gamma radiation rate ranges from 0.5 to 2 mr/hr. These measurements indicate that external gamma radiation at mines is usually not a significant health hazard. However, pockets of high-grade ore are sometimes encountered in the mine, and measurements taken near faces of ore containing several percent of uranium have shown gamma readings in excess of 10 mr/hr. If extensive orebodies of such grades are mined, every effort should be made to obtain good estimates of the gamma-radiation dose and to control the exposure of the miners. The only feasible method is to limit working time. Again, it is probable that in the presence of extensive high-grade orebodies ventilation control of radon and its daughters would be difficult if not impossible, and exposure limitation might have to be used to control hazards from these elements.

13–4. URANIUM MILLING

Uranium ore milling presents problems entirely different from those encountered in mining. In contrast to the mines, there is sufficient natural ventilation in the mills to prevent significant radon concentrations from building up in working areas. The only exception occurs where crushed ores are stored in unventilated bins. Even in such circumstances, no one would work in the bins except briefly, and the probability of significant exposures to radon is very small. The main health problems in the mills arise in sampling, crushing, and grinding areas, where the airborne dusts contain all the radioactive elements in the ore, and in the final packing areas, where essentially pure uranium compounds are dried and barrelled. In all other areas of the mills wet processes are employed, and the dust exposures are minimal.

13–4.1 Crushing and grinding uranium ores. Crushing and handling large quantities of ore present severe dust-control problems which are not easily solved. Changes in composition of the host material and of the moisture content of the ore are important factors in the creation of dust during these operations. As these factors are usually beyond the control of the mill, concentrations of atmospheric dust in the crushing and sampling areas may vary over wide ranges. Surveys of the uranium refineries have shown that the atmospheric concentrations of dust are quite variable, with many samples showing levels of uranium and radium in excess of the threshold limits for these elements. Since exposure of workers is difficult to evaluate by atmospheric sampling alone, it is desirable to study the operators to see if they are absorbing significant amounts of radioactive elements. Urine samples from crusher operators have been analyzed for this purpose. High urinary uranium excretion (about 50 μg uranium/liter) indicates absorption of significant amounts. Only one sample contained more than 50 μg uranium/liter; the majority were below 10 μg/liter. Limited medical examinations of these workers have shown no evidence of damage by uranium. Thus, the information available indicates that exposure to uranium dusts has not produced a health hazard.

13–4.2 Radium hazard. The degree of hazard produced by airborne radium has been of concern because this element is known to be exceedingly toxic when fixed in the body. In addition, the atmospheric concentrations of radium in the crushing areas are commonly found to exceed the threshold limit of 24 micromicrograms per cubic meter of air. Some radium inhaled as dust will be retained, and a portion of this will be fixed in the body. Eventually a dangerous body burden of radium could be accumulated.

To determine whether any of the men working in apparently high concentrations of radium were building up a significant body burden of this element, detailed studies were made on crusher operators who had worked for as long as 6 years under dusty conditions. The studies included the determination of breath radon levels, urinary radium levels, and whole-body gamma-ray measurements. No detectable body burdens of radium were found; in all cases the urinary excretion of radium was less than 2 micromicrograms/liter. These results showed that men exposed for several years had not retained any significant quantity of radium and that their current exposure was not producing a significant absorption.

While no extensive data have been reported on radium retention and excretion by human beings continuously exposed to airborne radium, calculations can be made from the available information. Norris [2] esti-mates that after 100 days exposure the daily excretion would be 95 percent of the daily intake, and that the rate of accumulation would be 5 percent of the daily dose. By using this estimate and the further assumption that 5 percent of the radium eliminated is excreted in the urine, it can be cal-culated that a daily urinary output of 20 micromicrograms of radium in-dicates that the individual accumulates approximately 0.1 microgram of radium (the maximum permissible body burden) in 5000 working days, or about 20 years. Thus, it appears that threshold limits for airborne radium and uranium incorporate a safety factor where exposures in uranium-ore processing plants are concerned. In addition to environmental samples, urine specimens should be obtained periodically from the workers in high-exposure areas. Analyses of these samples for radium and uranium would check the effectiveness of control measures.

13–4.3 Uranium concentrates. In the final packaging of the concen-trates, uranium is the element of primary health significance since radium and other radioactive elements are largely removed during ore processing. However, very high atmospheric concentrations of uranium can be pro-duced in those areas unless operations are well controlled. Samples taken at some of the refineries have shown levels of airborne uranium in the order of milligrams per cubic meter of air. In such circumstances, it is imperative that the operators wear respirators until dust-control measures are in-stituted. Some plants have developed methods of drying and barrelling the final product that prevent the dissemination of dust into the workroom air and, by collecting the dust that is produced, prevent the loss of a valu-able product. All plants should have such installations to control the potential health hazards.

Exposure to external gamma radiation is not a significant health hazard in handling uranium ores in processing plants. As mentioned previously, the dose rate from large bodies of ore above ground is in the range of from 0.5 to 2 mr/hr, and these levels are seldom reached in a processing plant. The freshly separated final product has a very low gamma-radiation rate, therefore external radiation is of no particular concern at this stage of the processing.

References

1. *Control of Radon and Daughters in Uranium Mines and Calculations on Biologic Effects*, Public Health Service Bulletin No. 494. Washington, D. C.: U. S. Government Printing Office, 1957.

2. W. P. Norris, Paper presented at the Second Annual Conference on Plutonium, Radium, and Mesothorium, Radiobiology Laboratory, University of Utah College of Medicine, 1954.

3 areas covered extensively

APPENDIX

MAJOR URANIUM DISTRICTS OF THE UNITED STATES*

A–1. THE COLORADO PLATEAU

Big Indian Wash—Lisbon Valley District, San Juan County, Utah [5].†
The Big Indian Wash-Lisbon Valley uranium district is in San Juan
County, Utah. The first uranium mined in the area came from the Big
Buck mines in the Cutler formation of Permian age, where small-scale
production began in 1948 and continued sporadically until 1953. Uranium
was first discovered in the Chinle formation of Triassic age in 1952, and
by 1956, over 3,000,000 tons of ore had been blocked out. Large uranium
deposits occur on the southern flank of the Lisbon Valley anticline, which
trends northwest.

The Lisbon Valley fault, a major displacement, and minor associated
faults cut the anticline logitudinally and place the Jurassic Morrison formation in contact with the Pennsylvanian Hermosa formation. This fault
dips steeply northeast and has a normal displacement of at least 3800 feet.

Sedimentary rocks exposed in the district range in age from the Hermosa
formation (Pennsylvanian) to the Mancos shale (Upper Cretaceous). Ore
in the Chinle formation is restricted to the basal Moss Back member.
At some places the ore horizon lies directly on beveled beds of the more
steeply dipping Cutler formation. At others it is separated from the
Cutler by a few feet of barren gray mudstone.

In the Big Indian Wash-Lisbon Valley area, uranium deposits lie within
a half-mile-wide strip bordering the Chinle escarpment and paralleling
the strike for a distance of 15 miles. Most known orebodies are in the
northern portion of the anticline, adjacent to Big Indian Wash, and all
are more or less elongated parallel to the strike of the beds. All except
one occur in the interval 6200 to 6700 feet above sea level. The single
exception, which is about 5840 feet above sea level, lies along the Lisbon
Valley fault in the southern part of the mining district. Maximum thickness of ore in the Moss Back is 30 feet; the average is 8 feet. Host rocks
include medium- and fine-grained sandstones, siltstones, and conglomerates containing pebbles of mudstone and limestone. The most productive
host is fine- to medium-grained sandstone with calcareous cement. Car-

---

*By Donald L. Everhart, U. S. Atomic Energy Commission.
† References for the Appendix are included with those at the end of Chapter 1.

414

bonized plant matter is widespread in the orebodies, but the average content of carbon, even in rich ore, may not exceed 0.5 percent. Ore does not impregnate the host rock uniformly, nor does it follow in detail primary textures such as bedding; instead, it characteristically occurs in irregular pods and stringers, which exhibit only crude parallelism with bedding.

The dominant ore mineral is uraninite containing minute intergrowths of coffinite. The most abundant vanadium minerals are vandium hydromica and montroseite with very fine intergrowths of dolorisite. The oxidized minerals tyuyamunite, corvusite, and pascoite are found along and adjacent to joint surfaces.

Both uraninite and montroseite replace calcite cement, and uraninite replaces coalified logs and carbonaceous debris. Fairly abundant pyrite commonly replaces fossil plant material. Small quantities of barite, fluorite, greenockite, sphalerite, and galena have also been reported. Dominant minerals in the sandstones and siltstones are quartz, plagioclase, and microcline, and muscovite is abundant locally. Cements are calcite, quartz, barite, clay aggregates, and chlorite.

Laguna District, Valencia County, New Mexico. The Laguna district, about 30 miles due east of Grants and 6 miles north of Laguna, in Valencia County, New Mexico, contains some of the largest reserves in the United States. The largest of the productive properties, including the Jackpile, and Woodrow mines, are operated by the Anaconda Mining Company.

Structurally, the Laguna district occupies the east side of the McCarty syncline and is near the north end of the western Lucero homocline. The general region is only slightly deformed, although it is only a few miles southeast of the Mt. Taylor volcanic centers. The Recapture, Westwater Canyon, and Brushy Basin members of the Morrison formation are exposed on the flanks of mesas, with a regional dip of two to three degrees northwest.

The district is marked by extremely broad and shallow folds, plunging northwest in the dip of the beds. Two large shallow anticlines underlie the valleys of Arroyo Paguate and Arroyo Gigante, with an intervening syncline. Smaller shallow "wrinkles" of similar orientation occur on the crests of the larger anticlines. Uranium deposits occupy the smaller "secondary" synclines, the crests of anticlines, and structural terraces.

Uranium mineralization in this district has occurred almost altogether in the Morrison formation [6]. Most of the orebodies consist of impregnations of coffinite and uraninite in beds as much as 30 feet thick. Uranium distribution within the deposits appears to be largely controlled by sedimentary structures and rock types. Ore tends to be concentrated in sandstone of variable grain size and composition, and the thickest ore in some deposits occupies sedimentary depressions.

General characteristics of ore in this district include:

(1) Uranium deposits are generally in the thicker parts of sandstone units, commonly where they exceed 150 feet.

(2) The ore sandstone is yellow-gray in color.

(3) The ore sandstone contains abundant carbonaceous debris and, in some deposits, much asphaltic material.

(4) The ore sandstone contains abundant claystone lenses and concretions.

A significant and somewhat unusual type of uranium deposit occurs in Anaconda's Woodrow mine in the Laguna district, where uranium ore has been produced from a nearly vertical pipe-like structure in the Morrison formation. The inside of the pipe, which appears to be a collapse structure, is 20 to 30 feet in diameter and has been dropped from 25 to 40 feet in relation to the surrounding rocks. Uranium oxides, pyrite, and minor amounts of other sulfides occur in or near the broken rock in the pipe.

Ambrosia Lake District, McKinley County, New Mexico. The Ambrosia Lake uranium district, in McKinley County, New Mexico, lies about 12 miles northeast of Prewitt, a station on the Santa Fe Railway. Uranium ore was discovered here by drilling in April 1955. Several million tons have been blocked out in the district by a number of mining companies.

Strata exposed range from the Chinle formation of Upper Triassic age to the Mesaverde formation of Upper Cretaceous age. The major uranium deposits occur in the Westwater Canyon member of the Morrison formation (Jurassic).

The dominant structural feature is the Thoreau homocline, a northeast homoclinal dip off the northeast flank of the Zuni uplift. Five fairly well-defined anticlinal folds have been mapped: the Prewitt, Silver Spur, South Ambrosia, Poison Canyon, and Gay Eagle anticlines [7]. Domes are present on two of these folds. The Ambrosia Lake dome at the south end of the South Ambrosia anticline is pronounced. Faulting is almost entirely restricted to the crests of anticlines. Most faults are nearly vertical, and show very little movement. Three prominent directions of faulting can be discerned: N 10–30°E, N 50–70°E, and N 10–20°W. The first two directions are those of the major fracture sets.

Both anticlinal and fault traps as well as stratigraphic traps are present. The most obvious trap is the Ambrosia dome, around which most of the ore deposits are clustered.

The uranium mineral in the Ambrosia Lake area is coffinite associated with asphaltite. The Westwater Canyon sandstone, the host rock, is poorly sorted, ranging from a pebble conglomerate to a medium- to coarse-grained sandstone. Clay is the principal cementing material, but calcite occurs to a minor extent. The coarsest host rocks contain the highest percentage of uranium, although small lenses of fine-grained material within a coarse-grained rock may be richer than the coarse surroundings.

In places in the ore zone calcite is so highly concentrated that it gives the appearance of one large cleavage face, up to a square foot in area. Outside the ore zone, calcite appears only as a minor cement, which would suggest that the uraniferous solutions also brought in these larger concentrations of calcite.

Over a large portion of the area of the Westwater sandstone, hematite cementing material gives the sandstone a reddish hue. Uranium in the Ambrosia Lake area occurs in bleached zones of the Westwater. In the bleached zone, the Westwater is generally gray and weathers yellow on an exposed face.

There is no specific stratigraphic horizon in the Westwater that is everywhere mineralized. Ore may occur anywhere from the Westwater-Brushy Basin contact to the Westwater-Recapture Creek contact. Sandstone lenses in the Brush Basin have been mineralized. There is at least one report of uraniferous sandstone outcrop of the Recapture Creek near the Westwater contact. The mineralized zones in the Ambrosia Lake area range in thickness from less than a foot to over 100 feet.

A–2. THE WYOMING BASINS

The Lucky Mc Mine is near the Gas Hills anticline, Fremont County, Wyoming, 50 miles east of Riverton, Wyoming. Here the Wind River formation was deposited on an irregular surface eroded on sedimentary rocks of Mesozoic age. Formations exposed on the flanks of the Gas Hills anticline range from the Chugwater formation (Triassic) to the Frontier formation (Cretaceous). Sedimentary rocks, in age ranging from Eocene to Miocene, are exposed on the Beaver Rim escarpment several miles to the south.

The Lucky Mc Mine is in the upper part of the Wind River formation, host for most deposits in the area. This formation, which dips gently to the south in this area, ranges from very thin to 500 feet in thickness. Claystones and siltstones predominate in the lower part of the Wind River formation, but cross-bedded very coarse-grained arkosic sandstones, conglomerates, and thin mudstones make up the thicker upper part.

The host rocks are poorly cemented, coarse-grained, gray and brown arkosic sandstones and conglomerates interbedded with thin gray and brown lenses of carbonaceous shale and mudstone.

The primary ore minerals, uraninite and coffinite, are disseminated in microscopic particles in dark very coarse-grained angular arkosic sandstone cemented by gypsum and calcium carbonate. Waxy gray-green uraniferous carbonate-fluorapatite, found as cement and in fracture fillings, may also be primary. The ore contains large amounts of finely divided pyrite, which imparts the dark coloration. Liebigite, a light-green secondary uranium carbonate, commonly occurs on fracture faces and fills seams in the richest primary ore.

Many secondary minerals are found in this deposit. In addition to liebigite, there are meta-autunite, yellow uranium phosphate, phosphuranylite, sabugalite, rutherfordine, metazeunerite, metatorbernite, and uranophane.

The Sno-Ball Mine is in the Crooks Gap section of the Green Mountains, Fremont County, Wyoming, about 65 miles north of Rawlins. The region exhibits complex structural features and has an equally complex geologic history.

Most of the uranium deposits are in the Wasatch formation, which averages over 800 feet in thickness and is composed of an alternating series of boulder beds, arkosic conglomerates, fine- to coarse-grained arkosic sandstones, siltstones, and carbonaceous shales.

At the Sno-Ball Mine, mineral deposition is confined to the lower beds of the Wasatch, in lenses of very coarse-grained arkosic sandstone and conglomerates of granite cobbles. The mineralized zones are distributed irregularly.

Most ore mined in the open pit has come from the top of a persistent carbonaceous mudstone layer, which dips approximately 15 degrees east. This ore zone attains a thickness of several feet, swells and pinches in the direction of the dip, and is irregular in shape along the strike. Uranium is disseminated as grain coatings and as interstitial or cementing material in beds of coarse-grained arkosic sandstone and in upper parts of the carbonaceous mudstone immediately underlying or imbedded with the sandstone ore. Carbonaceous fossil plant fragments are abundant throughout the ore zones, in many places associated with the highest grade ore. A few small steeply dipping faults and fractures have been mineralized, but bedding planes generally seem to contain more uranium than fractures.

The Washakie Basin of southern Wyoming and northern Colorado also contains economically significant deposits in the Browns Park formation of Miocene (?) age. The basin covers about 1500 square miles. The Browns Park formation comprises sandstones, shales, and tuffaceous beds unconformably overlying older strata. Two uranium deposits, similar in many respects, are the Poison Basin claims, 6 miles west of Baggs, Wyoming, and the Gertrude claims, northeast of Maybell, Moffat County, Colorado.

Uranophane with meta-autunite and schroeckingerite are the common secondary minerals and are disseminated in lenticular bedded deposits in fine- to medium-grained sandstones, which are often highly cross-bedded.

Drilling has disclosed gray unoxidized ore in both areas, but the identity of the uranium mineral has not been determined. Finely divided pyrite is a common gangue mineral in this ore. Fracturing and faulting are known to be important controls in the localized formation of these deposits. Visible quantities of carbonaceous materials are conspicuously lacking.

A marked resemblance exists between the many Wyoming deposits and those of the more thoroughly studied Colorado Plateau. Wyoming uranium deposits are distinct in the abundance of such compounds as phosphates and arsenates.

Widespread unconformities which separate strata of Tertiary age from older sedimentary rocks are common. Uranium deposits occur near such surfaces in several Wyoming areas. These surfaces are boundaries of marked lithologic and structural change which must have influenced the progress of migrating solutions.

Wyoming is a new uranium province characterized almost entirely by occurrences in continental sediments.

A-3. OTHER URANIUM PRODUCING DISTRICTS

Black Hills of South Dakota and Wyoming. In the Black Hills region, vanadium-uranium deposits occur in the Inyan Kara group of Cretaceous age, the outcrop of which encircles the Black Hills uplift [9]. The Inyan Kara group, comprising the Fall River, Fuson and Lakota formations, is folded into gentle anticlines and monoclines subsidiary to the major uplift. The Fall River sandstone in the upper part of the Inyan Kara group contains most of the large deposits. The ore-bearing rock is generally light-colored fine-grained sandstone, either interbedded with thin dark-colored shales or irregularly bedded with mudstone. The deposits are generally tubular layers of disseminated minerals. Limonite, hematite, calcite, and manganese oxide are associated with much of the ore. The deposits range from bodies a few feet across that contain a few tons of ore to bodies several hundred feet across that contain many thousands of tons of ore.

The most favorable areas for large deposits in the southern part of the Black Hills are where sandstone lenses containing abundant mudstone or shale coincide with structural terraces. Similar favorable conditions exist in the northern part of the region. Deposits in the Black Hills region are similar to the vanadium-uranium deposits in the Morrison formation of Jurassic age on the Colorado Plateau.

Marysvale, Utah. Since discovery of vein-type uranium deposits near Marysvale, Piute County, Utah, in 1948, significant tonnages of relatively high-grade ore have been mined from zones of primary and secondary uranium mineral concentrations in vein structures. The principal deposits are confined to an area less than a square mile centered about 4 miles northeast of the town of Marysvale. Primary vein minerals include vein quartz, chalcedony, adularia, pyrite, marcasite, calcite, siderite, jordisite, fluorite, hematite, magnetite, and pitchblende [10]. Most commercial deposits of uranium are restricted to quartz-pyrite-adularia-fluorite-pitchblende veins. Some of the pitchblende-bearing veins contain molybdenum minerals. The assemblage of secondary minerals reported at Marysvale contains iron and manganese oxides, ilsemannite, autunite, torbernite, metatorbernite, schoreckingerite, uranophane, phosphuranylite, β-uranotil, tyuyamunite, rauvite, umohoite, zippeite, johannite, uranopilite, and sooty pitchblende.

Host rocks for the veins include volcanic rocks of post-Oligocene age, quartz monzonite and other rocks that intrude the older rocks, and flows and tuffs of late Tertiary age that unconformably overlap the older rocks. Most of the ore mined has been from veins in quartz monzonite.

The host rocks are cut by three sets of vertical to moderately steep faults that trend northeast, northwest, and north. Pitchblende and secondary uranium minerals are most common in northeast-trending faults, less common in northwest-trending faults, and rare or absent in north-trending faults. The uranium-bearing veins pinch and swell, and the ore is commonly localized in shoots in both the primary and secondary zones.

Spokane Indian Reservation, Washington. Important deposits of uranium are found on the Spokane Indian Reservation, Stevens County, Washington, about 50 miles northwest of Spokane. Here autunite and uranophane, in amounts constituting commercial orebodies, occur at the contact of the Loon Lake granite of Cretaceous (?) age which intrudes the Deer Trail argillite of late Paleozoic (?) age [11]. Uraninite and pyrite have been found deep in the contact zone. The Loon Lake granite is a coarse-grained intrusive rock. No primary uranium mineral has been identified in the granite, but secondary minerals are found as much as 20 feet from the contact. Although termed argillite, the Deer Trail is composed of schists and phyllites with quartzite lenses in the vicinity of the deposit. Mineralization extended at least 40 feet into the metamorphosed sedimentary rocks along shear zones parallel with the contact, with no apparent replacement of the host rock.

Cochetopa District, Saguache County, Colorado. An area of uranium vein deposits containing commercial ore reserves occurs in the Cochetopa mining district in the northwest corner of Saguache County, Colorado.

The area is underlain by pre-Cambrian schist, granite and gneiss, on which rest the Morrison (Jurassic), Dakota (Cretaceous), and Mancos (Cretaceous) formations [12]. Faults in the pre-Cambrian rocks, the Morrison and the Dakota formations, are favorable sites for uranium.

In the mine area, a major high-angle reverse fault (the Los Ochos fault), trending easterly, is traceable for several miles. Steeply dipping northeast-trending pitchblende-bearing zones, intensely sheared at the contact of the granite and the Morrison formation, intersect the Los Ochos fault.

Silicification of the Morrison formation has conditioned the rocks, prior to uranium mineralization, as favorable hosts for uranium orebodies. The primary mineral assemblage in the veins includes pitchblende, marcasite, chalcedony, and ilsemannite. Quartz and barite constitute the gangue minerals.

Ralston Creek District, Jefferson County, Colorado. A producing vein deposit district lies in the Ralston Creek area, 8 miles northwest of Golden, in Jefferson County, Colorado. Several thousand tons of relatively high-grade (more than 0.7 percent U_3O_8) ore have been shipped from this district.

Uranium minerals in the Ralston Creek area include pitchblende and minor amounts of secondary autunite, torbernite, and uranophane associated with base metal sulfides in Tertiary fault breccia [13]. Two type of deposits have been described: (1) pitchblende in breccia faults in quartz-biotite gneiss and schist, and hornblende gneiss and (2) pitchblende in a broken, brecciated vein in granite at its contact with quartz-biotite schist. Most of the ore is in northwesterly and northeasterly trending veins.

Pitchblende was deposited before all sulfides, with the exception of minor pyrite and marcasite.

Tallahassee Creek District, Fremont County, Colorado. Modest amounts of ore have been shipped from three small mines in the Tallahassee Creek area in Fremont County, Colorado, about 20 miles northwest of Canon City. Geologic investigations here have disclosed two distinct types of uranium orebodies [14]. One at the Sunshine mine contains autunite precipitated from ground waters in fractures in volcanic boulders. These boulders fill a channel scoured into poorly sorted volcanic debris; the debris was deposited as the result of temporary ponding of Tallahassee Creek.

The other type, exemplified by the Mary L mine, contains black ura-niferous organic material in a bedded Tertiary sandstone. The uranium, believed to have been carried upward by hydrothermal solutions and deposited in the first favorable sedimentary horizon, is in bodies that pinch and swell with the thinning and thickening of the sandstone, which rests on an uneven erosional surface of pre-Cambrian rocks.

Lakeview District, Oregon. Uranium deposits in altered volcanic rocks occur in the Lakeview district of southern Lake County, Oregon. In the White King mine development work has been carried out in Tertiary volcanic breccia, which in places has been completely silicified to a light colored lustrous mass of opalite [15]. Silicification extends over large areas. A pale yellow mineral, identified as novacekite, coats closely spaced small fractures in some parts of the opalite. It appears to be a secondary product, developed during the present weathering cycle. Other minerals found in the fractured opalite are realgar, orpiment, pyrite, and uraniferous organic matter. These are embedded in the opalite and appear to have been deposited simultaneously with the silicification.

At the Lucky Lass mine, a complex of volcanic rocks has been extensively altered by hydrothermal solutions. Silicification is minor; the alteration is chiefly argillic. Numerous small veins filled with autunite occur in the altered lava and less abundantly in parts of the tuff.

Texas Gulf Coastal Plain. Uranium deposits occur in tuff and tuffaceous sandstone formations (late Eocene or early Oligocene) in a belt in the Gulf Coast Region of Texas [9].

The deposits, with minor vanadium and copper, occur in the flat-lying Jackson formation of Eocene age and in the overlying Oligocene beds. The ore-bearing beds consist of poorly bedded and mostly unconsolidated light-colored tuff, sand, and sandy clay. Yellow and green uranium phosphate and silicate minerals occur along fractures, bedding planes, and are disseminated in the rock. Large amounts of arsenic and molybdenum occur with the uranium. The best mineralized rock appears to be associated with hydrated iron oxides, bentonite, and rocks characterized by mixed and irregular bedding. Carbonaceous material is rare and commonly shows no association with the ore. The deposits range from bodies a few feet across that contain a few tons of ore to bodies several hundred feet across that contain several hundred thousand tons.

Note: Bracketed numbers apply to references at the end of Chapter 1.

INDEX

Abernathyite, 12, 92, 97
Absite, 91, 99
Ace Mine, 306
Acetone-HCL process, 265
Acid concentration, 117
Acid cure process, 332
Acid curing at high solids, 134
Acid leach, of shale, 398
Acid leach pulps, filtering, 187
Acid leaching, 115
  advantages, 116
  Blind River area, 279
  conditions, 116 ff.
  cyanide residues, 140
  lignite, 392
  methods, 125 ff.
  Moab Mill Reduction Company, 350
  Pachuca tank for, 126
  pulp densities in, 126
  under pressure, 136
  recovery of vanadium by, 148
  South Africa, 362
  Shiprock Uranium Mill, 336
  Vitro Uranium Company, 327
Acid liquors, percolation leaching
  with, 188
Acid pulps, counter-current
  decantation of, 185
  countercurrent washing in
    thickeners, 187
  classifiers and cyclones, 186
Acid processes, clarifying pregnant
  solutions from, 189
Acid systems, liquid-solids separation
  in, 185
Addition of oxidant, 123
Adsorption cycle, ion exchange, 209
Adsorption reactions in carbonate
  liquors, 206
Advantages of the pressure leach, 138
African Shield, 6
Agitation equipment, 126 ff.
Air agitation, 126
Air, as an oxidizing agent, 308

Air oxidation, 159
  catalysts, 161
Alkaline leaching of uranium ores,
  153 ff.
Alkaline systems, liquid-solids
  separations in, 183
Alkyl amines, extraction with, 250
Alkyl orthophosphoric acids, 242
Alkyl phosphates, effect of nature of
  alkyl group, 246
Alkyl phosphoric acids, 242, 246
  aqueous solubility of, 246
  extraction with, 249
  preparation of, 244
  removal of uranium from, 248
Alkyl pyrophosphoric acids, 242
Alpha radiation, 408
Alumina, from leached zone, 381
Ambrosia Lake district, New Mexico,
  37
American Smelting and Refining
  Company, 44
Amex process, 263
Amines, 250
  commercially available, 254
  effect of structure of, 250
  extraction, diluent for, 251
  removal of uranium from, 254
  selectivity of, 251
  solvent extraction of lignite by,
    394
Ammonium carbonate pressure
  leaching, 168
Ammonium dithionate, oxidant for
  tetravalent uranium, 158
Anaconda Copper Mining Company,
  164
Anaconda plant, Bluewater, New
  Mexico, 186
Analysis, colorimetric method, 73
  coulometric method, 81
  fluorometric method, 69
  polarographic method, 78
  of uranium ores, 65

volumetric methods, 65
X-ray spectrochemical method, 81
Andersonite, 93
Anionic complexes, 192
Apatite, 101
Aqueous leaching with agitation, 126
Aqueous solubility of alkyl phosphoric
    acids, 246
Argentina, 20
Arizona, 7
Arsenate ions, effect on resin
    capacity, 201
Asphaltic ores, roasting of, 105
Asphaltite, 100
Assays, chemical and radiometric,
    comparison of, 26
Associations, of uranium and carbon,
    100
  of uranium and carbon, as an
    organo-uranium complex, 100
  with fossil organic matter, 100
Australia, 5, 18, 97, 98, 99, 109
Autunite, 12, 13, 21, 97

Background count, 26
Backwash and settling, column, 211
Bancroft area, 17, 97, 142
Batch leaching, 127
Bayleyite, 93
Beaverlodge, Saskatchewan, 111, 165
  carbonate leaching in autoclaves,
    311
  crushing, 309
  flotation of pyrite at, 318
  grinding, 309
  heat exchangers, 310
  liquid-solid separation, 312, 316
  ore preparation, 309
  uranium precipitation, 312
  uranium recovery, 316
Beaverlodge area, carbonate leaching
    of uranium ore, 307
  geology and mineralogy, 307
Beaverlodge district, 15
Beaverlodge Mill, 306
Becquerelite, 92
Belgian Congo, 18, 97
Beneficiation, 108
Beta-uranotil, 93
Bicarbonate ion in carbonate
    leaching, 155
Bicroft Uranium Mines, Ltd., 142

Big Indian Wash—Lisbon valley
    district, 11, 97, 101, 146
Black Hills of South Dakota, 11, 12
Blind River area, 16, 98, 138, 273
  acid leaching, 279
  countercurrent decantation, 286
  crushing, 274
  drying uranium product, 299
  filtration, 279
  geology and mineralogy, 274
  grinding, 275
  ion-exchange recovery in, 291
  Lime-NaOH precipitation, 301
  liquid-solid separation, 286
  MgO precipitation, 298
  neutral thickening, 279
  nitrate elution, ion-exchange step,
    296
  ore preparation, 274
  Pachucas, 283
  precipitation from ion-exchange
    eluates, 298
  tailings neutralization and disposal
    in, 304
  two-stage filtration, 287
Blind River leach liquors, clarification
    of, 291
Blind River ores, chloride elution in
    ion-exchange step, 294
  leaching, 282
Blockson Chemical Company, 375
Blockson process, 375, 377
Bluewater plant, 164
Bonnie Chemical Plant, 375
Brannerite, 17, 19, 91, 98, 274
Brannerite, leaching, 98

Cactus extract, 172
Calcining, leached zone material, 384
Cameron district, 10
Canada, 5, 273
Canada, sources, 14
Canadian Shield, 6
Carbonaceous material, removal of, 104
Carbonate/bicarbonate ratio, effect on
    resin capacity, 207
Carbonate concentration effect on
    resin capacity, 206
Carbonate dissolution, chemistry of,
    154
Carbonate leach liquors in ion
    exchange, 206

Carbonate leach pulps, counter-current decantation washing in thickeners of, 184
filtration of, 183
Carbonate leach solutions, resin-in-pulp process for, 156
recovery of uranium from, 155
Carbonate leaching, autoclaves, Beaverlodge, 311
bicarbonate ion in, 155
clarifying pregnant solutions from, 184
efficiency, 156
grind required, 157
high temperatures and pressures, 166
ion exchange, elution reactions, 207
methods of dissolution in, 162
Pachuca tanks in, 165
rate of extraction in, 158
roasting, 158
Separan, use in, 165
uranium ores, 153 ff.
Beaverlodge, 307
Carbonate liquors, adsorption reactions in, 206
effect of other ions in, 207
percolation leaching with, 184
Carbonate solutions, filtering the uranium concentrate from, 185
Carbonate stripping, 248
Carnotite, 10, 13, 19, 92, 97, 103, 154, 164
Caustic soda rejuvenation, 225
Cations, uranium, extraction of, 244
Centrifugal extractors, in solvent extraction, 260
Chattanooga shale, 14, 374
Chemical changes in salt roasting, 103
Chemical costs, reduction in, 227
Chemical poison, ion-exchange recovery, 219
Chemistry of carbonate dissolution, 154
of the ion-exchange process, 192
Chloride consumption, reducing, 227
Chloride eluates, solvent extraction from, 265
Chloride elution in ion exchange, 204
ion-exchange step, 294
Chloride ions, effect on resin capacity, 201
Churn drilling, 30

Clarification, of Blind River leach liquors, 291
Climax Uranium Company mill, Grand Junction, Colorado, 104, 148, 188
Cobalt, concentrations in leach liquors, 222
poisoning, 221
removing from the resin, 222
Cochetopa District, Colorado, 11
Coffinite, 13, 100, 119, 157
solubility of, 94
Colloidal solution of silica, 219
Colorado Plateau, 5, 7, 232, 243
Colorimetric method of analysis, 73
Column, backwash and settling, 211
flush, 210
Column contactors, in solvent extraction, 259
Columnar ion exchange, 207
elution in, 211
equipment for, 207
extraction in, 207
multistage elution in, 211
Combination air-mechanical agitation, 126
Concentrate sampling, 57
Concentration, effect of higher acid, 119
ferric iron, 119
rocks and water, 3
uranium ores, 108
Coning, 50
Constituents, that affect capacity of resin, 197
Control, of oxidation, 123
Control sampling, 65
Copper, catalyst for increasing the rate of oxidation, 161
Core drilling, 29
Costs, mining, 42
sampling, 57
solvent, 242
Coulometric methods of analysis, 81
Countercurrent decantation, acid pulps, 185
Blind River area, 286
Countercurrent washing of acid pulps in classifiers and cyclones, 186
in thickeners, 187
Counters, use of, 25
Crushing, Beaverlodge, 309
Blind River area, 274

Moab Mill of Uranium Reduction
    Company, 348
  Shiprock Uranium Mill, 335
  Vitro Uranium Company, 325
Crushing hazards, in uranium ores, 411
Crustal abundance, 3
Cuprosklodowskite, 93
Curite, 92
Cyanide residues, 357
  acid leaching of, 140
Cyclones, 186
  for liquid-solids separation in shale
    leaching, 400

Daggafontein, 111, 356
Daggafontein Mill, 359
Dakota lignite, 390
Dapex process: see EHPA
Davidite, 19, 91, 98, 137
  leaching, 98
Dakota lignite, 373
DDPA: see Dodecyl phosphoric acid
DDPA process, (Dodecyl phosphoric
    acid), 261
Delta, 1
Density of ion-exchange resins, 195
Deposits, types of, 7
Dewindite, 92
Dibenzoylmethane, use in spectro-
    photometric determination, 76
Di-2-ethylhexyl phosphoric acid, 338
Diesel exhaust gases, 406
Diethyl ether extraction, 237
Diluent, amine extraction, 251
  kerosene, 245, 251
  organic solvents, 241
Dioctyl phosphoric acid, 246
Dissolution, methods of in carbonate
    leaching, 162
Distribution isotherm, 238
Districts, geology of, 4
Dodecyl phosphoric acid, 245, 246,
    247, 329
Dressing, ore, 108
Drill-hole logging, 31
Drilling, churn, 30
  core, 29
  patterns, 31
  percussion: see Wagon drilling
  rotary, 30
  underground, 30
  wagon, 30

Drying uranium product, Blind River
    area, 299
Dumontite, 92
Dust control, sampling, 53
Dyson's deposits, 19
Dyson's mine, 97

Effect, of grind in acid leaching, 124
  of higher acid concentration, 119
  of impeller speed, 127
  of temperature on leaching rate, 123
EHPA: see Ethylhexyl phosphoric acid
EHPA (di-2-ethylhexyl phosphoric
    acid), 150
EHPA process, 261
Eldorado mine, 14
Eldorado Mining and Refining
    Limited, 306
Electrolyte balance, in elution circuit,
    213
  in RIP, 218
Ellaton, 356
Eluate recycle, 213
Eluex process, 205, 264
Elution, in column ion exchange, 211
  in RIP, 217
  resin backwash after, 215
Elution circuit, electrolyte balance in,
    213
  solution balance in, 213
Elution reactions in acid leaching, 203
Entrainment, solvent, 240
Epiianthinite, 92
Equipment, leaching, 125 ff.
  size reduction, for sampling, 52
  two-stage leaching, 130
Eschynite, 91
Ethers, 242, 244
Ethylhexyl phosphoric acid, 247
Euxenite, 91
Exploration, 24 ff.
  drilling, 29
  mine openings, 29
  physical, 28
  stripping, 29
  trenching, 29
Exploration program, phases, 27
Extraction, coefficient, 238
  columnar ion exchange, 207
  diethyl ether, 237
  factors affecting in RIP, 216
  of anionic complexes, 250

with alkyl amines, 250
with alkyl pyrophosphoric acids,
    249

Faraday Uranium Mines, 142
Ferghanite, 92
Fergusonite, 91
Ferric iron, 117, 119
    concentration, 119
    extraction, 243
Ferric iron to ferrous, reduction at
    Shiprock Uranium Mill, 339
Ferroin, 68
Fertilizer, from leached zone, 381
Filter cakes, 182
Filtering acid leach pulps, 187
Filtering the uranium concentrate, 189
    from carbonate solutions, 185
Filtration, 172
    and thickening, in acid leaching
        lignite, 393
    Blind River area, 279
    of carbonate leach pulps, 183
Flocculating agents, 172
Flocculants, developments in use of,
    173
    effect of reagent dilution on
        behavior of, 177
    influence of slurry dilution on
        effectiveness of, 174
    method of adding to slurry, 177
    quantity, 180
    screening tests for, 173
    storage and preparation, 177
    use of, 177
Flocculation, degree of, 181
    effect of composition of the
        pregnant liquor on, 181
    role of particle size in, 181
Florida, 13
Florida phosphate leached zone,
    recovery from, 379
Florida phosphates, 101, 372
Flotation, 111, 112
    pyrite, Beaverlodge, 318
Flow rates in ion exchange, 208
Fluorescence analysis, 69
Fluorometer, 70
Fluorometric methods of analysis, 69
Flush, column, 210
    in RIP, 217
Fourmarierite, 92

France, 19
Freddies Consolidated, 356
Free State Geduld, 356

Gamma radiation, 410
Gamma rays, properties of, 25
Gas Hills area, Wyoming, 41
Geiger counters, 24
Geochemistry, 3
Geologic studies, 27
Geology, 3 ff.
Glues, 172
Grab sampling, 49
Grants district, 10, 41, 97
Gravity concentration, 108
Great Bear Lake, 5, 14
Grind, effect of in acid leaching, 124
    required in carbonate leaching, 157
Grinding, Beaverlodge, 275, 309
    hazards, in uranium ores, 411
    Moab Mill Reduction Company, 349
    Shiprock Uranium Mill, 336
    Vitro Uranium Company, 327
Guar gum, 172
    influence of slurry pH on
        effectiveness of, 177
Gummite, 92
Gunnar, 1, 16

Hand sampling, 49
Happy Jack deposits, 1, 98
Harmony and Virginia, 356
Hazards, in uranium mining and
    milling, 406
HDPA: see Heptadecyl phosphoric acid
Health and safety problems in
    uranium mining and milling,
    406
Heat exchangers, Beaverlodge, 310
Heavy Minerals Company, 386
Hecla Mining Company, 34
Heptadecyl phosphoric acid, 245, 246,
    247
Hexavalent uranium, 97
Higgins contactor, 230
High-lime ores, 164
High-speed mechanical agitation, 126
Homestake Mining Company, 35
Homestake-New Mexico Partners, 37
Hot digestion, 134
Hydrated arsenates, 92
Hydrated carbonates, 93

Hydrated molybdate, 92
Hydrated oxides, 91, 97
Hydrated phosphates, 92
Hydrated silicates, 93
Hydrated sulfates, 93
Hydrated vanadates, 92
Hydration of ion-exchange resins, 194
Hydraulic characteristics of ion-
    exchange resins, 195
Hydrochloric acid recovery, at Vitro
    Uranium Company, 330
Hydrogen peroxide, oxidant for
    tetravalent uranium, 158

Ianthinite, 92
Impeller speed, effects of, 127
Indicated ore, 32
Inferred ore, 32
Infilco CST exchanger, 231
Inflammability of solvent, 241
International Minerals and Chemicals
    Corporation, 375
Ion exchange, adsorption cycle, 209
    adsorption reactions, 198
    advantages of, 192
    carbonate leach liquors in, 206
    chloride elution in, 204
    columnar, 207
    elution in column, 211
    elution reactions in acid leaching,
        203
    elution reactions in carbonate
        leaching, 207
    flow rates in, 208
    Moab Mill Reduction Company,
        352
    neutral salt elutions in, 206
    nitrate elution in, 203
    processing of pregnant liquor in, 209
    rates of, 196
    resin-in-pulp, 216
    resin life, 197
    selectivity, 196
    solution characteristics, acid leach
        liquors, 197
    South Africa, 364
    sulfuric acid elution in, 205
    uranium recovery by, 191
Ion-exchange eluates, solvent
    extraction, 264
Ion-exchange equipment, advances in,
    228

Ion-exchange operations,
    improvements in, 227
Ion-exchange process, chemistry of,
    192
Ion-exchange recovery, Blind River
    area, 291
    chemical poison, 219
    from shale, 403
    "poisons," 219
    problems in, 219
Ion-exchange step, chloride elution in
    the, 294
Iron, effect on resin capacity, 200

Johannite, 93, 98
Jones reductor, 68

Kasolite, 93
Kerosene, diluent, 245, 251
Kerr-McGee Company, 135, 185, 331
Kilborn Engineering, Toronto, 142
Kolm, 100

Lake Athabasca, 306
Lake Athabasca district, 5
Lake County, Oregon, 97
Lakeview district, Oregon, 11
Lapointe Picker, 111
La Sal Mine, 35
La Sal Mining and Development
    Company, 35
Layout of continuous leaching
    circuits, 128
Leach, pressure, advantages of, 138
    single-stage, 131
Leach liquors, cobalt concentration in,
    222
Leached zone, alumina from, 381
    fertilizer from, 381
    material, beneficiation of, 381
    material, calcining of, 384
    ores, solvent extraction, recovery
        from, 267
    process for recovery of uranium
        from, 379
    uranium content of, 379
Leaching, acid, under pressure, 136
    alkaline, of uranium ores, 153 ff.
    batch, 127
    Blind River ore, 282
    brannerite, 98
    carbonate, advantages, 153

carbonate, bicarbonate ion in, 155
carbonate, limitations, 153
carbonate, of uranium ores, 153 ff.
conditions, Blind River Area, 138
davidite, 98
percolation, 133
percolation, with acid liquors, 188
pitchblende, 94
solvent, of ores, 265
two-stage, counter, 128
two-stage, equipment for, 130
two-stage, gold ore residues, 129
two-stage countercurrent, benefits
    of, 130
uraninite, 94
with sodium carbonate solution, 307
Leaching circuits, layout of, 128
Leaching countercurrently,
    advantages of, 129
Leaching efficiency, carbonate, 156
Leaching equipment, 125 ff.
Leaching methods, acid, 125 ff.
Leaching rate, effect of temperature
    on, 123
Liebigite, 93
Lignite, 7, 105, 372, 373, 390 ff.
    acid leaching of, 392
    acid leaching, filtration and
        thickening in, 393
    heating value of, 390
    roasting of, 105, 391
Lignite ash, 130
    two-stage countercurrent leaching
        of, 393
Lignite deposits, 12
Lignite leach solutions, solvent
    extraction of, 393
Lime-NaOH precipitation, in Blind
    River area, 301
Liquid-solids separations, 172
    in acid systems, 185
    in alkaline systems, 183
Lisbon Valley district of Utah, 101
Loading cycle in RIP, 217
Locust bean gum, 172
Longwall retreat, 35
Loss of uranium by occlusion, 117
Luckachukai district, 10
Luckachukai Mountains, 332

Manganese, as oxidant in South
    Africa, 362

Manganese dioxide, as oxidant, 121
Manganese recovery, in South Africa,
    368
Marysvale, Utah, 5, 11, 97
    ore-buying station, 50
Measured ore, 32
Mechanical agitation, 126
Mechanical sampling, 50
(Meta) autunite, 92
    torbernite, 92
    zeunerite, 13, 92
Metallurgical classification, 93 ff.
MgO precipitation, Blind River area,
    298
Mi Vida, 1, 37
Microlite, 90
Milliken Lake mill, 273
Milling operations, uranium, 272
Milling practice, 138
Mill-run sampling, 52
Mine-run sampling, 50
Mine, water, 39
Mineralogy, 89
Minerals, classes, 93
    vanadium, 101
Mining, 24 ff., 33 ff.
    at Shiprock, 335
    panel, 35
Mining costs, 42
Mining districts, major, 9
Mining methods, 33
Mixer-settlers, 256
Moab Mill, 146, 345
Moab Mill Reduction Company, acid
        leaching at, 350
    crushing at, 348
    geology and mineralogy at, 345
    grinding at, 349
    ion exchange at, 352
    ore preparation at, 347
    precipitation at, 354
    resin-in-pulp ion exchange at, 352
    sampling at, 348
    sand-slime separation at, 350
    uranium leaching at, 350
Moisture content, ore sampling for,
    45
Molybdenum, poisoning, 223
Monazite, 372, 373, 386 ff.
    rare earths from, 386
    solvent extraction recovery of
        thorium and uranium from, 386

thorium from, 386
trisodium phosphate from, 386
uranium oxide content of, 386
uranium recovery from, 386
Monododecyl phosphoric acid
        (DDPA), 245, 246
Monoheptadecyl phosphoric acid
        (HDPA), 245, 246
Monosodium phosphate stream, 377
Monticello mill, 184
Monticello sampling plant, 45
Monticello, Utah, 162
Monument Valley district, 10
Multiple oxides, 90
Multistage elution, in columnar ion
        exchange, 211
    in RIP, 217
Multistage operation, 255

Neutral complexes, extraction of, 244
Neutral salt elutions in ion exchange,
        206
Neutral thickening, Blind River area,
        279
New Klerksdorp, 356
New Mexico, 7
Nitrate eluates, solvent extraction
        from, 265
Nitrate elution, acidity used for, 204
    ion exchange, 203
    ion-exchange step, Blind River
        area, 296
Nitrate ions, effect on resin capacity,
        201
Nitrate losses, reducing, 228
Nitric acid leach liquors, solvent
        extraction from, 244
Nitrilotriacetic (NTA), use in
        spectrophotometric
        determination, 78
Nitrophosphate process, 385
Nonyl pyrophosphoric acid, 375
North Dakota, 5
Novacekite, 92

Occlusion, loss of uranium by, 117
Occurrence, 1 ff.
Octyl phosphoric acid, 246, 247
Olin-Mathieson Chemical Company,
        375
OPA process, 266

Ore, indicated, 32
    inferred, 32
    measured, 32
    Vitro Uranium Company, 325
    weighing, 45
Ore dressing, 108
Ores containing hexavalent uranium,
        97
Ores containing tetravalent uranium,
        93
Ore preparation, Beaverlodge, 309
    Moab Mill of Uranium Reduction
        Company, 347
    Shiprock Uranium Mill, 335
    Vitro Uranium Company, 325
Ore production, in the U. S., 7
Ore reserve estimates, 32
Ore reserves, U. S., 7
Ore sampling, for moisture content, 45
    for uranium content, 48
Oxidant, addition of, 123
    control of, 123
    for tetravalent uranium, 121
    for UO_2, 119
    manganese dioxide, 121
    sodium chlorate, 121, 282
Oxidation, tetravalent uranium, 119,
        159
Oxidation state of uranium, effect on
        solvent extraction, 243
Oxidimetric titration of uranium, 4, 65
Oxidizing agent, air as, 308

Pachuca tank, for acid leaching, 126,
        362
    in Blind River area, 283
    in carbonate leaching, 165
Panel mining, 35
Parsonsite, 92
Particle size, of ion-exchange resins,
        194
    role of in flocculation, 181
Percolation leaching, 133
    with acid liquors, 188
    with carbonate liquors, 184
Percussion drilling: see Wagon Drilling
Peroxide, use in spectro photometric
        determination, 77
PH and acidity, effect on resin
        capacity, 198
Phase disengagement, 241
Phosphate, 7, 101

Phosphate ions, effect on resin
    capacity, 201
Phosphate rock, 13, 372
    recovery from, 375
Phosphates, solvent extraction,
    recovery from, 266
Phosphine oxides, 244
Phosphoric acid, recovery from, 375
    solvent extraction of uranium from,
    375
    uranium from, 372
Phosphuranylite, 92
Physical concentration of uranium
    ores, 108
Physical poison, ion-exchange
    recovery, 219
Pitchblende, 5, 14, 15, 17, 18, 20, 89,
    93, 119, 274, 307
    forms, 94
    leaching of, 94
Podbielniak extractor, 260
Poisoning, anionic cobalt, 221
    molybdenum, 223
    polythionates, 220
    silica, 219
    thorium, 224
    titanium, 223
    zirconium, 223
Poisons, ion exchange, at Moab Mill
    Reduction Company, 353
    ion-exchange recovery, 219
    removal with caustic soda, 225
Polarographic methods of analysis,
    78
Polonium hazard, 408
Polyacrylamide, 173
Polycrase, 91
Polysaccharides, 172
Polythionates, poisoning, 220
Port Pirie, 19, 144
Port Radium, 14, 306
Porter column, 232
Portugal, 5, 19
Potassium dichromate, oxidant for
    tetravalent uranium, 159
Potassium permanganate, oxidant for
    tetravalent uranium, 159
Precipitation, eluate in South Africa,
    367
    from ion-exchange eluates, Blind
    River area, 298
    from sodium carbonate leach solu-

tions at Shiprock Uranium
    Mill, 344
Precipitation, Moab Mill Reduction
    Company, 354
    uranium plus 6, 117
    uranium, Beaverlodge, 312
    uranium in RIP, 218
    uranium, Vitro Uranium Company,
    328
    Vitro Uranium Company, 331
Pregnant eluate, Shiprock Uranium
    Mill, 344
Pregnant liquor, effect of composition
    on flocculation, 181
    processing in ion exchange, 209
Pregnant pulp, processing of by RIP,
    217
Pregnant solutions, clarifying from
    acid processes, 188
    clarifying from carbonate leaching,
    184
    improving clarity of, 182
Preliminary ore treatment, 103 ff.
President Brand, 356
President Steyn, 356
Pressure-leaching, of shale, 398
    of shale with oxygen overpressure,
    401
Priorite, 91
Provinces, 6
Pulp densities in acid leaching, 125
Pulp-to-resin ratio in RIP, 217
Pyrite, 111
    recovery from shale, 397
Pyrite flotation, in South Africa, 369
Pyrochlore, 90, 99

Quartering, 50

Rabbittite, 93
Radiation detection equipment, 24 ff.
Radiation dosage, 408
Radiation hazards, 408
Radioactive equilibrium, 26
Radioactive sorting, 111
Radium, threshold limit for, 409
Radium hazard, 408
Radium Hill, 5, 19, 98, 99, 108
Radon inhalation, 407
Radon mine, 34
Rail haulage, in mines, 35
Ralston Creek district, 5, 11

Rand, 1, 17
Rare earths, from monazite, 386
Rare Metals Corporation, Tuba City, Arizona, 186
Rate of extraction in carbonate leaching, 158
Rauvite, 92
Raw leach process, at Shiprock, 333
Raw-ore carbonate leach, 164
Reagent dilution, 177
  effect of on behavior of flocculants, 177
Recapture creek, 415, 417
Reconnaissance, preliminary, 27
Recovery, by precipitation at Vitro Uranium Company, 328
  uranium, by ion exchange, 191
  uranium, by ion exchange at Shiprock Uranium Mill, 338
Red cake, 150, 164
Redox potential, 121
Reducing chloride consumption, 227
Reducing nitrate losses, 228
Reduction, in lead reductor, 68
  in zinc amalgam column, 66
Reefs, 356
Refining, Vitro Uranium Company, 328
Refractory uranium minerals, 98
Removal of carbonaceous material, 104
Renardite, 92
Reserve estimates, ore, 32
Resin, characteristics, 193
  exchange capacity of, 194
  removing silica from, 220
  structures, 193
Resin backwash after elution, 215
Resin capacity, effect of carbonate/bicarbonate ratio on, 207
  effect of chloride and nitrate ions on, 201
  effect of iron, 200
  effect of pH and acidity, 198
  effect of phosphate and arsenate ions on, 201
  effect of sulfate concentration, 200
  effect of temperature on, 202
  effect of total carbonate concentration, 206
  effect of uranium concentration, 198

  effect of vanadium on, 200
Resin-in-pulp, electrolyte balance, 218
  elution in, 217
  extraction, factors affecting, 216
  flush in, 217
  ion exchange, 216
  ion exchange at Moab Mill Reduction Company, 352
  loading cycle in, 217
  multistage in, 217
  precipitation of uranium in, 218
  process for carbonate leach solutions, 156
  processing of pregnant pulp by, 217
  pulp to-resin ratio in, 217
  retention time in, 217
  solution balance in, 218
Resins, hydration of, 194
  ion-exchange, density of, 195
    hydraulic characteristics of, 195
    losses in, 195
  particle size of, 194
Retention time in RIP, 217
Retorting, shale, 397
Riverton, Wyoming, 97
Roasting, asphaltic ores, 105
  in carbonate leaching, 158
  lignites, 105, 391
  shales, 105, 397
  to improve settling and filtering, 106
  uranium ores, 103 ff.
  Vitro Uranium Company, 327
Rotary drilling, 30
Rum Jungle, 18, 97
Rutherfordine, 93

Sabugalite, 92
Saleite, 19, 92, 97
Salt roasting, 103, 150, 162
  chemical changes in, 103
Samarskite, 91
Sample pulp preparation, 55
Sampling, concentrate, 57
  control, 65
  dust control in, 53
  grab, 49
  hand, 49
  mechanical, 50
  mill-run, 52
  mine-run, 50
  Moab Mill of Uranium Reduction Company, 348

operating costs for, 57
Shiprock Uranium Mill, 335
size reduction equipment for, 52
split-shovel, 50
trench, 49
uranium ores and concentrates, 44
Sampling plant, concentrate, 59
    Monticello, 45
San Rafael Swell district, 10
Sand-slime separation, 112
    Moab Mill Reduction Company,
        350
Saturation capacity, 238
Schoepite, 92, 98
Schroeckingerite, 93, 98
Schwartzwalder mine, 5
Scintillation counters, 25
Screening tests for flocculants, 173
Selectivity in solvent extraction, 239
Sengierite, 92
Separan, 280
    influence of slurry pH on
        effectiveness of, 177
    use in carbonate leaching, 165
Separations, liquid-solids, 172
Shale, 7
    acid leach of, 398
    ion-exchange recovery from, 403
    pressure leaching of, 398
    pressure-leaching with oxygen
        overpressure, 401
    recovery of pyrite from, 397
    retorting, 397
Shale leach slurries, thickening, 403
Shale leaching, cyclones for liquid-
    solids separation in, 400
Shale roasting, 397
Shales, 13, 372, 374, 396
    Chattanooga, 100
    roasting of, 105
    Tennessee, 100
Shinkolobwe, 5, 18
Ship Rock Uranium Mill, 135, 331
    acid leaching at, 336
    crushing at, 335
    grinding at, 336
    mining at, 335
    ore preparation at, 335
    precipitation from sodium
        carbonate leach solutions at,
        344
    pregnant eluate at, 344

raw leach process at, 333
reduction of ferric iron to ferrous at,
    339
sampling at, 335
solvent extraction at, 338
solvent extraction circuit at, 340
solvent losses at, 342
solvent stripping circuit at, 340
uranium leaching at, 336
uranium recovery by ion exchange
    at, 338
vanadium recovery by solvent
    extraction at, 344
Silica, factors which affect stability of,
    219
    means for removing from the resin,
        220
Silica dust, 406
Silica poisoning, 219
Silicates, 97
Silver Reef district, 5
Simple oxides, 89
Simple silicates, 90
Single-stage leach with pregnant
    solution recycle, 131
Sklodowskite, 93
Slurry, method of adding flocculant to,
    177
    solvent extraction from, 263
Slurry dilution, influence on
    effectiveness of flocculants, 173
Slurry pH, influence of on effectiveness
    of Guar Gum and Separan, 177
Soddyite, 93
Sodium carbonate solution, leaching
    with, 307, 344
Sodium chlorate, as oxidant, 121, 282
Sodium dithionate, oxidant for
    tetravalent uranium, 158
Sodium diuranate, 155
Sodium fluoride in fluorometry, 69
Sodium hydroxide, decomposition, 386
    recovery of uranium, 155
Sodium peroxide, oxidant for
    tetravalent uranium, 158
    use in spectrophotometric
        determination, 77
Sodium uranyl tricarbonate, solubility
    of, 155
Solid-liquid separation, Beaverlodge,
    312, 316
    in South Africa, 363

in the Blind River area, 286
Shiprock Uranium Mill, 337
Vitro Uranium Company, 328
Solubility, coffinite, 94
sodium uranyl tricarbonate, 155
solvent, 240
Solution balance, in elution circuit, 213
in RIP, 218
Solvent, cost of, 242
diluent, 241
inflammability of, 241
phase disengagement, 241
properties of the, 238
toxicity of, 241
Solvent entrainment, 240
Solvent extraction, 237
centrifugal extractors in, 260
chemistry of, 238
column contactors in, 258
effect of oxidation state of uranium
on, 243
equipment used in, 255
from nitrate and chloride eluates,
265
from nitric acid leach liquors, 244
from slurries, 263
lignite by amines, 394
lignite leach solutions, 393
nature of cations present, 243
rate of, 255
selectivity in, 239
Shiprock Uranium mill, 338
superphosphates, 267
uranium from phosphoric acid, 375
recovery from ion exchange eluates,
264
recovery from leached zone ores, 267
recovery from phosphates, 266
recovery of thorium and uranium
from monazite, 386
recovery of vanadium by, 264
vanadium recovery by, at Shiprock
Uranium Mill, 344
Vitro Uranium Company, 329
Solvent extraction circuit, at Shiprock
Uranium mill, 340
Solvent extraction processes, 261
Solvent leaching, of ores, 265
TBP process, 265
Solvent losses, at Shiprock Uranium
Mill, 342
Solvent solubility, 240

Solvent stripping, at Vitro Uranium
Company, 330
Solvent stripping circuit at Shiprock
Uranium Mill, 340
Solvents, organic, stability of, 241
South Africa, 1, 140
acid leaching in, 362
geology and mineralogy in, 356
ion exchange in, 364
liquid-solid separation in, 363
manganese as oxidant in, 362
manganese recovery in, 368
Pachuca leaching tanks in, 362
precipitation of eluate in, 367
pyrite flotation in, 369
sources, 17
sulfuric acid production, 358, 370
uranium leaching in, 362
South African mines, 110
uranium mills, 354
South Australia, 144
South Dakota, 12
lignite, 373
South Reduction Plant, 111
Spain, 21
Spectrophotometric methods of
analysis, 73
Split-shovel sampling, 50
Spokane Indian Reservation,
Washington, 11, 97
Stability of organic solvents, 241
Starches, 172
Stilfontein, 356
Stillwellite, 19
Stockpiling, uranium ore, 56
Stripping, 237, 239, 248, 254
Sulfate concentration, effect on resin
capacity, 198
Sulfuric acid, autogenously generated,
136
elution in ion exchange, 205
production in South Africa, 358,
370
Superphosphates, solvent extraction
of, 267
Swartzite, 93
Sweden, 20 ff.
Synthetic polyacrylamide, 165
Synthetic polymers, 172

Tailings neutralization and disposal,
in Blind River area, 304

Tallahassee Creek district, Colorado, 11
TBP: *see* Tributyl phosphate
TBP (tributyl phosphate) in kerosene, 151
solvent leaching process, 265
Temperature, effect on resin capacity, 202
Temple Mountain district, 100
Tennessee Corporation, 375
Tennessee shale, 14, 374, 396
Tennessee Valley Authority process, 385
Tetravalent uranium, 93
oxidants for, 121
oxidation of, 119
Texas, 5, 11
Thickeners, countercurrent decantation washing in, 184
countercurrent washing of acid pulps in, 187
Thickener underflows, washing of, 182
Thickening, 172
shale leach slurries, 403
Thiocyanate, use in spectrophotometric determination, 73
Thompson district, 10
Thorium, from monazite, 373, 386
poisoning, 224
Thorogummite, 90
Thucholite, 17, 100, 274, 357
Titanium, poisoning, 223
Todilto, 1
Todilto limestone, 164
Todilto limestone ores, 97
Torbernite, 12, 13, 21, 97
Toxic elements, in uranium ores, 407
Toxicity of solvent, 241
Trackless equipment, 37
Treatment, preliminary ore, 103 ff.
Trench sampling, 49
Trialkyl phosphates, 242
Trialkyl phosphine oxides, 242, 244
Tributyl phosphate, 237, 244, 248, 338, 385
use in spectrophotometric determination, 78
Trisodium phosphate, from monazite, 386
Troegerite, 92
Two-stage countercurrent leaching, 128
benefits of, 130

Two-stage filtration, in Blind River area, 287
Two-stage leaching, equipment for, 130
of gold ore residues, 129
of lignite ash, 130
Tyuyamunite, 13, 92, 97, 164

Umohoite, 92
Underground drilling, 30
UO_2, oxidation of, 155
Uranates, 157 ff.
Uraniferous lignite, 100, 390
Uraniferous phosphates, 372
Uraninite, 11, 19, 89, 93, 98, 100, 119, 154, 274
forms, 94
leaching of, 94
Uranium, recovery from Beaverlodge, 316
from carbonate leach solutions, 155
Uranium concentration, effect on resin capacity, 200
Uranium content, ore sampling for, 48
Uranium ions, extraction of neutral complexes, 244
neutral complexes, 242
Uranium leaching, at Moab Mill Reduction Company, 350
at Shiprock Uranium Mill, 336
in South Africa, 362
Vitro Uranium Company, 327
Uranium minerals, 89
Uranium ores, roasting of, 103 ff.
Uranium Reduction Company, 146
plant, Moab, Utah, 189
Uranoan thorogummite, 90
Uranocircite, 92
Uranophane, 12, 93, 97
Uranopilite, 93, 98
Uranosphaerite, 92
Uranospinite, 92, 97
Uranothorite, 97
Uranyl ion, 117, 192
Uranyl salts, 91
Uranyl sulfate complex, 192
Uranyl tricarbonate complex, 192
Uranyl tricarbonate ion, 154
Uravan mineral belt, 10, 41
Urgeirica, 5, 20
U. S., ore reserves, 7

U. S. Phosphoric Products Division, 375
Utah, 7, 146
Utex Exploration Company, 37
Uvanite, 92

Vaal Reefs, 356
Vanadium, 101
  effect on resin capacity, 201
  interference in polarographic analysis, 79
  recovery by acid leaching, 148
  recovery by solvent extraction at Shiprock Uranium Mill, 344
  recovery of by solvent extraction, 264
  solubilization by salt roasting, 103
Vandenbrandite, 92
Vegetable gums, 172
Verna mine, 5
Visual settling tests, 173
Vitro Uranium Company, 187
  liquid-solid separation, 328
  ore preparation, 325
  precipitation at, 331
  recovery of uranium by, 323 ff.
  refining, 328
  solvent extraction at, 329, 330
  uranium leaching, 327
Vogelstruisbult Gold Mining Areas Limited, 111, 356

Voglite, 93
Volumetric methods of analysis, 64

Wagon drilling, 30
Walpurgite, 92
Washington, 97
Water, mine, 39
Waxco process, 263
Weighing, ore, 45
Weiss-Swinton pulsating column, 232
Welkom, 356
West Rand Consolidated Mines, Ltd., 192
Western Holdings, 356
Westwater Canyon, 415 ff.
White Canyon district, 10, 40, 97
White's deposits, 19
Winchester fixed bed—RIP column, 232
Witwatersrand, 17, 356
Woodrow mine, 415, 416
Wyoming basins, 5, 11

X-ray spectrochemical methods of analysis, 81

Yellow cake, 164

Zeunerite, 12, 98
Zippeite, 93, 98
Zirconium, poisoning, 223